THE ORIGIN OF
THE ZODIAC

Books by Rupert Gleadow

THE ORIGIN OF THE ZODIAC   *1969*

THE UNCLOUDED EYE   *1953*

MAGIC AND DIVINATION   *1941*

ASTROLOGY IN EVERYDAY LIFE   *1940*

Jupiter leaving Aries for Taurus
(*Painting by Baldassare Peruzzi in the Farnesina Palace, Rome*)

THE ORIGIN OF
THE ZODIAC

Rupert Gleadow

Atheneum   NEW YORK   1969

The author would like to make the following acknowledgments:
to Mr Cyril Fagan for help during absence from home;
to his wife Helen Gleadow for plates 1, 4, 20, and 23;
to the Alinari Organization for permission to reproduce the
    frontispiece;
to the Edwards Egyptological Library of University College,
    London, for Plates 15, 16, 18, 19 and 20
to the Trustees of the Science Museum, Dr H. R. Calvert, and
    Mr H. A. Saunders, for the use of the globe mentioned on
    page 200;
to Mr G. F. Kunz and J. B. Lippincott Co., Philadelphia, for Plate 2;
to the Warburg Institute and Professor B. L. van der Waerden for
    Plate 10;
to the Trustees of the British Museum for the remaining plates.

TO MY WIFE HELEN

Ἐκ Διὸς ἀρχώμεσθα

From Zeus begin we, never unmentioned we
Of mortal race may leave Him; everywhere the ways
Are full of Zeus, and all the market-places of men
And all the seas are full, and all the roads and harbours.
Him do we need at every time and in every place,
For we are of His lineage; and He kindly grants
Favouring signs to men, stirring the people to toil,
Reminding them that they must earn their livelihood.
He also tells when soil is best for beeves and cattle
And when the hour is right to trench the rising plants
And sow the seed; for He Himself in heaven placed
The constellations, and He planned what signs are best
For men from year to year, to tell His just decrees,
That every task may fill duly its proper hour
And all things may be brought to pass in decent order,
To Him both first and last do men and creatures pray.
All hail, Great Father, wonder and primal boon to men,
Thou are the earliest race. Ye too, ye Muses, ye
Honey-sweet voices; grant, and aid my invoking prayer,
To sing of the stars in all my heaven-sequent song.

Aratos, Phainomena, 1–18.

Contents

		page
1	The Zodiac As We Know It	15
2	The Rediscovery of the Ancient Zodiac	27
3	What Astrology Is and Does	34
4	Medieval Magic and Psychology	41
5	The Twelve Gods: Plato and Augustus	62
6	The Zodiac in China	87
7	From Mexico to Tibet	110
8	Persia and the Four Elements	115
9	The Bible and Birthstones	122
10	India and the Asterisms	137
11	Babylonian Myths and Omens	152

(i) The Eighteen Signs, 163; (ii) The Eleven Signs, 164

| 12 | The Horoscope of Eternity | 175 |

(i) The Calendrical Basis, 176; (ii) The Zodiacs of Denderah, 180; (iii) The Decans, 182; (iv) The Standard Diagram, 186; (v) The Hour-Stars, 190; (vi) Planetary Dates computed from the Heliacal Rising of Sirius, 195; (vii) Decans or Pentads? 197; (viii) The Mysterious Text from Abydos, 200

13	The Naming of the Constellations	206
	NOTES AND REFERENCES	221
	INDEX	231

List of Tables

1   Longitudes of Planets in the Horoscope of Agostino Chigi   61

2   Longitudes of Planets in Tarrutius' Horoscope of Rome   68

3   Plants of the Signs and Planets   85–6

4   Chinese Names of the Planets   91

5   The 12 Kung   100

6   The 24 Solar Terms   100

7   The Twelve Branches, or Horary Circle   102

8   The 28 Chinese Asterisms, or *Hsiu*   104–5

9   Asterisms and Hour circle compared   106

10   The Far Eastern Circle of Animals   108

11   Mexican Month-names   110

12   Toltec and Nagual Day-names   113

13   Jewels of the High Priest's Breastplate   135

14   Some Symbols, Animals, Colours and Gems attributed to the 12 Signs   136

15   The Hindu Zodiac   141

16   The 28 Hindu Asterisms, or Nakshatras   150–51

17   The Babylonian Zodiac of 18 Constellations   163

18   Full and Empty Degrees   185

19   Egyptian Moon-markers   191–2

20   Egyptian Planetary Dates Computed from the Heliacal Rising of Sirius   196

21   The 36 Egyptian decans   *facing page* 200

22   Planetary Positions at the Inauguration of the Sothic Calendar   205

23   Exaltations of the Planets   211

24   The Hour-circle or Dodecaoros   219

List of Illustrations

Jupiter leaving Aries for Taurus *frontispiece*
(from the horoscope of Agostino Chigi in the Farnesina
Palace, Rome, painted by Baldassare Peruzzi)

1 Horoscope of the Emperor Augustus, calculated in the
Hellenistic zodiac *between pages* 64–5

2 Medieval zodiacal man, with appropriate gems
(from G. F. Kunz, *Curious Lore of Precious Stones*, Philadelphia, 1913)

3 Medieval biped Sagittarius
(F. Boll, *Sphaera*, p. 131)

4 Zodiacal coins and gems:
(a) Capricorn on a denarius of Augustus, Lugdunum 12 B.C.
(after Mattingly, *Coins of the Roman Empire*, I, Pl. 11, No. 13)
(b) Phoenix on a coin of Antoninus Pius, A.D. 139
(After G. Dattari, *Numi Augg. Alexandrini* (Cairo 1901)
Pl. xxxii, No. 2428)
(c) Scorpio on a coin of Antiochus IV of Commagene
(A.D. 38–72)
(B.M. Cat. of *Greek Coins of Galatia*, etc., 1899, Pl. xv, No. 8)
(d) Ring-stone of Scorpio holding Libra, early Roman
Empire
(Duffield Osborne, *Engraved Gems*, New York, 1912, Pl.
xxvii, No. 8)
(e) Pan in zodiac (f) Sun in zodiac (g) the 3 watery signs
(S. Reinach, *Pierres Gravées*, Paris, 1895, Pl. 69)

5 Parapegma found at Miletus
(*Sitzber, Akad.* Berlin, 904, p. 92)

6 Poseidon and Hermes (Neptune and Mercury) on the Puteal
Albani
(H. Stuart Jones, *Catalogue of Sculptures in the Museo
Capitolino*, No. 29)

7 T'ang mirror with circle of animals *between pages* 96–7
(E. Chavannes, *Le Cycle Turc*, Leyden, 1906, Fig. VII at end)

8 Mithraic zodiac
(from F. Cumont, *Textes et Monuments des Mystères de Mithra*,
Brussels, 1896, II 389, Fig. 304)

9   Macara the Indian Capricorn and Kumbha   *between pages* 96–7
    the Waterpot (Erard Mollien, *Recherches sur le zodiaque indien*,
    Mem. Acad. Inscr. et Belles-Lettres, 1853, plate at end)

10 Comparison of Sagittarius, Capricorn, and Aquarius in Baby-
    lon and Egypt
    (B. L. van der Waerden in *Archiv für Orientforschung* XVI,
    227, after Wm. J. Hinke, *A New Boundary-Stone*, pp. 98–103)

11 Scorpion-man on a boundary-stone of 12th century B.C.
    (L. W. King, *Babylonian Boundary-Stones*, London 1912,
    Pl. XCI)

12 The Babylonian God-with-Streams
    (S. Langdon, *Semitic Mythology*, Fig. 48 on p. 95)

13 Virgo the grain-goddess in the Persian period
    (Meissner, *Babylonien und Assyrien*, II, 407)

14 Circular zodiac of Denderah   *between pages* 128–9
    (F. J. Lauth, *Les zodiaques de Denderah*, Munich 1865, frontis-
    piece)

15 Horoscope from Athribis
    (W. M. Flinders Petrie, *Athribis*, British School of Archæo-
    logy in Egypt, 1908)

16 Standard Diagram of Decans with Orion, Sirius and Planets
    (Tomb of Seti I in R. Lepsius, *Denkmäler*, Abth. III, Pl. 137)

17 Hour-stars and target-priest on a temple roof
    (Tomb of Rameses VI, Lepsius, id., III, 228)

18 Nût diagram from cenotaph of Seti I at Abydos   *between pages* 160–1
    (H. Frankfort, *Cenotaph of Seti I*, Pl. lxxxi)

19 Constellations of the Ram and Boat in the Ramesseum
    (Lepsius, id. III, 170)

20 Constellation of the Boat. Inset: The god Re in his boat, from
    The Book of the Dead, Ch. cxviii, Budge
    (Drawing by Helen Gleadow)

21 Marble plate from Egypt, Greco-Roman period, showing
    zodiac and hour-circle
    (Wm. J. Hinke, *A New Boundary-Stone*, p. 107, Fig. 41)

22 The Sigla of the 12 Signs
    (After O. Neugebauer)

23 The original 'Horoscope of Eternity', 2767 B.C.   *facing page* 192
    (Drawing by Helen Gleadow)

THE ORIGIN OF
THE ZODIAC

I. *The Zodiac As We Know It*

ZODIAC is a word that is commonly known but few would be prepared to say just what the zodiac is. The ancient Greek word *zodiakos* meant (a circle) 'of animals', or perhaps even 'of little pictures of animals', but why, where, and when the animals were chosen is an intriguing question which this book hopes to answer. Meanwhile the identity of the twelve signs can best be remembered with the aid of the traditional rhyme:

> The Ram, the Bull, the Heavenly Twins,
> And next the Crab the Lion shines,
>   The Virgin and the Scales,
> The Scorpion, Archer, and Sea-Goat,
> The Man that bears the Watering-Pot,
>   The Fish with glittering tails.

Everyone has heard that constellations bearing these twelve names do exist in the sky, and may also realize that every person on earth is supposed to be 'born under' one of them. The sign under which one is born can be quite readily ascertained if the hour of birth is known. As the idea of being 'born under' a sign is often repugnant to scientists, it is necessary to differentiate between the science of astronomy and the practice of astrology. Astronomy is concerned with measuring the constitution and movements of the heavenly bodies, and astronomers are usually supposed to be determined to believe that celestial bodies have no traceable influence on human life. Astrology, on the other hand, is the supposed science and art of interpreting the influence of the heavenly bodies on mankind. Usually astrology is thought by astronomers to be a delusion, but obviously it is not possible to recount the history of a subject while affecting towards it an attitude of superior disbelief. It will be necessary therefore to assume that the claims of both astronomy and astrology deserve to be taken equally seriously.

15

The zodiac is a circle of twelve constellations, each of exactly thirty degrees extent, lying along the path of the sun, and by means of which the positions of the sun, moon and planets can be measured. It has often been said that it originated in Babylon, and this, though not entirely true, is not implausible, for no other ancient civilization believed so implicitly in the doctrine 'As above, so below'. To a Babylonian or Assyrian it seemed quite rational to suppose that events on earth followed or resembled those in heaven, since the same divine powers were in charge of both. It is not known why Jupiter, as a planet, became the 'natural significator' of wealth, success, prosperity and expansion, while Saturn represented poverty and restriction, rather than the other way round. Possibly Saturn's association with law and righteousness is due to the astronomical fact that his path appears to conform most strictly to that of the sun; but this does not explain why Venus became 'the planet of love and friendship', or why Mars became connected with violence, maleness, athletics, and war.

The study of the stars differs from most other methods of predicting the future in appearing to be more objective. The stars provide data which are the same for every observer. This is not the case in practices in which the observer himself provides the data he is to interpret. Men have not normally distinguished between methods using subjective data, such as clairvoyance, and those requiring objective data, such as the study of handwriting or the stars. In some cases it might be thought difficult to make such a distinction: in psychometry or object-reading, the diviner holds an object such as a pen or watch which has been commonly used by the person on whose behalf the consultation is being made; and in augury, the birds and their behaviour are equally visible to everyone in the neighbourhood. The intention, however, is in all cases much the same, to discover something unknown in order to act on the information made available.

The zodiac, however, which was often used for trying to find the answer to such problems, and was largely instrumental in the development of astronomical science, is a circle drawn through that part of the sky which includes the track of the sun, moon, and planets. Since the earth, as it rotates round the sun, is tipped at an angle of 23° 27″ to the horizontal, the alternating phenomena of summer and winter are produced, and half of the zodiac lies to the north of the (celestial) equator and half to the south. The sun's path through the zodiac is called the ecliptic, which means the line on which eclipses may occur, and does not alter at all from year to year. The ecliptic is thus the most constant of all celestial phenomena. But a circle has no natural beginning, and man therefore had to ordain a beginning from which celestial phenomena could be measured. Nowadays this seems to be most readily provided by the equator, which is a great circle in the sky lying directly over the earth's equator. Another great circle is imagined as lying at right angles to the first and passing through the north and south poles. The north and south poles of the sky are, naturally, those points on the celestial sphere which are immediately over the terrestrial poles. Measurements made along the equator are spoken of as made in 'right ascension', and those towards the poles as made in 'declination'.

In earlier times, when most celestial measurements were designed to give the position of the sun, moon, or a planet, it was more con-venient to measure from the path these bodies actually follow. This had the advantage that high numbers were not required; measure-ments along the solar path were given in signs of the zodiac, and measurements at right angles to this were said to be in 'latitude'. But how did the zodiac come to have 360 degrees, and to be divided into twelve signs?

The idea of dividing all circles into 360 degrees originated inde-pendently in Babylon, Egypt, and China, as an obvious approxima-tion to the length of the year, which brings the sky back to the same point after 365·2422 days. Similarly, the division of the year into twelve is due to the fact that this is a more convenient number than can be obtained from an inconstant variation between twelve, thirteen, and fourteen months, as used to happen in countries where the calendar was wholly determined by the moon. All months are, however, originally moon-periods, as their name tells us. And in Islamic countries the month still begins, as it used to in ancient Greece and many other lands, with the first appearance of the new crescent of the moon after sunset.

The zodiac originated, then, as a time-measuring device, without any notion of people being 'born under' different signs. So there is no need to reject the zodiac as a superstition, which originally it

17

certainly was not. Where and how it was first used is the main subject of this book, together with the related questions of why the signs were twelve in number, and where and how they received the names which they still bear.

The importance of the number twelve in the study of the stars is not due merely to the fact that it is almost the number of new moons in a year. A lunar year comprises 354 days, so that it is eleven days short of a full solar year, and on the 355th day begins the thirteenth lunar month. Apart from this the number 12 is useful in itself because it is the lowest number having two pairs of factors: 3×4, or 2×6. It is small enough for a classification into twelve to be carried easily in one's head, which is not the case with the lunar numbers 27 and 28; a classification into 28 possible types is obviously more troublesome to remember than a division into only twelve. This element of convenience explains the frequent choice of twelve as a symbolic or 'magic' number, as in the twelve apostles, the twelve stones of the high priest's breastplate, the twelve days of Christmas, similar lists in other folk-songs, and the thirteen of the witches' coven (representing the sun and the twelve months or signs).

'Mere superstition' is never any explanation of anything, at least among fairly backward peoples; for when there is no practical reason for a belief, there is no reason for it ever to have grown up at all. Only a relatively sophisticated culture like our own would believe in superstitions of no known origin or purpose, such as that black cats should be 'lucky', though nobody knows why. Today, many people think it superstitious to believe that a person is influenced by the sign under which he or she was born. Others take the effect to be perfectly real and factual, probably because it is not in any way a guess or a matter of choice, but a firm datum obtained by calculation.

For centuries it has been customary in the West—though not in India—to begin the zodiac from the vernal equinox. This is the point where the sun appears to cross the equator from south to north at the spring equinox of the northern hemisphere; and the event occurs annually on March 20th, 21st, or 22nd. It is, however, fairly obvious, and also known from ancient records, that in earlier times men, even at a high state of civilization, were frequently unable to locate these dates exactly, or those of the other equinoxes and solstices, by observing the sky with the instruments available at the time.

There is an even more crucial difficulty: the equinox never occurs in exactly the same spot two years in succession, but its place slowly rotates round the sky, taking about 25,800 years to complete the circuit. This phenomenon is called the Precession of the Equinoxes, and in consequence of it the beginning of the (tropical) zodiac, which is generally known as the First Point of Aries, also moves slowly backwards round the sky at the same rate, amounting to 50 seconds of arc—that is to say, of space, not of time—annually. If it were normally measured from the so-called First Point of Aries, the zodiac would be a moving one, just as the equinoxes and solstices, which are so often marked in diaries, are moving points, recording astronomical events which never occur in exactly the same spot on the sun's path for two years in succession.

It is obvious that early astronomers, working with only the most primitive instruments, if any, would not have chosen to measure their zodiac from an invisible moving point which they were unable to observe. Yet this is precisely what the First Point of Aries is. It has never been anything other than an invisible point; that it also moved was not at first taken for granted, but was discovered to be a fact by Hipparchus about 120 B.C. It seems therefore fairly certain that the original zodiac, in terms of which astrology was doubtless invented, was measured from points which were both visible and fixed, namely the Fixed Stars.

Hence we now have two zodiacs, the tropical or moving zodiac, which is measured from the tropics, and the fixed or sidereal zodiac, which is measured from the fixed stars, but moves forward, when related to the calendar, by one day every 72 years. The difference between the two zodiacs is known by the Indian name of 'ayanamsha', and is gradually increasing at the rate mentioned above, fifty seconds a year; it was thought to amount to 24 degrees exactly in April 1947, so that the year when there was no difference at all must have been A.D. 220. About that date, and for a century or two on either side, astrologers cannot have known which zodiac they were using.

19

The word 'sidereal', by which the zodiac of constellations is distinguished, merely means 'of the stars'; the word 'tropical', which applies to the other version of the zodiac, means that it is measured from the four turning-points of the sun, which are called the tropics. Two of these are not strictly turning-points at all, but only marking-points, being the places where the apparent sun crosses the equator northbound (in March) or southbound (in September). The other two, the Tropics of Cancer and Capricorn, are circles drawn on the sky to mark the positions where the sun reaches its greatest distance from the equator, or on the earth to mark the latitude where this happens directly overhead. These points are called solstices, because the sun appears to stand still, in the sense that it changes from northward to southward motion, or vice versa.

It is often supposed that the constellations received their names on account of fancied resemblances. This is not very plausible in view of the fact that most constellations do not resemble anything at all. There are only two or three whose shape does explain their name, Gemini and Scorpio, and in part Leo. Gemini is so called because it contains two fairly bright stars of approximately the same magnitude, and Scorpio does have, in countries where it is not obscured by street lighting, a tail like that of a scorpion. Leo's shape reminds one of a couchant beast, which explains why it was known to the Babylonians as The Great Dog. Orion in Egypt was always a human figure, but surely the name of the Virgin (which means nothing more remarkable than a young girl) makes it plain that the name was not derived from any fortuitous resemblance.

Remembering that the people who invented these names were quite untouched by the modern predilection for materialism, one ought not to be surprised at finding no material resemblance to virgins, men bearing water-pots, and so forth. The zodiac was not created in an endeavour to establish in heaven signs for supposedly superstitious purposes, but was simply an early attempt to create a calendar based on observation. When the moon was full in the Virgin it told the Babylonians that they could soon expect to see the young corn standing up fresh and virginal in the furrows. This was far more use to them than having months called after historical characters like Julius and Augustus, or mere numbers like the Latin *septem*, *octo*, *novem* and *decem*. Months named after gods, heroes, or numbers would not have been specially useful or memorable; they were much more likely to be named after the events of that season of the year.

Before we can say for certain that the zodiac contains elements of observation, we must try to discover where the observations were expected to be made, whether in the sky or on the earth.

It is obvious that the zodiac would have been much more useful to early civilizations as a calendar incorporating allusions to climatic conditions than as a scheme designed to facilitate fortune-telling. Besides, what is 'fortune-telling'? We know that men practised it centuries ago, but what methods did they use, and what is the connection between that and the belief in being 'born under' one of the twelve signs?

The study of the future is a perfectly normal human practice, and has been almost universal on earth. Only the current fashion for materialism has decreed that prediction of the future must be impossible. This belief, though compulsory in some countries and plausible in others, has not been able to render non-existent the actual faculties which men and women have used. The faculty to perceive what is happening elsewhere in time and space is one which, to some extent, we all possess, though in a sophisticated country few care to develop it, while most prefer to be thought to believe what every one else believes. It is argued that a man cannot 'know' the future because it has not yet happened. This may appear to be good logic, yet the trend of the future is often regrettably plain. It is sometimes quite easy to foresee the future, without needing to call on any special faculties.

Intuition is not by any means just a mysterious and unexplained certitude. It was defined by Jung as 'perception by way of the unconscious, or perception of unconscious contents'. So the act of trying to set one's intuition to work could result, in some circumstances, in what might be called a piece of fortune-telling. There would be nothing abnormal or mysterious about this; we ought not to feel obliged to deny or devaluate such capacities in ourselves, when we know that they have always existed and been widely used among people at very different stages of culture, as for instance the Roman augurs, the Chinese students of the 'I Ching', and the Tibetan State Oracle before it was suppressed by the Chinese conquerors. There is no need to suppose that the use of any such faculties must necessarily be dishonest, insincere, or even incorrect. Admittedly 'controls' cannot be established in order to make the data the same for every observer; but before condemning divination one ought at least to try to practise it for oneself, in order to discover how the faculty works, and what states of mind inhibit it. The present writer has found the Tarot much more reliable than either geomancy or astromancy, but has not experimented much with other methods. This, however, does not imply anything against the other methods, since one's inability to use them may always be for some personal and individual reason.

There is thus a good reason why prediction should be possible, in general, regardless of the method used; it is that the inner self, or unconscious, or 'spirit', has often already decided what result it intends to produce, or what event to provoke, as the conclusion of a current line of thought or action. It will not have told the conscious mind, so the person himself will not consciously know, but in trying to discover this event one is not trying to discover something which 'does not exist', but on the contrary something which has already been definitely decided, though not by the conscious mind. So foretelling the future, when it is thus attempted, is not impossible at all. It only differs from other and more occasional forms of foreknowledge in that it is not involuntary, but is done deliberately, and, if successful, is just another form of telepathy, and is no more impossible or extraordinary than that.

So any person who maintains that it is always and necessarily impossible to know the future cannot be held to know what he is talking about unless he is prepared to say what methods he himself has used to try to know it, and what limitations or difficulties the practitioner must expect to encounter in trying to do so.

Predicting the future is thus merely a question of having learnt how to set one's intuition to work, and to recognize what types of question one is unlikely to be able to answer; for instance, some methods are useless with questions of time or dates. After all, the study of the unconscious is now a completely respectable academic subject, and there is no obvious reason why some awareness of expected events should not be included in the unconscious, provided we restrict ourselves to the future of persons present in the room. There is an adequate reason why questions of general interest, such as what horse will win tomorrow's race, should in most cases remain unanswered, being outside the foreknowledge of the unconscious, because usually there is no close or direct link between the querent and the quesited, that is to say, between the asker of the question and the answer, or the persons to whom the event is actually going to happen.

This, however, is only mentioned incidentally as an explanation of the widespread practice of prediction; for obviously nothing could be more superstitious than to rule that all the successes prediction has ever scored must be attributed to 'pure chance', ignoring the influence of the unconscious.

How the zodiac became involved with the belief in predicting the future is uncertain. The automatic classification of people by the period during which they were born was perhaps not the original method. Plato, in the *Phaedrus*, speaks of the 'soul', or as we should nowadays say, the 'unconscious', choosing to follow one of the twelve gods. And naturally these gods were not mere idols made of wood and stone—or mud, as Christians have often supposed, being perhaps misled by the apocryphal story of Bel and the Dragon—but were quite genuine patterns which actually worked in the collective mind. Besides, the choice of which god to follow would not be made by the conscious mind; if it were, many women would choose before the age of twenty to devote themselves to Aphrodite as the goddess of love, and then later would want to make a choice more in accord with their real nature, when they found that life as a temple prostitute was not their ideal. The 'choice', as Plato called it, was not really a conscious one, but merely the recognition of what kind of spirit was trying to express itself through one's inner being; for instance, if one has a natural inclination for poetry, music, or divination, then one's ruling power is plainly Apollo.

So perhaps originally, when it was still thought that the 'soul' exercised a choice in order to discover its real nature, the classification may have been according to the way people chose to occupy their time, all huntsmen being 'ruled' by Diana, and 'the servants of Poseidon' being merely another way of saying 'sailors'. But later, when this purely religious attitude to the problem of choice began to fade or to appear too difficult, men began to think of the rulers of the zodiac no longer as spiritual powers, but as the physical bodies of the 'planet sacred to Hermes' and the rest, and later still as mere planets.

The twelve signs were justifiably called in Greek a zodiac, since they are all animals except one inanimate object, The Scales, naturally sacred to Hephaistos the smith, and three and a half human signs, namely the Twins, the Virgin, the Waterman, and the former half of the Archer.

Not being a physical body, the zodiac has no gravitational pull: hence the alarm and discomfort felt by scientists at the idea of people believing in it, and their strong desire to disprove any 'mysterious influence of the stars'. Yet the influence interpreted by astrologers in calculating horoscopes is quite simply gravitational attraction, for in every horoscope the longitudes of the planets are calculated from the centre of the earth and not from the place of observation. This, of course, was not the practice two thousand years ago; but if the difference it makes, called parallax, were allowed for, and the planets' light used instead of their weight, the moon's position when it is near the horizon could be over a degree out, and in that case horoscopes for its return to its natal place would be two hours wrong, which would alter them completely.

Not many astrologers would now attribute to the zodiac a physical influence in the form of radiation from the fixed stars. If such an influence existed, the zodiac should not be divided into twelve segments of thirty degrees each, but should respond principally to the location of the Milky Way and of stars of the first two magnitudes, which it does not. A simpler solution would be to compare the zodiac to the earth's magnetic field, in consonance with the theory of relativity. Even so, no explanation arises for a division into twelve rather than any other number; and the signs would have to be measured from the sun's perigee and apogee, or else from the four natural turning-points of the tropical year (the equinoxes and solstices), for which there is no extant evidence.

A third possible explanation of how there could be a correspondence between events in the zodiac and events on earth might be 'synchronicity'. By this word, coined by C. G. Jung, is meant that every event—in so far as it is produced not by one urgently overriding force, but by various approximately equal but not quite constant or calculable forces—is characteristic of the moment at which it occurs and of the interacting forces then in play.

If this principle be sound, then to some extent divination should be possible, provided that the diviner could quite suppress the influence of his own personal expectation and preference—which he would certainly find difficult. This would explain reported cases of diviners foretelling events with which they had no apparent connection. And similarly the birth of a child to independent life would be characteristic of the moment, and thus a horoscope could have a degree of meaning without obliging us to believe in any 'mysterious influence of the stars'.

The focus of this notion is that patterns of thinking do exist, and not only in our conscious minds, but most of all in instinct. Common examples are the untaught skill of birds in building nests, or in migration, or the group-mind of a termitary. These patterns are called archetypes, and Jung has shown that they do not need to be communicated in language, but occur spontaneously, without communication or instruction, consciously or unconsciously, in widely separated individuals. So the group-mind of the human race is real, and does work in certain patterns, of which the zodiac could be one.

What of the origin of this particular archetype? Some archetypes, such as Sun-god and Earth-mother, grow out of the inescapable analogies of natural phenomena; another example is the association of the colour red with blood, war, vitality, and the planet Mars, which becomes very red when in perigee. Others, such as the Christian cross and the Muslim crescent, have been invented at a particular period and may not influence all humanity. These started as mere signs or emblems of a community, but became so charged with meaning that they rapidly rose to the rank of psychological symbols, and finally, to those who accept them, inevitable patterns. An archetype is an apparently inevitable mental pattern common to large groups of people; it may be described as a natural metaphor, like the Balance of Justice, which to us now is an inevitable notion, but was not so to palaeolithic man.

There is nothing patently inevitable about the signs of the zodiac; we could easily imagine them in another order. And if their names are arbitrary, as they seem to be, where is the inevitability which must characterize a universal idea?

In the psychological realm we all know the enormous importance

25

of first impressions. A bird, when it emerges from the shell, adopts as its parent the first living creature it sees, and this impression is ineffaceable, as Konrad Lorenz and others have demonstrated.

An idea, in fact, tends to work in the terms in which it was conceived, or perhaps rather, in whatever terms best express the original idea. Monsieur Guillotin was horrified by the political use to which his invention was put, but in effect it remained what it always was, a humane killer. The Christian Churches were all founded to propagate the teaching of Christ, and though they have often done the opposite they are still thought of as organizations to that end. Islam still wears the shape of its desert origin, and Communism the shape of the protest it now no longer needs to make. So possibly the zodiac may still work in its ancient shape despite the ignorance and defiance of astrologers.

2. The Rediscovery of the Ancient Zodiac

BEFORE the equinox could be reliably located men would not have chosen to measure the zodiac from such a point. Two thousand years ago there may have been half a dozen men on earth who could locate the equinox, but there is no reason to think there was anyone at all in 1000 B.C. Those astrologers today who maintain that the zodiac is incredibly ancient, and that it has always been measured from the equinox, are evidently up against a difficult problem.

Nowadays an astrologer has only to look up in his ephemeris to see where the equinox falls; the problem has been solved for him by the ephemeris-maker, so that he forgets that it ever was a problem. Twenty centuries ago, however, the position of the equinox was so unimportant that it was largely ignored, as we can see from the following quotation from Manilius: 'So one degree in tropical signs is to be distinguished, which moves the world and alters the seasons ... Some place this power in the eighth degree, others prefer the tenth, and there has even been a writer who has allotted to the first degree the alteration and shortening of the days.' (Book III *ad fin.*) Manilius, who is still a well-known writer on astrology, will not have been the only person to think that it did not greatly matter if one was a bit vague about where the true equinox fell. For quite evidently, as can be confirmed by quotations from the Michigan Astrological Papyrus, from Pliny (*Nat. Hist.* XVIII, 59), from Columella (IX, 14), from the *Apotelesmatica of Pseudo-Manetho*, from Achilles Tatius, and elsewhere, the sign Aries was not normally in those days taken to begin from the spring equinox.

This, however, is a relatively recent rediscovery, and the credit for it belongs to an Irishman named Cyril Fagan, who first published his findings in 1947. His reasoning collided head-on with the habits and beliefs of astrologers, who for some fifteen hundred years had been quite happily using a zodiac measured from the equinox.

27

When the light of this rediscovery began to shine in at the windows of occidental astrologers, naturally their first temptation was to pull down the blinds. For the revelation raised several awkward questions. Was the current zodiac now to be abandoned, though it had worked to everyone's apparent satisfaction for 2,000 years? Did the original version of the zodiac work better, or indeed did it work at all? Much difficulty was caused by asking which zodiac should be called fixed, and which should be labelled movable. And, worst of all, were all horoscopes now to be altered?

It is now evident that all horoscopes ought to be altered, because the oldest version of the zodiac was without doubt that measured from the fixed stars. And the stars from which it was measured are known: they were Aldebaran, or the Bull's Eye, in 15° of Taurus; Antares, or the Scorpion's Heart, exactly opposite in 15° of Scorpio; Regulus, the Lion's Heart, in 5° of Leo; and Spica, the Ear of Corn, in 29° of Virgo. But since European astrologers have for centuries been using the movable zodiac, owing to precession the Bull's Eye has moved forwards outside the constellation of the Bull and is now said to be in 8° of the Twins; and similarly the Scorpion's Heart is now said to be not in the Scorpion at all, but in Sagittarius, and the Lion's Heart is in the Virgin. In fact, till recently the original form of the zodiac was quite unknown in the occident, or rather, though the constellations were not unknown, they were not used.

But the alteration caused no small jolt, partly because followers of the sidereal version of the zodiac were able to show that their system worked at least as well as the other, and partly because their measuring-point lay no fewer than 24° away (in 1947) from the First Point of Aries. This meant that four-fifths of the entire population were no longer born under the sign to which they had been accustomed, but under the preceding constellation. Four-fifths of all Leonians were indignant at being pushed backwards into Cancer, four-fifths of all Cancerians complained that they could not possibly be under Gemini, the Geminians proved that they could not be under Taurus, and so on until the entire circle was in an uproar.

Everyone took for granted that the constellations must have the same influence as the signs of the same name—which was indefensible and self-contradictory—and on this basis proved the sidereal zodiac impossible, and thus excused themselves, in their own eyes, from examining the evidence. One lady even held a meeting for the express purpose of getting the sidereal zodiac condemned by the popular vote of an audience which had never studied it, but only heard a debate on the subject. At this meeting certain statistics were not allowed to be read out, for fear they might prove the case, and the chairman rather thoughtlessly remarked at the end: 'We need more statistics!' Such was the chaos in the world of astrology.

Although there is no need to suppose that the zodiac has any physical influence, sidereal astrologers were probably gratified by the discovery of a quite outstandingly large ultra-violet nebula one degree east of Spica, that is to say, on the measuring-point of the sidereal zodiac.*

The latest developments, though they have no relevance to the history or meaning of the zodiac, have been rather unexpected, at any rate by those who set a high value on promiscuous disbelief. For if astrology does not work at all, there can be no question of one astrological method being any better or worse than any other; on that supposition all methods must be equally worthless. One system of prediction might for a time have a run of luck, but no system, however apparently irrational, could be any worse than any other.

But since the rediscovery of the original version of the zodiac, and in spite of all the resistance of tradition and inertia, it appears that more and more students of astrology are becoming converted to its use, and the tropical version is being gradually abandoned, except by those professional astrologers who have been committed to the other for too long to risk change. The reason for this alteration of view appears to be not mere theoretical argument, but the empirical results of work done. Nevertheless, any comparative evidence, however convincing, must be, on the above assumption, illusory.

In the last thirty years astrologers have realized the value of supporting their belief with statistics. Up to the present the best figures produced have been those of Donald A. Bradley in a very thorough publication called *Profession and Birthdate*.† Working on the published birthdates of 2,492 American clergymen, Mr Bradley found for the sun's position between 79° and 109° of tropical longitude a probability ratio of −4·54, which is rated at odds of well over

* *Sky and Telescope Magazine*, U.S.A., May 1959.
† Llewellyn Publications, California.

100,000 to 1 against the result being merely accidental. This was supported by odds of nearly 1,000 to 1 for the frequency of Mercury in Aries, and about 30 to 1 for Mars or Venus in Aries and Leo respectively. Further, Mr Bradley's figures consistently favoured the sidereal zodiac against the tropical, which of course they ought not to do if the zodiac is entirely meaningless.

On the other side, in the nineteen forties an American astronomer named Hynek decided to disprove some part of astrology, and chose for this purpose the aphorism that the aspects of Mercury indicate the intelligence of the person born. His results succeeded in disproving this, to the annoyance of the more dogmatic astrologers; but the more empirical declared that they had long since discovered for themselves the falsity of this traditional aphorism, as of various others in the textbooks. In fact had Dr Hynek consulted them they could have saved him trouble!

The difficulty always is to obtain sufficient birth-data, especially if the hour is wanted; and the hour is always said to be the most important factor. One cannot easily look up the dates of birth of a thousand divorced couples to compare with those of a thousand happily married couples; and yet such a comparison ought to be illuminating.

An even more curious development is the latest 'synetic' zodiac. The measurement of the circle from Spica in 29° Virgo may have been traditional, but it left open the question of whether that point was exact or only approximate. It is hard to imagine any empirical test which would decide the matter.

Yet a solution was found, and published over the signature of Garth Allen in *American Astrology Magazine* for May 1957. The method employed was based on disasters causing much loss of life. The Krakatoa eruption on August 27th, 1883, cost over 30,000 lives, and that of Mont Pelée in Martinique, on May 8th, 1902, took even more. It has long been traditional to cast horoscopes for the sun's passage across the equator and through the tropics of Capricorn and Cancer—the equinoxes and solstices. It was now thought that, if the sidereal version of the zodiac were superior, there should be significance in horoscopes drawn for the entry of the Sun and Moon into the constellations. Mr Allen computed the Moon's entry into Capricorn preceding both these disasters, and found them suggestive but inexact. They suggested that Saturn should be exactly on the horizon, so he recalculated the charts for that moment, and in both of them the moon turned out to be in the same minute of longitude, merely 29° 54' Sagittarius sidereal. This, he thought, might mean that the celestial longitude which he was calling 29° 54' Sagittarius ought to be called 0° 0' Capricorn.

He then made similar calculations for many of the worst disasters in American history—the 20 worst train wrecks, 126 worst mine disasters, explosions, fires in public buildings, and so forth. In 14 of the 126 mine disasters Saturn was within 100 minutes of an angular cusp, and the odds against this happening by chance he computed at nearly 100,000 to 1. The alteration in the Moon's longitude did not, as one might expect, sometimes strengthen and sometimes weaken the indications of disaster; a correction of −6' consistently strengthened and a correction of +6' consistently weakened the indications. Finally, by using the Sun as well as the Moon, a correction of −6' 5" was arrived at. In consequence every horoscope may now be marked not only SZ or TZ, according as the sidereal or tropical zodiac is being used, but 'Sy Z' for 'synetic'.

The entries of the Moon into the tropical signs were so patently useless that in fact they were never used; and to anyone accustomed to the vagueness of predictions from 'solar entries' into the signs of that zodiac in the last hundred years it must seem very surprising that so precise a correction as −6' 5" should seem possible, and even more that it should be accepted. Why are astrologers not taking the path of least resistance? Because, of course, to them astrology is not a superstition where method does not matter, but a serious branch of study, what in Latin is called *disciplina* and in current usage a science.

When we attempt to trace the history of the zodiac, we shall find that the sidereal version is the older. The younger version was adopted, more or less by mistake, through the enormous prestige of Claudius Ptolemy, who wrote apparently favouring it between A.D. 120 and 150. From the astronomical point of view this method of measurement, as used today, is the most convenient now that we have well-equipped observatories; but for an early civilization with neither tradition nor equipment it was out of the question. And if, as we have seen, an idea will continue to work in the racial mind in the terms in which it was first devised, then for astrological purposes the original mental pattern of the sidereal zodiac may evoke in that mind a greater response than the newer tropical pattern.

In either case it is worth quoting Ptolemy's reason for adopting the tropical zodiac: 'The zodiac, being a circle, has no natural beginning, so the sign of the Ram, which begins from the Vernal Equinox, is taken as the beginning of the twelve; and, as if the zodiac were a living being, they make it begin with the excessive moisture of spring, and make the other seasons follow, because all creatures in their first youth have an excess of moisture and, like the spring, are still delicate and growing.' (*Tetrabiblos* I, 10.)

Nothing could be less scientific than these words of the great scientist! For they state quite clearly that Cancer owes its influence to the fact of following the summer solstice. Then what happens in the southern hemisphere, where Cancer follows the winter solstice? Logically, the influence of Cancer must be replaced by that of Capricorn. But Ptolemy, of course, had never heard of the southern hemisphere, and so indefensible is his argument that modern astrologers have tacitly let it drop, even when they use his zodiac.

People are sometimes surprised that the great astronomers Hipparchus and Ptolemy should have concerned themselves with astrology. But are they likely to have respected the prejudices of our age rather than their own? To them it was a hypothesis worth exploring, like so many others.

In the same way we are obliged to accept the zodiac as a geocentric phenomenon. It has been claimed that, since the discovery that the earth is not the centre of the solar system, the sun and not the earth should be the centre of the horoscope. But we live on the earth, not on the sun, and accordingly the horoscope shows the directions of influences converging on the earth.

In tracing the history of the zodiac we are obliged, for brevity's sake, to speak as if the constellations and signs exerted an influence; but, as we have seen, this influence, if it exists, may come from the racial mind and not from cosmic rays or gravitational pull. It may, in fact, be a projection of thought, a piece of racial imagination, and yet a valid projection if the racial mind does work in that way.

This will seem improbable to the extraverted person who likes to think nothing so real as historical facts and kickable objects. But meaning is not a function of either historical fact or physical sensation. The power of an idea is independent of both past history and physical substance. Since the power of a collective idea can be tremendous in politics, perhaps it may also be in other ways.

Meanwhile, the obscure part of the trail is its beginning in the past. So let us begin at the end and work backwards, exploring history, tradition, and the implications for human imagination of the expected correspondences of sky and earth.

3. *What Astrology Is and Does*

WHEN a person having no knowledge of astrology first comes across the subject, very probably one of the earliest questions he may want to ask will be: 'How scientific is it?' or 'How reliable is it?' The answer is that, if by 'scientific' you mean 'regularly using consistently factual data interpreted according to known and consistent principles', it is completely scientific. When a person declares that at his birth the sun was in so many degrees, minutes, and seconds of some given sign, and also states the year and place of his birth, this enables anyone to calculate that his Ascendant (which means the degree of the zodiac rising on the eastern horizon) was in however many degrees and minutes of whatever sign it actually was. Reliable, however, astrology is not—not because predictions sometimes fail, but because different students may make diametrically opposite predictions. In science this never happens, though scientists make predictions every day; and a learned study which, however consistently it follows its principles, yet leaves room for different students to come to opposite conclusions, cannot fairly be called reliable.

It was in the generation after Aristotle that astrology took the Greek world by storm. Many astonishing predictions were made, and in the stories these predictions usually came true, for there is rarely any point in telling a story about a prediction which failed—though we shall cite one in a future chapter.

It is not obvious why it should ever have appeared likely that character or events might be foretold by noting what planets or constellations were rising at the birth of a baby. But nevertheless it remains true that the horoscopic datum, and therefore the horoscope itself, is a scientific fact from which no one will ever escape so long as he lives. Foretelling the future, for instance, from the fact that on a certain day both the Moon and Venus were seen from Babylon inside a single halo, was a common practice in Babylonian civilization; but why men began to imagine that the chart of the heavens for the moment of birth represented a kind of indelible stamp made

34

on the 'native', as the person born is called, is a mystery to which nobody has yet suggested any solution. Yet since the analysis of character and the prediction of events, by astrology, have played a considerable part in several ancient civilizations, and still continue in our own time, it may be of interest to describe how they were done and for that matter still are done.

By derivation the word 'horoscope' means 'a consideration of the hour', and is quite correctly applied, since considerations drawn from a mere knowledge of the month of birth are not sufficient and do not constitute a horoscope.

The sun, on whose heat and light our lives depend, is naturally the most important body in any horoscope. It is said to represent the desires of the heart and to be the most essential element of character. The two other most important elements of the horoscope are the Moon and the Ascendant. The Moon is taken to represent one's manner and general style of behaviour; but the Ascendant, which has sometimes been thought to represent the body, derives its influence exclusively from the sign of the zodiac rising on the eastern horizon, modified by any planets which may be rising also. Thus if a man has the Sun conjoined to the restrictive influence of Saturn, but the Moon affected by the expansive influence of Jupiter, he will be habitually and chronically depressed, but his friends will not realize this because he will try to compensate for it by a cheerful or jovial manner. But conversely, if his Sun is in conjunction with Jupiter and his Moon afflicted by Saturn, he will be a born optimist but in manner and clothes rather careless and dirty.

But apart from the Sun, Moon and Ascendant every planet has its own character. Jupiter represents cheerfulness, expansion, optimism and prosperity, but Saturn the opposite—restriction, pessimism and poverty. Venus is the planet of love and friendship, and she and Jupiter are called benefics because the events they cause are the sort men like; Mars and Saturn, on the other hand, are called malefics, because the events attributed to them are most frequently harmful. Mars is not always and unmitigatedly evil, for, although he is the planet of violence, he also 'rules' (i.e. corresponds to) sport, all forms of muscular exertion, and masculinity. Venus, of course, is always regarded as feminine, and no doubt it was on account of astrology that the planet came to have this character. Mercury, the little

35

planet of children which never runs more than 28° from the Sun its father, has no sex, but 'rules' trade and commerce, ambiguity, reading and writing, and thievery—perhaps because small children, though they often have a vivid sense of 'me' and 'mine', inevitably only develop later a sense of 'you' and 'yours'.

After Uranus had been discovered, at the end of the eighteenth century, it was decided by astrologers, or 'discovered' as they would say, that this was a very dangerous planet, having rulership over electricity and inventions, dramatic events, and the unexpected generally. Similarly Neptune, discovered in 1840, signifies renunciations and many other forms of catastrophe, nervous agitation, and all morbid forms of excitement. Though Uranus can occasionally act as a benefic, enabling people to take advantage of opportunities against which most sensible neighbours would warn them, the influence of Neptune is almost uniformly disastrous, particularly in combination with Mars, for that corresponds to unwise acts performed in a fit of violent agitation. Pluto, however, discovered in 1930, is not so bad; this is frequently the influence under which young people first leave home.

The distances apart of the planets determine whether they have any influence on each other. For instance, if Mars and Jupiter are 60, 90, 120, or 180 degrees apart, they are thought to exert a combined influence weaker but similar to that which they would exert if they were in conjunction. The margin of error allowed for 'aspects' has usually averaged, in Europe, eight degrees. And until recently occidental astrologers used to think that 'aspects' measuring approximately one-third ('trine') or one-sixth ('sextile') of the zodiac were 'good', but those which divided the circle by two ('opposition') or four ('square') were 'bad'. At one stage any misfortune, such as a broken arm, could be attributed to a 'bad' aspect of any planet, even Jupiter or Venus, and the fact that the aspect was 'bad' was held to outweigh completely the fact that the planet was 'good'. In India, on the other hand, all planets in signs 120 degrees apart are considered to be 'in trine', though their actual distance apart may vary from 91° to 149°.

Events are predicted by various techniques. Nowadays it is frequently the custom in the West to set up a chart for the moment when the Sun or Moon reaches either the exact minute and second of longitude that it held at birth, or the opposite point. The 'solar return' thus calculated describes the events of the ensuing year, and the 'lunar return' (or demi-lunar) those of the ensuing month or fortnight. These charts need to be calculated with considerable accuracy, for it makes all the difference between a dramatic disaster and an extravagant triumph, whether the planet on the ascendant be Uranus or Jupiter or Saturn; or maybe no planet at all is there.

Another technique which used to be very popular for foretelling the future was the 'day for a year' method. By this the horoscope was 'progressed' so that, for example, the planets for the thirtieth day after birth made mutual aspects, and also aspects to the horoscope of birth, from which the events of the thirtieth year of life could be foretold. There was also a somewhat similar system called 'primary directions', in which a measure of, usually, one degree was taken to be equivalent to one year. An intermittent argument went on, however, as to whether the motion corresponding to one year should be exactly one degree or the average daily motion of the Sun, namely 59' 8", or even the amount of motion actually accomplished by the Sun on the corresponding date in the native's youth. It is easy to see that if Venus, the planet of love and friendship, comes to an aspect of Mars, the 'natural significator' of masculinity, the native, if a female, would be expected to have a love-affair or get married; but if the Sun came to a 'bad' aspect of Uranus, the planet of the unexpected, then an unforeseen distraction or disappointment would be more likely.

In casting a horoscope the first thing necessary is a circle to represent the heavens. Some centuries ago it was quite common to evade the difficulty of drawing a circle by drawing a traditional square form divided into twelve compartments, but nowadays convenient 'books of blank maps' can easily be obtained from specialist booksellers. In every horoscope cast in the northern hemisphere, south is at the top and north at the bottom; east, representing that which is coming into being, is on the left, and west on the right. The whole space of the horoscope is almost always divided into twelve segments, which are called 'houses', and are drawn on the diagram as if they were all equal. But careful inspection of the figures written against the 'cusps' which divide them will usually reveal that they vary widely from the 30° which would make them all equal. A few horoscopes may be drawn according to the 'equal house' systems, either counting from the Ascendant or from the Midheaven, but most horoscopes have very unequal houses. The figures are given in various published tables, except for the equal house systems, which do not require any. The commonest system is that called after the well-known seventeenth-century astrologer Placidus. It became popular because it was adopted by the principal English publisher of astrological literature, but cannot possibly be right because in the Arctic Circle it frequently fails to work. In the sixteenth century the most popular system in Europe was probably that called after Regiomontanus, but it fell out of use, not because it was wrong but because tables according to the rival system of Placidus were more easily available. The only theoretically impregnable system is that of Campanus (that is to say, Giovanni Campanella, who died about 1297). This divides the celestial sphere in what one would think was the most reasonable and scientific way, by means of the three great circles which all intersect one another at right angles—namely, the horizon, the meridian, and the prime vertical; but even in the latitude of England its results are so surprising that sooner than accept such unequal houses many astrologers still use other systems.

Over two thousand years ago, when astrology was still at its beginnings, there were only eight houses, and this is probably the reason why the eighth house is called the House of Death; at one time it was the last. More recently there have been twelve houses, and it may be of interest to give a list of the departments of life to which they correspond:

First: personality generally.
Second: money and finance.
Third: brothers and sisters, short journeys.
Fourth: one parent, usually the father, the last period of life.
Fifth: children, pleasure, theatres, gambling.
Sixth: health and servants, the armed forces.
Seventh: marriage and open enemies.
Eighth: death and other people's money.
Ninth: religion and long journeys.
Tenth: profession and standing in the world, one parent.
Eleventh: friends, also children again.
Twelfth: secret enemies, hospitals.

The first thing in a horoscope that an astrologer needs to know is what sort of a chart it is, for besides being that of a man, a dog, a limited company, or a government, it may be a solar or lunar return applying to any of these. When he has been told this essential information, the astrologer looks first to see which planets are nearest to the meridian and horizon, for these are the most vital sensitive points; and it is noteworthy that persons born at midnight have more ambition than those born at noon. It is as though those born at noon do not feel that they have to make any special effort to remain at the top, having been born there, whereas those born at midnight, being almost equally strongly under the influence of the Sun, want admiration and feel that they deserve it, but never seem to have enough of it, because the earth gets in their way.

One clearly practical use for a horoscope is in ascertaining whether or not two people will get on well together. Naturally it is not possible to foresee whether they will actually meet; but if they meet and marry it is quite easy to tell even without knowing the precise hour of birth of either, whether there will be serious disagreement. This technique is referred to by Jung in his book *The Interpretation of Nature and the Psyche*. All that is necessary is to consider the planets in each horoscope as making whatever aspects they do make to those of the other. If the Sun in one chart falls on the Moon of the other, then the relationship will be harmonious. If, on the other hand, Saturn or Mars of the one falls on Neptune of the other, sooner or later there will be disruption. In such a case divorce would not be for mere infidelity, but because the couple decide that they simply cannot bear to live together. There are on record marriages which have ended in crimes of violence, but the surprising thing is that these unfortunate cases can always be forecast, not only by an exceptionally gifted astrologer, but by any person able to read the chart.

Here, then, as an example of a horoscope, is that of the emperor Augustus. It has been calculated not in the sidereal zodiac, as used today, even less in the Tropical Zodiac used in the Middle Ages, but in the Hellenistic Zodiac, which Theogenes or any other astrologer would probably have used at the time. As can be seen, the Sun was close to the rising point, and the Moon in Capricorn. The date usually given for the emperor's birth is September 23rd, 63 B.C.; but since we know from his coins that he had the Moon in Capricorn,

39

and are also told that he had an excellent horoscope, there is no question of his having been born when the Moon was in Aquarius, or the Sun disastrously 'afflicted'; and since both these things were the case on September 23rd, Augustus was obviously born on the 22nd, when the Moon was very well aspected and in the right sign.

Indian astrology differs from occidental astrology in various ways, principally in that it divides the life of every person into several periods of which the West knows nothing. These periods come under the dominion not only of the seven planets known to the ancients, but also of Rahu and Ketu. These are not planets at all, but simply the points where the Moon, which never gets more than about 8° away from the ecliptic, actually crosses it. In position they are always exactly opposite one another, and their motion amounts to 3' retrograde per day.

Another point occasionally marked on horoscopes is the so-called 'Part of Fortune'. This is not a planet but an imaginary point found by adding to the Ascendant the distance from the Sun to the Moon. Naturally it has no influence of its own, but its aspects are thought to give some idea of the native's destiny or of some characteristics of it. By using the planets instead of the Moon there is a whole series of other 'parts' or points which can be calculated in a similar manner. They have evocative names like 'the pomegranate' and 'the lightning-flash', but are little regarded and not often encountered.

4. *Medieval Magic and Psychology*

In the last twenty centuries the sign of the Virgin has aged about thirty years. She used to be a pretty girl of fifteen, and now she is represented as a hard and selfish 'old maid'. How has this come about?

One might expect that so long as the signs of the zodiac are unaltered their characters would remain the same century after century. Astrologers would certainly think so. But on what, in fact, is their character based? Partly on symbolism, but partly also on observation. The sociological value of the writings of astrologers is the picture they give us of the mental attitudes of their epoch, the social structure, the professions, and so forth.[1] All this is observed. But other elements in the character of each sign are provided by the symbol and its attributions, to which astrologers feel that observation should somehow be made to fit.

Since Claudius Ptolemy decided to regularize the distribution of signs between the four 'elements' (fire, earth, air and water) and the three 'qualities', it has been necessary to think of Virgo as the mutable sign of Earth; and since Earth was considered a cold, practical element, Virgo had to be represented as cold and practical.

The three 'qualities' were derived from Ptolemy's system of measuring the zodiac from the solstices and equinoxes. The most important and effective signs were those which followed on the cardinal points, and were called Cardinal; they were said to act of themselves. Next came the Fixed signs, which were stable rather than active, and finally the Mutable or Common signs, which depended on the action of others. The Virgin is one of these.

Further, the ruling planet of Virgo is Mercury, the messenger of the gods, whose realm of activity covers writing, thinking, commerce, theft and communication; so the Virgin had no choice but to be intellectual and the perfect secretary, whose gift is for dealing with subtleties and little things.

Such are the *a priori* characteristics to which the sign of the Virgin has been expected to conform, regardless of observation. They comprise a large part of the following typical description of Virgo, to be found in Vivian Robson's *Student's Textbook of Astrology*, printed in 1922. The words entirely in capitals are suggested by the symbol of the VIRGIN, and those with a capital letter are derived from the attributions of Mercury, Earth, or the Mutable Quality, but those in italics suggest *Leo* rather than Virgo.

Cool, Practical, Discriminating, *very Critical, often destructively so*, Impassive, Faddy Over Little Things, very Inquisitive, MODEST, RETIRING, faithful, Intellectual, *strong opinions*, fond of Art, Literature, Science, and Mathematics, fond of collecting, Good Memory and Reasoning Power, not very original, slow to anger and forgiveness, QUIET, Persuasive, Very Good At Detail Work, fond of Gardening, Reading, COOKING AND NEEDLEWORK, etc.; often servile to *rich and distinguished people, fond of telling people their faults*, worry over Little Things but *brave in emergency, insist on respect*, often rather OLD-MAIDISH.

This description differs quite remarkably from the descriptions of fifteen or twenty centuries earlier. Although, from the symbol and its ruler Mercury we have to be told that the Virgonian is quiet and persuasive, at the same time she insists on being respected, is brave but snobbish, indulges frequently in destructive criticism, and is fond of telling people their faults. This may be the typical old maid of fifty, or it may be the self-centred and bossy Lion, but it is far indeed from the pretty maid of fifteen who was the original symbol.

The pretty maid was an angel—she had wings. She represented Astraea, the goddess or heavenly power of Justice, who dwelt on earth in the Golden Age. No wonder that her natives were described as the most helpful and charming in the zodiac! But Ptolemy, when he made Virgo a sign of Earth, could not help but cut off her wings; so now we are presented with this cold, selfish, viperish old maid!

There is, however, a factor of continuity in this surprising change. It is not wholly to be accounted for by a change in social manners (much for the worse, apparently), nor yet by animadversions upon the altered interpretation of the symbol and the possibly defective observational powers of astrologers. For the sign of the Virgin, as tropically measured in 1947, covered the last 24 degrees of the constellation Leo, and only the first 6 degrees of the constellation Virgo. And the Lion, if we read the old astrologers, is a great one for making himself respected, is 'brave in emergency' but not otherwise, is hard and overbearing, destructively critical, and not above telling people their faults.

So we cannot leap to the conclusion that the characters of the zodiac are nonsense. From that one area of the sky which is now called Virgo and two thousand years ago was labelled Leo, astrologers have observed that the people born are cold, overbearing, selfish, critical, and brave in emergency. Two thousand years ago they tacked this observation on to the symbol of the fearless and dominating Lion; more recently they have changed the interpretation of the Virgin in order to make her fit that character. The fact that they have done so suggests that their observations were perhaps not wholly without foundation. The archetype of the zodiac may have been working twenty centuries ago.

For Virgo is not the only sign to have changed its character; the rulership of Mars over Scorpio is another attribution which has become with the passing centuries more problematic. Scorpio, we have been told in recent textbooks, is deep, profound, secretive, fond of mysterious things, penetrating, obscure, and hard to understand. It seems to follow from this that it has not been understood. For anything more in contradiction to the forthright character of Mars would be hard to find. This seems to be a case where the experience of astrologers has moved gradually farther and farther away from the traditional ruling planet, until in the end it is only lip-service to claim Mars as ruler of Scorpio.

The situation was not the same in the seventeenth century, if we can take on trust that human character was really so unpleasant as the astrologers of those days represented it. For their descriptions of the signs were more outspokenly offensive, and form a possibly useful social comparison to our own.

William Lilly in 1647 gives Scorpio the following description: 'A corpulent, strong, able body, somewhat a broad or square face; a dusky, muddy complexion, and sad dark hair, much and crisping; a hairy body, somewhat bow-legged, short necked; a squat well-trussed fellow.'

43

The character to go with this is that of Mars when 'well dignified': 'In feats of war and courage invincible, scorning that any should exceed him; subject to no reason, bold, confident, immovable, contentious, challenging all honour to themselves; valiant, lovers of war and things pertaining thereto, hazarding himself in all perils, unwilling to obey or submit to anybody; a boaster of his own acts; one that slights all things in comparison of victory, and yet of prudent behaviour in his own affairs.' When 'ill dignified' he is 'a prattler, without modesty or honesty, a lover of slaughter and quarrels', and many other things besides.

In the early nineteenth century this becomes (Zadkiel 1835): 'A well-set form of middle stature, rather corpulent; swarthy complexion, black curling hair, broad and plain face. The temper is very unsociable and rash; they are generally revengeful, ungrateful, quarrelsome and wicked; yet of good genius and ready apprehension, excelling in mystery, etc.'

'Mystery' means of course mysterious studies like astrology and occultism. The bad character of Scorpio has for centuries been legendary, in fact Lilly in his translation of Bonatti's aphorisms[2] goes so far as to call its natives 𝕿𝖗𝖆𝖎𝖙𝖔𝖗𝖘 . But the supposed wickedness of this sign was due in part to the accident that one of the few genuinely suggestive resemblances to be seen in the sky is to the tail of a poisonous insect, and in part to the fact that by Ptolemy's scheme of rulerships it was allotted to a malefic planet, namely Mars. Aquarius, which modern astrologers have idealized on account of the incoming 'Aquarian Age', was given a perfectly odious character by Vettius Valens, simply because it was ruled by Saturn.

But the description of character was only one use to which the zodiac was put. A knowledge of it was required for predicting the future, and also for the practice of magic, and therefore during the dark ecclesiastical ages, when only the Church kept alive the flame of learning, the question often arose whether astrology was permissible and orthodox, or whether it ought not rather to be condemned. There are several reasons why one might expect it to be condemned, although belief in it was very general.[3]

For between astrology and magic there could be no very clear distinction so long as men believed that the verification of predictions could be contrived by obliging demons. Besides, astrology could be a public nuisance. Tertullian (about A.D. 155–222) reports with glee that astrologers had been officially expelled from Rome because they were so much consulted by persons wishing to know how long the emperor would live, and whether he could or would be murdered.

By churchmen astrology was rarely regarded as impossible, but quite frequently as dangerous; for if the future could be predicted, were men still responsible for their actions? Might they not begin to pretend that sin had been forced upon them by the stars? The most common attitude to this danger was that of Abelard and Hugh of St Victor, who lived in the eleventh century. They distinguished *naturalia* from *contingentia*, and admitted that prediction was possible of such 'natural' things as sickness, fertility, and the weather, but not of such things as were dependent on God's providence or man's free will. The opponents of astrology liked to claim that it taught determinism, but this was not always a quite honest accusation.

The solution of the problem is quite easy once you know it, but took centuries to discover. Yet an observant astrologer, in the course of ten or twenty years, must easily find among his acquaintances several persons who at different times suffer the same aspect, for example the transit of Uranus over the Sun by conjunction or opposition. Observing them, he expects to notice that, while the aspect is in force, each recipient of it will undergo an experience of the type described in his textbooks as 'Uranian'; but he cannot tell in advance upon what level any given native will take the aspect. Some resent and fight the change in their circumstances, most are made unhappy by having to adapt themselves, a few by taking the tide at flood gain worldly advantage, but others increase their understanding, make spiritual progress, and suffer little or nothing. The influence will arrive in any case, but the free will consists in deciding to use it well or badly, cheerfully or sadly.

It was hard to make this distinction in medieval times, because it was often thought that if anything was predictable by astrology, then everything must be predictable. There seems no reason for this sweeping assumption; it is the usual over-simplification of seeking a one-factor solution, just as some people nowadays talk as if everything could be explained by economics. In Augustine's time people

45

would try to catch the astrologer out by presenting the horoscope of an animal for delineation, and Augustine, though he had abandoned astrology, says that the best astrologers could not be taken in this trap. Modern astrologers, on the other hand, admit that the same horoscope can apply to a man, a dog, and a limited company, if they come into being at the same place and moment.

Augustine, however, was cured of his belief in astrology by learning that a slave and a rich friend had been born at the same moment in two houses not a mile apart—'whence I concluded for certain', says he, 'that true predictions made by consulting the stars were not due to skill but to luck, and false ones not to lack of skill but to lack of luck'.[4] This is a typical piece of that static thinking which regards the horoscope as a story complete in every detail, like a novel whose end is determined before you begin to read, rather than a chart of currents and winds to be used for navigation.

St John Chrysostom, who was born in Antioch in 347 and became Patriarch of Constantinople, argues that it is not the function of astronomy to learn from the stars who are being born, but merely to predict from the hour of birth what is going to happen, which, says Thorndike, 'seems a quite fallacious distinction upon his part'. Although Thorndike agrees in this with St Augustine, all modern astrologers would be against him, and accept Chrysostom's distinction. Chrysostom is trying to argue against astrology, but such was the spirit of his age that he could not help accepting it in part. He criticizes the Magi for their coming to Bethlehem, since as astrologers they ought to have known that their visit would cause trouble, and also for calling Jesus 'King of the Jews', whereas later Christ told Pilate that His Kingdom was not of this world. That, however, is a trap into which fell also the early Christians and even the Churches from time to time.

Not infrequently in medieval times there was discussion whether the planets were living beings—'animals', as it is sometimes translated. If so, they might be capable of sin, as was supposed by Bildad the Shuhite in the Book of Job.[5] Plato was the father of all those who allowed the planets to have souls, and Bernard Sylvester called them gods without being accused of heresy.

The horoscope of Christ was another dangerous topic, since no one wanted to be accused of making God subject to the controlling influence of the heavenly bodies He had created. Roger Bacon wrote to the Pope that in the opinions of astrologers God had willed the nativity of His Son to be in harmony with the constellations, in so far as Jesus partook of human nature.

St Hildegard of Bingen, about 1140, suggested that Christ perhaps chose astrologically favourable moments for the performance of His miracles, although she also claimed that the revelations of the stars concerned the past only, and not the future. Since Our Lord Him-self had said, 'There shall be signs in the sun, and in the moon, and in the stars',[6] and since His birth had been announced by a star, it was natural enough for Christians to believe in astrology. But Thorndike suggests that the story of the star and the three Magi was only inserted into the Gospel to conciliate the very wide belief in astrology in the second century. For it will have seemed only natural to the readers of that time that the birth of the sublimest of all beings should be announced with portents by the sublimest of all sciences.

There is only one record of an astrologer being burnt at the stake, and that was Cecco d'Ascoli in 1327. He had broken a ban imposed upon him by the Inquisitor of Bologna, forbidding him to teach and condemning two of his books; hence he counted as a relapsed heretic. The real reason for his death may well have been personal enmity, since his writings that have come down to us are no more offensive than those of such orthodox thinkers as Albert the Great and Cardinal d'Ailly. He does not advocate, though he suggests the possibility of, conjuring demons out of the sky by incantation.

When medieval characters disapproved of astrology, they almost always did so on the ground that it was possible but wicked. Very unusually Hippolytus, in his so-called *Refutation of All Heresies* (about A.D. 200), maintained that it was irrational and impracticable. This obliged him, of course, to contend that magic likewise was an impossible imposture. His attitude sounds more modern, but why assume that the magician and astrologer are conscious frauds, rather than self-deceived? Hippolytus, like all refuters of heresies, was an uncharitable character.

The difficulty is the common one of trying to have an opinion upon a subject where one is not an expert. What should one say about an unlikely science such as astrology? If one has a real sense of security, and a faith unweakened by any dogmatic obligation to

47

believe or disbelieve without evidence, then one finds it superfluous to have rigid views about the special subjects of others. Yet such security is rare. Hence the need to believe, or disbelieve, in order to feel certain about a picture of the world which is fundamentally weak and invalid because based on dogma rather than understanding.

Ungrounded disbelief is only the reverse of groundless belief, and both are equally superstitious. Faith is not blind; faith is knowledge of what one can do. Those who have faith do not need to go about believing and disbelieving in things for the pleasure of it. And hence there is no occasion to think that one need either believe or disbelieve in astrology. If one is an expert on the subject, one knows what can be done with it; if not, one has only one's own experience on which to erect a supposition, and one knows that that experience is inadequate. The attitude of such a man as Hippolytus, who claims to have proved that it cannot work and rules all evidence unnecessary, is peculiarly unintelligent—though not of course unparalleled in modern times.

Despite the disapproval of Hippolytus and Augustine, and the isolated case of Cecco d'Ascoli, the profession of astrologer does not seem to have been a dangerous one in medieval Europe. Many eminent thinkers accepted astrology in varying degrees, and many astrologers had wealthy patrons and grew rich.

In France the earliest wealthy astrologer known to us is Caecilius Argicius Arborius, who lived at Dax in Aquitaine in the third century A.D., and was the grandfather of the well-known Latin poet Ausonius.[7] His astrology, however, resembles that of the Greco-Roman world, and scholars have concluded that it came to him via Marseilles, and not from the Druids, although we are told by Roman writers that they were experts in divination and discussed the motions of the heavens. A Latin play called *Querolus*, satirizing astrologers, was acted in Aquitaine in the fifth century.

From this time on there were many successful astrologers in France and Italy. Louis XIII employed Morin de Villefranche, and Pope Paul III employed Gauricus, who obligingly proved that Luther would go to Hell because he was born under that much-abused sign Scorpio. This was particularly easy since Luther, like many other people, had several planets in that sign. Not improbably, however,

Gauricus faked not only the hour but also the year, since Cardan and Junctinus and Melanchthon are all agreed against him.

We do not know the name of any astrologer accredited to an English king, but Henry VII's portrait is found in a manuscript of Guido Bonatti's enormous astrological textbook, which had been specially copied for him. Bonatti had a now-forgotten method of judging what he called 'revolutions', meaning in this case the Sun's entry into the cardinal signs. This consisted in determining which planet was to be 'lord of the year', according to rather complicated rules; no planet, for instance, could be lord of the year if it was retrograde or too close to the Sun. He also illustrates the rather useful propensity of astrologers for copying older textbooks without adapting them, when he says that Mars in Taurus in a 'revolution', if oriental, signifies peace both in the parts of Babylon and in the West, but if occidental, epidemics; if retrograde, diseases among children, but if direct, hatred from women—on the authority of Albumasar.

Bonatti's career was long and successful, and his greatest achievement was the defence of Forlì in 1282. At this time he was a prominent and wealthy citizen, well over sixty, and his patron was the town's military commander, Guido da Montefeltro.

Bonatti was very precise in selecting hours for the start of Montefeltro's aggressions. On the chosen day he would mount the tower of San Mercuriale—well-omened name!—and give three signals on a bell, first for the moment to arm, then to mount, and finally to set out.

So successful were these expeditions that after a time Pope Martin IV dispatched an army in order to subjugate Forlì. Montefeltro then consulted Bonatti, who must have spoken to him somewhat as follows: 'I cannot promise you victory in the field, for the signs are contradictory; and besides, I have the horoscope of the enemy commander, which I obtained from a colleague, and for him there are signs of victory and feasting. You, however, are not due to suffer anything unpleasant. We must give all the influences a chance to work—it is no use hoping that some of them will fail—so I suggest that you withdraw your army from the town, and give the women instructions to feast the enemy lavishly; any little rape or seduction will be easily forgiven when we return, for once the enemy troops are drunk we shall rush in and massacre them!'

Montefeltro agreed, the massacre went off as planned, and everyone was delighted, including the women, and especially Bonatti, who was wounded while carrying medicines to the injured; for, since he had predicted this, his reputation now stood higher than ever. The only unsatisfied person was the Pope, who, as soon as convenient, sent a larger army. This time Forlì submitted in earnest, and Montefeltro moved to a district where his military talents would stand a better chance. No doubt Bonatti had advised him that resistance was useless at the moment; and Montefeltro thus becomes one of the clearest examples of the astrological use of free will. He lost his city in either case, but he chose to do so without bloodshed. Later he made his peace with the Pope, and died in the Franciscan Order. Bonatti may possibly have done the same, for quite a number of Franciscans had written on astrology and astrological medicine. ✔

Nor was such study entirely dogmatism and guesswork; it did attempt to relate the human body to the forces of the universe in which we live, and out of this the desire to experiment developed.

A common and easy form of experiment was the strictly astrological one of a 'decumbiture', or horoscope set for the moment of a patient taking to his bed. If in such a case Saturn or Mars was found on the meridian or horizon, the patient would be expected to die, but if Jupiter or Venus, then he would recover quickly; and the Moon's sign, or the sign rising, should indicate that part of the body where the trouble was chiefly located. In general, Aries as the first sign was taken to rule the head, and so on through the zodiac until the last sign, Pisces, ruled the feet (see Plate 2). But this was evidently a little too simple; for Virgo, which rules the bowels, a much commoner site of infection than the feet, rises at sunrise in September, and from then on until the following March cannot rise at all during the hours of daylight. So a scheme was elaborated whereby the head was not always ruled by Aries, but each planet could signify any part of the body, depending on how far it was from its own sign. And a planet in its own sign—that is to say in a sign which it ruled, in its exaltation, or in its triplicity, 'term', or 'face'—was always thought to be well-disposed, even if by nature it was one of the malefics.

It was also expected, of course, that any person having the Sun or the malefic planets in Aries would be especially liable to headaches, and so on all round the circle.

50

At this date the zodiac was simply a tradition whose origin, although unknown, was presumed to be divine. The uses to which it was put were still being elaborated, and there are many extant pictures in which the signs were associated with the seasons; but in Europe they were almost all based on the equinox as starting-point.

One of the first medieval thinkers to appreciate the value of experiment was Albert the Great, a famous churchman who gave much study to astrology and magic, and died two years before Bonatti's triumph at Forlì. He was one of the first to publish lists of observed details on which generalizations might be based, although his observations were neither planned nor systematic. Unlike Augustine and Gregory the Great, he accepted astrology, and solved the problem of free will very easily. 'There is in man a double spring of action, namely nature and the will; and nature for its part is ruled by the stars, while the will is free; but unless it resists it is swept along by nature and becomes mechanical.'[8] This appears to be very true; but for 'will' one might equally well write 'higher self' or 'incarnating entity'.

There was of course a distinct slump in astronomical knowledge in the Middle Ages, but in spite of this astrology never died out, though it sometimes became, through ignorance, as futile as the modern Sunday newspapers with their division of the calendar and the whole population into only twelve types. The Venerable Bede, for example, did nothing unusual when he compiled a list of rules for divination from thunder according to the direction and time of day at which it was heard; many such are known from Constantinople.

Another substitute for horoscopical calculation was the attempt to predict a child's character from the letters of its name, the day of the week on which it was born ('Monday's child is fair of face', and so forth), or, slightly more astronomical, from the day of the moon's age. One fourteenth-century moon-book claims to have been written by Adam from his own experience! The other most popular suppositious author was the prophet Daniel.

But these moon-books can only have been designed for the unlearned. In the time of Charlemagne's successor, Louis the Pious, every great lord had his own astrologer, and William the Conqueror's chaplain was devoted to star-gazing; hence, perhaps, the representation of Halley's Comet in the Bayeux Tapestry. England in the twelfth century had two well-known astrologers, Daniel of Morley and Roger of Hereford; yet in the reign of Henry I considerable consternation was felt when the Archbishop of York died unshriven with a textbook of astrology under his pillow! Since he was already unpopular, the coffin was stoned and the people wished to refuse him Christian burial. The book was the well-known work by Firmicus Maternus, written in Sicily in the fourth century.

By this time the revival of learning, through translations from the Arabic, was going strong. It began perhaps as early as the tenth century, and one of the most famous of Arab astrologers was Albumasar, who died in 886, after spending many years as official astrologer to the Caliph of Baghdad. His book on 'revolutions' was republished in 1905.

Alcandrus, who is quoted by the Emperor Frederick II's magician Michael Scot, gave a list of the 28 'Mansions of the Moon', but since he tells us to discover under which mansion a man is born by a numerological calculation of his name and his mother's, his astronomical knowledge was apparently inconsiderable.

The same remark would apply to some of the methods of the medieval Greek alchemists,[9] which profess to declare whether a sick man will recover, or a runaway slave be found, by turning his name into a number, adding the number of days since the Sun entered Gemini (which was regarded as the beginning of summer), then dividing by 7 or 9 and judging by the house of the horoscope in which the remainder fell.

About the same time John of Salisbury rebukes Thomas à Becket for persistently consulting all kinds of fortune-tellers, even after he became Archbishop of Canterbury.[10] And, as an attempt to satirize astrology, and fortune-telling in general, a 'hermaphrodite's horoscope' was invented in Latin verse, which may be translated as follows:

'Tis said my parents, while my mother carried me,
   Inquired of heaven what the child would be.
Mars said: 'A girl'; Phoebus: 'A boy'; but 'Neither's right!'
   Cried Juno: hence I was hermaphrodite.
They asked my death. 'Hanging,' said Mars; 'With steel run
     through,'

Said Juno; Phoebus: 'Drowning.' All came true.
A tree o'erhangs a stream; I climb; but from its sheath
By chance my sword slips; on to it I fall.
Caught by the foot, my head the wave beneath,
The poor hermaphrodite is pierc'd, hanged, drown'd and all![11]

The eleventh century is the time when we first find diagrams of the astrological man, a human figure with the signs of the zodiac applied to the different parts of the body. One of the earliest bears this legend: 'According to the ravings of the philosophers the twelve signs are thus denoted.'

The distinction between astronomy and astrology begins to be perceptible in the writings of Isidore of Seville about A.D. 630, but was first formulated about the time of Hugh of St Victor, who died in 1141. Hugh distinguished *mathematica*, the science of abstract quantity, from *matesis* (without an H), which meant astrology. In the next century Albert the Great made the distinction dependent upon the length of the E in *mathesis*.

The incapacity of medieval astrologers to use their zodiac accurately is very plain in two books attributed to Hermes Trismegistos. In the *De Revolutionibus Nativitatum*, of unknown date but printed at Basle in 1559, the Father of Wisdom is made to recommend that the sun's motion be taken 'with the instrument mentioned in the Almagest (which the Greeks call The Great Construction)', and that the return of the sun and planets to their places should be calculated by their mean motions, not their actual motions, the length of the solar year being taken as $365\frac{1}{4}$ days less one-hundredth part of a day. This book is the ancestor of the modern custom of calculating annual horoscopes both for individuals and for political prediction, but it assumes the impossibility of computing the exact time of the equinox, besides suggesting that Hermes lived later than Ptolemy. The same difficulty occurs in another book attributed to him.

The interpretation of the signs of the zodiac in terms of mythology and analogy was usual and, as today, very few writers speculated on the origin of the names. One who did was Helpericus, a ninth-century monk who wrote on the ecclesiastical calendar. Some of the names he finds quite simple: Aquarius and Pisces are explained by

53

the rainy season, Leo by the heat, and Libra by the equinox; in Cancer the sun begins to walk backwards. The Scorpion's sting and the Archer's arrow are both compared to the sting of hail-showers, and Capricorn is the lower turning-point of the sun because kids graze uphill, 'as everyone knows'. The Ram, however, was either named because the sun breaks up the frozen earth as a ram attacks with its horns, or else because rams, having slept on their left side all the winter, now start to sleep on their right. In the month of Taurus oxen work to prepare the ripening of the corn, but the explanation of Gemini is an incoherent allusion to Castor and Pollux. Virgo, finally, is so called because the earth is exhausted and no longer bears any fruit—the transition from the pretty girl to the old maid is on the way.

Both in India and in the Greco-Roman world there was a doctrine of a Great Year, at the end of which the planets, and consequently the world, would return to the state of the beginning. Astrologers rather naturally imagined that at creation all the planets stood in the first degree of Aries, and could not help concluding that when this universal conjunction should be repeated there would come an apocatastasis, or restoration of all things; and this, no doubt, is one origin of the doctrine of the millennium and the return of the Golden Age—the other being a misapplication to the physical plane of the doctrine that the soul's ultimate destiny is perfect adaptation and union with God. If the conjunction of all the planets occurred in any other part of the zodiac, the restoration of all things was not expected; in the Middle Ages it was thought that such a conjunction in Capricorn would produce another Deluge, and in Cancer would result in destruction of the world by fire.[12]

The idea is an archetypal one—not just a Freudian longing to return to the peaceful existence of the womb—because it is ultimately unavoidable: the only logical ultimate aim is perfect adaptation on all levels, which means not just the heat-death of entropy, but union with the Creative Force. Hence we find the doctrine of the millennium cropping up everywhere, in the Revelation of St John, in Shelley ('The world's great age begins anew'), in Virgil, in Yeats, in More's *Utopia* and Marx's Socialist state, because the astronomical possibility of a universal conjunction chimes in with the universal yearning for perfection in the human heart.

The length of the Great Year was a matter of speculation, and in India became too long to be interesting, but this was because it could not then be accurately calculated. To discover when all the planets will be conjoined in the first degree of Aries would take an electronic computer, now that three more planets are known. The period of the Great Year, however, could fairly be taken as a little under 26,000 years, since this is the period of the Precession of the Equinoxes.

When the zodiac was first invented, precession was not imagined, and the sun was thought to cross the equator in the constellation Aries always at the same point. In fact the point of crossing moves westward at a speed of about 50·2 seconds of arc per year. Hence it takes about two thousand years to pass through a constellation, and nearly 26,000 to make the tour of the sky. If Mr Fagan is right in concluding that the oldest measured zodiac was defined by the star Aldebàran in the exact middle of Taurus, then the Vernal Equinoctial Point of the northern hemisphere entered the constellation Taurus about 4139 B.C., entered Aries about 1953 B.C., when incidentally the cult of the ram-god Amun was becoming so important in Egypt, then entered Pisces in A.D. 220, the Fish being the symbol of the Christian Era, and will enter Aquarius about A.D. 2375.

Most astrologers think that the Aquarian Age will start earlier than that, perhaps indeed has already begun with the discovery of Uranus in 1784; but the transition must take one or two centuries, and Christianity did not become an official religion till about A.D. 330. Other modern astrologers give different dates, and having seen upon celestial globes unequal boundaries between the constellations, they leap to the conclusion that these boundaries are sacrosanct and of great occult significance, not realizing that they are only three or four hundred years old. In ancient times there were no accurate boundaries, except in the zodiac, which was divided for convenience into twelve equal divisions. The doctrine of unequal divisions, though sometimes true of the Indian and Chinese asterisms, is not true of the zodiac when used for measurement.

The interpretation of history in the light of planetary and precessional cycles was first conspicuously developed by Peter of Abano, who might therefore be regarded as the father of the present notion of the Aquarian Age, which is to last from now for the next two

55

thousand years. His own historical schemes are highly implausible, but he was the first to give a reasonably accurate estimate of the speed of precession—one degree in 70 years, which is only 2 years short. He is best known, however, as a magician, indeed more souls are said to have been damned through reading his book than any other. Unfortunately the book surviving under his name is almost certainly spurious and, like all the blacker forms of magic, rather disgusting.

The method of medieval magic was largely concerned with the making of images, and much of this practice goes back to Thabit ibn Kurrah, or Thebit ben Corat, who was not an Arab but a Sabian, that is to say an old-fashioned pagan who had inherited the sparse remains of ancient Babylonian religion, combined with some of the many other religious influences of the Middle East in earlier times. He was also astrologer to the Caliph of Baghdad, and died in the same year as Alfred the Great. Like most other users of magical images, he maintains that each must be made under the appropriate sign of the zodiac, but unlike them he thinks the material of the image unimportant. Here is a sample from his book:

When you want to make an image for a man who wishes to become the head of a city or province, or judge of a prefecture or a town, the method is the same. First begin by making a mould in which to cast the image. Carve the head of the image when the Dragon's Head is in the Ascendant, and let the lord of the ascendant be a benefic, free from aspect of the malefics. Carve the body of the image under whatever rising sign the Moon shall be in, carve the shoulders and breasts with Venus in the ascendant, the haunches with the Sun rising in one of its dignities, the thighs with Mercury in the ascendant, and he must not be retrograde or combust, but should be unafflicted and in one of his fortunate places; and the feet under the ascendant of the Moon in conjunction with Venus.

When you have drawn out the figure thus, proceeding in order, you may start to cast it, of gold if you will, or any metal you like, under the ascendant of his birth if you know it, or else under the ascendant of the time when he asked the question. And you shall name the image by the name by which he is generally known. And see that the ascendant be fortunate, and its lord, and the tenth house, and that the malefics be remote from the ascendant and its lord, and let the lord of the eleventh be one of the benefics, in aspect of the ascendant and its lord; and let the lord of the tenth be in conjunction with the lord of the ascendant in a friendly conjunction or with complete mutual reception. When you have done this and made the image in this manner, he will obtain what he desires from his king and be given the post he seeks. Preserve the image as I have told you, and it will do the work if God wills.

Needless to say, there is another image for depriving a man of royal favour, but this, like those for creating friendship and enmity, must be buried with the recital of a magic spell. So must the image made with Scorpio rising to keep away scorpions. Sometimes instead of 'If Allah wills', Thabit says, 'Do this and you shall see marvels.'

Other effects supposed to be obtainable from the use of magical images were to give rheumatic pains, to heat baths at night, to congregate ten thousand birds or bees, and to prevent sexual intercourse in a given area. Roger Bacon believed in the value of astrological amulets, so did Albert the Great, Peter of Abano, Louis XI, and many others—and in modern times the great yogi Sri Yukteswar, guru of Yogananda.[13] Pope Boniface VIII valued highly a zodiacal seal made for him by Arnald of Villanova as an antidote to pains in the kidneys. This seal must have been made by some such procedure as the following, which Arnald gives as instruction for making the seal of Capricorn:[14]

When the Sun is in Capricorn take gold or silver and make a seal of it, and while it is being struck with the hammer say: 'Arise O Lord my God and set me free, for Thou art my hope and my patience from my youth up.' The psalm is *Deus in adjutorium meum intende*, etc. And carve upon it a figure of Capricorn while the Sun is in it, and around the edge thus: CHANARIEL, SANCTUS BARTHOLOMAEUS, and on the rest of the circumference the following inscription: Glory to GOD in the highest and on earth peace to men of goodwill; and in the middle JESU BRASIM. The virtues of this seal in general are:

57

It avails against the bites of poisonous beasts and mad dogs, and against gout in the knees.

Aquinas, that pillar of orthodoxy, without denying the virtue of gems, denies that it could be increased by carving figures on them, since words and figures are not material and cannot influence the constitution of matter. But this materialist explanation misses the point, since the effect of amulets, if there is any, might be psychological and not physical. Apart from this, Aquinas accepted the rule of superiors over inferiors, that is, the influence of celestial bodies over earthly bodies, saying that it was amply proved;[15] and he was inclined to admit that the planets were moved by angels, though he would not allow them to have soul and intelligence as Plato and Aristotle had thought.

Plato and Aristotle, though neither explicitly mentions the zodiac or the art of prediction from the heavens, are not irrelevant to the study of astrology. Indeed, in the Middle Ages they were supposed to be the head and fount of it—and not without a reason. Roger Bacon in the thirteenth century cannot be blamed for accepting as a genuine work of Aristotle *The Secret of Secrets*, which purported to be the essence of the teaching that Alexander the Great, between the ages of thirteen and sixteen, had received from Aristotle, who was his tutor. There is much good advice in this book, and only here and there is it explicitly astrological; for instance, 'When you wish to take a laxative, let the Moon be in Scorpio or Libra or Pisces, but be careful to avoid the Moon's application to Saturn, for then she makes the medicine and humours in the body to congeal.'

To make a talisman for lordship and dominion, let the ascendant be in Leo—this is quite right since Alexander the Great was born with the sun in Leo conjoined to Regulus—and let the sun be in 13° Aries, the Moon in 3° Taurus, Saturn in Aquarius, Jupiter in Sagittarius, and Mars in Virgo. You then melt together the metals of the planets (putting in as much of Saturn as will equal all the rest) on a Thursday morning in the hour of Jupiter, make a signet ring, inlay it with a red ruby, and engrave on it a black man riding on a lion, crowned, winged, and carrying a standard, and before him there should march six beardless men with the wings of birds.

In medieval myth, even the birth of Alexander was supposed to have been arranged by astrology. St Basil, who wrote in Greek before 379, had never heard of a king who took steps to have his son born under a favourable constellation; but Augustine, writing in Latin less than fifty years later, had heard of a sage who selected an astrological hour for intercourse with his wife, in order to beget a marvellous son. It seems to have been agreed that Nectanebus was a king of Egypt who used to defeat his enemies by conjuring armies out of the air by magic. Eventually, however, like Guido da Monte-feltro, he found that the time had come when the planets were against him, so he disguised himself, emigrated to Macedon, and set up as an astrologer. His skill was so remarkable that he was soon known at court, and in the absence of King Philip he became intimate with the queen, Olympias. Thus he, rather than Philip, was the true father of Alexander. Needless to say, he achieved this by making a wax image of the queen, and appeared to her in the likeness of the god Ammon, with many other marvellous details. Finally when the day of the birth arrived he stood beside her and obliged her to hold back until the most favourable moment, crying: 'No, no! He who is born now will be ugly and unsuccessful! Do not let the child come forth!'

Another curiosity of the *Secret of Secrets* is that it speaks of the two zodiacs.[16] The eighth sphere, that of the fixed stars, is supposed to move by precession inside the ninth, which contains the equinoctial points and is immovable and invisible. We can no longer accept as genuine a work in which Aristotle advises Alexander to remember the story of Cain and Abel; but even in Aristotle's genuine works there is reason enough to make him the father of medieval astrology.

Perhaps the sidereal system of measuring the zodiac did not die out completely. In Italy there are astrological frescoes in various Renaissance buildings, for instance the Schifanoja Palace at Ferrara, the Palazzo della Ragione at Padua, and the Farnesina in Rome. The paintings in the Farnesina are by Baldassare Peruzzi, illustrating the horoscope of his patron Agostino Chigi. They are in panels all round and on the ceiling of the Sala di Galatea, and represent no fewer than eighteen constellations in addition to the signs of the zodiac and the planets.

The room runs almost due north and south, the northern end being canted a little towards the west. The painting at the north end represents Leo, and that at the south end Aquarius, while between them, running along the middle of the ceiling, are two larger pictures, the northern one portraying the Wain, the southern one Pegasus and Perseus. This gives us an approximate hour of birth; for when the meridian passes through Aquarius in the south, it also passes through the Wain and Pegasus, and of course Leo, which is invisible under the earth. Perseus is possibly emphasized because he was in the east, to provide another indication of the hour of birth, or perhaps only for mythological reasons: Pegasus sprang from a drop of blood when Perseus cut off the Gorgon's head.

In 1934 a little book on these frescoes was published by Fritz Saxl, with the horoscope computed by Arthur Beer. Both writers were rather keen to exhibit their contempt for their subject of study; hence Beer places Saturn neatly on the midheaven, while Saxl blandly speaks of Agostino Chigi's excellent horoscope! The frescoes give no hint of Saturn being on the midheaven, indeed from the position of the constellation Cygnus it seems rather more likely that the sidereal time was about 22 hours, and the hour of birth would therefore be about 5 p.m. Beer sets up his chart for 6.15 and calls it seven o'clock.

The date is given correctly as December 1st, 1466. This does not fit the tropical zodiac, which was thought to be the only one then in use; for in that system the Moon is in Libra and Venus in 0° Aquarius, whereas the frescoes show Venus in Capricorn and the Moon in Virgo. Beer gets over the difficulty by claiming that the signs are taken 'within their true limits', and gives a table of the extent of the constellations in tropical longitude in 1466. But if that were so, the horoscope would be purely visual and have no astrological reference at all. There is no record of astrologers bothering themselves with unequal constellations, although they too sometimes fall into the same fallacy, and speak as though the dotted lines drawn between constellations had some divine sanction.

But even the 'true limits' do not make Beer's example fit, for they put Jupiter in 3° Taurus, and Peruzzi, as can be seen from our frontispiece, took Jupiter to be entering Taurus but still in touch with Aries. Oddly enough, this is the precise position he occupied in the sidereal zodiac.

TABLE I *Longitudes of Planets in the Horoscope of Agostino Chigi*

Constellation	Extent (according to A. Beer)	Beginning (15th century)			Tropical Positions of Planets	Sidereal position of Planets
Aries	24° from	20°	trop. long.			29° 54′ Jupiter
Taurus	32°	44°	,,	,,	Jupiter 17°	
Gemini	34°	76°	,,	,,		
Cancer	20°	110°	,,	,,		
Leo	36°	130°	,,	,,		
Virgo	43°	166°	,,	,,		Moon 20°
Libra	20°	209°	,,	,,	Moon 8°	Mars 20°
Scorpio	27°	229°	,,	,,	Mars 7° Mercury 29°	Mercury 12°
Sagittarius	34°	256°	,,	,,	Sun 18½°	Sun 1°
Capricorn	24°	290°	,,	,,		Venus 13°
Aquarius	32°	314°	,,	,,	Venus 0°	
Pisces	34°	346°–20°	,,	,,	Saturn 26°	Saturn 9°

5. The Twelve Gods: Plato and Augustus

'WE tend,' says Aristotle, 'to think of the stars as mere bodies or items arranged in order, quite without soul or life. We ought rather to regard them as possessed of life and activity, for the consequences of this will not seem unreasonable ... We ought to regard the action of the planets as comparable to that of animals and plants.'[1]

And Plato says, in the Timaeus,[2] that mortal men were created by the lesser gods working with the Creator, in order that they should be partly not immortal.

> He divided the whole mixture into souls equal in number to the stars, and assigned each soul to a star ... and declared to them the laws of destiny, according to which their first birth would be one and the same for all—no one should suffer a disadvantage at his hands ... He who lived well during his appointed time was to return and dwell in his native star, and there he would have a blessed and congenial existence. But if he failed in attaining this, at the second birth he would pass into a woman, and if, when in that state of being, he did not desist from evil, he would continually be changed into some brute who resembled him in the evil nature which he had acquired, and would not cease from his toils and transformations until he followed the revolution of the same and the like within him, and overcame by the help of reason the turbulent and irrational mob of later accretions, made up of fire and air and water and earth, and returned to the form of his first and better state. Having given all these laws to His creatures, that He might be guiltless of future evil in any of them, the Creator sowed some of them in the earth, and some in the moon, and some in the other instruments of time; and when He had sown them, He committed to the younger gods the fashioning of their mortal bodies.

The 'younger gods' were thought in the Middle Ages to be an allusion to the signs of the zodiac. So it is not surprising that Plato and Aristotle should have been regarded as the great justifiers of astrology in those—as we now think—superstitious times.

Yet by condemning people for being unscientific we render ourselves incapable of understanding what their beliefs have meant to them. This is well illustrated by some words of Otto Neugebauer[3]:

> But there exists a third type (of astrology), standing between the omina type ('when this and this happens in the skies, then such and such a major event will be the consequence') and the individual birth horoscope, namely, the 'general prognostication', explained in full detail in the first two books of the *Tetrabiblos*. This type of astrology is actually primitive cosmic physics built on a vast generalization of the influence of the position of the sun in the zodiac on the weather on earth. The influence of the moon is considered as of almost equal importance, and from this point of departure an intricate system of characterization of the parts of the zodiac, the nature of the planets, and their mutual relations is developed. This whole astronomical meteorology is, to be sure, based on utterly naive analogies and generalizations, but it is certainly no more naive and plays no more with words than the most admired philosophical systems of antiquity. It would be of great interest for the understanding of ancient physics and science in general to know where and when this system was developed. The question arises whether this is a Greek invention, replacing the Babylonian omen literature, which must at any rate have lost most of its interest with the end of independent Mesopotamian rule, whether it precedes the invention of the horoscopic art for individuals or merely represents an attempt to rationalize the latter on more general principles.

By the fifth century A.D., when Proclus wrote his commentaries on Plato's *Dialogues*, astrology had become an ingredient of the whole culture of the Greco-Roman world, and Proclus, when discussing the *Republic*,[4] even gives rules for working out the relation between the horoscope of birth and that of conception, which later became known

63

as the 'trutine of Hermes', or 'pre-natal epoch'. Although these rules cannot apply in the Arctic Circle, textbooks on them have been published in the twentieth century. In Greco-Roman times the horoscope of conception was often used, and sometimes thought more important, but the preference for the horoscope of birth does not rest only on the fact that the event is easier to observe. It is also the beginning of independent life, and furthermore no one has ever proved the somewhat unlikely proposition that the incarnating entity times its descent for the moment of conception; according to Buddhists it waits till six months before birth. On the other hand the horoscope is that of the personality, not of the immortal self.

All these points will have been discussed by Platonists, Neoplatonists, and other learned men of the Roman Empire, but to popularize astrology no one contributed more than the Emperor Augustus himself. 'While in retirement at Apollonia,' says Suetonius[5] —and this was when he was eighteen, just before Caesar's death— 'Augustus mounted with Agrippa to the studio of the astrologer Theogenes. Agrippa was the first to try his fortune, and when a great and almost incredible career was predicted for him, Augustus persisted in concealing the time of his birth and in refusing to disclose it, through diffidence and fear that he might be found to be less eminent. When at last he gave it unwillingly and hesitatingly, and only after many urgent requests, Theogenes sprang up and threw himself at his feet. From that time on Augustus had such faith in his destiny, that he made his horoscope public and issued a silver coin stamped with the sign of the constellation Capricorn, under which he was born.'✓ (One of these coins is illustrated in Plate 4(a).)

The date of Augustus's birth is given as September 23rd, 64 B.C.; but the coin is evidence that it should probably be one day earlier. For Roman astrologers called a man Capricornian if he had the Moon in that constellation, whereas modern usage prefers to go by the Sun or Ascendant. The question is, which of five possible zodiacs did Theogenes use? Eudoxus had put the equinox in 15° Aries, Cleostratos of Tenedos in 12°, Naburiannu in 10°, Kidinnu (the founder of the Hellenistic zodiac) in 8°, and Hipparchus in 0°! And all these systems were still current.

In the modern tropical zodiac the Moon was in 27.3° Capricorn, but that zodiac had only been invented less than a century before

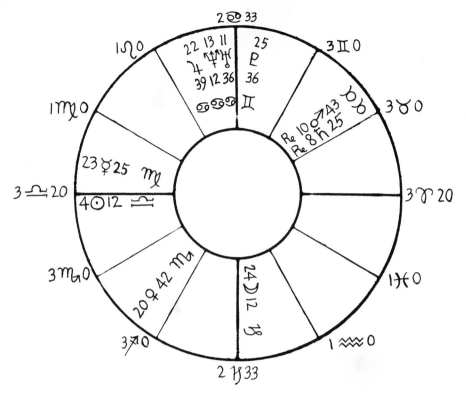

1. Horoscope of the Emperor Augustus, calculated in the
Hellenistic zodiac (*see pages* 39 *and* 64–5)

Born at sunrise, September 22nd, 63 B.C. The date usually given is
September 23rd, but this is impossible because Suetonius says that the
astrologer fell down and worshipped Augustus because of his wonderful
horoscope; and on the 23rd the Moon was in square to Mars and Saturn,
which makes a very bad horoscope indeed. On the 22nd, however, she was
in sextile to Venus and in opposition to an exalted Jupiter, which quite
explains Theogenes' behaviour. Besides, everyone knows from his coins
(Illustration 4(a)) that Augustus had Moon in Capricorn, and on the
23rd it went into Aquarius.

Calculated with Hynes' and with Bryant Tuckerman's tables, but Pluto's
longitude has not been corrected for perturbations, so it must be regarded
as approximate (Noesselt's tables).

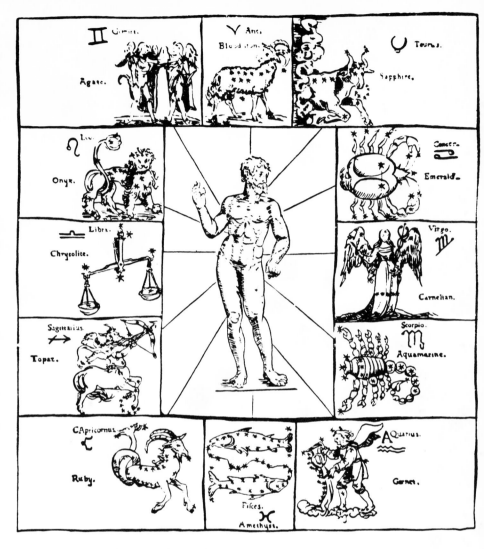

2. Medieval zodiacal man, with appropriate gems

3. Medieval biped Sagittarius

4. (*facing page*) Zodiacal coins and gems (*see pages* (*a*) 64–5 *and* (*b*) 177)

d

u

a

b

c

c

e

f

g

5. (*above*) Parapegma found at Miletus (*see page* 77)

6. (*right*) Poseidon and Hermes (Neptune and Mercury) on the Puteal Albani

Augustus went to Apollonia, and not yet been popularized by Ptolemy. In the Spica zodiac the Moon's longitude would have been measured as 1·2° Aquarius, and in the Hellenistic zodiac, which is far the most likely for Theogenes to have used, the Moon's position would have been called 5° Aquarius. Further, the Moon at dawn on 23rd was going to the square aspect of Mars and Saturn, at which no astrologer would prostrate himself in worship! The obvious conclusion is that Augustus was born on September 22nd, when the Moon was unquestionably in Capricorn and strengthened by a beautiful and close opposition to Jupiter in its exaltation, both being in close aspect to the rising Mercury, which was also exalted. Granted Augustus' devotion to his horoscope, the date of 22nd is unescapable, and Plate 4(a), which shows the Goat holding the Urn, should not be taken as conclusive evidence that the Moon was on the cusp between Capricorn and Aquarius. (The Ascendant was Mercury in Virgo, with the Sun a little below it just entering Libra.)

It is not probable that Augustus waited to act until the proper sign of the zodiac was rising, but Tiberius may have retired to Capri to escape the designs of maleficent planets. Suetonius wrote of him: 'He was rather neglectful of gods and religions, being addicted to astrology, and fully persuaded that all things are brought about by fate. Yet he was immoderately afraid of thunder, and if the sky became threatening he never failed to put on a laurel wreath, because of the common saying that that kind of leaf is never touched by lightning.'[6]

Astrology is known to have been practised in Rome in the third century B.C.—Plautus mentions it. It gained ground as representing Stoic rationalism and determinism against religion; rather the opposite of the present situation. No doubt Romans, like modern historians, often fell into the false antithesis of thinking that determinism excludes freewill, on the false premise that if anything is determined then everything must be. But apart from Augustus, the men who did most to popularize astrology were scholars of the first rank, Posidonius of Apamea, Nigidius Figulus, and Thrasyllus. Thrasyllus was the editor of the current edition of Plato's works; Tiberius met him in Rhodes in 6 B.C., brought him to Rome, and remained his personal friend for forty years, so that Thrasyllus, born an Alexandrine Greek, was for a long time the most influential man in the Roman Empire. In their time both Augustus and Tiberius expelled professional astrologers from Rome, which shows that then as now there was a distinction between scholarly study and the exploitation of public credulity.

By A.D. 11 astrology was so popular that Augustus made illegal the use of divination to discover the date of anyone's death, and published his own horoscope in order to show that it was not time for him to die. He died three years later, but of course the temptation remained, since the succession was so often uncertain, and under Caligula citizens whom the emperor did not like were commonly tried for treason on the excuse of illegal divination.

Nor was it always safe to be the astrologer, for the emperor might ask: 'And what of your own horoscope?' If the astrologer claims that all is well, he is put to death just to prove him wrong. Among various stories of this kind one is of an astrologer, possibly called Asclation, who answers: 'I am destined to be eaten by dogs.' The emperor therefore orders him to be crucified, but at the critical moment a torrential thunderstorm breaks out, the executioners run for shelter, so do the keepers of some ferocious circus dogs, and the astrologer has the satisfaction of disappointing the emperor. The best answer to this awkward question was perhaps discovered by Thrasyllus: 'I stand at this moment in the most imminent peril.'

Tiberius' hour of birth has not come down to us, but he had the Sun in Scorpio and the Moon in Libra, the Moon being in aspect of Venus and Jupiter, which makes for charm, but also of Mars and Saturn, which does the reverse. Evidently Mars and Saturn were more prominent than Jupiter and Venus!

Nero appears a rather worse character. He was born at exact sunrise with the Sun and Mars in conjunction in Sagittarius, both in square to an elevated Saturn; and the Moon in Leo closely square to Jupiter would account for his love of flaunting himself in theatres.

Seneca, who was Nero's tutor, writes: 'Aristotle says that we should always be respectful in the presence of the gods; and surely this is never more true than when we are discussing the planets.'[7] But he also complains that the Chaldeans only speak of the influence of five stars (apart from the sun and moon), and asks: 'Do you think the others shine for nothing? We must be under their influence too.'[8]

66

Cicero was less favourable to astrology, though he repeated Plato's argument for thinking the planets to be living and divine. 'The marvellous and incredible regularity', he says, 'of the stars in their eternal and unvarying courses, shows that they have divine power and intelligence, in fact anyone who cannot see that they possess the power of gods would seem to be quite incapable of understanding anything.'[9] In his book *On Divination*, however, he gives ten pages to an attack on astrology, calling it 'incredible mad folly which is daily refuted by experience', and argues that the weather, which it can at least feel, should have more influence on a new-born baby than the signs of the zodiac.

An attempt was even made to work out the horoscope of Rome. According to Plutarch, this was the achievement of an astrologer called Tarrutius in the first century B.C. Tarrutius dated the conception of Romulus to a total eclipse of the sun which occurred on 23rd Khoiak of the Egyptian calendar, in the first year of the second Olympiad, which corresponds to June 25th (Julian), 772 B.C.; and he put the birth on 21st Thoth at sunrise, which equates to March 25th. The eclipse he mentions actually occurred on June 24th. The foundation of the city he then gave as the third year of the sixth Olympiad (which would be 754 B.C., not 753), on 9th Pharmuthi, which would be October 4th, between the second and third hour.

It will be noticed that Romulus is supposed to have founded Rome at the age of nineteen. This is probably because Tarrutius knew the 'Metonic cycle', whereby new moons occur on the same day of the month after nineteen years, and perhaps he wanted both the foundation of the city and the conception of its founder to be marked by eclipses. As so often happens with these ancient and much-copied documents, the astronomical data do not fit, and one is left to guess which points are erroneous.

Manilius puts Rome under Libra, doubtless in the same way that Augustus was under Capricorn, for he says

Hesperiam sua Libra tenet, qua condita Roma
(Italy doth the Balance rule, the sign of Rome's foundation).[10]

To put Rome under Libra is symbolically right enough, for Libra is the constellation of law and administration. According to statistics more lawyers and administrators are born under Libra than under

67

any other constellation, and Rome's great contribution to the civilization of Europe was her law and her administrative system. There is, however, one other characteristic of Rome which is as ancient and undying as her law, and that is her desire to have some-one for whom to legislate, in other words her traditional imperialism. No city in the world can equal Rome in this, and she should there-fore, along with Libra, have been founded under Aries or Leo, and preferably both.

The date usually given was traditional, namely the festival of the Parilia, which fell a.d.vii kal. mai., on April 21st, and we are further told by Solinus and Lydus that the Sun was in Taurus, Jupiter in Pisces, and the four remaining planets in Scorpio—which is physically impossible. There is no getting at 'the truth' in such a complicated state of affairs, but it is possible to calculate a horoscope of Rome for April 753 (the usual year) with the Moon in Libra. If the Sun be put on the midheaven in the imperialistic Aries, with the full Moon opposite, then the imperialistic Leo will rise. By a curious chance the sign and constellation Aries were both full of planets at the time, and the Libran full moon occurred on April 11th (Julian).[11]

TABLE 2 *Longitudes of Planets in Tarrutius' Horoscope of Rome*

	tropical longitude		*sidereal longitude (Spica 29° 0' Virgo)*	
Sun	13° 30'	Aries	26° 50'	Aries
Moon	14° 54'	Libra	28° 14'	Libra
Mercury	7° 48'	Aries	21° 08'	Aries
Venus	3° 48'	Aries	17° 08'	Aries
Mars	13° 12'	Pisces	26° 32'	Pisces
Jupiter	8° 42'	Aries	22° 2'	Aries
Saturn	15° 54'	Scorpio	29° 14'	Scorpio
Uranus	6° 30'	Aries	19° 50'	Aries
Neptune	17° 48'	Aries	0° 28'	Taurus
Midheaven	14°	Aries	27°	Aries
Ascendant	0°	Leo	13°	Leo

It is not surprising that a city should be thought to have a horo-scope when we remember that the oldest form of prediction from celestial phenomena was for war or peace, plenty of dearth, in fact, for public and not for individual affairs. But the old astrologers had not the modern need to think of the planets as causes rather than significators. If a raven proclaimed the end of an epoch by alighting on the left, that would not make it, for them, the cause of the ensuing disaster, even if it quoth: 'Nevermore!' One could, at a stretch, imagine some causative influence at work in the horoscope of the foundation of a city, but why bother, when no causative influence can be adduced in the ancient practice of 'horary astrology'?

For the 'horary art' is astrological divination, or the art of answering questions by noting the time of asking. It differs from ordinary divination in that the practitioner is less free to choose what symbols shall be significant to his unconscious mind. Such are the rules that twelve astrologers, confronted with the same chart, ought to give twelve very similar answers; and although the basic quality of the answer, the yes or no of it, depends upon the planets, the details and circumstances are derived from a knowledge of the many associations of the signs of the zodiac.

Here for example is a question asked one Saturday morning in A.D. 479. The astrologer was Palchus, an Egyptian living in Smyrna under the emperor Zeno of Constantinople, and the date was the 20th Epiphi (Egyptian calendar) in the 195th year of the Era of Diocletian. In the Gregorian calendar the date was July 14th; the time, 8.30 a.m.

The question was of the safety of a ship bound for Smyrna from Alexandria, which had failed to arrive. With the omission of one or two technical terms, this is the astrologer's answer as translated by Richard Garnett[12]:

> Finding that the lords of the day and hour, being Saturn and Mars, were both in the ascendant, and observing that the moon was applying to an aspect of Saturn, I said that the ship had encountered a violent storm, but had escaped, inasmuch as Venus and the moon were beheld by Jupiter ... The nature of the question not having been disclosed to me, I said it concerned a ship, because the Part of Fortune was in Sagittarius, rising nigh Argo, and its lord was in a watery sign.

This, incidentally, would surprise modern astrologers, for Sagittarius is not now thought to have anything to do with shipping. The Part of Fortune is an imaginary point obtained by adding to the

Ascendant the difference in longitude between the Sun and Moon. Since it does not exist as a material body, some astrologers think better to do without it; and it was not, at the time, 'rising nigh Argo', but Argo would rise when its position came to the ascendant, about nine and a half hours later. Furthermore, the Part of Fortune was just passing out of Sagittarius and into Capricorn. That, however, is by the way.

Palchus continues:

> And observing that the Ascendant was in a bi-corporeal sign, and that (several other technicalities) were one and all in bi-corporeal signs, I said that the ship's company would pass from one vessel to another. And as Venus, who has dominion over birds, was in opposition to Sagittarius, I said they would bring some birds with them. And because the moon was in the house of Mars and in the terms of Mercury, I said they would probably bring some books or papers, and some brazen vessels on account of the moon being in Scorpio.

Scorpio being the house of Mars, the vessels might equally well have been of iron; but we must always allow a diviner to use his intuition. The double-bodied signs are not only the Twins and the Two Fishes, but, since Ptolemy had such a mania for symmetry, the Archer, half man and half horse, and also the Virgin with her ear of corn. The Balance, with its two scales, ought to be 'double-bodied' but is not.

'And observing that Aesculapius was rising along with the moon'— this again means 'would rise when the moon rose', for the moon was far below the horizon; and 'Aesculapius' is the constellation Ophiuchus, the Serpent-bearer, well outside the zodiac—'I said they would bring medicines.'

> Being asked concerning the time of their arrival, I said that this would take place when the Moon entered Aquarius. They arrived accordingly, and being questioned respecting their detention, replied that it was owing to a violent tempest, and that, the sea being cloven, their prow struck against a rock and was broken, and that they were mightily tossed to and fro. But having made a harbour, they shifted into another vessel the

cargo they had brought with them, which consisted of birds, and blank writing paper on account of Mercury being aphaeretic [i.e. he signified death rather than life], and cooking vessels on account of Scorpio, and a full medicine chest by reason of Aesculapius.

This is believed to be the earliest recorded reading of a horary chart, and if it all happened as described it certainly was a great success. By 'paper' is meant of course papyrus, which stood high on the list of Egyptian exports.

Palchus, who, as the reader can now judge for himself, was nothing if not brilliant, will also provide us with a splendid example of the use of the zodiac in making elections of favourable times for starting things. This is the technique of trying to ensure the success of an undertaking by beginning it at an astrologically favourable moment. It means that not only must the horoscope of the moment be good in itself, but, more important still, its comparison to the horoscopes of the people concerned must be favourable likewise. It is no use choosing a moment when the Moon is in conjunction to both the benefics, Venus and Jupiter, and failing to notice that the degree upon the Ascendant is the very same degree where Saturn stood at your birth! But if you are going mining, any astrologer would say that the Moon should be in Capricorn, which rules mines, or else in Taurus (the earth) and in aspect of Saturn. The Moon in an airy sign would mean no mining, and in a watery sign would threaten flooding.

The art of making elections has existed for two thousand years, yet many modern astrologers do not believe in it, having had experience of its failures. Sometimes it is downright impossible to find any moment at all which will favour the native in a particular direction before a certain date; and at other times the 'election' remains blandly ineffective. The reason for this is clear enough, even without abandoning the presuppositions of astrology. The real time of beginning any undertaking is when it is effectively decided upon, when there is no longer any question of going back, not the moment of birth of the idea, and not the purely formal moment of carrying out an already fixed intention, except in the case of official functions like the foundation of a city or the opening of a congress. But it can be seen from this that the effective time of the 'election' will not be the time you choose, but the time when you chose the time!

Here then is one of the earliest known examples of an 'election' which went wrong. It too is taken from Palchus.[13]

Pamprepios was a native of Egyptian Thebes who came to Athens and taught philosophy there in the fifth century A.D. He was one of those unreliable characters who are too clever by half, and bring interested in occult science had contrived to gain a reputation as a magician before he was expelled from the city. He then went to Byzantium, trying always to move in the highest circles, and having left there, not perhaps by choice, he met in Asia Minor a certain Leontios, whom he persuaded to set himself up as emperor in opposition to the legitimate ruler Zeno in Constantinople. This then is Palchus' account of the coronation of Leontios:

> He was crowned at a time elected by two astrologers, and at once lost both his kingdom and his luck ... Those who made the election much fancied the rising of Sun, Jupiter, and Mars, with Mercury succedent to them, and the good aspects of the Moon to Saturn and Jupiter. But they did not pay attention to the fact that Mercury, ruler of the day and of the next ensuing hour was in evil case; for he was at his greatest elongation from the Sun, which makes him to signify violent death, and his only aspect was to Saturn. Also Venus, being isolated, could not cure the evil, for the Sun intercepted her. Nor did they observe that the Moon, being the dispositor (or ruler) of the Sun, Ascendant, Jupiter, Mars, and the preceding new moon, was in her fall and afflicted. And the fact that the Sun, Ascendant, and Jupiter were together did not suffice to outweigh those other aspects and prevent them from working.

Modern astrologers would agree that the election was badly made, but in the main for different reasons. Though they would readily grant that bad aspects can interfere with good ones, the converse proposition might be less easy to defend. They would ignore the fact that Mercury rules the first hour on Wednesday, nor would they think it a sign of danger to find him so far away from the Sun. They would however be horrified to discover that the Moon was in her fall (that is, in Scorpio), beneath the earth, and applying to a conjunction of Saturn, which is a sure sign of failure! There are also at least two errors in the text, since the Moon is incorrectly stated to be in Cancer, and the longitudes of Mars and Jupiter are interchanged.

As it turned out, Leontios and his lieutenant Illus were defeated at the castle of Papyrion by a land and sea expedition under John the Scythian. They fled, and waited a long time in another castle for the brother of Illus, but on learning that he had been killed by John they realized that their astrologer had deceived them, so they cut off his head and hung his body from the battlements. And any modern astrologer would admit that, if he really chose a time when the Moon was going to conjunction of Saturn, he certainly deserved it.

If we recalculate with modern methods the horoscopes by Palchus to be found in various Greek manuscripts in Paris and Florence,[13] we find that the positions of the planets average, in most of them, 3 degrees less in longitude than is computed by our tables. This cannot be due to carelessness or inefficiency on the part of Palchus, for the error is consistently on the same side; it can only mean that Palchus was not measuring the zodiac from the equinox. His zodiac in fact was sidereal, not tropical, and his equinox lay in 27° Pisces.

In the Michigan Astrological Papyrus No. 1, of the second century A.D., we find the explicit statement[14]: 'The marking-points of the Sun are four, two equinoctial in the eighth degrees of Aries and Libra, and the tropics, the summer tropic in the eighth degree of Cancer and the winter tropic in the eighth degree of Capricorn.' This statement was long out of date; but again in the *Apotelesmatica* of Pseudo-Manetho, a work of the second to fourth centuries A.D. reflecting the older tradition, we are told:[15] 'The circle that turns the season of fiery summer is described in the sky by the all-seeing Sun in its course upon the eighth degree of Cancer.'

The eighth degree, however, was not universally accepted, for Manilius says at the very end of his third book:[16] 'So one degree in tropical signs is to be distinguished, which moves the world and alters the seasons ... Some place this power in the eighth degree, others prefer the tenth, and there has even been a writer who has allotted to the first degree the alteration and shortening of the days.'

And Columella, writing about A.D. 60, has a similar comment:[17] 'Winter which begins about viii kal.Jan. in the eighth degree of

Capricorn ... And I am not overlooking Hipparchus' argument, which teaches that the solstices and equinoxes happen not in the eighth but in the first degrees of signs. In this rustic science I follow the calendar of Eudoxus and Meton, which fits in with the public festivals.'

These quotations, with one or two others,[18] explain a difficulty which astrologers have had to overlook for centuries. For when they used to claim that their science was many thousands of years old, and also that the twelve visible constellations were much less important than the invisible 'signs', they had no sound way of explaining why the names of both were the same. For the date when the two zodiacs coincided must in any case be less than two thousand years ago, since the difference between them does not yet amount to 30 degrees; and if the names are older than two thousand years, it is hard to believe that they became tacked on to the visible constellations some time after they had been chosen to express the influences of invisible signs—especially since the name of the Twins does seem to refer to the two stars Castor and Pollux, and the name of the Scorpion to the curling tail seen in the eastern half of that constellation. And the only other explanation was to assume that the names had been given 26,000 years B.C., leaving a rather hungry gap in history.

To discover the precession of the equinoxes at all would in any case take several centuries; for if the vernal equinox were marked by the day when Spica rose at dusk—the acronychal rising, as it is called—then a century later this measurement would only be in error by a day and a half, and, allowing for variations of visibility, this might easily be disregarded, especially as it was difficult to check.

The actual time required for the making of the discovery seems to have been from about 500 B.C., when the Babylonian astronomer Naburiannu located the equinoctial point in 10 degrees of the constellation Aries, through the time of Kidinnu, who about 373 B.C. located it in 8 degrees of that constellation, until some time between 150 and 126 B.C., the end of Hipparchus' life.

But although precession had been discovered, it was not at once adopted and taken seriously by users of the zodiac. It was much easier to accept Kidinnu's statement that the equinoxes were in the eighth degrees of the constellations and then do nothing about it—

since they moved at a rate vaguely guessed to be one degree in a century, to ignore this and treat them as fixed. Thus arose the Hellenistic Zodiac, which was a tropical zodiac measured from its tropics in the eighth degrees of Aries, Cancer, Libra, and Capricorn. This is the zodiac used by Manetho and the Michigan Papyrus, and referred to by Columella, Manilius and Pliny. Correct about 373 B.C., it continued in common use in the time of Augustus, when it was already 5 degrees out, and indeed for some time after. The reason may have been that Greek astronomers did not know from which stars the zodiac had originally been measured. Possibly this key fact was kept as a religious secret by whatever Babylonian or Egyptian priest first divulged the practice of individual astrology.

Hipparchus was the founder of the Tropical Zodiac because he first suggested that it might be convenient to measure the zodiac from the tropical points. Ptolemy in his *Tetrabiblos* justifies this on astrological grounds, as if it were the proper way to analyse human character from the stars, but it seems more likely that Hipparchus adopted it for the same reason that the equinoctial 'First Point of Aries' is still used as the chief celestial measuring-point, namely as the best way of fixing the calendar conveniently to the seasons. The ancient world had long been bothered by its many lunar calendars, which were about eleven days short, as the Muslim calendar still is, and therefore had to be adjusted every two or three years with the insertion of a whole extra month—as the Muslim calendar is not.

The location of the equinox came in fact as a godsend to agriculture, which hitherto had been forced to time its operations by the stars—hence the traditional injunctions found in Virgil, Hesiod, and other agricultural writers. Hesiod was giving sound and valuable advice to farmers when he wrote:[19]

> Begin your harvest when the Pleiads come
> To rising, and your ploughing when they set.

But, after Julius Caesar's reform of the Roman calendar in 46 B.C., Virgil's corresponding instructions (in the rather engaging translation of John Jackson) were an archaism:[20]

Twice men gather the teeming produce; two are the seasons of

75

harvest; either so soon as Taÿgete the Pleiad has shown her fair face to the earth, and spurned beneath her foot the despised streams of Ocean, or when she flees before the sign of the watery Fish, and descends from heaven—a sadder maid—into the wintry waves.

The Pleiades are invisible for about forty days while the sun is in the end of Aries and in Taurus, but the exact length of time depends on the latitude, the visibility, and the nature of the horizon. The name is thought to mean 'The Sailing Stars', because their morning rising marks for Hesiod the beginning of the season of navigation. The Greeks, however, thought it might mean 'The Doves'. The Hyades on the other hand, which the Greeks took to mean 'The Rainy Ones', may possibly mean 'The Little Pigs', which was their name in Latin.

The next step was the invention of parapegmata. A parapegma (with a long E in the Greek) was a stone tablet with 360 holes arranged in rows of thirty, corresponding to the Sun's longitude in the Tropical Zodiac, and thus forming a zodiacal calendar. It was presumably put up like a public notice-board in the agora of any Greek town, and every day the responsible official would put in the proper hole a stick, which might be marked on the head with the date in the civil calendar. Thus the 22nd of Hecatombaion would be marked with the letters $\Theta\ \Phi$ (meaning '9 waning', since the days in the last third of the month were numbered backwards), and this would be inserted into whatever degree of the Cancer row was appropriate that year. The normal length of the Athenian year was 354 days, and New Year's Day was kept as close as possible to the summer solstice by inserting a month called Second Poseideon whenever necessary.

Plate 5 shows part of a broken parapegma found at Miletus.[21] A translation of the right-hand column of fragment B follows. The large isolated $\varLambda$ at the beginning means '30', referring to the thirty days of Aquarius (some signs have thirty-one days), and thirty holes can be counted in this column, but nine of them occur over the word 'Andromeda' because for nine days there would be no risings or settings to observe; the rest, by chance, fall for the most part on successive days, but altogether there are eighteen blank days out of

76

thirty, signified by the eighteen holes between the lines of text, and twelve holes at the beginnings of lines:

Λ

    ◦ Sun in Aquarius

    ◦ (Leo) begins its morning setting

and Lyra sets

    oo
    ◦ Bird's evening setting begins

    ooooooooo
    ◦ Andromeda begins morning rising

    oo
    ◦ Waterbearer in middle of rising

    ◦ Horse begins morning rising

    o
    ◦ Centaur completes morning setting

    ◦ Hydrus completes morning setting

    ◦ Cetus begins evening

setting

    ◦ Arrow sets, west winds

constant

    oooo
    ◦ Bird completes evening setting

    ◦ (Arcturus) evening rising

The invention of the parapegma was ascribed to the philosopher Democritos, the 'laughing philosopher' and principal exponent in ancient Greece of atomic materialism—strange though it seems nowadays that a materialist should laugh. He was indeed a man of very wide knowledge, but the invention may equally well have been made by one of the contemporary astronomers, perhaps Meton or Euktemon. The date of it must in any case have been about 400 B.C., and this shows that the zodiac, as a calendar, must have been already known in Greece at that date.

The zodiac at this stage was a division of the ecliptic circle into twelve equal divisions of 30 degrees each, but we cannot assume that these divisions had the characteristics which we associate nowadays with the twelve signs. They may well have had no ruling planets and

77

no supposed influence on human character, for horoscopic astrology was possibly unknown in Greece in 400 B.C. And in any case the precession of the equinoxes was still undiscovered, so no distinction will have been made between signs and constellations, and the constellations of that time will have been twelve equal divisions, the tropics and equinoxes being in the eighth degrees of the first, fourth, seventh and tenth of them.

The earliest allusion to horoscopic astrology in Greek literature was probably that passage of Eudoxus in which he expressly dissociated himself from the astrological predictions of the 'Chaldeans'. But the passage has not survived, and we only have the statement on authority of Cicero, some four centuries later.[22]

Plato was a contemporary of Eudoxus, born twenty years earlier and dying eight years later, so he must at least have heard of predictional astrology, since Eudoxus came to stay in his house. But Plato's zodiac is not by any means all that modern astrologers might desire; for it suggests that the rulership of planets over signs was not yet irremovably established, if indeed established at all; and thus conceivably the art of personal astrology was still only in an early stage of growth, or had as yet been only partly revealed by the initiates of Babylon or Egypt.

Plato's use of the zodiac can best be illustrated by direct quotation:[23]

Zeus, the mighty lord holding the reins of a winged chariot, leads the way in heaven, ordering all and caring for all; and there follows him the heavenly array of gods and demigods, divided into eleven bands; for only Hestia is left at home in the house of heaven; but the rest of the twelve greater deities march in their appointed order. And they see in the interior of heaven many blessed sights; and there are ways to and fro, along which the happy gods are passing, each one fulfilling his own work; and anyone may follow whom he pleases, for jealousy has no place in the heavenly choir.

The eleven companies have been supposed to refer to the zodiac of only eleven signs, in which the Scorpion's claws occupied the space allotted afterwards to Libra; but no less probably Plato meant that Zeus the sky-god should go first, leading eleven companies besides his own. For Plato speaks of the planet Mercury as 'the planet sacred to Hermes',[24] showing that, for him, Hermes was a divine power to which, incidentally, a planet was dedicated. Only later did Zeus in Greek and Jupiter in Latin come to be thought of no longer as the supreme god of heaven, but simply as the power of a particular planet. This loss of their principal gods, who became no more than the mechanical powers of planets, may be one reason why the Greeks and Romans welcomed so eagerly the gods of the Orient, Cybele, Isis and Osiris, Sarapis, Mithra, who were genuinely potent and had not been devalued by either astrology or rationalism.

Plato knew also that men could be born under the influence of a god. He says in the *Phaedrus*:[25]

Now the lover who is the attendant of Zeus is better able to bear the winged god [i.e. Eros], and can endure a heavier burden; but the attendants and companions of Ares [i.e. Mars], when under the influence of love, if they fancy that they have been at all wronged, are ready to kill and put an end to themselves and their beloved. And in like manner he who follows in the train of any other god honours him, and imitates him as far as he is able while the impression lasts; and this is his way of life and the manner of his behaviour to his beloved and to every other in the first period of his earthly existence. Everyone chooses the object of his affections according to his character, and this he makes his god, and fashions and adorns as a sort of image which he is to fall down and worship. The followers of Zeus desire that their beloved should have a soul like him; and, therefore, they seek some philosophical and imperial nature, and when they have found him and loved him, they do all they can to create such a nature in him ... But those who are the followers of Hera seek a royal love, and when they have found him they do the same with him; and in like manner the followers of Apollo, and of every other god walking in the ways of their god, seek a love who is to be like their god, and when they have found him, they themselves imitate their god, and persuade their love to do the same, and bring him into harmony with the form and ways of the god as far as they can; for they have no feelings of envy or mean enmity towards their beloved, but they do their utmost to

79

create in him the greatest likeness of themselves and the god whom they honour.

So here is Plato genuinely saying that 'followers of Mars' — which may or may not mean persons born under Mars — are capable of murder when crossed in love, but that 'those who have the nature of Zeus' (who is not of necessity the same as Jupiter) are more patient. And the 'followers of Hera' may be those born under Aquarius.

But it is most important to distinguish Plato's spiritual attitude to the zodiac from the more mechanical attitude of the average astrologer. Plato had no use for the angry assumption which is sometimes vented in the words: 'I did not ask to be born.' He was convinced, on the contrary, that the soul chooses to descend, and even if it chooses unwisely it is none the less responsible for its presence here. Hence the 'followers of Zeus' are not those born under the mechanical influence of a celestial sign or planet, but those who have chosen to manifest according to, or to be guided principally by, that particular mode of the Creative Force which among the Greeks was called Zeus. All the gods are part of God, but some express one aspect and some another, and so do we ourselves.

Further, though Plato calls the planets 'visible gods', and 'animals', that is to say living powers, the rulers of the twelve signs are not for him the planets, since they are specifically stated to be invisible;[26] they were the twelve principal manifestations of the Creative Force which runs the universe.

So the Twelve Gods of Plato are neither the planets nor the signs of the zodiac. They are the Dodeka Theoi, the twelve Greek gods who were pictured on the central milestone of Athens, from which all distances were measured. And Plato is not the only one to tell us of the Twelve Gods; the full list comes from Manilius:[27]

Pallas rules the woolly Ram, and Venus guards the Bull,
Apollo has the handsome Twins, and Mercury the Crab,
Jove, with the Mother of the Gods, himself is Leo's lord;
The Virgin with her Ear of Corn to Ceres falls; the Scales
To Vulcan's smithy; while to Mars the warlike Scorpion cleaves;
The Hunter's human part Diana rules, but what's of horse
Is ruled by Vesta, with the straitened stars of Capricorn;

Aquarius is Juno's sign, as opposite to Jove,
And Neptune owns the pair of Fish that in the heaven move.

This list of gods is arranged so far as possible in opposite pairs, and is not inappropriate, except that Vesta, who is Hestia the hearth-goddess, has no particular connection with horses or goats. The attribution of Cancer to Mercury, though it may shock modern astrologers, comes from Egypt, and is further justified by the myth in which the infant Hermes, while still in his cradle, found a tortoise at the mouth of his cave on Mount Cyllene and made its shell into a lyre, on which he immediately played. And Cancer, though called the Crab by the Greeks and Babylonians, is basically just a hard-shelled creature, a tortoise to the Chinese and a scarab to the Egyptians.

Pallas Athene, or in Latin Minerva, is perfectly suitable for Aries, which rules the head and is a warlike sign, since she sprang fully armed from the head of Zeus. For the Ear of Corn no ruler could be more suitable than Demeter-Ceres. Diana as the huntress is obviously correct for Sagittarius, and her brother Apollo, the spirit of music and prophecy, rules the opposite sign. The many-breasted 'Diana of the Ephesians' would equate with the Mother of the Gods and be placed in Leo. Taurus and Scorpio have their usual rulers, and the Scales, as the only manufactured object in the list, are naturally given to Vulcan the craftsman. As for the Fishes, their allotment to Neptune ought to be welcomed by astrologers, who have been trying for the past hundred years to hand them over to the planet of that name!

The Twelve Gods are illustrated in a most beautiful wellhead sculpture (Plate 6) now in the Capitoline Museum in Rome,[28] and also on the Altar of Gabii now in the Louvre.

The division into twelve evidently fascinated Plato, as it has so many others, and he stipulates: 'We will divide the city into portions, first founding temples to Hestia, to Zeus, and to Athene, in a spot which we will call the Acropolis, and surround with a circular wall, making the division of the entire city and country radiate from this point. The twelve portions shall be equalized by the provision that those which are of good land shall be smaller, while those of inferior quality shall be larger.' And later: 'There are to be twelve hamlets in the twelve country districts, each with a temple to the proper one

81

of the Twelve Gods, but Zeus, Athene and Hestia have temples everywhere.'[29]

Zeus has temples everywhere as the supreme god of the present world—though he is not the Creator. If he ruled any sign of the zodiac in Plato's time, it was still Leo and not Sagittarius. Athene has temples everywhere as patron goddess of Attica and Athens, and Hestia as goddess of the home. But Plato was not quite satisfied with the list of the Twelve Gods, and suggested that the god of the underworld, Pluto or Hades, ought to be included. 'The law will say', he writes,[30] 'that there are twelve feasts dedicated to the Twelve Gods', and he adds that Pluto is to have his feast in the twelfth month and not be excluded as a denizen of the underworld, for warlike men should realize that he is the best friend of man.

The twelfth month, both at Athens and for Plato,[31] would be that preceding the summer solstice, and since he begins his list with Zeus, who rules over Leo, perhaps he meant to substitute Pluto god of the underworld for Hermes ruler of Cancer, the guide of souls to the world below. Yet one cannot help feeling that the power to be excluded should have been Hestia, the hearth-goddess, who according to the passage in the *Phaedrus*[32] 'alone remains in the house of the gods' and does not make the circuit of heaven with the others. By this means Pluto could have ruled Capricorn, which was then the place of the winter solstice and, as the lowest part of the sun's path, the natural symbol of death and resurrection.

Modern astrologers would like Pluto the planet, discovered in 1930, to rule either Aries or Scorpio, and they can quote Plato's statement that Pluto the god is 'the best friend of warlike men'. But planets and gods should not be equated too easily. Uranus, whose name means 'heaven', has fitted well enough to Aquarius the sign of the rain-cloud, but Neptune the planet, though commonly allotted to Pisces, has shown no evidence of affinity for the sea, and Pluto the planet may yet turn out to have no connection with the underworld either through Scorpio as the sign associated with death or through Capricorn as the sign of the descent into hell.

And Capricorn, being the sign of the lowest depths, is also the sign of reascent. In Porphyry's essay 'On the Cave of the Nymphs', written towards A.D. 300, we are told that souls descend into generation in Cancer and begin their return to heaven in Capricorn.

Cancer is warm and moist, the sign of the summer tropic, when the material world is most powerful; Capricorn is stony and hard, where material seductions are overcome by deep thought and aspiration. There is a picture by Blake which illustrates the Cave of the Nymphs, from the passage in the *Odyssey* where it is described.[33]

Plato, who taught reincarnation, certainly knew of these astrological speculations, but to say so is not to accuse him of 'being' an astrologer, nor of 'believing in' astrology, as the superstitious materialist may fear. The average modern scholar ignores the gods, and thereby becomes incapable of understanding Plato when he talks about them; his nearest approach to understanding involves the mental substitution for the word 'gods' of some such phrase as 'the forces of the unconscious'—which of course is not far out, but does imply an attempt to devaluate the gods and get them so far as possible under control of the conscious rationalizing intellect. This will work so long as the weather is fair and you are alone in your study, but the intellect is not an impenetrable bomb-proof shelter against the earthquakes of the unconscious. To Plato the gods were certainly not dead; his modern admirers think they are. In consequence they worship them under other names: the Earth-Mother has been rechristened Matter, Hermes is called Science or Rationalism, and so forth.

The object of such renaming is evident; it rises from that fear of the unconscious which always infects the conscious mind when the latter is striving for exclusive control and trying to pretend that Reason is the only tool that it possesses. Instead of admitting God to be Wisdom, Love, and Power, it likes to pretend that logical analysis can keep the world under control, that the human mind will never have any more capacities than it has at present, and that the only reality is what it can understand, namely that static half of Wisdom which can be boiled down and safely catalogued as technique and information. The advantage of saying 'Science' instead of 'Hermes', and 'Matter' instead of 'Demeter', is the implication that there simply is no power or love to bother about, only facts, only information. And as if this defence against the power of creation were not enough, some thinkers assure us that the mind does not exist, but is simply a misleading word to describe certain phenomena. But 'Matter is the only Reality' only makes sense if we translate it

83

'Demeter is the only Reality', for only in virtue of the Power inherent in material phenomena do we have any material experience at all. Materialism is just the worship of the Great Mother under another name.

To a universal mind like Plato's there is no invidious distinction between science and religion, or between psychology and astronomy. The problem is to adapt ourselves to the world in which we live, and any religion which enables us to do this is a true religion, and of necessity in harmony with science and astronomy and psychology. When an astronomer hates astrology, or a materialist hates religion, he is uncritically copying the intolerance of the monotheistic Church, which claimed that there was only one valid adaptation to life. To Greek astronomers the zodiac may have been only a calendar, and to astrologers only a mechanical method of divination, but that it had a spiritual significance for the greater minds is shown by a remark put into the mouth of Aristophanes in the *Symposium*:[34] 'Hoar-frost and hail and blight spring from the excesses and disorders of this element of love, which to know in relation to the revolutions of the heavenly bodies and the seasons of the year is termed astronomy. Furthermore all sacrifices and the whole province of divination, which is the art of communion between gods and men — these I say are concerned only with the preservation of the good and the cure of the evil love.'

In other words, all human problems are of relationship, and all relationships are symbolized in the zodiac, where the twelve types make all possible combinations as they circle round the focus of life; and divination is the art of reconciling conscious and unconscious, whether by the interpretation of dreams, as in psycho-analysis, or by ritual, as in religion. Divination is now despised in obedience to the negative superstition that no such thing can be possible, or else exaggerated by the positive superstition that one can extract from the unconscious, by methods which do not emerge from it, such as numerology, mere facts which are not in it in any case, such as the date of the next election or the winner of the two-thirty. The divination mentioned by Aristophanes is the reconciliation of conscious and unconscious, and this is closely allied to the reconciliation of God and man.

Plato, at the end of his life, or one of his immediate pupils, wrote a short dialogue called *Epinomis*, the aim of which, according to Mr Harward, was to reform Hellenic religion by substituting the worship of the planets for that of the Greek gods and goddesses—although, of course, this aim is only put forward in very guarded terms, in order not to offend the Delphic Oracle. More probably Mr Harward's opinion should be attributed to the monotheistic prejudice which for so long has obliged classical scholars to pretend that the Greeks found their gods unsatisfactory. If we cannot recognize the divinity of Athena, Plato certainly could.

That the zodiac had been brought to Greece about 400 B.C. and used for parapegmata is certain. Whether it came from Babylon or Egypt we shall consider in a later chapter. Meanwhile the *Epinomis* only tells us that Plato at the end of his life accepted the zodiac as an archetype, a deeply religious symbol of the harmony of the Many and the One; and that is exactly what it is.

TABLE 3 *Plants of the Signs and Planets* according to the Greek astrologers

(from the *Catalogus Codicum Astrologorum Graecorum*, VIII (3), 151 (best), 139 foll.; VII, 232; VIII (2), 159; XII, 126; VIII (4) 253–262.)

ARIES	Sage (*salvia triloba*); water milfoil (*myriophyllum spicatum*).
TAURUS	Vervain (*verbena officinalis*); clover (*trifolium*).
GEMINI	Holy vervain (*v. supina*); wild *gladiolus*.
CANCER	Comfrey (*symphytum bulbosum*); *mandragora officinalis*.
LEO	*Cyclamen graecum* or *neapolitanum*; another unidentified.
VIRGO	Calaminth (*calamintha*).*
LIBRA	Scorpion-tail (*scorpiurus sulcata*); 'needle-plant' (*belonike*).
SCORPIO	*Artemisia*; houndstongue (*cynoglossum*).
SAGITTARIUS	Pimpernel (blue or red) (*anagallis*).*
CAPRICORN	Sorrel (*rumex patientia*); stinking tutsan (*hypericum hircinum*), which smells of goat.
AQUARIUS	Edder-wort (*dracunculus*); fennel (*foeniculum*); buttercup (*ranunculus*).
PISCES	*Aristolochia* (long- or round-leaved birthwort).

* Other(s) unidentified
See *Wild Flowers of Attica*, by S. C. Atchley (Oxford, 1938).

SATURN   Asphodel (*asphodelus*); white heliotrope (*h. europaeum*); houseleek (*sempervivum*); frothy poppy (*silene viscosum*).

JUPITER   Agrimony (*eupatorium*); 'chrysacanthus'.

MARS   Lambstongue (*arnoglossum*); butterburr (*petasites*); *peucedanum* (hog's fennel).

SUN   Sunspurge (*euphorbia helioscopia*); chicory (*cichorium intybus*).

VENUS   Vervain (as Taurus); white rose (*r. sempervirens*); man orchis; Venus's allheal, i.e. maidenhair fern (*adiantum capillus-Veneris*).

MERCURY   Mullein (*verbascum*); cinquefoil (*potentilla*).

MOON   Paeony (*paeonia*); helenium (*inaula h.*; but this would seem to be a solar plant).

6. *The Zodiac in China*

NOT so long ago, if you asked a Chinese his age, he would reply simply with the name of an animal. He would say, for example: Dog, Rat, or Monkey—naming the year of his birth. Twelve animals—the Rat, the Ox, the Tiger, the Hare, the Dragon, the Serpent, the Horse, the Sheep, the Monkey, the Cock, the Dog, the Boar—formed the Chinese 'circle of animals'; and, except for the Ox falling into second place, it does not bear much resemblance to our Western zodiac. There is, however, a partial resemblance. The star Spica (Alpha Virginis) was called by the Chinese Kio (also spelt Chio and Güo) and regarded as the lower Horn of the Dragon, the upper horn being Arcturus; and if we therefore equate the Dragon with Libra, which adjoins Spica, we shall have the Serpent for Scorpio, which is very appropriate; the Horse for Sagittarius, which is right; the Sheep for Capricorn, which is again suitable since the Chinese regard goats and sheep as much the same animal; then the Monkey in place of the Man with the Urn, which is not far out; and the Tiger very properly in the place of our Lion. The Hare, however, which would thus correspond to Virgo, does not equate to our constellation Lepus the Hare, for the latter is not in the zodiac but lies south of Orion's feet.

At first sight, it seems, no Chinese scholar is likely to thank us for this comparison. For in the first place it leaves six of the animals unaccounted for—the Rat, Ox, Hare, Cock, Dog, and Boar—even if we accept the Dragon in place of the Scorpion's Claws which are commonly called Libra. Secondly, it is an hour-circle, and therefore like any clock is numbered clockwise, whereas the zodiac is numbered widdershins; hence any resemblance to the zodiac should be in reverse order. Thirdly, it is closely related to the twenty-eight *hsiu* (asterisms, or mansions) of Chinese astronomy, which are not a zodiac. Fourthly (if more reasons were needed), the Chinese equate the Rat with Aries, the Ox with Taurus, and so on round the circle. The Rat rules the third watch of the night, just after midnight, noon is the hour of the Horse, and sunset that of the Cock.

If the circle of animals is transferred from service as marking the twelve months, and used instead to signify the twelve double-hours of the day, a reversal of order of the signs is only to be expected. Scorpio is visibly to the left of Libra when we look at the nocturnal sky, and if Libra culminates in the south at sunset, Scorpio will follow two hours later; hence the same sequence seems to apply. On the other hand from noon to 2 p.m. the sun has moved one-twelfth of a circle to the right, hence the hands of a clock move to the right, and the hour-circle of animals must be counted in that direction. The Chinese day began at midnight, so if Aries as the first sign is given the first double-hour and the direction North, Taurus will rule from 2 till 4 a.m. and correspond to the direction NNE, although visibly Taurus lies to the left of Aries, not to the right.

Thus there ought really to be two circles: an annual circle, the zodiac, counted from right to left, the direction of motion of the sun and moon among the stars; and a diurnal circle, or hour-circle, counted from left to right, the direction of motion of the sun across the sky. And in China both exist.

Our Western zodiac has been known there for several centuries, having been introduced, to all intents and purposes, by the first Jesuit mission under Matteo Ricci, who reached Peking in 1601. Knowledge of it had come through earlier by way of the Central Asian caravan-route, but the Chinese did not use our zodiac until the Jesuits arrived and were able to teach them something of practical value concerning it.

Native Chinese astronomy was based, as we should expect, on different ideas from those of Egypt and Babylon. Instead of paying their chief attention to the ecliptic, of which no more than one-half is ever visible at one time, the Chinese seem to have relied originally on the circumpolar stars, which, weather permitting, are visible all night every night of the year.

The Chinese Empire called itself The Middle Kingdom as being the earthly counterpart of the Middle Kingdom of Heaven, the region of the never-setting stars. The Emperor gave audience seated facing south because he represented the very centre of the central kingdom, namely the Pole Star. This suggests that the custom arose at a date when, as today, there was a star of perceptible brightness very close to the pole; perhaps 3067 *i* Draconis (*T'ien-yi*) which was pole star about 2668 B.C., or else either 42 or 184 Draconis (*T'ai-yi*) about 2260 B.C.[1]

Around the Middle Kingdom the Chinese divided the sky into four palaces, called by the names of the four cardinal points. But in terms of remoteness from the equator the Northern Palace was no more northerly than any other; and the Eastern Palace, comprising the constellation of the Green Dragon, centred on Antares, cannot in the nature of things be any more easterly than any other part of the sky, except when it happens to be rising.

The doctrine of the Palaces is rather obscure, and it has even been claimed that the asterisms within them were counted clockwise in two of them and widdershins in the other two, thereby explaining (with some considerable effort) why the months in the primitive Turkish calendar were named after numbers, but the numbers run in the wrong order![2] Yet this is not impossible, if we remember that the Green Dragon, which corresponds to Spring and the element of Wood, has its head to the south and tail to the north, and so does the White Tiger, which corresponds to Metal and Autumn; but the Red Bird (Fire and Summer) and the Black Tortoise (Earth and Winter) both have their heads to the west and tails to the east, although they are on opposite sides of the sky.

Not until the first or second century A.D., in the time of the later Han, do we find the Chinese giving a name to the ecliptic. They then honoured it with the title of The Yellow Road (*hoang-tao*), the equator being called The Red Road; thus they recognized at that time the superior importance of the ecliptic. However, the 28 asterisms are older than this period, and were not divisions of the ecliptic but of the equator, therefore they cannot rightly be called a zodiac. Further, they were not originally called by the names of animals, any more than were the twelve divisions of the year.

The Mongol chief Argoun wrote to Philippe le Bel in the year of the Ox, which was 1289, as 1955 was for Tibetans 'the year of the Wood Sheep'. This use of a cycle of animals for numbering years appears to be later than their use for numbering months or hours. And if the animals are not an arbitrary list, but had some original appropriateness, then they are likely to have been used first of all to describe the months.

In fact, according to Gustave Schlegel, the choice of animals was made from the seasons at which their activity was most conspicuous. The Cock, for example, is bellicose, and was therefore chosen for October, when preparations for war are made. (The Cock is the Pleiades.) The ape *semnopithecus schistosus* gives birth in November, the tenth month of the Chinese year, when the full moon would, about 1000 B.C., rise near the asterism of Shên the Ape, which is Orion's head. In a similar way the Horse gives birth during the twelfth moon, Snakes come out of the earth at the end of winter (first moon), Hares give birth in March and April, Tigers migrate in April and May, Rats are commonest in July, and Pigs were put out in August to trample and manure the water-logged ground.[3]

That a race should have named its months after the natural phenomena of the seasons is not improbable, and thus far Schlegel may be right; but his actual explanations are not acceptable now because they are thought to put the origin of the animals names too early. We cannot, in order to make Chinese astronomy look ancient, claim that it influenced Babylon rather than the other way round, or that the contact happened in a gratuitously remote antiquity.

According to Carl Bezold,[4] Babylon and China had the same names for the constellations of the two Bears, Draco, Coma Berenices, Orion, and Andromeda. He also showed a distinct Babylonian influence on the astrology of the *Shi-ki*. For in this book, as on Babylonian omen-tablets, sentences are found in which an if-clause describing some celestial phenomenon (for instance 'if there be a halo round the full moon in Fang') is followed by a prediction in one word: 'hunger', 'war', or the like. Mars in Fang (which is part of Scorpio) has the same effect as Mars in Scorpio in Babylon, and Bezold gives seven examples of this, in one of which Mars is actually called by the name of the constellation Boötes; and it was a Babylonian custom to call a planet by the name of a star or constellation whose influence was supposed to be similar. This is the normal type of Babylonian celestial prediction, and was already ancient and traditional when Asshurbanipal built up his great library at Nineveh in the seventh century B.C. Nothing leads us to suppose that this typically Babylonian method was of Chinese origin, so it seems more natural to conclude that it came to China from Babylon; and

Bezold thought that this must have happened before the end of the sixth century B.C.

A similar interchange of names or symbolism is implied in those texts which speak of Venus being worshipped as the White Emperor, Jupiter as the Green (or Blue) Emperor, and the star Denebola (Beta Leonis, the Lion's Tail) as the Yellow Emperor.[5]

The regular Chinese names of the planets are these, with their elements and directions:

TABLE 4

Jupiter	*suei-sing*	wood	east
Mars	*yong-ho*	fire	south
Saturn	*chen-sing*	earth	centre
Venus	*t'ai-po*	metal	west
Mercury	*ch'en-sing*	water	north

A purely Chinese type of political prediction, though of later date, is given in the sixth century A.D. by Wei Shou, who describes the traditional catastrophes attributed to various animals.[6] These occur whenever a monster is born on earth, or a miraculous beast is seen in the sky. A two-headed calf means that the temple of the ancestors will be destroyed. A horse in the sky means war, and a cock with horns prefigures the usurpation of royal prerogative by a minor official. The Calamities of the Goat signify that the ruler is not enlightened and makes mistakes in government—nowadays we should expect this every year!—but the Calamities of the Pig are said to be even worse: 'Of all the signs of evil augury, these are much the most common; they signify that a person holding public office is perverse.'

A more cheering view of life is taken in the following passage from a Buddhist text of uncertain date and Central Asian origin:[7]

When the twelve animals have accomplished their meritorious work, they make a solemn vow in the presence of all the Buddhas to see to it that night and day there shall always be one of them travelling, preaching, and converting, while the other eleven remain quietly practising goodness. The Rat begins on the first day of the seventh moon, and converts all beings who have the form of rats. He persuades them to give up evil actions and exhorts them to do good. The others in succession do the same, and when the thirteenth day comes the Rat begins again. In the same way they go on until the end of the twelve months, and the twelve years, with a view to bringing all living beings under the Rule. It is for this reason there are so many meritorious actions upon the earth, since even the animals preach and convert, teaching the unsurpassable doctrine of the Buddha.

To go back, however, to earlier times, a purely solar calendar is not convenient for primitive peoples, since the sun makes the stars invisible, and a purely lunar calendar, though much easier to observe, is useless as a guide to the seasons. To reconcile the two the Chinese had, according to Saussure,[8] a particularly simple self-operating system. With them the full moon to the right of Kio was always the last of the year, and the full moon to the left of it was always the first, regardless whether the year had twelve or thirteen moons. Kio, which was called The Root of Heaven and Chief of the Asterisms, was the star Spica; and it is curious that Spica was also the sidereal marking-star of the zodiac, as we shall later see. This may be only chance, but the Chinese could equally well have chosen several other equatorial stars, particularly Markab, Altair, Antares, Alphard, Procyon, Betelgeuze, the Pleiades or Hyades.

Again, for primitive peoples, to count the number of full moons in a year, and arrange to meet for the autumn fair after a given number, is not so easy, nor so reliable seasonally, as to arrange the meeting when the moon shall be full in conjunction with a particular group of stars. For this purpose the Chinese chose two constellations, Scorpio and Orion. When the Moon was full in conjunction with Antares (Hsin, the Heart of the Green Dragon) they met for the festival of the Renewal of Fire in spring; and the convocation of vassals for the harvest festival, and the execution of criminals at the end of the year, was timed by the full moon near Orion.[9]

At present the full moon of Antares falls about May 31st, and that of Orion about December 17th, which shows the effect of precession, for both these dates are far too late. In the twenty-fourth century B.C., the ostensible date of the Canon of Yao, they would have been about March 30th and October 18th. This, however, does not enable us to date the system at all accurately, since the constellations are so large and the climate may have somewhat altered.

The Chinese had another simple dodge for making the calendar regulate itself. At first, allegedly since the time of the Yellow Emperor, their year had had 366 days, but this was shortened under the Chou to 365¼, and thenceforward the Chinese circle of the sky was divided not into 360 degrees but into 365¼ *tou*, this being a closely approximate average to the daily motion of the sun.

The subdivision of the seasons also became more accurate, through the invention of a method supposedly due to Chou-kong, brother of the first Chou emperor. A 'circle of declination' is drawn from pole to pole of the sky, passing through the sun at the winter solstice, and this is called The First *Chong-ki*. Then the twelve *chong-ki* are intervals of 30·4375 days, twelfth-parts of the circle of 365¼ days, and the fourth, seventh, and tenth of these gave the official (but slightly inexact) Chinese dates of the two equinoxes and the summer solstice.

However, the moon's synodical revolution (her period from new to new) is distinctly less than 30·4375 days, being in fact 29 days 12 hours 44 minutes 2·9 seconds; it could therefore happen that an entire moon, or month, would pass without containing a *chong-ki*. Such a month was regarded as an extra or intercalary month, and bore the same name as the preceding month, followed by the hieroglyph of the 'Prince-between-two-doors'.[10] By this means an extra month was put in whenever required, and the lunar calendar was kept in harmony with the solar seasons. This method is much superior to the ancient Greek system of inserting one or even two extra months whenever the calendar was found to be badly out.

Being a time system and not a spatial system, the *chong-ki* do not provide equal divisions of the ecliptic, and so cannot properly be called a zodiac; but their use suggests that a division into twelve was practised under the Chou, perhaps as early as Chou-Kong himself (1111 B.C.), and possibly even earlier.

When we come to look into the matter of dates, there are four questions to be answered. What is the earliest Chinese record of the 28 asterisms, of the 12 divisions of the sky, and of the two sets of animal names?

The earliest Chinese astronomical document is the Yao-tien, or Canon of Yao, which forms the first chapter of the Shu King, or Book of History, supposedly compiled by Confucius in the early fifth century B.C.[11] This was, so to speak, the first press-cutting book on record, for it consisted of famous speeches and enactments; but in its present form it was long thought to be of early Han date, and merely a reconstruction from memory, with perhaps a few fragments discovered in remote localities; for it was assumed that no Chinese book could be older than the Burning of the Books in 213 B.C.

More recently, with a better knowledge of the evolution of the Chinese language, scholars have decided not to believe in the total destruction of China's early literature. This does not mean, however, that we can take any ancient text at its face value; for Chinese scholars did not copy their texts in the perfunctory manner of medieval monks, without bothering to understand what they were writing; being scholars, and not merely scribes, they made sense of their texts, brought them up to date, and sometimes wrote commentaries on them. In consequence, of course, no Chinese text can be relied on as a verbatim expression of the thought of its ostensible author.

Further, in the early centuries A.D. Chinese astronomers were learning to compute backwards what the appearance of the sky would have been at epochs in the past, and having done so they thought it only natural to insert into ancient books statements of what they knew to have been the case. Hence the allegations of scholars that such statements are largely 'forgeries' of the sixth century A.D. or even later.

This is why we cannot take too seriously the statement that in the twenty-ninth year of Lu-siang, which would be 544 B.C., the cold winter was attributed to the fact that Jupiter had gone too far, and instead of being in *Sing-ki* (Sagittarius–Capricorn) had gone on into *hiuen-hiao* (Capricorn–Aquarius). We can, however, parallel the phenomenon, which is only due to the slight eccentricity of Jupiter's orbit; for

in December	1931	Jupiter turned retrograde in	22½°	Leo	tropical
in January	1933	,, ,, ,,	,, 23°	Virgo	,,
in February	1934	,, ,, ,,	,, 23°	Libra	,,
in March	1935	,, ,, ,,	,, 23°	Scorpio	,,
in April	1936	,, ,, ,,	,, 24°	Sagittarius	,,
in May	1937	,, ,, ,,	,, 27°	Capricorn	,,
in June	1938	,, ,, ,,	,, 2°	Pisces	,,

omitting Aquarius altogether.

94

In its final form, however, the Canon of Yao has come down to us as follows, describing how two pairs of brothers were appointed by Yao to observe the cardinal points:

He separately commanded the second brother Hsî to reside at Yü-î, in what was called the Bright Valley, and (there) respectfully to receive as a guest the rising sun, and to adjust and arrange the labours of the spring. 'The day', (said he), 'is of the medium length, and the culminating star is Niâo;—you may thus exactly determine mid-spring. The people are dispersed (in the fields), and birds and beasts breed and copulate.'

He further commanded the third brother Hsî to reside at Nan-kiâo (in what was called the Brilliant Capital), to adjust and arrange the transformations of the summer, and respectfully to observe the exact limit (of the shadow). 'The day', (said he), 'is at its longest, and the star is Hwo;—you may thus exactly determine midsummer. The people are more dispersed; and birds and beasts have their feathers and hair thin, and change their coats.'

He separately commanded the second brother Ho to reside at the west, in what was called the Dark Valley, and (there) respectfully to convoy the setting sun, and to adjust and arrange the completing labours of the autumn. 'The night', (said he), 'is of the medium length, and the star is Hsü;—you may thus exactly determine mid-autumn. The people feel at ease, and birds and beasts have their coats in good condition.'

He further commanded the third brother Ho to reside in the northern region, in what was called the Sombre Capital, and (there) to adjust and examine the changes of the winter. 'The day', (said he), 'is at its shortest, and the star is Mâo;—you may thus exactly determine mid-winter. The people keep in their houses, and the coats of birds and beasts are downy and thick.'

The Tî said, Ah! you, Hsîs and Hos, a round year consists of three hundred, sixty, and six days. Do you, by means of the intercalary month, fix the four seasons, and complete (the period of) the year. (Thereafter) the various officers being regulated in accordance with this, all the works (of the year) will be fully performed.

This text goes back to a time when the determination of the seasons was still regarded as difficult, and the dates implied are as follows[12] (in the astronomical era, by which $-2357 =$ B.C. 2358):

Mao	=Pleiades	-2357
Niao	=Alphard	-2152
Huo=Fang	=Beta Scorpii	-2619
or else	Delta Scorpii	-2477
Hsü	=Beta Aquarii	-1858

These dates, however, cannot be taken seriously, for several reasons. The constellations Huo and Niao are far too large to provide any date at all. Hsü and Mao are smaller, but differ in date by half a millennium. Hence it is an illusion to suppose that one can date the Canon of Yao by the precession of the equinoxes. For if, as does seem to be the case in the opinion of most reputable sinologists, the marking-stars of the 28 asterisms were chosen to coincide with an already existing set of circumpolar marking-stars, then the precession of the equinoxes has nothing to do with the case. The main difficulty is that the literary and archaeological evidence all points to Chinese astronomy having grown up in the Shang period, roughly between 1600 and 1100; but if we take the Pleiades seriously as a seasonal marker, there is no escaping from the twenty-fourth century.

Of course the mention of four asterisms in the Yao-tien does not imply that the whole system of 28 was known. Stars are mentioned on the oracle-bones discovered at Anyang, and from these it seems certain that the Four Palaces were recognized as early as 1300 B.C., in the reign of Wu Ting. Particular mention is made of the Bird Star (Niao hsing, Alphard) and the Fire Star (Huo hsing, Antares).

A little later comes the Shih King, or Book of Odes, also supposedly compiled by Confucius, but containing poems now thought to date from the ninth and eighth centuries. It mentions at least eight of the asterisms. Next in date comes the Yueh Ling, which may be as old as 850 or as late as 420 B.C. It mentions all but five of the asterisms. And finally the full list was almost certainly in existence by 350.[13]

The Yueh Ling speaks in this style: 'In the first month of spring the Sun is in the constellation Ing Shih (Pegasus); Shen (Orion) culminates at sunset, and Wei (the Scorpion's tail) at dawn. In the

7. (*left*) T'ang mirror with circle of animals

8. (*below*) Mithraic zodiac (*see pages* 118 *and* 120)

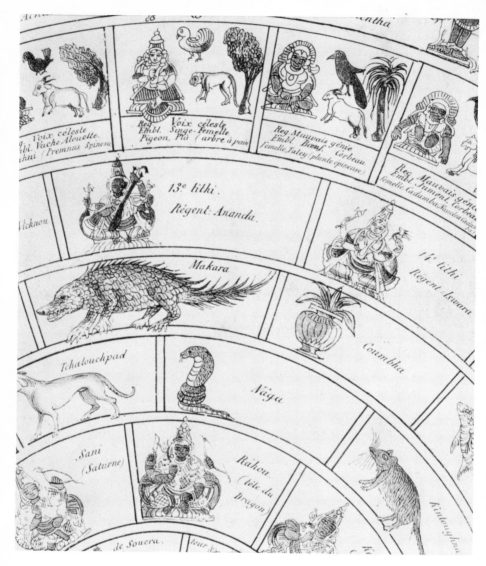

9. Macara the Indian Capricorn and Kumbha the Waterpot (*see page* 141)

(*facing page*)

10. (*left*) Comparison of Sagittarius, Capricorn, and Aquarius in Babylon and Egypt

11. (*right*) Scorpion-man on a boundary-stone of 12th century B.C. (*see page* 167)

12. The Babylonian God-with-Streams (*see pages* 167–8)

13. Virgo the grain-goddess in the Persian period (*see page* 171)

second month of spring the sun is in K'uei (Andromeda with Pisces); Hou (Canis Major and Argo) culminates at sunset, and Kien (the head of Sagittarius) at dawn; equinox, the swallows arrive.'

Each month has its agricultural and social duties, depending on the season—to plough or to sow, not to pull down nests or kill pregnant animals, to care for the aged by providing them with walking-sticks, and so forth—and there are many other correspondences. In the second month of autumn, for instance, the divine ruler is Shao Hao, its animals are the hairy ones, its smell is metallic; one sacrifices to the spirit of the gate and puts the liver on top. The Son of Heaven wears white and goes out in the war-chariot drawn by white horses with black manes and tails, and decorated with white flags. He eats sesame and dog's flesh out of rectangular dishes.[14]

> He orders the Grand Recorder to guard the statutes and maintain the laws, and especially to observe the motions in the heavens of the sun and moon, and of the zodiacal stars in which the conjunctions of these bodies take place, so that there should be no error as to where they rest and what they pass over; that there should be no failure in the record of all these things, according to the regular practice of early times.

The astronomical information in these books has of course been brought up to date in the usual Chinese manner, and now corresponds to a date A.D. rather than to its own ostensible time; but the asterisms are not yet alluded to by their animal names. Indeed it is not quite certain how early these occur, but unless they originated in Turkestan, as Chavannes suggested,[6] then they probably came from the West about the time of Alexander the Great. It is known that trade relations between India and China expanded in the third century B.C., and it has been thought that the name China (Sanskrit *Cina*, and in similar forms, sometimes with S instead of C, in many Western languages) perpetuates the name of the Ch'in Dynasty, which ruled from 249 to 206 B.C.

The best-known minister of that dynasty, and probably the first low-born capitalist to become a nationally important figure in China, was Lü-pu-wey, who was appointed Grand Counsellor in 250, and dismissed, to the delight of his many enemies, in 237.

97

Legend tells that he seduced the queen and so became the father of the ensuing emperor, the notorious Cheng, who called himself Shih-Hoang-Ti—First Yellow Emperor—although the original Yellow Emperor had reigned some four-and-twenty centuries earlier. It was Cheng who committed the historic crime of decreeing the Burning of the Books.

Lü-pu-wey had realized that the Ch'in Dynasty, and its whole province, was backward and uncultured compared to the rest of China, which it had recently conquered, and he therefore assembled scholars from many parts and caused them to compile a book of annals, including a vast amount of miscellaneous information. Then, with the vanity of the self-made, he himself assumed the authorship, calling it Lü-shih Ch'un Ch'iu—'Mr Lü's Spring and Autumn'.[15]

Lü-pu-wey, being a wealthy merchant and importer, may well have been interested in foreign parts; he was a Taoist, and Lao-tse the founder of Taoism was said to have travelled to India and the West, perhaps even to the Caspian Sea; and we are told in the *Spring and Autumn* that in ancient times the empire was governed by 71 sages, an unlikely number which recalls the Indian doctrine of 71 divine rulers to a *manvantara*, or phase of manifested life. This being so, it seems possible that knowledge of the circle of animals may first have come to China in the time of Lü-pu-wey.

Lists of asterisms in China begin either with Kio (Spica), which is the native system, or else with Mao (the Pleiades), which is the Indian method. Lists beginning with Mao were compiled under Buddhist influence, for when the first Buddhist missionaries arrived from India, certainly no later than the third century B.C., they most likely brought with them the traditional Indian list, in which Krittika (the Pleiades) stood first. It was already long out of date, and precession has since obliged the Hindus to transfer the head of the list successively backwards to Bharani, then to Açvini, and now to Revati. But before precession was known it would not occur to anyone that the reference-points of the sky were becoming gradually obsolete.

The Chinese, however, had always measured their year from the winter solstice—in so far as they showed any preference for one of the four cardinal points—and their calendar began halfway between the winter solstice and the vernal equinox, in the middle of February.

Why then this choice of Kio as the first asterism, which it never was in India? Saussure thought it was chosen because the first full moon of the year appeared there in Shang times, and Shinjo suggested because the handle of the Big Dipper points towards it, the Big Dipper's handle being used as a seasonal marker according as it points east or west, up or down. With these two possible alternative reasons, it would be rash to lay too much stress on the use of Spica as the original marking-star of the zodiac, which would imply that a system essentially Chinese was measured by a fiducial imported from the Middle East.

The Chinese constellations have little in common with those of Europe; of the 48 in the Ptolemaic canon, only 10 were found by Professor Needham to have positive resemblances in China.[16] On the other hand we do discover in Censorinus,[17] a Latin writer of the third century A.D., a twelve-year cycle of predictions of plenty and scarcity of the fruits of the earth, which is closely paralleled in the Chi Ni Tzu.[16]

Besides the circle of 28 asterisms, the *hsiu*, there existed in China a circle of 12 divisions which may have been even older. These are called the Twelve Kung, and their principal use was apparently to predict plenty or scarcity, peace, or war, in the provinces they ruled, from the colour, brilliance, and course of the planet Jupiter when passing through or in opposition to them. The rulership of a sign over a province was determined by the constellation chiefly worshipped in each. In Sung, for example, the people worshipped Ta-Ho, the Great Fire, which is part of Scorpio, and in Tsin (Shansi) Orion's Belt. In contrast to modern times, Jupiter's influence was not supposed to be good in itself, but depended on the appearance of the planet.

It has been thought that this cycle took its origin from Jupiter's twelve-year period.[18] On the other hand the number 12 is unavoidable in astronomy because of the $12\frac{1}{2}$ lunations in the tropical year; and it is equally possible that the twelvefold division may have come from Babylon, as Bezold believed, and was originally a month-number rather than a year-number. That 'Twelve is the number of Heaven' is warranted in the Li-ki by the fact that the emperor's sacrificial robe was embroidered with the sun, moon and stars, and his crown bore twelve strings of pearls.

99

TABLE 5 *The 12 Kung*

Name	Meaning of Name	Beginning in the asterisms	Extent	
hsing-chi	recording star	tou 12°	30°	Winter Palace, North, water
hsüan-hsiao	empty depth	nü 8°	30°	Dark Warrior or Tortoise
chü-shih	?	wei 16°	31°	
hsiang-lou	?	k'uei 5°	30°	Autumn Palace, West, metal
ta-liang	great splendour	wei 7°	30°	White Tiger
shih-ch'en	Orion	pi 12°	31°	
shun-shou	head of the red quail	ching 16°	30°	Summer Palace, South, fire
shun-huo	body of the red quail	liu 9°	31°	Red Quail
shun-wei	tail of the red quail	chang 18°	30°	
shou-hsing	longevity (Spica)	chen 12°	31°	Spring Palace, East, wood,
ta-huo	great fire (Antares)	ti 5°	30°	Green Dragon
che-mu	the ford(?), or woodcutting	wei 10°	31°	

The 12 Kung, also called Tzhu, correspond to the 12-year cycle of Jupiter.

Besides the divisions into 12 and 28, the Chinese have a division of the year into 24 'solar terms', given by Giles as follows:[19]

TABLE 6

Begins about		Name	Meaning of name	Sun in tropical sign
February	5th	li ch'un	spring begins	Aquarius
„	19th	yü shui	rain water	Pisces
March	5th	ching chih	excited insects	„
„	20th	ch'un fên	vernal equinox	Aries
April	5th	ch'ing ming	clear and bright	„
„	20th	ku yü	grain rains	Taurus
May	5th	li hsia	summer begins	„
„	21st	hsiao man	grain fills	Gemini
June	6th	mang chung	grain in ear	„
„	21st	hsia chih	summer solstice	Cancer
July	7th	hsiao shu	slight heat	„
„	23rd	ta shu	great heat	Leo
August	7th	li ch'iu	autumn begins	„
„	23rd	ch'u shu	limit of heat	Virgo
September	8th	pai lu	white dew	„
„	23rd	ch'iu fên	autumn equinox	Libra
October	8th	han lu	cold dew	„
„	23rd	shuang chiang	hoar-frost descends	Scorpio
November	7th	li tung	winter begins	„
„	22nd	hsiao hsüeh	little snow	Sagittarius
December	7th	ta hsüeh	heavy snow	„
„	22nd	tung chih	winter solstice	Capricorn
January	6th	hsiao han	little cold	„
„	21st	ta han	severe cold	Aquarius

The number 28 looks like an attempt to provide one asterism, or 'mansion', for every night of the moon's revolution; and so it might be, in a sufficiently backward state of culture. But it could not be accurate enough to serve as the basis of a calendar, since the length of the moon's sidereal revolution (between two successive conjunctions to a given star) is only 27 days 7 hours 43 minutes — an inexactitude of nearly one-third of a day in every month, or four days in a year.

Further, the Chinese asterisms were not originally intended to serve this purpose, since they follow the equator rather than the ecliptic. The moon can be near, but never actually in, the *hsiu* of the Ape, since the Ape is part of Orion, where the moon never goes. More probably, therefore, they were intended to serve as hour-markers for telling the time at night.

In Han times (from 206 B.C.) and perhaps earlier, the Chinese divided the day into 60 parts, beginning from midnight,[20] and this system is found also at Babylon and in the Vedas. Furthermore, both the Vedas and the Chinese give the proportion of the longest day to 24 hours as 18: 30, and this works out at 14 hours 24 minutes, which is exactly the length of the longest day at Babylon as computed by Claudius Ptolemy in the second century A.D. So here is evidence of the transmission of astronomical knowledge and tradition, rather than fresh observation, from the Hellenized region of the Middle East to India and China.

Is it possible that the 28 mansions spread in the opposite direction, from China across Central Asia, and reached the Middle East via Turkestan and Persia? For the Parsees and Arabs have such systems, as well as the Hindus. Of the 28 asterisms, there are only 5 peculiar to China; 17 the Chinese have in common with the Hindus, and 18 in common with the Arabs; which suggests that the Arabs did not derive them from the Hindus. Or conceivably they could have originated in Persia, and spread thence to China, India, and Arabia.

The Chinese marking-stars, as Burgess and Chu Kho-Chen have shown,[21] follow the equator of the twenty-fourth century B.C. more closely than they do the equator of any later time, and more closely than do the Arab or Indian marking-stars. It is therefore possible that the Chinese system of asterisms grew up in or some time after the twenty-fourth century B.C. as an equatorial system of hour-divisions, chosen to fit in with the upper and lower culminations of circumpolar hour-stars which were already in use. But while it is true that the Chinese marking-stars follow the equator of the twenty-fourth century better than they do that of any later time, they do not follow it very closely. In particular, seven in succession (Nos. 6 to 12), all selected from the zodiacal constellations Scorpio, Sagittarius, Capricorn and Aquarius, were at that date no less than 13 degrees to the south of the equator; and since there are several stars bright enough to be used instead, standing higher in the sky and nearer to the equator—especially Altair, Eta Ophiuchi, Lambda Aquilae and Epsilon Pegasi—it seems almost possible that some of the determining stars may have been altered to mark the zodiac rather than the equator. However, a curve drawn through the determining stars of the *hsiu* can only be rough at the best of times, and it may be rather more plausible to agree with Professor Needham that this curve can be taken to fit the sixteenth century as easily as the twenty-fourth.[22]

In any case the circle of animals is not the original Chinese system, and hardly anyone believes that it can be traced there so early as the sixth century B.C.; the fourth or third century is much more likely. The question remains, which is the older, the hour-circle of 12 animals, or the circle of 28? In order to solve this problem we must scrutinize the two lists.

TABLE 7 *The Twelve Branches, or Horary Circle*

	Hour	Direction	Name	Meaning of Name	Animal.
1.	midnight	North	tzŭ	a child	Rat
2.	1–3 a.m.	NNE	ch'ou	(uncertain)	Ox
3.	3–5 a.m.	ENE	yin	to revere (?)	Tiger
4.	5–7 a.m.	East	mao	to burst forth	Hare
5.	7–9 a.m.	ESE	ch'en	a lucky time	Dragon
6.	9–11 a.m.	SSE	ssŭ	(uncertain)	Serpent
7.	noon	South	wu	noon (?)	Horse
8.	1–3 p.m.	SSW	wei	not yet (?)	Sheep
9.	3–5 p.m.	WSW	shen	continuation	Monkey
10.	5–7 p.m.	West	yu	ripeness, completion	Cock
11.	7–9 p.m.	WNW	hsü	(uncertain)	Dog
12.	9–11 p.m.	NNW	hai	(uncertain)	Boar

These animals are often represented in Chinese art, for instance on old mirrors, or carved in jade. The first, fourth, and tenth names have an obvious reference to the hour of the day, and such may well be the origin of all. But this does not apply to the animal names. The Cock does not, as with us, signify dawn, and even if it did, what hour would the Sheep or Tiger signify? Since these names have no obvious appropriateness, they may be derived from some other system.

The 28 asterisms are as follows — their numbers are given in both the Chinese and Buddhist systems, but they will be alluded to by the latter, following the practice of earlier writers. They are not equal in extent; the largest covers over 30 degrees, the smallest about 2 degrees. (See Table 8 on pages 104–5.)

Of these 28 asterisms, only the Deer and the Ox (Nos. 9 and 26) bore animal names originally; and these were preserved when the full cycle of animal names was devised. The descriptive names, being unsystematic, are clearly older; in some cases the meaning has been forgotten, and fancied resemblances are to be found in Nos. 8, 14, 18, 19, and 22, and possibly also in Nos. 15, 17, and 27.

But if we look down the list of 28 animals, we may well be struck by a certain duplication of ideas, as if this were an expansion of an originally smaller number of names. There are two adjacent dragons, then serpent and worm adjacent, and two kinds of deer with a horse between them; monkey and ape make a pair, followed by three birds together, then dog and wolf. It is often assumed that the twelve animals of the hour-circle were selected in reverse order from the 28, but this pairing makes it appear more probable that the 28 are an inflation of the 12. In that case J.-B. Biot may have been right to suppose that the original number of asterisms was 24, though not for the reason that he gave. He suggested that the extra four might have been put in to mark the equinoxes and solstices in the time of Chou-kung (1100 B.C.). They would then have had to be Nos. 24, 3, 10, and 17, and the dates indicated would be as follows:

Vernal Equinox, no. 17, Wei (pheasant) = 35 Arietis R.A. 0° in 1031 B.C.
Summer Solstice, no. 24, Liu (muntjak) = Delta Hydrae R.A. 90° in 913 B.C.
Autumn Equinox, no. 3, Ti (badger) = Alpha Librae R.A. 180° in 1280 B.C.
Winter Solstice, no. 10, Nü (bat) = Epsilon Aquarii R.A. 270° in 1009 B.C.

TABLE 8 *The 28 Chinese Asterisms, or Hsiu*

Chinese Number	Buddhist Number	Animal	Name	Meaning of name	Extent	Principal Stars
18	1	Cock	Mao	(uncertain)	11°	Pleiades
19	2	Raven	Pi 畢	handnet; writing-tablet	16°	Hyades
20	3	Monkey	tsŭi	lips	2°	λφ Orionis
21	4	Ape	shen	(uncertain)	9°	Orion's head and shoulder
Southern Palace						
22	5	Tapir	ching	the well	33°	μ Geminorum
23	6	Sheep	kuei	the spirits or ghosts	4°	θ Cancri
24	7	Muntjak	liu	the willow-tree	15°	δ Hydrae
25	8	Horse	hsing	the star	7°	α Hydrae (Alphard)
26	9	Deer	chang	the hornless deer*	18°	κνμ Hydrae
27	10	Serpent	i	the wings of a bird	18°	α Crateris
28	11	Worm	chén	to revolve†	17°	γ Corvi
Eastern Palace	12	Hornless Dragon	kio	the horn	12°	Spica
2	13	Dragon	k'ang	strong, violent; neck	9°	κλ Virginis
3	14	Badger	ti	to hang down (?); root	15°	αβ Librae
4	15	Hare	fang	the room	5°	βδπ Scorpii
5	16	Fox	hsin	the heart	5°	Antares
6	17	Tiger	wei 尾	the tail	18°	εμ Scorpii
7	18	Leopard	chi	spread out fanwise‡	11°	γ etc. Sagittarii

Northern	8	19	Gryphon	tou	the (southern) dipper	26°	$\mu\phi$ Sagittarii
Palace	9	20	Ox	niu	the ox; the herd-boy	8°	$\alpha\beta$ Capricorni
	10	21	Bat	nü	the woman, serving-maid	12°	ϵ Aquarii
	11	22	Rat	hsü	empty	10°	β Aquarii
	12	23	Swallow	wei 危	precipitous, rooftop	17°	α Aquarii
	13	24	Boar	shih	the mansion	16°	α Pegasi
	14	25	Porcupine	pi 壁	the fortified wall	9°	γ Pegasi
Western	15	26	Wolf	k'uei	legs	16°	$\beta\zeta\eta$ Andromedae
Palace	16	27	Dog	lou	the tether	12°	$\alpha\beta$ Arietis
	17	28	Pheasant	wei 胃	the stomach	14°	35 Arietis

* or, extended net   † or, chariot-platform   ‡ or, winnowing-basket

The mean date of this table 1096 B.C., and the margin of error $183\frac{1}{2}$ years on either side (just over 3 degrees). This is evidently possible, but there seems no reason to accept it, rather the contrary, since at that epoch the system of *hsiu* had hardly settled into its final shape. Further, there would be no need to insert four extra asterisms unless the original system had contained four which had been supposed to mark the equinoxes and solstices in earlier times. And although Dr Chatley [23] declares that the four marking-stars of the equatorial belt in early times were Alphard, Antares, Beta Aquarii, and the Pleiades, these stars can only have been used as a rough guide before the birth of exact celestial measurement, for the dates when they would have been exact are centuries apart:

Hsing (Alphard) marked the summer solstice in 2153 B.C.
Fang (Beta Scorpii) marked the autumn equinox in 2620 B.C.
Hsü (Beta Aquarii) marked the winter solstice in 1859 B.C.
Mao (Pleiades) marked the vernal equinox in 2219 B.C.
Antares marked the autumnal equinox in 2922 B.C.

It is thus not at all probable that the *hsiu* were ever combined with a system of seasonal marking-stars; and the four which would have marked the seasons in 1100 B.C. are all too large to be later insertions.

But, to return to the later period when the animal cycle had been imported, there is surely some significance in the intrusion of the horse between two deer. Should we reduce the 28 to 24 by excising the Horse and every seventh therefrom? If we do this, we lose the Hare, Rat, and Cock, and the remainder form an uninterrupted sequence of twelve pairs, which we can compare with the horary circle:

TABLE 9 *Asterisms and Hour-circle compared*

24 *Asterisms*	12 *Branches*	24 *Asterisms*	12 *Branches*
1. Two dragons	5. dragon	7. dog and wolf	11. dog
2. badger and fox	4. hare	8. raven and pheasant	10. cock
3. tiger and leopard	3. tiger	9. monkey and ape	9. monkey
4. gryphon and ox	2. ox	10. sheep and tapir	8. sheep
5. bat and swallow	1. rat	11. deer and muntjak	7. horse
6. boar and porcupine	12. boar	12. serpent and worm	6. serpent

All but two of these pairs are obvious; for the muntjak is a kind of hornless deer; the porcupine's name in several languages means 'spiny pig'; and the bat and swallow both fly round the house. So obvious, in fact, is the principle of pairing that is seems hard to discredit it even by the oddly assorted couples sheep and tapir, gryphon and ox. Are the words rightly translated?

The word *han* 犴 translated by Giles as 'tapir' in reference to the asterisms, in other connections means 'a wild dog like a fox but smaller', or else a watchdog or possibly a jackal. Since we already have both dog and wolf in the circle, this can hardly apply: Giles is doubtless right to translate the word differently. In the third century B.C., however, the meaning may not have been what it is today, and the Chinese are also capable of having seen a resemblance not obvious to the Westerner.

The animal *hsieh* 獬 is 'a fabulous animal with a single horn like a unicorn. It dwells in the desert, and being able to discriminate right from wrong, gores wicked people when it sees them. It eats fire in its ravenous fury, even to its own destruction'. Thus Giles, enlarging upon the Chinese Imperial Encyclopaedia, the *Ku-chin T'u-shu Chi-ch'eng*, where the animal is illustrated.[24] Like most Chinese dragons, it resembles a Pekingese dog more than anything else, and the horn is placed on its nose. More terse than Giles, the Encyclopaedia says: 'like a sheep one horn four feet' — and a sheep, of course, means equally a goat. Not unnaturally Couvreur translates it 'unicorn'.

But a unicorn is found in the horary cycle of the Mimaut Papyrus! Hence it, too, may have come from the West; and if so, one would expect it to be paired with the Sheep rather than the Ox. The Ox, however, is one of the only two asterisms which had an animal name originally; there could therefore be no question of altering the Ox, but the Unicorn, if it needed a place, could fit in beside it since both are horned. The difficulty about the Tapir and the Sheep remains, but can hardly be held to cancel out the whole principle of pairing.

To return, then, to the comparison from which we started, the circle of animals would seem to have come to China, and the Far East generally, in the following form, which has a significant resemblance to the zodiac:

TABLE 10 *The Far Eastern Circle of Animals*

Dog	Dragon (in Thailand Great Dragon; in Persia crocodile)
Pig (in Japan Boar)	Snake (in Thailand Small Dragon) (♍)
Rat or Mouse	Horse (♐)
Ox (in Thailand Cow)	Sheep or Goat (in Thailand Goat) (♑)
Tiger (in Mongolia Panther)	Monkey or Ape (in Japan long-tailed monkey) (♒)
Hare (in Thailand Rabbit)	Bird (Cock or Hen in Japan, Persia and Thailand)[25]

When these names were applied to the already existing set of asterisms, there was no difficulty in making them fit, for there was only one name in common, namely the Ox, which was located at Alpha and Beta Capricorni. But had it been our zodiac, as a year-circle, which was imported into China, then after the equation of the Bull with Niu the Ox (No. 20), we should have had the Twins, instead of the Boar, equated with Shih the Mansion (No. 24), and the Crab instead of the Dog given to Lou the Tether (No. 27). Three things show that the idea which came to China was not at first the year-circle of the zodiac, but the hour-circle, or dodeca-oros: first, the equation of the animals being counter to the order of the asterisms; secondly, the circle being exclusively animal, without any human figures; and thirdly, though it bears a partial resemblance to our zodiac, the Chinese circle of animals is patently not our zodiac and was not put to the same use.

In favour of there having at first been 24 asterisms, not 28, the evidence is the list of pairs obtained by excising the Horse, Hare, Rat, and Cock, and the fact that, if one were merely trying to inflate the 12 up to 28, it is not at all clear why the Bat and Swallow, two flying creatures, should be chosen as fit companions for the Rat. But a formidable difficulty remains: the four excised animals correspond to the most ancient marking-stars of Chinese astronomy, which we cannot suppose to have been omitted from the original list of asterisms. Nor is it really likely that the four large asterisms which marked the cardinal points in 1100 B.C. were merely afterthoughts. And the table of twenty-four pairs really proves nothing, since in order to inflate the twelve up to 28 the obvious procedure is to invent a pair for each and then add four; and since we have seen already that it was the circle of 12 hour-animals which came to China, one can hardly doubt that this procedure was followed.

How then do we explain the extra four? The Cock and the Hare take no explaining, for each is part of a regular trio, three birds in the one case, and in the other three animals which haunt the fringes of cultivation. Nor is the Horse so intrusive as it appears; it is part of the hour-circle, and the two Deer come next to it because one of them was there already, being one of the only two asterisms which had an animal name. The Rat or Mouse, for all its resemblance to a Bat, does look out of place between two flying creatures, but it appears to be the original member of the group, and one can at least say of all three that they haunt the house without being reckoned domestic animals.

Why then does the Rat come first in the Chinese circle? Perhaps because the Chinese day began at midnight, which happened to be the hour of the Rat. This, if true, would explain why the Rat, ruling the first hour, was equated to Aries the first sign. But how did midnight come to be the hour of the Rat? Possibly for no particular reason, since we know that in the dodeca-oros the sequence of animals was much less constant than in the zodiac. In the Middle East, however, where the hour-circle originated, the day was reckoned to begin not at midnight but at sunset, so the first hour would be, in summer, from about 7 to 9 p.m. We can imagine this being ruled by whatever animal corresponded to Aries and came first on the list; but if we are right to put the Dragon in Libra, this must have been the Dog. And if the Dog rules at 8 p.m., the Rat will rule at midnight.

In conclusion, then, the number of asterisms would seem to have been originally 28 in China, not 27 or 24, and this may have been an accident, determined by the number of convenient groups of marking-stars which had been chosen, or it may have been decided under Indian influence, or it may have grown up as a set of moon-stations in such ancient times that its inexactitude would not have mattered. The Indian *nakshatras* existed as a system by about 800 or possibly even 1000 B.C.; but there is no proving whether they had an influence on Chinese astronomy or conversely, for the system of *hsiu* grew up about the same time, and the two may have been independent. The animal circle was not Chinese in origin, but was imported about the third or fourth century B.C.

It is worth remembering that all the most ancient zodiacs began with the Pleiades and ended with the asterism Al Butain, 'the belly', whose longitude was Aries 17° 09'.

7. *From Mexico to Tibet*

WHEN Alexander von Humboldt returned from Mexico and published, in 1816, his great travel-book *Vues des Cordillères*,[1] he claimed to have discovered a striking similarity between the zodiac of Mexico and that of Tibet. This idea is extremely surprising, since the Mexican calendar is not based on the numbers 12, 28, and 30, like most calendars of Europe and Asia, but upon 13 and 20. The solar year consisted of 18 'months' of 20 days each, making 360 days; more important, however, was the period of Venus, which consists astronomically of 584 days, but ritually was made to consist of 260, that is, 13 of the 'months' of 20 days. The 20 days bore, of course, names instead of numbers — the notion of merely numbering things. and otherwise leaving them anonymous, had not yet been invented — and the months also bore names, which according to Bowditch[2] had the following meanings:

TABLE 11   *Mexican Month-names*

pop	=mat	yax	=green, fresh
uo	=frog	zac	=white
zip	=error, swollen, rotten tree, or sunset (?)	ceh	=deer, flint knife for killing deer
zotz	=bat	mac	=lid
tzec	=chastisement or scorpion	kankin	=yellow sun
xul	=end	moan	=cloudy day or head of a bird
yaxkin	=beginning of summer, new sun, rainy season	pax	=a drum
		kayab	=song or turtle
mol	=a claw; to collect	cumhu	=thunder
chen	=a well or spring	uayeb	=bed, repose

These names for the most part are patently seasonal, and give no handle for any connection with the zodiac. The 20 names of the days, however, are taken mostly from animals, and are therefore more promising. Each day had also its ruling god or goddess, but if

Fritz Roeck can be relied on, these did not always fall in the expected places; Quetzal-coatl, for instance, the Feathered Serpent, ruled the second day, called Wind, and not the fifth day, which was called Coatl (serpent); the fire-god ruled the day called Water, and the god and goddess of death ruled the day called Dog, not, as one might have expected, the day called Skull. With their mania for human sacrifice the Mexicans naturally wanted a day of this name, and they had two feasts of the dead in successive 'months'.

The calendar systems of pre-Columbian peoples often seem to have a good deal in common, and it may be that astrology, in some form or other, was widespread, for in 1698 the bishop of Chiapas, F. Nuñez de la Vega, wrote as follows in a pastoral letter referring to the Nagualists among the Quiché: 'They believe that the birth of men is regulated by the course of the stars and planets; they observe the time of the day and of the month at which a child is born, and predict the conditions of its life and destiny, both favourable and unfavourable. And the worst of it is that these perverted men have written down their signs and rules and so deceive the erring and the ignorant.' Too bad!

But although the bishop was writing more than 200 years after Columbus, it does not seem certain that these perverted wizards were putting into practice in southern Mexico astrological rules imported by Spaniards who had studied the writings of King Alphonso the Wise (1252–84), or of Firmicus Maternus and Peter of Abano. Possibly they had their own methods. Among the Nagualists, for example, a boy was given at his initiation into manhood a protecting spirit in animal form, and although the nature of this spirit was sometimes discovered by the local magician in a dream, the animals used may have an astrological connection with the 31 animals which gave their names to the days of the Nagual calendar. It has been suggested by Roeck, on the strength of this, that totemism may have an astrological origin, but this, like some of his other conclusions, is more enthusiastic than convincing.

If prediction by astrology did exist in pre-Columbian America, it was probably found only in the higher cultures. The Navaho,[3] for example, have no knowledge of the zodiac, and though a few of them will use for their 'sand-paintings' an occasional theme of astronomical inspiration, most regard the subject of constellations as too difficult to be interesting. But Toltec astronomy did have something in common with Chinese, in so far as both divided the world into five directions instead of four—north, south, east, west, and centre. Further, the four outward directions were ruled, as in China, by four cosmic creatures comparable to the Four Holy Creatures of Christianity and Judaism—the Bull, Lion, Eagle, and Man that are associated with the evangelists. Roeck[4] has the following comparative table which he believes to indicate some continuity of cultural contact, rather than just the expression of similar archetypal ideas in different places:

	EGYPT	Magic papyrus	TIBET	CHINA	MEXICO
	The Four Sons of Horus	(Berlin) (Parthey II, 101)	Spirits of the Seasons	Four Cosmic Beings (Constellations)	Ritual Masks of the 4 Regents
South	Hawk	Hawk (fire)	Garuda-vulture	Red Bird	Vulture
West	Jackal	Crocodile (water)	Black Dog	White Tiger (originally Spotted Dog)	Dog
North	'Black-faced Ape' (i.e. dog-headed baboon)	Horus-child on lotus (earth)	Horse and Rider	Black Warrior on Tortoise	Death's-head
East	Man	Snake (air)	Man-dragon	Green Dragon	Crocodile

This table is not above criticism, as can be seen. When however we come to the comparison of the animal names of the Chinese and Tibetan asterisms with the Mexican names of the 20 days, Roeck's equations are not very persuasive, any more than those of Humboldt with the twelve Tibetan months. (The Tibetan animal cycle is the same as the Chinese.) It would be guesswork to try to establish any definite theory of Toltec astronomy being copied from that of China or derived from Babylon, although some influence may have percolated. However, for the sake of comparison with the zodiacs of the old world, a list is given here of the 20 Mexican[5] day-names and the 31 animals of the Nagual calendar.

TABLE 12   *Toltec and Nagual Day-names*

Toltec	
* 1.	cipactli=swordfish or alligator
* 2.	èēcatl=wind
3.	calli=house
4.	cuetzpalin=lizard
* 5.	coatl=snake
6.	miquiztli=death's-head
7.	maçatl=stag
* 8.	tochtli=rabbit
9.	atl=water
10.	itzcuintli=dog
11.	ocomatli=ape
*12.	malinalli=straw rope
*13.	acatl=reed
*14.	ocelotl=jaguar
*15.	quauhtli=eagle
*16.	cozcaquauhtli=vulture
17.	olin=movement
*18.	tecpatl=flint
19.	quiauitl=rain
*20.	xochitl=flower

Nagual	
1.	'lion', i.e. puma
* 2.	snake
3.	stone
* 4.	alligator
5.	cotton-tree
6.	quetzal-bird
7.	stick
* 8.	rabbit
* 9.	cord
10.	leaf
11.	red cattle
12.	parrot
*13.	flower
14.	frog
15.	maggot
16.	treestump
17.	arrow
18.	broom
*19.	jaguar
20.	maize
21.	flute
*22.	greenstone
23.	crow
24.	fire
25.	pheasant
*26.	reed
27.	opossum
*28.	storm-wind
*29.	vulture
*30.	hawk
31.	bat

An asterisk (*) in either list signifies that a very similar name will be found in the other.

Eleven of the Toltec names are found in the Nagual list, but nine are not, and this suggests imitation and cultural contact rather than the handing on of an actual tradition. Comparison with the Chinese cycle shows that the Chinese have at most 6 names in common with the Toltec list and 8 with the Nagual list, but only 3, the snake, the rabbit or hare, and the jaguar or leopard, in common with both.

113

The Chinese and Tibetan list, being restricted to animals, naturally has little in common with the American lists, which are not. Further, if we compáre these American lists with the 28 'signs' given in the British Museum Papyrus 121, written in Egypt about the third century A.D., we find that the Toltec list has only 4 names in common with the Egyptian list (the stag, dog, leopard, and vulture), while the Nagual list has 6 or 7 (the lion, leopard, snake, ox, vulture, and hawk, and possibly the staff, being equated to the stick of the Naguals).

One cannot therefore seriously pretend that the American lists of signs are derived either from Egypt or from China. Can we claim that the idea behind them originated at one place on the earth's surface? Even that is not too plausible, for the natural procedure, when one begins to classify the stars, is to group them into convenient small groups and label each with the name of some object which it may possibly resemble, or of some seasonal phenomenon which it may annually indicate. There may be a seasonal significance in the Toltec names 'water', 'wind', and 'rain', or in the Nagual names 'fire' and 'maize'. But on the whole it is very rare for a constellation to resemble anything on earth except a winding river or snake (which occurs in all the lists), a triangle, a curve such as the Crown or the Scorpion's tail, a box or house (which occurs in Mexico and China), and a dipper (a box with a handle, which does equally well for a wain with shafts). There is no difficulty in seeing further resemblances, the difficulty lies rather in pretending that the Lion cannot equally well resemble a knife, which is what the Egyptians called it, or that the square of Pegasus is any more like a horse than a house.[6]

The American names may therefore quite well be of indigenous origin; and we cannot easily suppose that the whole notion of naming constellations was imported. The question is not so much of the origin of these apparently very capricious lists of names, but rather why and from whence the Chinese, Tibetans, and other peoples drew the idea that the names should be restricted to animals.

8. Persia and the Four Elements

PERSIA lies just east of Babylonia, on the way to India by land, and also at the beginning of the golden road to Samarkand and on to China. Geographically, therefore, it was well placed to take part in the spread of ancient ideas about astronomy. Its early history, however, is much less known than that of the Babylonian lowlands. The Amādai and the Parsua, that is to say the Medes and Persians, first come to our knowledge in 837 B.C., in an inscription of Shalmaneser III, King of Assyria. The Median Empire was established by Cyaxares (in his own language Huvakhshatara) between 633 and 584, and transferred to the Persians by Cyrus (Kurash) in 550. Medo-Persian art and civilization were mainly derived, through Assyria, from Babylonian models, but Persian religion was not of Babylonian origin and was not astrological. The supreme and omniscient Good God was Ahura-Mazda, opposed by the Evil God Angra-Mainyu or Ahriman, who was not omniscient. The goddess Anâhita, representing the planet Venus, first begins to be important in the reigns of Artaxerxes II and III (404–336), and at that period the people also worshipped the four elements, light, water, earth, and wind, of which light was divided into the light of the sun and that of the moon.

The Magi seem to have been originally a tribe who specialized in religious observances, like the Levites in Israel. No sacrifice was valid unless attended by a Magus. But later they became a caste, and in the Sassanian period (A.D. 224–642) the Chief of the Magi was appointed by the king, and himself appointed his assistants. By this time astrologers were, with physicians and poets, a regular class of the Persian bureaucracy; but their astrology was not distinguished from that which had spread to India from the Hellenistic world. Further, it was not till near the time of the Muslim conquest that some of the oldest surviving texts of the Persian religion were collected into the book we know as the Bundahish; hence the following account of the creation cannot claim any great antiquity.[1]

Auharmazd produced illumination between the sky and the earth, the constellation stars and those also not of the constellations, then the moon and afterwards the sun, as I shall relate. First he produced the celestial sphere, and the constellation stars are assigned to it by him; especially those twelve whose names are Varak (the Lamb), Tora (the Bull), Dopatkar (Gemini), Kalakang (the Crab), Ser (the Lion), Khusak (Virgo), Tarâzuk (the Balance), Gazdûm (the Scorpion), Nimasp (the Centaur), Vahik (Capricorn), Dûl (the Waterpot), and Mahik (the Fish); which, from their original creation, were divided into the twenty-eight subdivisions of the astronomers, of which the names are

unfortunately corrupt, and can therefore only profitably be discussed by an expert on the Pahlevi language. However, the third of them corresponds to the Pleiades, hence the first must equate with Açvini, which in the Indian system stood first when the equinox was there, that is, about the first century B.C. and for at least five hundred years thereafter.

In Sassanian times, and perhaps earlier, the Persians seem to have acknowledged four 'chieftains' of the four quarters of the sky. The chieftain of the north was called Haptôk-ring and can be reliably identified with the Wain; hence Vanand, chieftain of the south, may be Fomalhaut, because this star stands in the south when the Wain is underneath the Pole Star. Tishtar, or Tishtrya, chieftain of the east, was Sirius,[2] and this leaves Antares as the most probable identification of Satavês the chieftain of the west.

Tishtar, however, had an adventure which suggests that he was not only a star, but an angel whose home was in a constellation. This adventure is described in Chapter 7 of the Bundahish; it is a flood story, but without an ark.

The second conflict was waged with the water, because, as the star Tishtar was in Cancer, the water which is in the subdivision they call Avrak[3] was pouring, on the same day when the destroyer rushed in, and came again to notice for mischief (*avarak*) in the direction of the west. For every single month is the owner of one constellation; the month Tir is the fourth month of the year, and Cancer the fourth constellation from

Aries, so it is the owner of Cancer, into which Tishtar sprang, and displayed the characteristics of a producer of rain; and he brought on the water aloft by the strength of the wind. Co-operators with Tishtar were Vohuman and the angel Hôm, with the assistance of the angel Burg, and the righteous guardian spirits in orderly arrangement. Tishtar was converted into three forms, the form of a man and the form of a horse and the form of a bull; thirty days and nights he was distinguished in brilliance, and in each form he produced rain ten days and nights; as the astrologers say that every constellation has three forms.

Tishtar has become the guardian deity of Cancer, and there is a reference to the three decans, which in Egyptian astrology have presiding spirits with animal heads.

The wind, however, then blew the waters away, and so formed the ocean all round the edge of the world, but

the noxious creatures remained dead within the earth, and their venom and stench were mingled with the earth, and in order to carry that poison away from the earth Tishtar went down into the ocean in the form of a white horse with long hoofs. And Apâôsh, the demon, came meeting him in the likeness of a black horse with clumsy hoofs; a mile away from him fled Tishtar, through the fright which drove him away. And Tishtar begged for success from Auharmazd, and Auharmazd gave him strength and power, as it is said, that unto Tishtar was brought at once the strength of ten vigorous horses, ten vigorous camels, ten vigorous bulls, ten mountains, and ten rivers. A mile away from him fled Apâôsh the demon, through fright at his strength; on account of this they speak of an arrow-shot with Tishtar's strength in the sense of a mile.

Then, with a cloud for a jar—but the word for jar (*khumb*) is not the usual Pahlevi word for the waterpot of Aquarius—Tishtar made it rain once more for ten days and nights in order to wash away the venom of the noxious creatures which had been drowned; but he was not entirely successful, and the water remained salt. Evidently this myth is intended to explain the creation of the sea, which the Persians in their original mountain home would not have known.

A very similar story is told in the eighth Yasht of the Avesta, but there the purpose is merely seasonal, to explain the origin not of the ocean but of rain, and Apâôsh is accordingly the demon of drought.

The three shapes of Tishtar in the Avesta are 'a man of fifteen' (the ideal age according to the Persians), a bull with golden horns, and a white horse with golden ears and a golden caparison. In another part of the Avesta there is frequent reference to 'the star Tishtrya, the radiant, the glorious, and the Moon, which contains the seed of cattle in its beams'. This is because in old Persian myths a cloud, as a source of fertility, was compared to a bull; and the Moon, being masculine in both Zend and Pahlevi, and connected in the popular mind with rain, could therefore easily be compared to a bull. This is enough to make any astrologer recollect that the Moon is exalted in the sign of the Bull; and it is perhaps significant that the sacred bull of Mithraism, which was the reputed origin of all fertility, came also from this part of the world; for Mithra was a member of the Persian and Indian pantheons before he became established in a religion of his own. There were sacred bulls in Egypt too, but they were symbols of strength as well as fertility, and not especially connected with the Moon.

We seem, then, to be on the track of the Bull as a celestial symbol. But we cannot safely claim that its origin was among the Aryan peoples, because Persian civilization is so relatively late in time and so dependent on its predecessors. The Avesta seems to represent the religion of the Median Magi in the period just preceding Alexander the Great; but this religion was not that of the people, and did not become the State religion until the time of Shapur II (A.D. 310–79). By then the Zoroastrian mania for symmetry had decided that since the stars were created by Ormuzd, and were therefore good, the planets could only have been created by Ahriman, and were therefore all wicked.

There exists in the Avesta a Sirozah, or list of the thirty gods which rule the days of the month, but since a similar list is known from Assyrian times this cannot claim to be a Persian invention.

Again, in the thirty-fourth chapter of the Bundahish we learn that each sign of the zodiac is to reign for a thousand years; but as they follow each other in direct and not retrograde order, this cannot have any reference to the precession of the equinoxes.

Another Pahlevi text will serve to illustrate a use to which the zodiac was put in many countries other than Persia, namely the measurement of the calendar by means of noonday shadows. 'When the sun enters Cancer the shadow is one foot of the man, at fifteen of Cancer it is one foot; when the sun enters Leo it is one foot and a half, at fifteen of Leo it is two feet', and so on up to ten feet at the entry of Capricorn. This table, combined with other measurements found in the Bundahish, proves to have been computed in latitude 32° North, which is the latitude of Yazd, the last part of Persia where any Zoroastrians were to be found. A further table follows, stating that every thirty days the sun's midday shadow increases by one and a third feet, and here the shadow at the beginning of Leo is given as seven and a half feet, and at the beginning of Capricorn fourteen and two thirds. Every 'constellation' is allowed the same amount of increase or decrease, regardless of its obliquity.[4]

Thus the Zoroastrian religion adopted the zodiac, and in consequence it is accepted today among the Parsees of India, though their sacred books oblige them to consider the signs good and the planets bad. But the Persian contribution to the history of the zodiac was almost certainly the lore of the four elements. Fire, Earth, Air, and Water, before Claudius Ptolemy forced them into a neat scheme, had already been associated with the twelve constellations in various irregular ways, but the original worshippers of the elements appear to have been the Magi. To the Greeks and Romans they were known as fire-worshippers, but in fact they considered all four elements holy, and declared that none of them must be polluted by the contact of a corpse. Corpses therefore might not be buried, burnt, or thrown into rivers, and under the Sassanian dynasty, when this prescription had become law, they were exposed to the vultures; but this was not the law nor common practice under Darius and Artaxerxes.

Although the belief that a corpse could pollute fire does suggest that fire was regarded as a material substance, it is important to observe that, as far as the zodiac was concerned, the four elements are not and never were material substances, as our present mechano-morphic philosophy likes to believe. They were more nearly the four principles of the physically perceptible world, namely solidity, liquidity, gaseous conditions, and light.

The other Persian influence on the history of the zodiac was Mithraic. The great popularity of astrology in the Roman Empire was due in part to Mithraism, which was derived from the old Persian religion by a process of fermentation no longer easy to explain. For although the planets are regarded as wicked in the Bundahish, being creations of Ahriman, they were worshipped by the initiates of Mithra, and on the floor of a mithraeum at Ostia, near Rome, could still be seen the seven stations of the priests, in which, it is thought, they stood to invoke the planetary spirits.[5]

The earliest famous devotee of Mithraism was that Mithridates King of Pontus whom nobody could poison. He was eventually overcome by the Romans in 66 B.C., but his religion began to flourish at Rome in the following century, and was finally suppressed under Theodosius, soon after 394. Mithras was not officially a sun-god, but a hero who overcame the sun and then made friends with him. He conferred fertility on the earth by the slaughter of a bull, and sculptures of this sacrifice show it happening in the presence of a dog, serpent, scorpion, cup, and crow, all of which were among the constellations known to the Romans; often also a lion, and sometimes a cock, which is not a constellation. Probably the serpent is a symbol of earth, the cup of water, the crow of air, and the lion of fire.

The two dadophoroi, or torch-bearers, who stand on either side, suggest the alternate lengthening and shortening of the days, since one holds his torch upwards and the other down. They are certainly connected with the Two Pillars of Freemasonry and Kabbalism, which tradition says were copied by Solomon from the mysteries of Tyre.

It is hard not to believe that the exaltation of the Moon in Taurus comes from this cycle of thought. Equally, since Scorpio rises when Taurus sets, it is natural enough for a scorpion to be present at the death of the Bull. This is like the Greek story, also of astronomical origin, that Orion died of a scorpion's sting.

Mithraism was a military religion which made no place for women, but it carried belief in astrology to the remotest garrisons of the Roman Empire; for the signs of the zodiac were represented in every mithraeum; and by the time of its extermination by Christianity the zodiac had become deeply engrained in the

European mind. Having nothing plainly heretical about it, it was naturally not condemned.

Sculptures of the bull-sacrifice, or 'tauroctony', often show the signs of the zodiac, and sometimes in reversed order. One of the best known was found at the Walbrook in London, and another, surrounding a bust of Mithra born from the rock, at Housesteads in Northumberland.[6] On this one Sagittarius is shown as a man instead of a centaur.

Another Mithraic style was to draw the entire zodiac on the breast of the lion-headed god representing time, who is akin to Zervan and to the Orphic Phanes. Sometimes one sees this figure, naked except for the serpent wound spirally up him, with Aries and Libra on his breast and Cancer and Capricorn on his loins. The serpent, even though it has not its tail in its mouth, implies eternal recurrence, as in Plate 8.[7]

9. The Bible and Birthstones

In the Bible there is less astronomy than one might expect. Of the planets only two are mentioned, namely Saturn (*kijjûn*, which should be the same as the Assyrian *kaimanu*) in Amos v 26: 'Ye have borne Siccuth your king and *Chiun* your images, the star of your god, which ye made to yourselves'; and the morning star, which must be Venus, in Isaiah xiv 12: 'How art thou fallen from heaven, O day-star, son of the morning! how art thou cut down to the ground, which didst lay low the nations!'[1]

And of the constellations and stars Orion and the Pleiades are almost the only ones which can be identified with reasonable certainty. Mention has been alleged[2] of Boötes, Antares, Corvus, and the Hyades, but the latter two are almost certainly wrong.

The most famous reference occurs in the Lord's speech out of the whirlwind in the thirty-eighth chapter of Job: 'Canst thou bind the cluster of the Pleiades, or loose the bands of Orion? Canst thou lead forth the Mazzaroth in their season? or canst thou guide the Bear with her train?'

And there is a similar passage in the ninth chapter, verse nine, where Job says of God: 'Which maketh the Bear, Orion, and the Pleiades, and the chambers of the south.'

Also the prophet Amos exhorts us (Chapter v 8): 'Seek Him that maketh the Pleiades and Orion, and turneth the shadow of death into the morning, and maketh the day dark with night.'

Among these allusions, the 'chambers of the south' may well be the six southern signs of the zodiac, although we cannot be sure, for Mowinckel identified them, somewhat improbably, with the constellation Corvus. Similarly 'Mazzaroth' may mean simply the constellations in general, or a single constellation, or it may refer to the zodiac specifically. *Kimah*, the word translated 'Pleiades', is probably correct and seems to mean 'the heap'. *Kesîl* also is almost certainly correct as Orion, but not within the same boundaries as today. The word means 'fool', not however a silly fool, but the hubristic, insolent, or godless one whom the Arabs call *al-Jauza'*, the Giant; and the same accusation of disrespect to the gods is found in the Greek myth of Orion the hunter. But among the Arabs, as in Babylon and doubtless among the Hebrews, the constellation of the twins consisted only of the two stars Castor and Pollux, and the other stars of what we call Gemini were included in Orion.

As another example of changed boundaries in the sky, only the learned among the Arabs speak of *al-Hamal*, the Ram; popularly the constellation is limited to the three stars in the Ram's head, which are known as *al-Ashrat*, 'the mark', or *ash-sharatain*, 'the two marks'. And the Hebrews, like the Arabs and Babylonians, may well have made of Leo a large constellation extending from the middle of Cancer to the middle of Virgo. This, at least according to J. J. Hess,[3] is the meaning of the word *'ayish*, translated in the Book of Job as 'The Bear'.

For the zodiac one naturally turns to the forty-ninth chapter of Genesis, where Jacob blesses his sons; for we should expect there to have grown up, sooner or later, a standard identification of the twelve tribes with the twelve signs, and it would have to be based on this passage. In fact, however, the position is not so simple, for the blessings had not originally any astrological intention; Professor Skinner, who wrote the volume on Genesis in the *International Critical Commentary*, does not consider them all to be of the same date. Some seem to be based on etymology, others on tribal emblems; those on Zebulun, Gad, and Asher are of geographical origin, since Asher had fertile soil, Zebulun lived by the sea, and Gad was on the landward frontier; and those on Reuben, and on the twins Simeon and Levi, are curses, not blessings, referring supposedly to historical events.

The only easy identifications with the zodiac are those of Judah ('a lion's whelp', as in the fifth chapter of Revelation), Dan, who as a serpent must be equated with Scorpio, and Issachar—'a bony ass crouching between the panniers', which may refer to the two asses and manger in the constellation of Cancer.

However, comparing this list with that in the thirty-third chapter of Deuteronomy, where incidentally two other tribes are compared to lion and lioness, namely Dan and Gad, Skinner found in both one twin sign (either Simeon and Levi, or Ephraim and Manasseh) and one feminine, for which Jacob's daughter Dinah could be brought in to correspond to Virgo. Further, the animals mentioned are all found in or near the zodiac, including the Wolf to which Benjamin is compared; and Skinner concludes accordingly that there may be some astrological reference. If so, it can hardly have been meant in the original version of the text.

In equating the tribes with the signs, the Jewish Encyclopaedia places Judah in the east between Issachar and Zebulun, in opposition to Aries, Taurus and Gemini. This would make Judah correspond to Scorpio, and Issachar to Libra. Reuben stands in the south between Simeon and Gad, and in opposition to Cancer, Leo and Virgo; so the obvious attribution of Reuben to Aquarius is upheld. Ephraim, Manasseh and Benjamin occupy the west, so that Ephraim corresponds to Taurus, suitably enough in view of the remarks about Joseph in Deuteronomy xxxiii. And the north is the place of Dan Asher and Naphtali, Dan being Leo as Deuteronomy suggests.

This is a little surprising, the Lion of Judah being so well known; but then Jewish thought does not seem to have taken the zodiac too seriously. Medieval Jewish writers agree that the righteous Jew is above being influenced by the constellations, in view of Jeremiah x 2: 'Thus saith the Lord, Learn not the way of the nations, and be not dismayed at the signs of heaven; for the nations are dismayed at them.' And to consult or depend on astrologers seems at variance with the Jewish religion on account of Deuteronomy xviii 10–12: 'There shall not be found among you any one that maketh his son or his daughter to pass through the fire, one that useth divination, one that practiseth augury, or an enchanter, or a sorcerer, or a charmer, or a consulter with a familiar spirit, or a wizard, or a necromancer. For whosoever doeth these things is an abomination unto the Lord.'

Star-worship is condemned in 2 Kings xxiii 5; but inevitably zodiacal symbolism found its way into Jewish literature, and it was quite permissible to use it in a calendrical sense, as was done for instance by the famous liturgical poet Eleazar Kalir in a prayer for rain which he composed at the end of the eighth century, mentioning the signs of the zodiac in order in every other stanza:[4]

In God's hand is the key; without it can no one open; He maketh water to gush forth in the depth, to loose the bonds of him who is bound [that is, Isaac].

At the testing he poured out his heart like water; may his *Lambs* remain ever in life.

Be ever gracious to the people chosen in the beginning; may water increase corn and new wine on the fields of the firstborn; the meadows are green, *Oxen* and fat cattle multiply.

May his rich store in the rainy vault of heaven fill with rich water the valleys of the ox-lamers. [That is, Simeon and Levi, see Genesis xlix 6.]

The kindly and friendly one hearkens to our lovely song, may he not be angry for the murmuring at the waters of strife.

Well-pleasing be the prayer as acknowledgement of the *Twins* [that is, Moses and Aaron].

May water be allotted to the sowers in the music of the wheel of the Sun ...

The zodiac and planets were likewise adopted into the Qabalah, twelve of the thirty-two Paths of the Concealed Glory being given zodiacal correspondences; and the same correspondences occur in the 22 Tarot trumps, which are of Qabalistic origin. These are perfectly valid for the practising mystic who knows how to use them in meditation, but there is no point in describing them here; the fact that philosophical thinkers have never managed to agree upon an interpretation of the world bears witness to the existence of numerous paradoxes which mere thinking cannot resolve. Any valid system of meditation must, without abandoning thinking, make it possible to explore the further realm of direct realization, and thus to understand in experience the resolution of paradoxes which cannot be thought out. The Qabalah is such a system, but its correspondences to the zodiac represent stages of experience through which the human spirit passes time and again on many different levels. The nature and consequence of these experiences is often far from obvious, and hence to try to summarize them would only be misleading. Realization, to those who have not had it in the same form, often appears unlikely and unconvincing.

A correspondence to the four 'fixed' signs of the zodiac is often assumed in the four 'holy living creatures' from the first chapter of Ezekiel; they are often identified with the four evangelists, and frequently appear in Christian iconography. They are also represented on the 21st Tarot trump. 'Irenaeus seems to have been the first to play with this fancy', writes Dr Cooke; 'he identified the man with Matthew, the lion with John, the ox with Luke, and the eagle with Mark. A different series of identifications, however, became more popular: man—Matthew, lion—Mark, ox—Luke, eagle—John.'[5] This in fact is the version of Victorinus, but two further different versions were put forward, by Athanasius and by Augustine.

Astrologers, when they make the equation with the four fixed signs, use the eagle instead of Scorpio, and pretend that it represents the higher side of that maligned constellation. Yet the Eagle's longitude places it not close to Scorpio but over the junction of Sagittarius and Capricorn, to both of which it is symbolically appropriate, since the motto of Sagittarius is 'Onward and upward', and Capricorn is the goat which climbs to the mountain-top.

It was Zimmern[6] who first suggested that the Cherubim in the first chapter of Ezekiel represent the cardinal constellations of the third and fourth millennium B.C.; but he inevitably pointed out, what astrologers have since ignored, that if this Babylonian derivation is justified, then the Man does not represent Aquarius, but is the Scorpion-man of the Babylonian boundary-stones (see Plate 11); and the Eagle, of course, was used because Altair, its brightest star, standing consistently about 6 degrees north of the equator, was a more convenient seasonal marker than the stars of Aquarius, which are both dimmer and less high in the sky. So when we admire in the British Museum the 'winged bulls' or 'cherubim', which have a human head, the forefeet of a bull, the hind feet of a lion, and eagle's wings, we ought to remember that the human head represents Scorpio, not Aquarius, and the eagle's wings represent Altair, which was put in to make a fourth with Antares, Aldebaràn, and Regulus.

The four cherubim—the word means 'intercessors' according to Cooke and Langdon—occur again in the fourth chapter of the Revelation of St John, and are among the many supposedly astrological references in that book. But these references, even when developed by so able a scholar as Boll,[7] remain exceedingly unconvincing. Since we are told in the last verse of Chapter i that 'the seven stars are the angels of the seven churches', it seems improbable that the author was primarily interested in developing an astrological symbolism. Admittedly both Philo and Josephus[8] found a connection between the seven-branched candlestick and the seven planets; and Josephus also states that the twelve loaves of shewbread in the Temple refer to the signs of the zodiac. Further, the reference to the four Living Creatures being 'full of eyes' may indicate that they were originally constellations. And in Zechariah iv 10 the planets are apparently alluded to as 'the eyes of the Lord'. But on the other hand when we try to work out astrologically various passages in Revelation we are apt to be disappointed.

For instance, in the beginning of Chapter vi, the third and fourth horsemen can very easily be equated with Libra and Scorpio, since the fourth is Death and the third carries a balance; but if this is so, the first and second should correspond to Leo and Virgo, which they show no sign of doing. Similarly the scorpions in verses 7 to 10 of Chapter ix have been said to suggest the scorpions on Babylonian boundary-stones; and if Scorpio thus becomes the First Woe, the Second and Third should be Sagittarius and Capricorn respectively, which they can be in view of the mention of horses in the Second and an earthquake in the Third; but one cannot feel sure that the author intended anything of the kind.

It has also been thought[9] that the four-and-twenty elders of Chapter iv verse 4 are of astronomical Babylonian origin, and correspond to the 24 stars, or star-gods, which according to Diodorus Siculus[10] were allotted to the zodiac, twelve visible ones in nothern latitudes to rule the living, and twelve, more frequently invisible, in southern latitudes, to rule the dead. This equation has been accepted by some scholars and rejected by others. Dr Charles, who edited the book in the *International Critical Commentary*,[11] finds it too far-fetched, and explains the elders as the heavenly counterpart of the twenty-four priestly orders in 1 Chronicles xxiv 7–18.

An outstanding passage of possible zodiacal interest is the first six verses of Chapter xii of the Revelation:

And a great sign was seen in heaven; a woman arrayed with the sun, and the moon under her feet, and upon her head a crown of twelve stars; and she was with child: and she crieth out, travailing

127

in birth, and in pain to be delivered. And there was seen another sign in heaven; and behold, a great red dragon, having seven heads and ten horns, and upon his heads seven diadems. And his tail draweth the third part of the stars of heaven, and did cast them to the earth: and the dragon stood before the woman which was about to be delivered, that when she was delivered, he might devour her child. And she was delivered of a son, a man child, who is to rule all the nations with a rod of iron: and her child was caught up unto God, and unto His throne. And the woman fled into the wilderness, where she hath a place prepared of God, that there they may nourish her a thousand two hundred and threescore days.

This period of 1,260 days is exactly three and a half years of 360 days, and is no doubt the same as the 'time, times, and a half' mentioned in verse 14 of the same chapter. But again one cannot feel sure that this has not merely a political reference, since 1,260 days is not an astronomical period of any significance. The ten horns of verse 3 seem to be traditional,[12] and are certainly not astrological; the destruction of a third part of the stars sounds astronomical, and a similar story is found in the Bundahish,[13] but does not appear to correspond to anything observable in nature.

The woman clothed with the sun represents, according to most interpreters, the spiritual Israel as the spouse of God. For various reasons scholars have decided that she is an adaptation of an earlier sun-goddess, either the Egyptian Hat-Hor, who is crowned with the sun, or the Greek Leto, who wears[14] a veil of stars, or the Babylonian Damkina, the mother of Marduk,[15] or finally the 'Assyrian' Juno, who according to Martianus Capella wore as a crown the twelve precious stones listed in the table at the end of this chapter.[16] However, the allusion of the twelve stars to the zodiac is usually admitted, and might be regarded as the only certain reference to the zodiac in the Bible, were it not that we cannot call it certain. On the analogy of the seven spirits of the seven churches, the twelve stars may only mean the spirits of the twelve tribes of the spiritual Israel, and be no more astrological than the sun, moon, and eleven stars in Joseph's dream.[17]

We have to remember that the author of Revelation was deeply

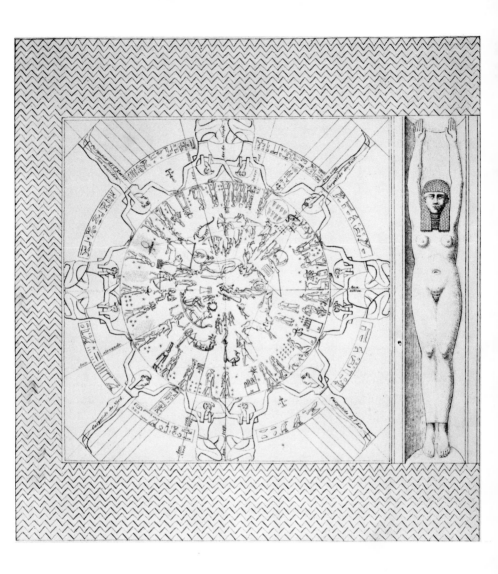

14. Circular zodiac of Denderah (*see page* 180)

15. Horoscope
from Athribis
(*see page* 182)

16. (*below*) Standard
Diagram of
Decans with Orion.
Sirius and Planets
(*see pages* 186–7)

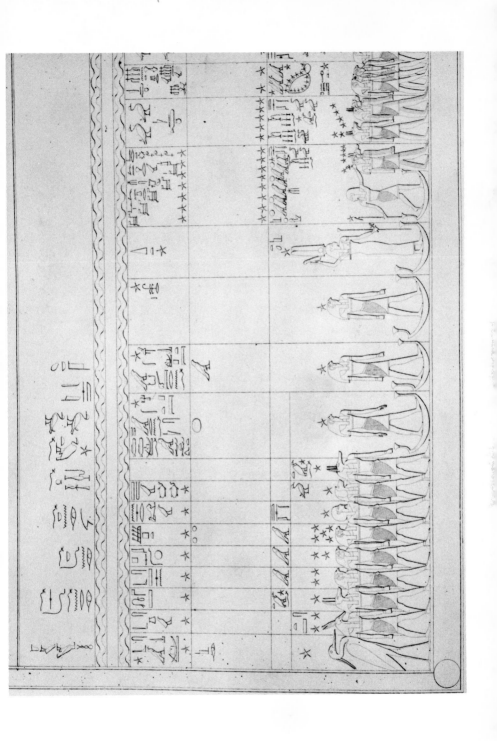

17. Hour-stars and target-priest on a temple roof (*see page* 190)

read in the Jewish apocalyptic literature of the last centuries B.C., and may fairly be expected to have a point of view not very different from that of the Book of Enoch or the Book of Jubilees. Jubilees is a calendrical work, written within about half a century of A.D. 1. It strongly condemns the traditional lunar calendar of the Jews, and urges the adoption of a solar year of 364 days.[18] The zodiac and planets are not even mentioned. Enoch is of slightly older date, and also advocates a solar year, but we learn that among the wickednesses of the fallen angels 'Barâqîjâl taught astrology. Kôkabêl taught the constellations,' and various other angels taught the knowledge of the signs of clouds, of the sun and moon, and so forth.[19] The author's astronomical knowledge was not great, as he shows by his endeavour to explain the varying length of the day;[20] and he frequently speaks of the fallen angels as fallen stars, which suggests a metaphorical rather than a literal approach to his subject-matter. But since astrology is classed with magic as a sin, it is not unlikely that the author of Revelation may have been equally opposed both to the zodiac and to astrology.

This will not prevent astrologers and others from trying to equate the twelve precious stones, which are the foundations of the New Jerusalem in Chapter xix 19–20, with the Twelve Tribes in the order enumerated in Chapter vi 5–8, and also with the signs of the zodiac. It is quite possible that an author of that date would have had the idea of making such a correspondence; but Dr Charles believed that the author's object was, on the contrary, to avoid any astrological reference, and show the Holy City 'as having nothing to do with the ethnic speculations of his own and past ages regarding the city of the gods'. As evidence of this Dr Charles points out that the stones are mentioned in reverse zodiacal order, beginning with Jasper (The Fishes) and ending with Amethyst (The Ram). He did not realize that the reverse order of the signs is the direct order of the Sun's progress through the houses which correspond to them; hence this does not weaken the possibility of an astrological interpretation. The fact which does militate against the astrological view is that the angel in Chapter xxi measures the city neither clockwise nor anticlockwise, but taking the sides of the square in the order East North South West (verse 13); and this order does suggest a wish to break the circle of astrological analogies.

But the equation of stones and signs which Dr Charles accepted is taken from Athanasius Kircher, who claimed that it could be found on Egyptian and Arabian monuments;[21] and when we reflect that his book, *Œdipus Ægyptiacus*, was published in 1653, this begins to seem doubtful. Further, if we accept the stones as running in the same manner as the gates of the city, in the order East North South West, we find ourselves with a diagram in which Aries and Libra stand next to one another in the north-west corner, and Virgo with Pisces similarly in the south-east, which is in plain defiance of astronomical fact. Thus it seems not improbable that the author of Revelation was indeed trying to avoid the astrological parallel.

The original list of twelve precious stones is of course that of the high priest's 'breastplate' or pouch in the Book of Exodus (xxviii 17–20 and xxxix 10–13). This list has also been interpolated in a garbled form into a passage of Ezekiel (xxviii 13).[22] The author of Revelation does not follow either list; and his catalogue of the Tribes (vii 5–8), which omits Dan and Ephraim in favour of Joseph and Manasseh, differs in both order and composition from the list in Ezekiel xlviii 31, where Ephraim and Manasseh are omitted; and both disagree with the much older list in Numbers ii, which omits Joseph and Levi.

There is no reason to suppose that any astrological reference was intended by the writer of Exodus, any more than by the authors of the forty-ninth chapter of Genesis. And we can only obtain an astronomically coherent scheme in Revelation if we assume that the order East North South West was an early copyist's error, and that the order intended was some circular order; though this might be East South West North, as in Numbers ii, or North East South West as in Ezekiel xlviii, or even East North West South. Dr Charles, however, has shown a possible reason for the order stated,[23] in putting first the six sons of Leah, then those of Rachel, and last those of Leah's handmaid.

In view of all this confusion we may just as well ignore Kircher's equation of amethyst with the Ram, and if we also ignore the order East North South West, we can take the first foundation to be Aries and run straight through the list. This is probably the origin of the popular catalogue which ends with amethyst for the Fishes.

To make matters worse (if that were necessary) Josephus gives two somewhat different lists of the correspondences of the stones with the Tribes, which are taken in order of birth. And the words he uses, when he refers the high priest's breastplate to the zodiac, are worthy of note.[24] He says: 'The two sardonyxes that were in the clasps on the high priest's shoulders indicate to us the sun and moon. And for the twelve stones, whether we understand by them the months, or the twelve signs of what the Greeks call the zodiac, we shall not be mistaken in their meaning.' In fact Josephus regards the zodiac as a Greek innovation rather than a Jewish tradition, but at the same time accepts the symbolism of the number 12 as corresponding to the months of the Hebrew calendar no less than to the twelve tribes.

The two *shoham*-stones which represented the sun and moon, and are here called sardonyxes, have been variously identified as reddish-brown onyx or possibly topaz (by Charles), as very dark (in the Midrash Bemibdar), and as aquamarine-beryls (by Kunz).[25]

But although Josephus, Philo of Alexandria, and others accepted the equation of the twelve jewels with the zodiac, the wearing of special birthstones is not too well attested in ancient times. Kunz suggests that it arose in Poland in the eighteenth century, among the Jewish population there, and mentions that Catherine de' Medici possessed a girdle of twelve stones which may or may not have been zodiacal. In view of her period (1509–89) we shall probably not be wrong in assuming that they were (see Plate 2).

Nor is it in the least unlikely that zodiacal stones were worn under the Roman Empire; for among surviving classical gems one may find a heliotrope bearing the head of Sarapis surrounded by the zodiac,[26] a green jasper bearing the symbols of the Moon, Capricorn, and Taurus, obviously in reference to the owner's horoscope, and a jewel which belonged to Tiberius and bore his sign of Scorpio as well as that of Capricorn for his predecessor Augustus (see Plate 4).

The most common list of birthstones is derived from that in the Book of Revelation, beginning with St Peter, Aries, and the month of March, and assuming the jasper for that month to be red. But in the course of time several alterations have been made, and lists discoverable in different countries often disagree. There is no possibility of finding an authentic list because there has never been one, and also because of the differences which have arisen in course of time

131

and through the difficulty of identifying the stones. As examples of these difficulties, the Authorized Version has reversed the order of the third and fourth stones in the Book of Exodus; the *topazion* is said by Pliny to have been a greenish stone, so that it cannot be our modern topaz; and the Apostles were supposed to be attributed to the twelve jewels of the Apocalypse in the order in which they occur in the synoptic Gospels, but the synoptic Gospels do not all give the names in the same order!

The most futile of all lists is that authorized by the National Association of Jewellers at its meeting in Kansas City in 1912 or 1913. This is nothing but a piece of unfounded salesmanship, and is wrong in principle because it ignores tradition and commits such solecisms as making aquamarine an alternative to bloodstone, including the pearl which is not a mineral, and using various stones not known in antiquity. If birthstones are to be worn at all, one would think that they should at least correspond to the signs of the zodiac, which are supposed to have some occult virtue, and not to the months, which are mere calendrical divisions and have none. To wear a month-stone is as meaningless as to wear the civic arms of one's birthplace. The use of a birthstone ought to imply a belief in the Law of Correspondences, and therefore like anything else should be done properly or not at all. And oddly enough Kunz, though he condemns the Kansas City lists so roundly, attributes the emerald to Aries and the carbuncle to Pisces!

Colour has notoriously a strong psychological effect on the mind. If there is to be an astrological correspondence as well, there should be something in common between the symbol and the thing symbolized. One cannot symbolize the Ocean or the Fishes by a red stone such as the carbuncle. Camillo Leonardi's *Speculum Lapidum*, published in Venice in 1502, attributes to the constellation of the Eagle a zodiacal influence comparable to that of the Crab. As symbology this is impossible; but an inspection of Leonardi's other attributions suggests that he did know what he was about, and hence Cancer is probably a slip for its opposite sign Capricorn, which would be correct.

The basic symbols are archetypal, that is to say, the human mind thinks in those terms and cannot be prevented from doing so. Gold, being the colour of the sun, represents the highest value, or God;

red, not blue, is the colour of blood, bloodshed, ferocity and energy; blue, not yellow, is the colour of the sea and therefore of the feminine aspect of God; and green, as the colour of growth, suggests peace and plenty. Regardless whether jewels can be consecrated with spiritual force or magnetized by the power of a personality, these laws of symbolism must be observed or there will be a conflict of opinion between the conscious mind, with its arbitrary wrong symbolism, and the unconscious, which cannot help knowing better. Even among Muslims the unconscious will not accept a green stone as a symbol of war in general, nor therefore of the constellation Scorpio which has produced so many famous soldiers.

The chemical composition of the various gems is not much help, since ruby, emerald, amethyst, and topaz are now all classed as varieties of corundum; emerald and aquamarine are greener and bluer varieties of beryl; and the various different-coloured chalcedonies, including carnelian, agate, chrysoprase, catseye, jasper, sard, and others, are all classed as quartz. For this reason we are almost entirely reduced to making the attributions by colour.

A 'correct' list of stones for the twelve signs would have to be one which was psychologically easy to associate with their other correspondances, and in accordance with tradition and the Qabalah. Such a list might run somehow as follows:

Aries must obviously have a red stone, hence red jasper would be a good choice; and ruby, traditionally a solar stone, suits the exaltation of the sun here.

Taurus: green jasper; emerald; malachite.

Gemini in the Middle Ages was thought to deserve a mixture of red, white, and dark stones, hence the best would be some variegated stone such as onyx (banded agate) or a striped chalcedony.

Cancer, in view of its association with the Moon and the sea, might well have moonstone, sea-green beryl, or turquoise.

Leo must have a yellow stone, presumably topaz, zircon, yellow jasper, or fire-opal.

Virgo, as sign of the green corn, could have the apple-green chrysoprase, chrysoberyl, which is much the same colour, or green felspar, which was associated in ancient Egypt with fertility. If thought of as a sign of purity, diamond or an uncoloured chalcedony would be required. But since ripe corn is also a suitable colour for Virgo, one could use light brown agate or onyx.

For *Libra* the correct stone would be jade, from its use in treating kidney-disease in China, the kidneys being 'ruled' by Libra; also chrysolite and peridot (olivine), which are transparent green stones, green being required because Libra is ruled by Venus.

Scorpio: bloodstone or haematite; carnelian (red chalcedony).

Sagittarius should for Qabalistic reasons have a blue stone, hence sapphire or star-sapphire; and this suits quite well in the sidereal zodiac, where the constellation is a mixture of air and earth, and associated with flight. Those who prefer the tropical zodiac, and think of this as a fiery sign, might choose rose-quartz.

For *Capricorn* tourmaline is appropriate by reason of its light-excluding qualities, in any colour including the dark blue indicolite; also the black opal.

Aquarius as the sky sign should have a sky-blue stone, but since it is a more watery sign than Sagittarius perhaps it should have the paler stone, aquamarine rather than sapphire. It might also have lapis lazuli, which was much prized in antiquity and so ought not to be omitted.

Pisces: the amethyst, though attributed here for the wrong reason, suits very well on account of the Jupiterian colour and also because it was supposed to be a preventive of drunkenness, which is associated with the planet Neptune and the Fishes. The opal also seems to belong here, and there is a purple fluorspar which much resembles amethyst.

The terminology of gems is not always reliable. Jacinth meant originally a hyacinth-blue stone, probably the sapphire, but the name is now used of an orange stone, which is ridiculous. Further, some gems found in jewellers' shops are dyed, the original colour having been removed by heating. This may not matter from the point of view of appearance, but obviously no person using a gem for magical purposes would choose a dyed stone.[27] This remains part of the curious lore of gems, despite the widespread belief that because one cannot work magic oneself, therefore no one else can! Those who try ought at least to do it properly.

THE BIBLE AND BIRTHSTONES

TABLE 13   *Jewels of the High Priest's Breastplate*

As translated in Exodus xxviii 17–20 and xxxix 10–13, Revised Version:

sard	topaz	carbuncle
emerald	sapphire	diamond
jacinth	agate	amethyst
beryl	onyx	jasper[28]

As in a model made in India in 1927 for the late Rev. G. A. Cooke, D.D., Regius Professor of Hebrew at Oxford (cp. Notes 5 and 22 of this chapter):

carnelian	peridot	emerald
carbuncle	lapis lazuli	sardonyx
brown agate	banded agate	amethyst
topaz	turquoise	aquamarine

135

TABLE 14   *Some Symbols, Animals, Colours and Gems attributed to the 12 Signs*

	Altar of Gabii (Louvre).	Ath. Kircher, II, ii, 177	Varaha Mihira, Pancha Sidd. I. 20.	Martianus Capella, Teubner, p. 34.	CCAG XII 68.	Theosophical Society (1912)	'777', by A. Crowley (2nd ed. 1955).
ARIES	Minerva owl	sheep amethyst red	blood-red	dendrites	siderite	sardonyx	ruby geranium tiger lily
TAURUS	Venus dove	cattle jacinth dark	white	heliotrope (stone)	yellow jacinth	carnelian	topaz mallow
GEMINI	Apollo tripod	apes chrysoprase yellow	green	keraunos (reddish onyx)	diamond heliotrope	topaz	alexandrite tourmaline magpie, orchid
CANCER	Hermes tortoise	water-creatures topaz blue (cyaneus)	darkish red	lychnis (fiery red)	green jasper, euchite	chalcedony	amber lotus
LEO	Jupiter eagle	forest beasts beryl golden	smoky white	astrites (?catseye)	agate selenite	jasper	catseye sunflower
VIRGO	Ceres basket	dogs chrysolite green	variegated	emerald	corallite, dendrite	emerald	peridot lily
LIBRA	Vulcan bonnet	birds sard purple	black	Scythian-emerald	sardine, emerald	beryl	emerald aloe
SCORPIO	Mars wolf	birds of prey sardonyx black	golden	jasper	hematite, pyrites	amethyst	snakestone cactus
SAGITTARIUS	Diana hound	military beasts(!) emerald flame-colour	yellow	rock crystal	amethyst	jacinth	jacinth rush
CAPRICORN	Vesta lamp	ruminants chalcedony white	whitish yellow	water-coloured gems	ophite chalcedony	chrysoprase	black diamond thistle, Indian hemp
AQUARIUS	Juno peacock	marine beasts sapphire deep blue	darkish white(!)	diamond	magnet	crystal	glass (sic) coconut
PISCES	Neptune dolphin	marsh and river beasts jasper ash-colour	fish-colour	hyacinth	beryl jacinth	sapphire	pearl opium

10. *India and the Asterisms*

'AN astrologer', says Varaha Mihira, 'ought to be of good family, friendly in his appearance, and fashionable in his dress; veracious, and not malignant. He must have well-proportioned, compact and full limbs, no bodily defect, and be a fine man, with nice hands, feet, nails, eyes, chin, teeth, ears, brows, and head, and with a deep and clear voice; for generally one's good and bad moral qualities are in unison with one's personal appearance. Now, good qualities in a man are: that he is pure, clever, free, eloquent, ready-witted, able to discern time and place, good in the highest sense of the word; not timid in society, unsurpassed by his fellow-students, skilful, not addicted to bad passions, well versed in the arts of expiation, of procuring prosperity, of incantation, and of anointing; further, that he is regular in worshipping the gods, in his observances and fasts; that he is able to raise the prestige of science by the wonderful perfection of his branch of study, and to solve satisfactorily any question, except in cases where supernatural agencies baffle human calculation; finally, that he knows both text and meaning of the works on mathematical astronomy, natural astrology, and horoscopy.'[1]

Modern Western astrologers do not realize that they need lessons in deportment and voice-production, and a manicure once a month! But India is of all countries that where astrology has stood highest in repute; marriages there are still made by astrological principles and, we are told, are almost always happy. Astrology has enjoyed in India not only high social standing but also a reputation for being incredibly ancient. The date of the most famous astronomical text-book, the Surya Siddhanta, is stated to be 2,163,102 B.C.![2] However, the immense age claimed for Indian astronomy and astrology is finding fewer and fewer supporters, even in India. Nor is this due only to a naive pursuit of the fashion for discounting the antiquity of antiquity; the scholarly principle of believing nothing beyond the evidence leads straight to error only in such a study as the Mystery Religions, where the evidence is that the evidence is insufficient.

137

But the difficulty with Hindu star-science is its incurable vagueness. Both Sir William Jones in the eighteenth century and Albiruni[3] in the eleventh—his travel book on India was published in 1031—found it impossible to obtain clear-cut answers to astronomical questions from their Hindu informants. India is supposed to be under Capricorn, the symbol of which is a crystal, hard and lucid; and this accords with the pre-eminence of Indian thinkers in the deep realms of religion and philosophy: but religion, in which India particularly excels, is under Sagittarius, where Mercury, the planet of accurate measurement, is at its weakest. (Hence the supposed quarrel between science, which measures regardless of meaning, and religion, which having found meaning does not trouble to measure.)

Indian astronomy abounds in enormous periods of time. The present epoch of history, the Kali Yuga or Iron Age, began at midnight—or perhaps at dawn, for Aryabhata was ambiguous on this point—on Friday, February 18th, 3102 B.C. at Ujjain in Central India; it will last 432,000 years. According to another tradition, the Kali Yuga began when all the planets were in conjunction in 0° Aries; but this did not happen in 3102 B.C. In any case the Age of Brass, which preceded the Age of Iron, was twice as long, the Silver Age before that was three times as long, and the Golden Age, when men were twenty-one cubits tall and lived four hundred years, was four times as long. For 432,000 years is only one-tenth of a *mahayuga*, and 1,000 *mahayugas* make a *kalpa*, at the end of which the world is destroyed by fire and recreated. Thus a *kalpa*, according to Brahmagupta, who wrote in A.D. 628, lasts for 4,320,000,000 years. This is longer even than the Pre-Cambrian Age, which recent geologists have put at a thousand million years!

It has been suggested that these long periods arose because Indian astrologers wanted to claim experience of all possible combinations of planets and signs of the zodiac. But the real reason was that they did not feel at home with fractions, and so instead of saying, as we do, that the length of the synodical month is 29 days 12 hours 44 minutes 2·8 seconds, they preferred to say that the sun and moon return to exactly the same relative position after a given number of whole days. But of course the shorter this period, the less accurate it would be; so they sought greater accuracy, just as we do, by adding to their figures. The difference is that we use a decimal point.

Another difference is that Hindu astronomers measured celestial distances by co-ordinates which are not at right angles to each other —which has rather naturally earned them the disapproval of modern scientists. They used the ecliptic, but the pole of the equator instead of the pole of the zodiac; hence their references are distinguished by the names of 'polar longitude' and 'polar latitude'.

Recent scholars have deducted a good deal from the age of the Surya Siddhanta. It is now thought to be mostly of the sixth century A.D., and to be a compendium of Indian astronomical knowledge after the influence of Alexandria had become established. Alexandria was not founded till 332 B.C., and remained the capital of the learned world until the Muslim conquest in 640.

Its influence on Indian astronomy and astrology was enormous. Many Greek technical terms were taken over directly, for instance *lipta* for minutes, *trikona* for trigon, *jamitra* for diameter (or opposition), *pandphara* for rising; and it is significant that the art of calculating a horoscope is called *hora*, Greek for hour. The great names in Indian astronomy are almost all subsequent to the spread of Greek learning: Aryabhata, 'the father of Indian epicyclic astronomy', lived at the end of the fifth century A.D., Varaha Mihira died in 587, Brahmagupta was thirty years old in 628. Earlier than any of these, writing about 378, was Pulisa of Saintra; and when we remember that Alexander becomes Sandro in Italy and Sandy in Scotland, this may well be Paulus of Alexandria. Alexandria itself was called in India Yavanapura, meaning simply The Ionian City, and Varaha Mihira knew the difference in longitude between Yavanapura and Ujjain, which was the Greenwich of Hindu astronomy.[4]

The great period of immigration of Greek knowledge must have been between the birth of Christ and A.D. 400; and it must have begun before Claudius Ptolemy wrote his Great Construction (A.D. 140) because the constants used in Indian astronomy are never quite the same as those of Ptolemy, with one exception: the Romaka Siddhanta quotes the length of the tropical year in the same figures as were given by Hipparchus. One reason for such differences is that the Indians preferred to convert the Greek figures into long periods of whole days, in their usual style, and another is that they used sidereal and not tropical periods. Some of Ptolemy's discoveries, for

139

instance the evection of the moon, are found in the Siddhantas, but sometimes their constants are more accurate than his: the Surya Siddhanta gives precession as 54 seconds per annum, against Ptolemy's 36″, and the correct figure nowadays is 50·2. The Surya Siddhanta also gives a more accurate estimate of the longitude of the sun's apogee, though this of course may have been improved with time; the climate of India does not readily preserve millennary manuscripts.

Despite efforts to prove the contrary,[5] heliacal risings, which were so useful to Greek farmers and sailors, and were the basis of Hesiod's *Works and Days* and of the parapegma shown in Plate 5, seem not to be mentioned in India before the time of Aryabhata. As late as A.D. 80 Hindu astronomers believed the moon to be farther away than the sun,[6] and it is quite possible that the names of the signs of the zodiac were then still unknown, although the existence of a twelve-fold division is mentioned in the Mahabhārata.[7]

The Alexandrian origin of the zodiac, or at least of its subdivision into 36 *drekkana* or decans, is suggested by such casual phrases as the following—from Varaha Mihira's astrological textbook the Brihat Jataka, in the picturesque translation of B. S. Row:[8]

> The first drekkana of Mesha [i.e. Aries] represents a man with a white cloth round his waist, dark complexion, pretending to protect, fearful red eyes and a lifted axe. The second drekkana of Mesha is sketched by Yavanas [i.e. Greeks] as representing a woman with red cloth, fond of ornaments and food, pot-belly, horse-face, thirsty and single-footed. The third drekkana of Mesha represents a man cruel, skilled in arts, yellowish, fond of work, unprincipled, with a lifted-up stick, angry and covered with purple clothes.

Another sign that the zodiac is not of Hindu origin is the existence of two sets of names, one transliterated from the Greek, presumably before the meanings were known, and the second a translation:

TABLE 15   *The Hindu Zodiac*

Greek name	Spelt in Sanskrit	Sanskrit name	Meaning of Sanskrit name
Krios	Kriya	Mesha (*or* Aja)	(Ram *or* Goat)
Tauros	Taurusi	Vrisha	Bull
Didumoi	Tituma	Mithuna	Couple (man and wife)
Karkinos	Karka	Karkata	Crab
Leōn	Leya	Simha	Lion
Parthenos	Pâthena	Kanya	Virgin
Zugos (=yoke)	Juka	Tulā	Balance
Skorpion	Kaurpya	Vrischika (*or* Ali)	Scorpion (*or* Bee)
Toxotēs (=archer)	Taukshika	Dhanus	Bow
Aigokerōs (=goat-horned)	Akokero	Makara (*or* Mriga)	Sea-monster *or* (Antelope)
Hydrokhoös (=water-pot)	Hridoga	Kumbha	Pot
Ikhthues	Ithusi	Mina	Fish

We shall see in the Babylonian chapter that *makara* the sea-monster is not likely to be a verbal corruption of *akokero*. By origin Capricorn is a sea-monster. Rather surprisingly, *Makara* is called 'the Indian Cupid', but this can be justified astrologically if we remember that the goat in Greece was a symbol of lust and that Mars is exalted in Capricorn; for Mars stands for creative energy, of which desire (Latin *cupīdo*) is the expression.

The Hindus, incidentally, have put the zodiac to a commoner use than any other people, in that they employ the twelve names to describe arcs of 30 degrees on any circle and not only along the ecliptic.

Before the influence of Alexandria began to be felt, Hindu cosmology had supposed a flat earth with the sun, moon, and planets circling an enormous mountain called Mount Meru. When this had to be modified, the earth-ball was imagined hanging in the centre of the world-egg, and Mount Meru became its axis, a golden mountain on which the gods lived at the north pole and the Asuras at the south pole.

Another halfway-house in the progress of ideas was the doctrine of the libration of the equinoxes. When it was found that the spring point did not remain stationary in Aries, someone suggested that perhaps it swung to and fro through an arc of 27 degrees to east and west of the beginning of the sidereal zodiac.[9] The time before it returns to this point is given in the Surya Siddhanta as 7,200 years. At the same period, before the theory of epicycles had been adopted to account for the retrogradation of the planets, the behaviour of Venus and Mercury in alternately preceding and following the sun was explained by saying that they were pulled this way and that with ropes of air by beings who were said to be forms of time.[10] The learned Westerner, if he likes to scorn such ideas, would do well to remember that in religious thought he is still far behind the Hindu, perhaps is hardly even an apprentice; and Hinduism includes atheism as a branch of religion.

What then did Indian astronomy amount to before the Hellenistic period? Did it owe anything directly to Babylon, and had the Hindus discovered the precession of the equinoxes?

Before the excavation of Mohenjo-Daro and Harappa, the Vedic period in India was variously dated between 4500 B.C. and A.D. 880. It is now generally agreed that Vedic literature grew up between 1500 and 1000 B.C. Before this time the Aryan-speaking tribes had not apparently entered the country; but their predecessors will have had the usual reasons for observing the stars. Thus B. G. Tilak discovered hints of the vernal equinox occurring in the neighbourhood of Orion (Mriga),[11] which would justify the earliest date suggested.

Sengupta says:[12] 'The chief requirements for the performance of Vedic sacrifices were to find as accurately as possible the equinoctial and solsticial dates, and thence to find the seasons. The Vedic months were synodic months and reckoned from a full moon to the next full moon.' Thibaut on the other hand[13] thought that the year at that epoch consisted of 12 months of 360 days with an intercalary month inserted whenever necessary. The fact is that the Hindus early started to use a period of 1,830 days, which is 67 lunations, and one cannot be sure whether this means 5 years of 366 days, or 5 years of 360 days plus one intercalary month of 30. At any rate in the literature of the Vedic period, which includes the Brahmanas and Samhitas, the sun and moon are the only heavenly bodies definitely mentioned; and since the Brahmanas are full of number symbolism, and the number 5 has no particular importance in them, it seems unlikely that the five planets were recognized as such.

But observation of the seasonal sacrifices in Vedic times did oblige men to notice certain changes due to precession. In the earliest period, according to Burgess and Sengupta, the winter solstice occurred when the moon was full in the constellation Maghâs, of which the principal star was Regulus. This gives as a date the year −2344, with a margin of error of several centuries either way, since the moon might be up to 6 degrees away from the star. At the same time the Pleiades rose due east—exact in −2926—and spring began one day after the new moon nearest to Spica. All this would agree with a date perhaps as early as the thirty-first century: but we shall not need to go so far back for the origin of the zodiac.

The asterism Māghas gave its name to the month of Māgha, which at first was supposed to run from the full moon in conjunction with Regulus to the following full moon between Denébola and Spica; but owing to precession it became necessary, if the month of Māgha was to remain close to its proper asterism, to reckon it from the preceding new moon instead of from the full, and later still to make it end with the full moon of Regulus instead of beginning there.[14]

Dr R. Shama Sastry, followed by M. Raja Rao and others, has tried to maintain that in the Vedic era the Hindus could calculate the periodical return of eclipses in different parts of the zodiac.[15] It is difficult to feel certain of this, for not all myths can be interpreted as descriptions of external natural phenomena, especially among an introverted people such as the Hindus, with whom a religious and psychological interpretation is never unlikely. Shama Sastry, however, gives an entirely astronomical interpretation to the myth of Rohita and to the Śunahśepa hymns: Aditi, the mother of the gods, whose name means Unity, is interpreted as the 58-year eclipse cycle, Rohita becomes a reddish-coloured eclipse recurring in one thousand days, and the fact that Visvamitra cursed 50 of his 101 sons is explained because 50 of the 101 eclipses in a twenty-year cycle are invisible from any given place. Shama Sastry also says that the first day of the Kali Yuga was a total solar eclipse, and as confirmation shows that the 239th day of 3101 B.C. was a nearly total lunar eclipse.

After the Vedic period astronomical knowledge continued unchanged until the early centuries A.D. The chief work was the wearisome technique of calculating the places of the sun and moon in the *nakshatras*; but the word *nakshatra*, which in the Brahmanas had only meant a star or constellation, no matter which, was now specialized to mean one of the set of 27 or 28 asterisms into which the circle of the zodiac was divided. We read for instance in the Mahabhārata:[16] 'I went out with the moon at the Pushya and have returned with the moon at the Sravana.' Pushya is the sixth asterism counting from the Pleiades and its principal stars are Gamma, Delta, and Theta Cancri; Sravana is the twenty-first, marked by Beta and Gamma Aquilae; so the speaker tells us that he was absent for just over half a sidereal month, and owing to the moon's varying speed this might be anything from twelve and a half to fourteen and a half days. He also tells us that he measures time sidereally by the moon's place among the stars, and not synodically by her amount of light. The Babylonians would have done it the other way.

The first known mention of the asterisms as a complete set is in the Atharva Veda.[17] The passage is rather tedious since it lists all 28 in similar terms, but it begins as follows: 'Marvellous all together, and brilliant in the sky are the swift serpents of the firmament! Desiring the friendship of the twenty-eight, I worship in my song the sky and the days. May Krittika be to me a subject of fortunate invocation, and also Rohini; may Mrigaçiras be propitious to me, Ardra fortunate, Punarvasu amiable, Pushya beautiful, Açlesha light, and Māgha a path for me; may the Former and both Phalgunis be that which is pure, and Hasta likewise ... '

But whereas in this prayer all the asterisms are asked to be propitious, sooner or later tradition grew up about their individual influence, just as with the signs of the zodiac. For instance, a late fragment of debased Sanskrit discovered in Turkestan reads:[18] 'A formula of medical herbs ... In this respect effective are Chitra, Mrigaçira, Sravana, Nidhana ... Causers of misfortune are Krittika, Phalguni, Ashadha ... Causers of success in this respect are Purva-Phalguni, Purva-Ashadha, Purva-Bhadrapada ... The fourteenth day again has Yama for its deity.' (Yama is the god of death.) Modern use of the asterisms is of course similar, but more detailed.

As we saw, the asterisms are not mentioned in China before the third century B.C.; and the Arabian system is very much later. It seems then, in default of any evidence from Babylon, that their country of origin must have been India, unless we prefer to think with a number of scholars including Thibaut[19] and Needham,[20] that they grew up separately in the two different countries. It is conceivable that the number may originally have been 24, since 6 of the Indian *nakshatras* are composed of pairs bearing the adjectives Former and Latter (Purva and Uttara). But most probably the total varies between 27 and 28 for the same reason that so many peoples used to use an intercalary month, and that our own year varies between 365 and 366 days. Not for nothing is the optional asterism, Abhijit, which bears the number 22 and not 28, marked by a star well outside the zodiacal belt—none other than Vega, which lies 61° 45′ north of the ecliptic.

The Chinese have to a far greater extent than most peoples the civil-service mentality; they could hardly think of astronomy without imagining its use for administration, and to them the engaging vagueness of a system which varied between 27 and 28 divisions was psychologically repugnant. If they received this system from India, they will have decided to use always an even number of asterisms because it is more convenient for accounting. There is something after all in the attribution of the Chinese to Libra, the sign of administration; for even Confucius and Mencius, who, being sages, ought to have known better, wanted to be administrators.

Originally, then, and perhaps as long ago as the twenty-third century B.C., the asterisms will have been simply a set of small constellations lying near the path of the moon, having no standard length or recognized dividing lines. Later they were provided with *yogataras*, that is, 'junction stars', at or near which each began, and later still they became 27 arcs of 13° 20′ each, the *yogataras* no longer marking the boundaries.

Of the pre-Alexandrian period of Indian astronomy hardly any books remain. There are fragments of the Garga Samhita, too corrupt and incomplete to be safely translated, and the Jyotisha Vedanga.[21] This little work makes no mention of the planets; it is entirely concerned with calculating the times of the full and new moon festivals, and the unexpected mention of Pisces (*mînât*) near the beginning, as first sign of the circle, is probably to be explained as an interpolation, since the zodiac is otherwise not referred to. At any rate this isolated reference is no safe basis for a theory that the zodiac was known in India at the time this book was composed; for

145

the winter solstice then fell in the first degree of Sravishtha, the summer solstice in the middle of Aslesha, the vernal equinox in 10° of Bharani, and the autumn equinox in 3° of Visakha; and this points to a date about the sixteenth or seventeenth century B.C.

During this phase few of the fixed stars seem to have attracted attention outside of the zodiacal belt; we only hear of Agastya, which is Canopus, and the Seven Rishis, which are the stars of the Great Bear. The five-year cycle of 1,830 days was in use, and there were five names, instead of numbers, for the individual years within the cycle. But towards the end of the period another system of calculation along the zodiac was invented, the *tithi*, which was the length of time the moon takes to gain twelve degrees of longitude over the sun. A *tithi* may be a little more or a little less than a day, according to the speed of the moon.

In all the earliest writings the first of the asterisms is Krittika, the Pleiades, and this is generally taken to mean that the vernal equinox fell near it. But since Krittika means 'razor', Erard Mollien suggested in 1852[22] that the name might metaphorically signify 'the dividing-line'; for the original Sanskrit name of the Pleiades was *bahulah*, meaning 'very many'—and this, rather than 'sailing stars', may be the meaning of the Greek word Pleiades. He added that the opposite asterism Visakha, marked by Alpha and Beta Librae, means 'divided in two', and gives for it the symbol ⊖, which bears a certain resemblance to the glyph of the constellation Libra ♎. Furthermore, Kartikeya the war-god, who was suckled by the Pleiades and takes his name from them, was created by Shiva in order to vanquish (according to Mollien) the two giants Taraka (meaning 'constellation') and Kraoncha (meaning 'obliquity'). Not only so, but almost the first act of Kartikeya was to conquer an enormous Ram!

All this sounds very zodiacal. On the other hand Varaha Mihira makes no mention of precession in the Pança Siddhantika, which is of the sixth century A.D., and the Surya Siddhanta still accepts the theory of the libration of the equinoxes. So it seems impossible to suppose that precession was recognized in India before Alexandrian times.

Albiruni in the eleventh century blames Varaha Mihira for not having understood precession, alleging that 'he had no knowledge of the motion of the fixed stars towards the east. The solstice has kept its place, but the constellations have migrated, just the very opposite of what Varaha Mihira has fancied.'[23] This, however, is only an earlier example of the controversy that burst out in the nineteen forties, when Western astrologers were confronted with two zodiacs and began to wonder which of the two was fixed and which had moved. It is of course a question of point of view. A farmer would naturally conclude that the stars move against the fixed background of the seasons; an astronomer might think that the seasons move against the fixed background of the stars. Only since they discovered that neither is really fixed have astronomers made the seasonal measuring-point official.

The same controversy continues to this day in India, where some astrologers use the tropical zodiac, called *sayana*, and others use various *nirayana* or sidereal zodiacs; and because the knowledge of the original fiducial star has been lost, they try to determine the true *ayanamsha*, that is, the amount of difference between the tropical and sidereal zodiacs. This question would not arise if the proper reference-point were known. It will be mentioned again in the last chapter.

As happened in Greece and Rome, there was probably a period of several centuries when the effect of precession, and the consequent distinction between tropical and sidereal measurement, was not clear to astrologers, and perhaps not even to astronomers, since the two were not then distinguished. Hence the fact that the fiducial point was called *Asvini-adi* only meant that it fell somewhere in the asterism Asvini, which extended to about 12° west of Beta Arietis; and in fact the vernal equinox lay in that space between the years − 300 and +572. *Asvini-adi* will have meant 'the first point of Asvini' by analogy with the first point of Aries; and from this it may have been transferred to mean the fiducial point of the whole zodiac. And then it was later noticed, owing to precession, that the *yogatara* of the asterism Revati, Zeta Piscium, the tropical longitude of which was 359° 50′ in A.D. 560, was very close to the equinoctial point. And thus arose the idea that the zodiac should be measured from the small star Zeta Piscium — a notion which some Indian astrologers still accept.

A curious example of the transmission of knowledge in India was discovered in Pondicherry by a certain Lieutenant-Colonel John Warren, who published a collection of essays on Indian astronomy in

1825.[24] Warren met a calendar-maker who calculated for him the time of an expected eclipse of the moon by arranging shells on the ground. The man had no textbook, but worked by memory of various astronomical formulae which he carried in his head. His method of working revealed quite clearly that it came down to him from the works of Varaha Mihira in the sixth century, the Roman Empire in the third century, and ultimately from Babylonian texts of the Hellenistic period and the methods exemplified in Seleucid cuneiform tablets of the second and third centuries B.C.

Divination began very early in India, as it does all over the world. The constellations *gyeshthagni* and *vikritau* are mentioned as unlucky in the Atharva Veda,[25] and the Laws of Manu[26] lay down that astrology and fortune-telling are impure occupations and as such forbidden to ascetics. On the other hand it is astonishing how many types of divination are mentioned by Varaha Mihira in the Brihat Samhita, which is for the most part a textbook on the stars: they vary from knowing the signs of a person's face, and how to judge a sword or a jewel, to prognostications from the movements of tortoises, goats, elephants, or wagtails, from boils, torn garments, lamps, and umbrellas, to divination from the objects bepissed by dogs! Indeed, so many are the signs to be noted that, 'since the symptoms cannot be observed uninterruptedly by one man, an astrologer, if well paid, ought to keep in his service four other persons conversant with the science.' These four should be always on the look-out for meteors in all directions. For, 'as was said by the great seer Garga, the king who does not honour a scholar accomplished in horoscopy and astronomy, clever in all branches and accessories, comes to grief.'[27] Considering how few modern kings have done this, and how many have come to grief, the statement is without doubt statistically true!

Varaha Mihira has a long chapter on architecture, a short one on the culture of trees, and condemns those who speak evil of women; but his lists of objects ruled by the signs and asterisms, and of the character and destiny they produce, are very short. There are, however, extensive prognostications for the raising and lowering of prices: for instance, if there be an unusual appearance of the sun whilst in Virgo, one should buy up fly-whisks, donkeys, camels, and horses; for then one will be able to sell them for double six months later, though after any shorter or longer period one will only make a loss. The fly-whisks—chowries—are included among the animals because they are made from the tails of yaks.

As in China, the influence of a planet is good when it shines clear and bright; but when it is dim and 'wounded', then suffering will come to those ruled by it. This appears to be a pre-zodiacal form of divination, and thus it is not improbable that astral divination existed in India long before the zodiac was imported in Alexandrian times. And India was probably the origin of the system of 27 or 28 *nakshatras* which were later taken up and modified by the Chinese and Arabs. The Indian names for the asterisms, unlike the zodiac, are not those of animals.

TABLE 16   *The 28 Hindu Asterisms, or Nakshatras*

			long.	R.A.
1. Açvini	two horsemen	βγ Arietis	12°	11°
2. Bharani	bearer, yoni	35, 39, 41 Arietis	17°30'	16°50'
3. Krittika	(uncertain)	Pleiades	12°	12°
4. Rohini	ruddy	Hyades	13°30'	13°40'
5. Mrigaçiras	antelope's head	λφ Orionis	4°20'	4°40'
6. Ardra	moist	α Orionis (Betelgeuze)	25°40'	27°30'
7. Punarvasu	again brilliant	Castor & Pollux	13°	14°
8. Pushya	nourishing	θγδ Cancri	3°	3°20'
9. Açlesha	embracer	ε Hydrae	20°	20°40'
10. Mâghas	mighty	Regulus	15°	15°
11. Purva Phalguni	(?like a bed)	δθ Leonis	11°	10°40'
12. Uttara Phalguni	(same)	β Leonis	15°	13°50'
13. Hasta	hand	αβγδ Corvi	10°	9°20'
14. Chitra	brilliant	Spica Virginis	19°	17°40'
15. Svati	sword	α Boötis (Arcturus)	14°	13°10'
16. Viçakha	with spreading branches	αβγ Librae	11°	11°
17. Anuradha	success	ζδ Scorpii	5°	5°
18. Jyestha	oldest	Antares	12°	12°
19. Mula	root	ζηθικλ Scorpii	13°	14°
20. Purva Ashadha	unsubdued	δε Sagittarii	6°	6°30'
21. Uttara Ashadha	(same)	ζσ Sagittarii	6°40'	7°
22. Abhijit	conquering	Vega	13°20'	14°30'
23. Çravana	ear	βγ Aquilae	10°	10°40'

24. Çravishtha	most famous	αβγδ Delphini	30°	30°40'
25. Çatabhishaj	having 100 physicians	λ Aquarii	6°	6°
26. Purva Bhadrapada	beautiful foot	αβ Pegasi	11°	10°30'
27. Uttara Bhadrapada	(same)	γ Pegasi + α Andromedae	22°50'	21°10'
28. Revati	wealthy	ζ Piscium	8°10'	7°40'

The meanings are rarely very certain. The last two columns give the extent of the asterisms in longitude and in right ascension respectively.

11. *Babylonian Myths and Omens*[1]

THE Babylonians have the greatest reputation of any ancient people for astronomical study, and it is often said that the zodiac had its origin among them. However, the earliest Mesopotamian cities, such as Kish, Shuruppak, Ur, and Jamdet Nasr were founded before 5000 B.C., and the latest known cuneiform text is of the year A.D. 75.[2] In so long a time astronomy must have evolved.

The first great civilization of the Euphrates and Tigris valley was the work of the Sumerians, who were not Semites and worshipped a vast and complicated pantheon of gods. The Accadians, who invaded and took over the Sumerian civilization, perhaps about 3000 B.C., were Semites, speaking a wholly different language, coming from South Arabia, and worshipping, apparently, only three gods, namely the Moon, Venus, and the Sun. They were obliged, however, when they became civilized, to change the sex of the Sun and Venus, for among them the Sun had been a mother-goddess and Athtar, the planet Venus, was male. The Moon remained masculine, but lost its Semitic name of Shahar and was called by the Sumerian name of Sin. To suit the Sumerian liturgy Shamash, the Sun, became masculine, and Ishtar, the evening star, became the goddess of love and war. Thus she retained a double nature; in the morning she was goddess of war, and was called the Male Ishtar, but in the evening she became the goddess of love, and was called the Female Ishtar.

The Accadian period was brought to an end by another Semitic invasion such as the first, but often called Amorite. It was only then that Babylon rose to eminence. The First Dynasty of Babylon ruled from 1830 to 1531 B.C., and its most famous king is Hammurabi (1728–1686). This period is often regarded as the first flowering of both astronomy and astrology, because of the Enuma Anu Enlil (or Ellil) series of tablets which has come down to us.[3] This is a collection of over 7,000 celestial omens and observations.

After this came the Cassite period, and then, about 1000 B.C., the

152

Assyrians devised their great menologies giving rituals of the months founded on earlier Babylonian and Sumerian practice. King Asshurbanipal, the famous antiquarian (668–626), issued a definitive text in fifteen tablets, twelve for the standard lunar months, and three extra for intercalary months.[4]

The Assyrian empire copied Babylonian customs in almost every respect, and when it fell in 612 astronomy (or astrology) was still valued by the kings of the Neo-Babylonian empire. Then came in succession the Persians (538–330), Alexander the Great and his successors the Seleucids, and finally the Arsacids (about 250 B.C. to A.D. 230).

The original God of the Sumerians was An, meaning apparently 'That which is above'—just like Horus in Egyptian—and this word was written as a determinative before all names of gods, on the principle that 'all the gods are part of God'. The Semites, however, seem to have believed in a single male Creator who was father of the tribe; hence the monotheism of the Jews and Arabs is not peculiar to them, but can be paralleled in less extreme form among the Phoenicians and Canaanites, the early Aramaeans of North Syria, the Minaeans and Sabians of Arabia Felix, and the Aksomites of Abyssinia. In origin therefore Allahh, and the Hebrew gods Elohim and Yaw (IAO), were not so different from Bel or Baal, whose name means simply The Lord. The Earth-Mother, on the other hand, was not a native idea among the Southern Semites; yet once discovered she was called Allat (feminine of Allahh), and by the time of Alexander the Great had become, under many local names, the *Tychè* or Fortune of many a city, and also the goddess who ordained the future for men, with definitely astrological implications.

It was held as a matter of common observation that the gods, most obviously the Sun and Moon but possibly others, ordered the course of agriculture and human fertility, and there was an ancient belief in Mesopotamia that they held a congress at the beginning of each year in order to determine the fates of earth-dwellers. In Babylon this great assembly was dated to the eighth day of the spring festival in the month of Nisan, and the presiding god was Marduk, as later Asshur in Assyria; but earlier it was Enlil the earth-god who presided, and before that Ea the Sumerian fish-man.[5] Thus fate was determined not by the stars but by the earth-god, or by the god of the subterranean fresh-water ocean, and in Syria by various mother-goddesses who were patronesses of cities.

Rather naturally, then, there are no astrological documents of the Sumerian period, and of the Old Babylonian era only one tablet of the usual 'omen' type has been recovered.[6] Yet omen-taking became a standard feature of Babylonian official life, though individual records can often not be dated because they survive only in Assyrian copies, and the Assyrians did not file them under date but under the nature of the phenomenon recorded.

Omens were taken at any time if anything notable appeared, but most of all on the first day of the month, that is, at the appearance of the new moon. Sometimes the sickle appears on the twenty-ninth day since the previous one, and sometimes on the thirtieth, so the month varied between 28 and 29 days. It was the Sumerian city of Nippur which first made observations accurate enough to predict the length of the month in advance, and hence the calendar of Nippur became the basis of the religious calendars of the Babylonians, Assyrians, Jews, Aramaeans, and Phoenicians.

Significance was allotted to the moon's colour and elevation, brightness or dimness, and the direction of its horns. Babylonian accuracy was much greater in regard to the moon than in any other direction, and when Kidinnu, about 380 B.C., defined the length of the lunar month as 29 days 12 hours 44 minutes $3\frac{1}{3}$ seconds he was profiting by two thousand years of continuous observation.[7] (Modern measurements give 2·9 seconds). But omens were also taken from all kinds of celestial phenomena, from the movement, colour, and stations of the planets, from mists and clouds and shooting stars, and very frequently from haloes. These things were located in heaven regardless of their distance from the earth, and by reference to the constellation in which they were seen.

Prognostication was thus common in Babylonia long before the zodiac was devised.

In the thirty-seventh year of Nebuchadnezzar king of Babylon [says tablet VAT 4956 (567 B.C.)], on the 1st of Nisan (the preceding month had 29 days) the new moon became visible behind the Hyades; duration of visibility 64 minutes. Saturn was over against the Southern Fish. On the morning of the 2nd a rainbow appeared in the west ... At the beginning of the night of the 8th the moon was one ell before the star at the hind foot of the Lion. On the 9th the sun in the west was surrounded by a halo. On the 12th Jupiter rose at dusk. On the 14th the god was visible with the god [that is, the sun and full moon were visible simultaneously]. 16 minutes passed between sunrise and moonset the next day. On the 15th it was overcast. On the 16th Venus appeared ... From the 8th of Second Adar till the 29th of Nisan the water rose 3 ells 8 fingers. This month a fox came into the city ... on the 9th Sivan summer solstice. On the 10th the moon passed 3½ ells above Antares. This month's prices were: 1 *gur* would fetch 12 *ka* of barley or 60 *ka* of dates ... On the night of the 6th the moon was surrounded by a halo and within it were the Pleiades and Hyades and Beta and Zeta Tauri ... On the night of the 29th reddish clouds were seen in the west ... There was an earthquake on the 22nd, Mercury being 3½ ells behind the fish-tail of Capricorn.[8]

Many similar documents are expressly addressed to the king. Here is one which reminds us of the parapegma quoted in Chapter III:

At the behest of my master and my mistress, an announcement in advance ... On Airu 30th, Saturn in Scorpio, Mars in Aries. On 2nd, heliacal setting of Sirius. On 6th, heliacal rising of Venus in Gemini in the west. Mercury appears in the east as Aldebaran, which has disappeared. 15th, full moon day. 20th, heliacal rising of Jupiter at the end of Taurus: Mercury's heliacal setting in the east as Aldebaran, which has disappeared. 26th, Venus reaches Cancer. 27th, last sickle of the moon.

The date of this is −239.[9]

Eclipses, however, could not always certainly be foretold, since at each occurrence of a given eclipse at a given place the shadow passes a little farther north (or south) than last time, and after five or six eclipses will miss entirely. Hence such a report as the following:

To the king my lord, thy servant Mar-Ishtar. Greeting to the king my lord. May Nabu and Marduk [that is, Mercury and Jupiter] be favourable to the king my lord. Length of days, comfort of body, and joy of heart may the great gods give to the king my lord. On the 27th day the moon was still visible. On the 28th, 29th, and 30th days we kept watch for an eclipse of the sun, but he went his way and did not have an eclipse. The moon was visible on the first day, which is the day expected for the month in question. Regarding Jupiter, about which I reported earlier to the king my lord: 'He is shining in the path of Anu in the region of Sibzianna; when the sickle disappeared he stood low on the horizon and could not be perceived, but we can say that he is in the path of Anu and such is his interpretation': now I report to the king my lord: 'He is retarded and therefore was not perceived, but he is in the path of Bel, below the constellation of the Chariot, he has really gone down as low as the Chariot. His interpretation was accordingly erroneous, but the interpretation of Jupiter in the path of Anu is as I earlier reported to the king my lord and would not be wrong. For the information of my lord the king.[10]

A great many ritual prohibitions were enforced on both king and people in connection with the observance of the calendar, and demons were always ready to take vengeance on any breach. There were days when the king must or must not wash his clothes, when he must recite a penitential psalm, when no one might go out in the street and no physician practise. This is the origin of the resentment at Jesus' healing on the Sabbath, for not only festivals but prohibitions and the intolerance of the Old Testament God seem to have been imitated from Babylon. Thus the Sabbath began as the four quarter-days of the moon, not as a festival or rest but as an ill-omened day on which it was unlucky to do business. In Assyria, and indeed since Hammurabi's time, all work was forbidden on the 7th, 14th, 19th, 21st, and 28th days, and in fact hardly any documents have ever been found dated on one of those days. On the other hand the Roman and Egyptian lucky and unlucky days are not derived from the Mesopotamian lunar system.[11]

The week and month began in the evening with the appearance of the sickle moon, and any days over the 28 were disregarded. The first day of the week was therefore Monday, not the Saturday of the Jews nor the Christian Sunday. 'The 26th and 27th were days of sorrow and penance,' says Langdon, 'preparatory to the 28th when the moon crossed the river of death and joined Nergal lord of the dead in the darkness of Arallu.' The 29th was unlucky for everything. 'The king shall not go out of the gate; he will meet with witchcraft in the wind of the street' on the 29th Tebit. If a man goes out on the 29th Nisan he will die, but if he goes out on the 29th Tammuz his wife will die. In the months of Nisan and Tebit it was illegal to take purgatives, and on the 13th Nisan we read: 'One may take a wife. One may not be merry. One should worship Sin.'[11]

Another feature of Babylonian life was a great fondness for consulting diviners, though that too, of course, was frequently forbidden on Mondays. There are extant lists of suitable signs of the zodiac for attempting various undertakings, for instance[12] to get a man's love for a woman the moon should be in Libra or Scorpio, and for the converse in Pisces or Gemini. For getting one's name favourably mentioned at court She (or rather He, Sin) should be in Pisces; to remove a spell, in Aquarius or Pisces; to bind or drown a ghost (a recognized way of getting rid of one), in Cancer; and to obtain a change of mind, in Leo. Many of these signs have nothing in common with modern astrological notions, but there is precedent for the traditional good influence of Jupiter, although in other documents, as in India and China, the goodness or badness of a planet depends on its luminosity: 'When Jupiter culminates, the gods will give peace, troubles will be cleared up and complications unravelled. Rain and floods will come' (so the crops will be good), 'the lands will dwell securely. Hostile kings will be at peace, the gods will receive prayers and hear supplications.'[13]

It is lucky for Mars to be dim, unlucky for him to be bright. 'When a planet stands at the left horn of the moon, the king will act mightily.' On the other hand, 'When Jupiter appears in the month Tammuz there will be corpses, and when Mars approaches Jupiter there will be great devastation in the land.'

Among these serious matters, written about 660 B.C., we come unexpectedly on a plaintive wail: 'The handmaiden of the king my lord has gone to Accad; I cannot wait, she has run away. Let the king my lord fetch her and give her to me. From Billi the son of Igibi the magician.'[14] One cannot help feeling that, had Billi been efficient as a magician he would not have needed police assistance.

It is highly significant that Hammurabi's laws, which mention

157

every kind of profession then existing, make no mention of the *mašmašu* or diviners.[15] This implies that only since the seventeenth century B.C. did prediction spread down from being a purely official matter for king and city, and begin to be practised for individuals.

The most famous set of Babylonian astronomical tablets is called the ᵐᵘˡAPIN series. The name means Plough Star, and refers to the constellation Triangulum, which lies between Aries and Andromeda but apparently included the Pleiades. These tablets, though only written about 700 B.C., give the results of observations going back to about 1300, and with their help an amazing number of Babylonian star-names have been placed in the sky. This was the great period of accurate observation in Babylonia, at any rate for the daily rising, setting, and culmination of stars, though more complicated phenomena such as computations in advance were done only approximately by simple arithmetical progression.[16]

In these tablets the ecliptic had not yet become the principal line of reference; the Babylonians spoke instead of the Three Ways of Enlil, Anu, and Ea. The Way of Anu was a band about 16° 40′ wide on either side of the equator, the Way of Enlil lay to the north of it and the Way of Ea to the south.[17] Thus the sun's path was divided into four sections, and it spent three months in the equatorial Way of Anu, three in the northerly Way of Enlil, the next three again in that of Anu, and the last three in the southerly Way of Ea. If these four zones were divided equally, the four points of passage would fall in the middles of the second, fifth, eighth, and eleventh signs of a tropical zodiac. Thus they are definitely older than the zodiac, and their equality determines the width of the Way of Anu.

Another important feature of Babylonian astronomy was the 'twelve times three', or 36 seasonal stars. The Egyptians also had a set of 36 seasonal stars, but theirs were of quite different origin, and not divided between the three Ways of Anu, Enlil, and Ea. In the fifth tablet of the Epic of Creation it is said of Marduk :[18]

> He constructed stations for the great gods. The stars their likenesses he fixed, even the Lumaši. He fixed the year and designed the signs [of the zodiac]. For the twelve months he placed three stars each. After he had defined the days of the year by signs, he established the place of Nibiru to fix all of

them, in order that none transgress or loiter. He appointed the places of Enlil and Ea with him [i.e. beside the Anu Way]. He opened gates on both sides, he made strong the lock-rails left and right. In her belly he placed the 'heights', and caused the new moon to shine forth, entrusting to him the night. He fixed him as a being of the night to determine the 'days'. Monthly without ceasing he magnified him with a crown: 'At the beginning of the month, the time of the shining forth over the land thou shalt shine with horns to determine six days, and on the seventh with a half crown. At the full moon verily thou art in opposition monthly, when the sun on the foundation of heaven has overtaken thee.'

Oddly enough, Nibiru is not taken by scholars to mean either the equinox or the fiducial star of the ecliptic, obvious though this might seem to the expectant reader. The word is translated 'place of crossing over', and refers in particular to the position of Jupiter in such a situation, especially on the meridian.

A good deal of puzzlement has been caused by the 36 stars, since they correspond to the twelve months, and one might expect that those in the Way of Enlil, being farthest north, should rise heliacally at the beginning of the month, those of Anu in the middle, and the stars of Ea at the end. However this does not work out, and furthermore the constellations' names are accompanied by numbers, of which those in the middle ring are double those of the inner ring and half those of the outer ring. Probably this refers to the length of watches of the night, which varies with the seasons. But the list of twelve times three stars has a different origin, though this too is not entirely certain. These stars correspond very largely to the old lists of twelve stars each, which are attributed to Elam, Accad, and Amurru, and this is a regional division rather than an astronomical one. Originally, one would expect, the Elamites, Accadians, and Amorites would each have made a choice of twelve stars to mark the months by their heliacal rising, and some of these would be the same, but others not. When in Hammurabi's time the scribes tried to develop a single system for the whole Babylonian empire, they conflated the local schemes, and whenever a gap was caused by two stars being the same in the local lists they filled it with a constellation that

159

rose at the same time of year, or even with a planet. Thus in the first lists of stars of Enlil, Anu, and Ea, the star of Enlil was only the most northerly of the three, and did not, as in later times, actually have to be over 16° 40' from the equator.[19]

Now since the [mul]APIN series dates from about 700 B.C. and makes no mention of the zodiac, presumably it was not yet known, for it was not required so long as the Babylonians were quite content with their Three Ways and their lunar calendar. But the names of months are often seasonal, so we ought to inquire whether the signs of the zodiac could be derived from seasonal phenomena. This leads us to one of the most curious blunders in the whole history of this curious subject.

Two astronomers, Mr and Mrs Maunder, writing in the *Monthly Notices of the Royal Astronomical Society* for March 1904, print the following list of meanings of the Accadian month-names, according to a certain Colonel Conder of the Royal Engineers:

> lambing, calving, bricks, harvest,
> very hot, dried up, thunder, irrigation,
> very cloudy, flood, very rainy, ploughing.

This list starts with the Lamb, a form of Aries, goes on with the Calf, of the nature of Taurus, gives 'very hot' in the fifth position, that of the Lion, and in place of the Goat-fish and Waterman says 'flood' and 'very rainy'. Mr and Mrs Maunder then comment:[20] 'It will be seen that this scheme has no zodiacal reference, but it is entirely climatic.' Yet why should the zodiac have no climatic reference?

If we draw up a table of Sumerian months, from which the Babylonian, Assyrian, and Hebrew month-names were derived, we find that a good number of them have seasonal references, such as 'brick-making', 'seed-corn', 'lighting braziers', 'wind and rain', and the rest are named from religious festivals. Indeed, according to Professor Langdon[21] 'a striking aspect of Sumero-Babylonian religion is the association of myths with each of the months and the attempt to find in the regnal constellations of the months figures which correspond to the ideas involved in the monthly myths'. Obviously therefore we must investigate the monthly myths in order to see whether by any chance they throw light on the origin of the zodiac.

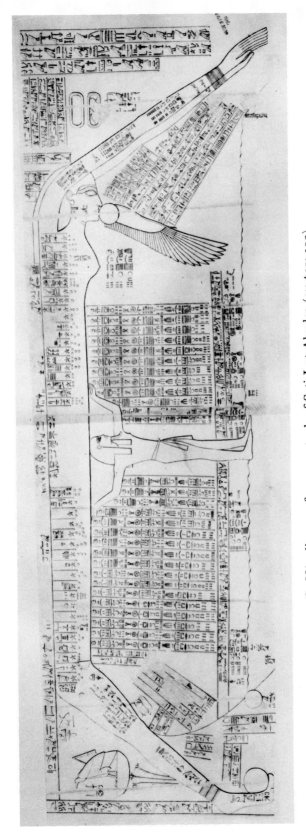

18. Nût diagram from cenotaph of Seti I at Abydos (*see page* 193)

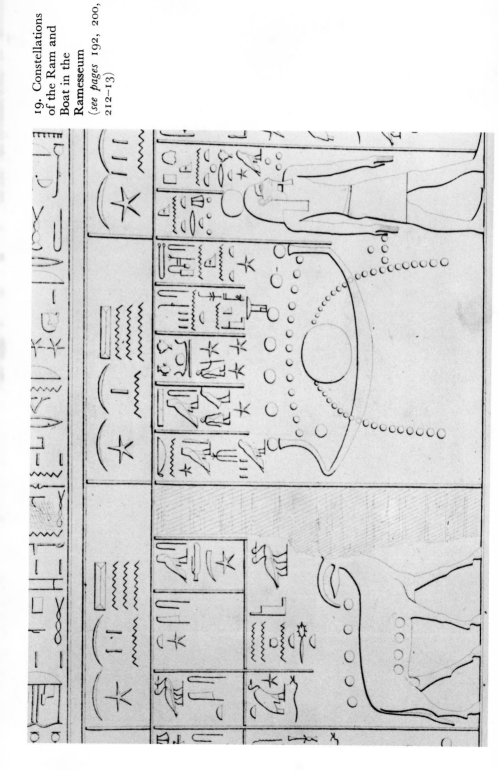

19. Constellations of the Ram and Boat in the **Ramesseum** (*see pages* 192, 200, 212–13)

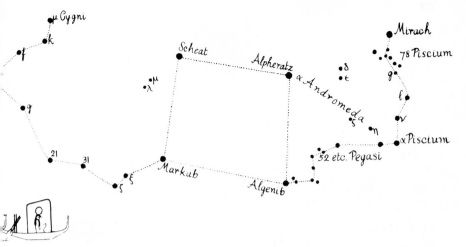

20. Constellation of the Boat (*see page* 200)

21. Marble plate from Egypt, Greco-Roman period, showing
zodiac and hour-circle

Modern.	Medieval.	Demotic.		Hieroglyphic.

22. The Sigla of the 12 Signs

These myths and festivals originated in the Sumerian period, between 3000 and 2000 B.C. The most famous is that of Tammuz, the beautiful shepherd loved by Ishtar. In the second month (Ayar) he celebrated with her the Sacred Marriage, but in the fourth, called after him, he died, the pasture being burnt up by the summer sun, and in the sixth, when the days become shorter than the nights, Ishtar descended into the lower world to bring him back. However, at Babylon Tammuz did not rise again until the 28th of Kislev, when the days begin to lengthen. Also in the fourth month, about June, the Sumerians celebrated the festival of the breaking of bread for Ninazu, another name for Tammuz, then the burning of torches in the fifth month was a festival of the dead, also for him, and 'purification', the name of the sixth month, refers to Ishtar's descent. Thus no less than four months are named from the Tammuz-Ishtar cycle. Indeed, Langdon suggested that the fire-festival may be the origin of the midsummer fire-festival on St John's Day both in North Africa and Europe, adding: 'And in Sardinia to this day the ritual of the Adonis gardens is incorporated in the festival for St John's Day.'[22]

Tammuz was identified with the constellation Orion, the name of which was Sib.zi.an.na, the Faithful Shepherd of Heaven. Orion's conjunction with the sun, when he is invisible and therefore might be said to have descended to the lower world, now takes place in June, but in 2000 B.C. it took place only about a month after the vernal equinox, hence the descent of Tammuz cannot have been in origin an astronomical myth, but only a seasonal one. Similar considerations preclude an astronomical origin for the festival of purification in the month of Elûl and the ox-procession at Nippur.

The first and seventh months were both marked by new-year festivals, since the early Semitic year began in the autumn and the Sumerian year in the spring. Hence the resemblance between the myths of the two months, both of which refer to the gods fixing the fates for the coming year. It seems, however, that the myth of the judgment of souls at the autumn equinox cannot be earlier than about 2000 B.C.

Both the eighth and ninth months are connected with the lighting of braziers, partly on account of the cold weather and partly also to symbolize the reascent of the sun from the shortest day. The tenth month, Tebit, was exceedingly unlucky, since ghosts were supposed to return from under the earth, and demons were especially active. This, together with the season of storms, may be why Capricorn and Aquarius, both sacred to the water-god Ea, the one kindly god in the Mesopotamian pantheon, were also regarded as demons in the train of Tiamat. Finally the last month, Adar, means 'threshing-floor', and was the season of the barley harvest in all Sumerian cities. So it does not look as though the monthly myths were astronomical in themselves, though attempts were later made to fit them together with various constellations, some of which were adopted into the zodiac.

But although the zodiac seems not yet known in 700 B.C., 410 is the date of the earliest surviving personal horoscope. It was cast for a son of Shuma-usur, son of Shuma-iddina, and placed Jupiter in Pisces, Venus in Taurus, Saturn in Cancer, Mars in Gemini, and Mercury invisible, with the Moon beneath the 'horn' of Scorpio, that is to say in Libra. The Ascendant is not mentioned in this or any other Babylonian horoscope that has come down to us. The predictions are very brief, indeed in the oldest example seem to say only that the horoscope was a good one. In other cases 'he will be lacking in wealth', 'his days will be long', 'he will have children'. The customers for some of the third-century horoscopes bear Greek names such as Aristokrates and Nikanor.[23]

This raises the question, how early were the Babylonians able to locate the equinox, and where in Aries or Taurus did they place it? Kugler, writing in 1914, stated that before the eighth century B.C. eclipses were not observed accurately enough to predict their recurrence with certainty, and systematic intercalation of extra months was not possible before 528 B.C.; hence the finest flower of Babylonian astronomy occurred as late as the third and second centuries. By then, however, the Babylonians had ceased to observe the equinox, so their longitudes were $5\frac{1}{2}°$ out. Had the beginning of the year been accurately, and not just empirically, geared to the equinox, the fact of precession would have become evident from the gradual change of date in the heliacal risings of important stars. But the Babylonians did not discover precession.[24]

By the seventh century, the great period of astronomy in Assyria, the epact of eleven days had been discovered, which is necessary to bring the lunar year of 354 days up to the solar year of 365; but not so long before that the beginning of the year, though computed in advance, still needed to be checked by observation. A seventh-century text says: 'The place of the celestial equator seek and the days to be filled in thou shalt know; then fix thou the year and add the epact.'[25] The beginning of the year was thus fixed at the new moon nearest to the spring equinox.

(i) The Eighteen Signs

Theoretically, then, the vernal equinox fell a fortnight before this new moon, on the fifteenth day of the twelfth month about 1000 B.C., and later, about 700, on the fifteenth of the first month. (The Easter full moon still falls on the fifteenth day of the first lunar month after the equinox.) There were twelve schematical months of 30 days each, connected with the heliacal rising of certain stars, and the sun's path was divided into four parts, though not yet into twelve.[26] The twelve equal signs, as opposed to the figures of constellations, are first mentioned in extant literature in the Persian period, 419 B.C., in tablet VAT 4924. But there is evidence of an earlier stage at which there were not twelve but eighteen constellations of the zodiac. The list is as follows:

TABLE 17 *The Babylonian Zodiac of 18 Constellations*

Zappu	tuft of hair	Pleiades
Gud.an.na	bull of heaven	Hyades
Sib.zi.an.na	faithful shepherd of heaven	Orion
Šugi	charioteer	Perseus
gamlu	scimitar	Auriga
maš.tab.ba.gal.gal	great twins	Gemini
al.lul	(?crab)	Praesepe
ur.gu.la	lion or lioness	Leo
ab.sin	furrow	Virgo
zibanitu	horn, (later) scales	Libra
gir.tab	scorpion	Scorpio
PA.BIL.SAG	(uncertain)	Sagittarius
suhur.maš	goat-fish	Capricorn
GÙ.LA	(?giant)	Aquarius
zibbati	tails	Pisces
šim.mah	great swallow	southern fish
anunitum	(a goddess)	northern fish
hunga (=agru)	hireling	Aries

163

Some scholars have thought this stage intermediate between an original set of 28 lunar mansions, as in eastern Asia, and the 12 equal signs, but there is no need to suppose so, for Babylonian interest in the moon was directed first of all to its light, depending on its relation to the sun, and so their mansions, had they existed, would have been the same as their days, and the first would have been the new sickle, regardless of the stars among which it appeared.

The eighteen are called 'constellations which stand in the path of the moon, and into the region of which the moons pass monthly, and which they touch'. One of the texts listing them is the first tablet of the ᵐᵘˡAPIN series, compiled between 1400 and 900 B.C. and extant in a tablet dated 687, the other is British Museum tablet 86378.[27]

The conclusion seems to be unavoidable that about 1000 B.C. in Babylonia the zodiac had not taken form, but most of its constellations were known under the same names as we have today. A tablet of about 400 shows a later stage of the evolution, when the 'Charioteer' and the 'Scimitar' are missing, the two goddesses of Pisces have been replaced by the single constellation *Iku*, and the 'Square Field' (Pegasus, of course) and the 'Tails' have been exchanged for the 'Band of the Fishes'. Finally, the twelve usual signs are given in a late-Babylonian text of the Seleucid period.[28] A similar intermediate stage is found in an extant ritual for consecrating a new statue of a god.[29]

(ii) *The Eleven Signs*

The most striking thing about these Babylonian irregular zodiacs is the absence of the Ram: it suggests that the zodiac was not invented by the Babylonians alone, but perhaps their constellations were used for a syncretistic scheme in which Greece or Egypt may also have had a share. There is, however, no doubt of the Babylonian origin of most of the constellations, above all Capricorn. The Greek word for Capricorn, *aigokerōs*, does not mean 'goat' but 'creature with horns like a goat', and not till Claudius Ptolemy made Capricorn an earthy sign did anyone dream of forgetting that it had a fish's tail. As such it is of common occurrence on Babylonian monuments, especially boundary-stones (see Plate 10).

In Babylonia ownership of land was not protected, as in Egypt, by a set of markers along the boundaries, but a full-sized 'boundary-stone' was set up in the middle of the field, and a small copy or tally was kept at home. The stone was inscribed with the owner's name and necessary details, and at the top were pictured in relief the gods or demons invoked to protect the owner and punish infringement.

The oldest surviving boundary-stone belonged to King Entemena about 3500 B.C., but it was the Cassites (1746–1170) who made their use common for private citizens; being mountain people they were prepared to fetch stone a distance of a hundred miles, there being no stone in Babylonia.

One cannot pretend that all the gods represented on boundary-stones are astronomical—they vary too much; but among the most popular choices were Anu 'father of the gods, king of heaven', Anunit his wife, Ea the king of the subterranean fresh-water ocean and god of springs, Enlil 'the sublime lord who determines the fate of the gods', and the other greater gods such as Ishtar, Shamash, and Nabu (Venus, the Sun, and Mercury).

The commonest symbols are the crescent moon on its back for the god Sin, a star for Ishtar, and the winged disk or four-rayed wheel of Shamash, also seven stars or points for the Pleiades, and various dragons. There are frequently more or fewer than twelve gods represented, nor is the order in any way consistent, hence they cannot be zodiacal symbols, although a good number of them do have constellations associated with them. Also common are figures of Scorpio and Capricorn.

The general principle is that a deity can be represented by his shrine (all shrines look much alike), by his weapon or his animal, or by any combination of these. The lightning-fork of Ramman the weather-god may appear on a shrine or alone, with or without his symbol, the crouching ox; and the ram's head has nothing to do with Aries, but belongs to Ea, and often occurs on the back of the goat-fish which is his animal symbol. Ea is the only one of the Sumerian and Babylonian gods who was never angry, and always ready to help both gods and men out of difficulties. He is often represented as a man walking in a great fish-shaped cloak, the head over his head and pointing upwards like a mitre, the tail at his heels, and the forward leg showing his human form. He is said to have emerged four times at long intervals from the ocean to teach civilization to men, and each time he would retire into the water at night. Capricorn his symbolic creature symbolizes this dual life, and has as yet no association with the planet Saturn, which has never been reputed to help people out of scrapes. Saturn was represented by the lion-headed dragon and the god Nergal, who is the violent sun of summer and also the winter sun and god of the dead.

Among the titles of Ea[30] is 'antelope of the subterranean ocean', so there is no need to look further for the origin of Capricorn the fish-tailed goat. It is also called *kusarikku*, the fish-ram, and *suhurmashu*, skate-goat. The latter became the common name of the constellation Capricorn, and the former explains why a ram was also a symbol of Ea and sometimes appears on Capricorn's back. In late-Babylonian times the fish-ram and skate-goat were also used as monsters in the train of Tiâmat, but 'antelope of the Apsu' was a title of Ea as long ago as Sumerian times.

When Babylon rose to be chief of all cities, Marduk its local but hitherto minor deity had to be raised to the level of the great gods. A crisis was therefore engineered in heaven by the Babylonian scribes, and a monster appeared, Tiâmat, representing the salt and bitter sea (by contrast with the fresh waters of Ea). Tiâmat for merely grammatical reasons was feminine, and even Anu, the original creator, fled before her. Then Marduk undertook to do battle against Tiâmat on condition of being recognized as one of the great gods. He passed the preliminary test, which was to destroy and create again a garment provided by the examiners, and then successfully tore Tiâmat's body in two. Of the two halves heaven and earth were made. This was about three thousand years after the foundation of Ur and Kish.

Tiâmat had a train of eleven monsters, but this does not mean that she and they together comprised the zodiac, for she in herself comprised the whole of heaven, which did not exist so long as she lived. Marduk set the eleven demons in heaven as constellations, and they are not very zodiacal; they are the Viper, the Raging Serpent, the dragon Lakhamu, the Great Lion, the Gruesome Hound, the Scorpion-man, the destructive spirits of wrath, the Fish-man and Fish-ram.[31] To these were added Tiâmat and her husband Kingu, and the constellation Hydra, representing an unfortunate dragon called Mushkhusshu, which in Sumerian times had started life as a harmless vegetation-spirit but suffered, like other dragons, merely for being a dragon.

Very common on boundary-stones is the picture of a scorpion, and there sometimes occurs a scorpion-man drawing a bow (Plates 10 and 11). This looks like a combination of Scorpio and Sagittarius, and indeed Langdon says that the scorpion-man 'is universally identified with the archer Sagittarius'.[32] This explains why in some pictures the centaur has a scorpion's tail and a second scorpion beneath it. The two were not originally distinct, and only became so when the zodiac was schematized. This double nature may be the reason why Sagittarius was double-headed, with a human head facing forward and an animal head looking back. And this of course will have encouraged Ptolemy to make Sagittarius a double-bodied sign, although it seems now to be centuries since the two heads were mentioned in astrological literature.

There is no evidence that the scorpions on boundary-stones are astronomical; they might readily symbolize the curses with which these monuments are laden. Gilgamish, in the epic called after him, is terrified by a scorpion-man who guards the gates of sunrise, and such a figure would not be associated with one part of the zodiac more than another. Nor are the names of the two constellations any help: *gir.tab* means simply scorpion, and the name of Sagittarius, PA.BIL.SAG, cannot be interpreted because it never occurs in any other context. However, this sign was identified with Ninurta the god of war, and therefore, had the zodiac been a purely Mesopotamian invention, Sagittarius would surely have become the sign of war, whereas in fact it became something very different. But Scorpio as the sign of war may have its roots here.

Obviously, then, Scorpio, Sagittarius, and Capricorn are of Babylonian origin, since they occur in Mesopotamia well over a thousand years before they are carved in Egypt upon the zodiacs of Denderah and Esna. But this does not prove that they were already at that date constellations, much less signs of the zodiac or thirty degrees in extent.

Aquarius is a different matter. The god Hapi, watering from two jars, was an extremely ancient symbol of the Nile. But a similar figure would be natural anywhere. In Babylon there is a form of Ea which is sometimes called 'the god with streams', and sometimes he holds a pot, but more often the water flows spontaneously from his hands and arms,[33] as in Plate 12. He is not, however, particularly located in Aquarius. The Babylonian name of Aquarius is GU.LA, and this was at first taken for the name of a goddess patroness of childbirth and healing, whose wrath was celebrated by rest and mourning on the nineteenth day of the month. Later it was suggested that GU.LA might mean 'great star', which seemed unsuitable since no star of the first magnitude is found in this little constellation. The latest rendering is 'constellation of the great man', and its origin is supposed to be either the giant Enkidu watering an ox, or else the god of fresh water, Ea, also represented in Capricorn. These interpretations show how scholars have wanted to find a water-god here in order to explain Aquarius. The attempt has not been obviously successful, nor is it really necessary.

Enkidu was an extremely famous and interesting character, a friend of Gilgamish the Babylonian Hercules; and Gilgamish began his career as an historical personage, the fourth or fifth king of the First Dynasty of Erech, something before the year 3000 B.C. In myth, as probably in real life, Gilgamish became an appalling tyrant, and left 'not a son to his father nor a maiden to her mother,'[34] so to distract him from evil-doing the gods appealed to Aruru the earth-goddess, and she created Enkidu out of a piece of clay. He was naked and shaggy and behaved like a wild ox, in fact the euhemerists would say that he was a nomadic invasion. At any rate he was totally ignorant of civilized usages, so the people of Erech very wisely sent a harlot to seduce him; and she, having more brains than most, succeeded in educating him. He came to the city and wrestled with Gilgamish, and the two thenceforward became friends; so they left the city in peace while they went about the country wrestling with lions, bulls, and other public nuisances. Finally Enkidu died, and Gilgamish went to the nether world to fetch the plant of eternal life and restore his friend; but although he received the plant from the goddess of hell, he lost it on the way up! These two friends are very likely commemorated in the Great Twins, the constellation Gemini. Otherwise the most common twin-god is Nergal, as god both of the sun and of the lower world, and his emblem is two lions' heads back to back on a staff; but other gods also could be double-headed without any allusion to the constellation Gemini.

Besides the constellations already named, there is no reason to doubt the Babylonian origin of Taurus, Leo and Libra. UR.GU.LA (to be distinguished from GU.LA) does seem to mean a lion or lioness, although the Accadian version of the name means The Great Dog. Its position is known because it rises heliacally with Sirius and Hydra, Aquarius and Aquila set when it rises, and Libra rises when it culminates. Five of the individual stars are mentioned, of which our name Denebola is an Arabic version of KUN.UR.GU.LA, the Lion's Tail. In the same way Regulus (little king) is a translation of the Babylonian name of this star, LUGAL (=Sharru) meaning king.

Libra is often thought to be a late invention, somewhat unjustifiably suppressing the Scorpion's claws; indeed this is stated on a tablet in the British Museum, and also by Greek and Latin writers. The Accadian[35] name of Libra, *ziba.anna*, otherwise *zibanitu*, is of frequent occurrence, and means the 'horn' of the Scorpion, which must be its claws. The word *rin*, Scales, is found later, but Langdon remarks: 'About 2000 B.C. the constellation which governed this month [of Teshrit] was connected with the judgment of the living and the dead, the time when the gods fixed the fates, and consequently the Babylonians out of pure imagination saw the sign of the Scales, Libra, here ... Hence *zibanitu* also came to mean "Scales".' Then the exaltation of Saturn in this constellation caused him to be regarded as the planet of justice — though others have thought this was because his orbit is the least irregular of the planets. Also derived from this idea are the Mandaean angel of judgment, Abathur, the Islamic belief that in the ninth month Allahh will judge the souls of men, animals, birds, and spirits, and the Jewish day of Rosh ha-Shanah on the first of Teshrit, for which the 81st Psalm was composed.

Taurus the Bull seems to be a straightforward translation of the Babylonian *gud.anna*, bull of heaven, whose story is again connected with Gilgamish. When Gilgamish, with Enkidu's help, had demolished the terrible Humbaba, Ishtar, goddess of lechery, fell in love with him, but he repulsed her, pointing out quite justly that she was incapable of faithful affection: all her previous lovers she had herself brought to a bad end. Furious, Ishtar flew to heaven and demanded of Anu her father that he should create a Bull of Heaven to kill Gilgamish. Anu obliged, and this is the Bull that draws the Plough-star (the constellation Triangulum).[36]

A bull, however, is also the regular emblem of Adad, Hadad, or Ramman, the god of thunder and lightning, and this is the god signified by the bull on boundary-stones, not therefore the Bull of Heaven, and not zodiacal. But the Bull of Heaven, having been created at the desire of Ishtar, does naturally come to be ruled by Venus at the later date when planetary rulerships were invented. It was also represented by the white bull sacrificed at sunset on the fifth day of the Babylonian new-year festival, and is the origin of Virgil's 'white bull who with his golden horns opens the year'.[37] As will be later seen, this does go back to the time when the equinoctial new moon appeared in Taurus.

From the list of eighteen constellations six were later excluded, quite apart from those that were altered; and four of these six were in the region of Taurus and Gemini, namely the Pleiades, Orion, Perseus, and Auriga. In accordance with this we find a tablet of Nebuchadnezzar's time (604–561 B.C.) stating that the Moon's exaltation is in Perseus and the Pleiades.[38] Later it was said to be in 3° Taurus, and this is exactly the same spot, for the sidereal longitudes of the stars concerned are these:

Algol (Beta Persei)	1° Taurus
Alcyone, chief of the Pleiades	5° Taurus
Mirfak (Alpha Persei)	7° Taurus

So here is evidence that the Moon had an exaltation before the zodiac was reduced to twelve signs, and further that the exaltations are very much older than the rulership of signs by planets. The same tablet speaks of the exaltation of the Sun in the Square Field and the Hireling—the space which later became the Ram. Venus is given an exaltation in Leo as well as in Pisces, the others are the same as usual, Mercury in Virgo, Saturn in Libra, Mars in Capricorn, and Jupiter in Cancer.

Evidently, then, the famous mulAPIN list is precisely what it claims to be, a list of constellations athwart the path of the moon. To provide a scale of reference for accurate measurement of the moon's position, Perseus and the Pleiades (or rather, the Charioteer and the Tuft of Hair) would not both be necessary, since they overlap, nor would both Auriga and Orion, which have much the same extent whether in longitude or right ascension. Thus although Mr Fagan[39] claims that the exaltations of the planets originated in 786 B.C., when the new temple of Nabu, who is Mercury, was opened in Calah by Adad-nirari III, king of Assyria, yet 200 years later, in the time of Nebuchadnezzar, the Moon's exaltation, though in the right place, is not spoken of as in Taurus, and hence the zodiac, though it had probably been imagined, had not yet superseded the earlier system.

The constellation Taurus is of particular importance for the history of the zodiac because of the question when and in what sense the vernal equinox fell in it. Mr Fagan has calculated that, on the basis of twelve equal divisions based on Spica in 29° Virgo, the vernal equinox passed out of Taurus into Aries about 1963 B.C. The Babylonians were not capable of any such calculation, and would have reckoned the Taurean Age to persist so long as the first new moon of the year was seen as a rule in Taurus; until it was usually seen in Aries the Ariean Age would for them not have begun. This is why we find Langdon writing: 'A date anywhere between 1100–500 B.C. can be assumed for the beginning of the Aries period.'[39] On this principle to speak of the Ariean and Taurean Ages is not a mere curiosity or abstraction, nor does it suppose any mysterious influence of the precession of the equinoxes; it arose as a matter of observation among peoples having a lunar calendar. At this rate, of course, the Piscean Age would not begin till A.D. 1000, nor the Aquarian Age before 3000.

In the Sumerian period writing was under the patronage of the grain-goddess Nidaba, doubtless because she kept account of the stores. In Semitic times it was taken over by Nabu, the messenger of Bel (The Lord). Nabu's city was Borsippa, and in the sky he was the sun at the winter solstice, the planet Mercury, and the star Aldebaràn. His function was to write on the tablets of fate the decisions taken at the vernal congress of the gods, and for this reason Aldebaràn was called the Star of the Tablet, which also became its name in China. This was because, as the brightest star in Taurus, it rose heliacally at the end of April and thus announced the beginning of the Babylonian year.[40] The meaning of the Arabic name Aldebaràn is often thought to be 'the follower' because it follows the Pleiades, but Dr Langdon suggested that it might mean 'the forecaster', as a reminiscence of Nabu the divine scribe writing the predictions for the year.

The grain-goddess Nidaba, or Shala, is shown in Plate 13, and seems the obvious origin for Virgo. The name of the constellation is *absin*, the furrow, and its western half, without Spica, represented the bunch of dates of the goddess Sarpanitum, described in tablet VAT 9428[41] as 'she has a star on her head and a whip in her right hand, the thong of which stretches out over the tail of Leo'. (This doubtless explains why on the zodiacs of Esna, Virgo appears to hold Leo by the tail.) The illustration is of the Persian period, but three earlier texts give Spica, the ear of corn, as the only ruler of the month Elul, and it appears that the Sumerians knew it as the corn-goddess so long ago as Gudea's time. Virgo thus has a Babylonian and in fact a Sumerian origin.

The 'winged bulls' so famous in Babylonian and Assyrian sculpture are sometimes said to represent the four 'fixed signs' of astrology, but, as we saw in Chapter IX, this was not the original belief. The four 'fixed signs' were first so called by Claudius Ptolemy in the second century A.D., or at earliest by some follower of Hipparchus not long before. Winged bulls, however, existed in the Sumerian period; they were called *alad* by the Sumerians and *šedu* by the Babylonians, and the Hebrews are accused of worshipping them in Deuteronomy xxxii 17 and Psalm cvi 37. Most of them were underworld demons which fed on blood, but a few were good, such as those set up at the doors to defend kings' palaces, and we are also told that the good *šedu* has the form of a goat. Thus they do not always comprise the four animals usually expected; sometimes there is simply a winged human-headed bull with no lion about it, sometimes there are four leonine feet and no trace of a bull.[42]

Of the twelve constellations nine have now been discussed, and seven of them had a convincing Babylonian origin. With Aquarius and Gemini the evidence was less conclusive, and of the remaining three at least one, the Ram, was absent from the Babylonian zodiac.

The Fishes are not perhaps absent, but divided up. By the end of the Seleucid Era they were called The Tails, and KUN, meaning Tail, is the oldest name of this constellation. It was also called The Band, a double string or leash, and the two fishes tied together upon it are the goddesses Anunitum and Šimmah. Anunitum, the northern one of the two, means 'female dweller in heaven', or words to that effect, and represents the River Tigris, while Šimmah, the southern, though it refers to the Euphrates, means 'the swallow', and apparently is the emblem of an ancient goddess called Nina who used to fly over the sea in the shape of a swallow—probably a tern. So the 'swallow-fish' is not so much the flying-fish *exocetus* of the Indian Ocean, as a typical Babylonian conflation of two separate ideas, bird and fish. Thus the Babylonians saw in this area a tail, a band, a tern, a goddess, and two rivers, but that they also saw two fishes here before the reign of Esar-haddon is not to be considered certain. For the tail is not inevitably that of a fish.

Cancer likewise is problematic. Its name *al.lul* according to Langdon means 'the wicked or rebellious one', which reminds us of Orion; and though he asserts that it was definitely known as *bulug* the Crab, more recently Goessmann denies this, and declares that no one has any right to call it a crab or crayfish; its later name NAN.GAR means a carpenter or indoor worker, by intentional contrast to *hunga* the Hireling, an outdoor worker. But if NAN.-GAR[43] should really be read *kušu*, it possibly means a water-creature of some kind; this would not be surprising, but we must beware of discovering signs of the zodiac in Babylonia merely because we think we ought!

Finally, to return to Aries, this was the region where the city of Babylon had its heavenly counterpart. Its constellation was *Iku*, meaning The Square Field, identified sometimes with our Aries plus Cetus, but more obviously with the Square of Pegasus; and this reminds one that Babylon was a more or less square city and its most conspicuous feature, the temple of Marduk called Esagila, was a square tower of seven diminishing storeys. These storeys were painted in the colours of the planets, and though the colours have now vanished, in the mid-nineteenth century Rawlinson identified them on the remains of Ezida, the temple-tower of Nabu at Borsippa, and recorded them as follows: the lowest storey was black for Saturn; then brown-red for Jupiter; rose-red for Mars; gold for the Sun; white-gold for Venus; dark blue for Mercury; and the top-most storey silver for the Moon.[44]

Next to the Square the Babylonians had no Ram; its place was taken by *hunga* the Hireling. And yet, by one of those unexpected turns for which scholars must always be prepared, the Ram, which does not exist in the Babylonian zodiac, tries to sneak in by the back door in a very curious manner.

Cuneiform is a tedious script to write, and after a time the scribes indulged more and more in abbreviations. Thus PA.BIL.SAG (Sagittarius) became first PA.BIL and then simply PA; *maš.tab.ba.-gal.gal*, was reduced to *maš*, and Leo, UR.GU.LA, became A. Thus from 272 B.C. onwards the first sign of the zodiac was *hun*, short for *hun.ga*, the man who works for wages. But the original form of the word was *lu.hun.ga*, and this was shortened to *lu*, which can also mean Ram! There is, however, no question of this being the original meaning.

This coincidence might enable one to maintain a wholly Babylonian origin for the zodiac if the word *lu* could be proved to occur before the reign of Esarhaddon, who conquered Egypt; but even then there is no proof that the Babylonians would have understood it as meaning Ram rather than as an abbreviation of the old Sumerian word for Hireling. Furthermore the older form of zodiac, with eighteen signs and no Ram, was still in use, together with the Enuma-Anu-Enlil system, two or three hundred years later than Esarhaddon. Hence it is not possible to maintain that the zodiac existed before Babylon and Assyria had felt the influence of Egypt.

12. *The Horoscope of Eternity*

WHEN Julius Caesar decided to give the Romans a new calendar, the expert whom he chose to design it was an Egyptian—though probably of Greek descent—Sosigenes of Alexandria. This was because the Egyptians possessed the only wholly reliable calendar known to the ancient world. The Babylonians had a higher reputation as astronomers, and took more notice of celestial happenings; but their calendar was lunar and hopelessly erratic. Already in 488 B.C., when Darius I wanted to provide a better calendar for Persia, he had adopted the Egyptian system just as it stood.

The ancient Greeks, and after them the Romans, had great respect for the wisdom of the Egyptians; but modern professors have almost no idea in what that wisdom consisted. This is because learning is static and consists largely of information, while wisdom is dynamic and requires mastery of the art of life. Wisdom therefore is not the same as the ability to reason, and in any case the Greeks did not learn that from Egypt. Genuine wisdom cannot be written, nor congealed into asphorisms and avuncular advice. Being concerned with the problem of how to live, it is naturally apt to be religious, and the wisdom of the Egyptians was the ultimate driving-force behind the Mystery Religions; for they were all studies in the art of living. Man is always trying to get life under control, and among his methods of doing so are system, rule, legislation, dogma, and punishment. But the wise man does not try to get life under control; he adapts himself and swims with the stream instead of angrily trying to dam it.

Where wisdom and knowledge meet is in the solving of problems; and one problem for which the Egyptians alone of the ancient nations had found a reliable solution was the organization of the calendar. Modern scientists consider that the year should correspond as closely as possible to the period of the earth's revolution about the sun; and this is contrived in the Gregorian calendar by the insertion of a leap-year day once in four years, with an exception in centennial years and an exception against the exception in millennial years. But whether the year 10,000 will be a leap year nobody yet knows, and so by Egyptian standards the Gregorian calendar is irregular.

(i) *The Calendrical Basis*

In the ideal Egyptian calendar no irregularity was permitted. There were no leap years. Twelve months of thirty days each were followed, or preceded, by five days called 'epagomenal', and that was all.

The Egyptian year, therefore, was about a quarter of a day short, and in consequence its relationship to the seasons was not constant: it lost a day in four years, a month in about 120 years, and a whole year in fourteen and a half centuries. That is to say, 1,460 Gregorian years are equal to 1,461 Egyptian years, and after that time the Egyptian New Year's Day returns to its starting-point.

This return of their New Year's Day to its proper place was always important to the Egyptians, indeed it was the linch-pin of their whole astronomical system. Their agricultural year began with the rising of the Nile; but the inundation could be early or late, deep or shallow, depending on the melting of the snows in Abyssinia and Central Africa. Between A.D. 1873 and 1904 the interval between two successive risings varied from 336 to 415 days.[1] It must therefore have been a great convenience when the inundation could be predicted and anchored to a regular astronomical phenomenon. This phenomenon we know to have been the heliacal rising of Sirius.

The heliacal rising of a bright star such as Sirius, or of a planet, was a beautiful as well as an important occasion to those who first noticed these things. When a bright star can be seen in the west soon after sunset, each evening it shines lower and lower in the solar haze, until finally it can be seen no more. This is called its heliacal setting. Being now so close to the sun, it remains invisible for a period which the Egyptians averaged at seventy days, although it varies with the star's declination and the latitude of the place. At Babylon, for example, Sirius is absent sixty-nine days, but Spica, being farther north, only thirty-six.[2]

Then, when the sun has passed a little farther on in the zodiac, one morning when the sky towards dawn has lost its darkness and the

176

earth seems lit but empty, awaiting the sun, in the glow of the east appears a twinkling point between gold and silver which was not there the day before. This is the return of the star; and if it pre-signifies the rise of the Nile, the return of the flood and of all green things and crops, then it will be very important and well watched.

In a clear climate, with no street-lighting and no industrial smoke, and where dawn is the most comfortable and convenient hour to rise from bed, a survey of the half-lit sky is easily made, and the re-appearance of a star well known, but absent for the last month or two, is a practical guide.

This heliacal rising of Sirius is the origin of the legend of the phoenix; for the explanation which connects it with the 'anting' of birds, and their occasional love of playing with fire, is unconvincing because it bears no reference to Heliopolis.[3] The legend tells that there is only one phoenix, and that at the end of its life it returns to its birthplace, which is the 'Arabian Desert' between the Nile and the Red Sea. There it burns itself to death, and a new phoenix arises from the ashes of the old. Really the fire in which the phoenix dies is the glow of dawn. It is born in the 'Arabian Desert', because that is the eastern horizon of Egypt, and the length of its life is 1,460 years, which is 4 times 365. The event was known as 'the return of the phoenix to Heliopolis', and was commemorated by Antoninus Pius with a special issue of coins, which can be seen in Plate 4(b). This not only shows the respect in which the Romans held the Egyptian calendar, but also gives us a basic date for computing Egyptian eras.

Antoninus issued his coins, with the word AIΩN meaning Era, about A.D. 139, and Censorinus, writing in A.D. 238, states that 99 years earlier the Egyptian New Year's Day had fallen on July 21st. This therefore will be the date of the Phoenix Era, and if we count back in periods of 1,460 years we shall find the Birth of the Phoenix occurring within four years of 1320 and 2780 B.C. In fact, of course, the length of the solar year is not exactly $365\frac{1}{4}$ days, but 365·2422; nor is the length of the Phoenix Period constant—according to Petrie[4] it decreased from 1,466 years about 600 B.C. to 1,448 about A.D. 2000, and should average 1,508. Nevertheless, the Egyptian calendar must certainly have been inaugurated on its New Year's Day, and since it existed long before 1320 the most probable date is about 2780.

The Phoenix Era which fell about 1320 is known as the Era of Menophres, and the name is generally thought to be that of the king in whose reign it happened, Menpehrê Ramesses I, who reigned only 16 months. Before that the cycle takes us back to the reign of Zoser at the end of the Third Dynasty; and this explains the amazing reputation of his chief minister, Imhotep, who was the architect of the first of the large pyramids, the Step Pyramid of Saqqarah, and later was deified as the healing god of Memphis. Imhotep is known to have been an astronomer as well as an architect and physician, and it seems at present not very likely that the Sothic calendar was devised 1,460 years earlier again. That would have been about 4240 B.C., 1,000 years before the First Dynasty; and the mention of the five epagomenal days in the Pyramid Texts does not actually prove this.

Because it rotated slowly through the seasons, the Egyptian calendar has been called The Wandering Calendar. Even so it was vastly superior to the lunar calendars of antiquity; for the prime purpose of a calendar is agricultural, and in order to keep those lunar calendars in time with the seasons an extra month was interpolated by proclamation whenever needed. In consequence the accurate computation of dates is impossible, whether backwards or forwards. The only exception is the Muslim calendar, in which no epagomenal months are allowed, and in consequence that calendar too rotates through the seasons, losing about 11 days each year, whereas the Egyptian lost only one day in four years.

The Egyptian too had its disadvantage: the festivals of the gods rotated through the seasons regardless of suitability. The change amounted to only about a fortnight in a lifetime, and the Egyptians had long accepted this when, in 238 B.C., Ptolemy III published the Decree of Canopus, by which in every fourth year a sixth epagomenal day was added. This spoilt the beauty of the system, and now one has to know that the extra day was used only between 238 and 57 B.C., after which it was very properly suppressed.

In 238 the 1st of the month of Thoth (New Year's Day) had been October 22nd, and Sirius rose on 1st Payni, but after 26–5 B.C. Augustus fixed 1st Thoth on August 29th, or 30th in leap years, with Sirius rising on 25th Epiphi.

Nowadays Sirius rises in Egypt in the middle of August, far too late to be of any use in agriculture; but throughout dynastic times it did conveniently precede the rising of the Nile.

In the present century, as Petrie remarked,[5] the Egyptians have had four calendars in use at the same time. These are the official Muslim lunar calendar; the Gregorian, imported from Europe; the Alexandrian, of the Coptic Church; and the agricultural festivals still attached to the names of the Coptic months.

In ancient times likewise the Egyptians had more than one calendar. Khnumhotep in his tomb at Beni Hasan says:[6] 'I decreed the offerings' (that is to say, I ordered the food) 'at every feast of the necropolis, at the feast of the beginning of the year, at the feast of the opening of the year, the feast of the long year, the feast of the short year, the feast of the last day, the great feast, the feast of great heat, the feast of little heat, the feast of the five days added to the year, at the feast of sand-throwing, at the twelve monthly feasts, at the twelve half-monthly feasts, at every feast of the living and of the blessed dead.' And when the priests of Senusret III at Kahun were paid on the 29th day of the month, this is cross-dated in the Wandering Calendar.[7]

In the XII Dynasty the 'opening of the year' was apparently the actual rising of Sirius, and the 'beginning of the year' was the next new moon,[8] but later the terminology became confused.

But though the ideal year retrogressed steadily through the seasons, Sirius did not rise on the same day in all parts of the country, and for this reason it was found more practical to date the official calendar from the first new month thereafter. And the Egyptians did not count their months from the appearance of the new crescent, as in most other countries, but from the invisibility of the moon. This is why we are told in the 'dramatic text' from the cenotaph of Sety I at Abydos: 'Horus provides himself with his two eyes on the second day of the month.'[9] The 'short year' and the 'long year' will then be alternative lunar years, according as the year had contained thirteen or fourteen new moons.

Now the zodiac, like the Egyptian agricultural year, is a calendar fastened to an astronomical reference-point called its fiducial. But the fiducial of the zodiac is not Sirius because Sirius lies too far to the south, outside the ecliptical belt. Is there, despite this difference, some connection?

179

(ii) *The Zodiacs of Denderah*

Several representations of the zodiac were discovered in Egypt when Napoleon invaded the country in 1798, and pictures of them were published in his enormous *Description de l'Égypte*.[10] At first, of course, they were taken to be amazingly ancient, and the most famous among them is the circular zodiac of Denderah, now in the Louvre, but originally a ceiling in the temple of Hat-Hor, goddess of heaven and also of love and joy. Photographs of this zodiac often look rather confused because it is only in low relief; it is therefore reproduced here in a line-drawing (Plate 14). To the unpractised eye the signs of the zodiac may not look strange, but to the Egyptologist they have a distinctly foreign air.

The Crab, the most northerly of the twelve, is a very round-bodied object not far from the diagram's centre, and immediately over the Lion's head. A goddess holds the Lion by the tail, and behind her stands Isis with her ear of corn; this of course is Virgo with the star Spica. Harpocrates in the disk of the sun is represented on top of the Scales, but the lion below him has nothing to do with Leo of the zodiac. Scorpio, Sagittarius, and Capricorn, being farther south, lie near the outer circle of figures, which represent the decans.

This outer circle is not, oddly enough, intended to be aligned with the zodiac and constellations, and therefore the disk with eight decapitated figures, to be found beneath the Water-bearer, does not signify the moon eight days old. A little farther on in this outer series four rams' heads rise from a single stem, and the third figure behind them is a child on a lotus flower. Both of these are calendrical indications, and so is the hawk on top of a papyrus column, which marks the summer solstice. Beyond it is Sirius, represented as a cow lying in a boat; and the royal figure on the other side of it, under the Bull's hoofs, is Orion.

In the centre are the circumpolar constellations. The Wain or Dipper had always been thought of as a bull's foreleg, which was a common sight on the altar of sacrifice, and it is sometimes drawn with a bull's head at the broader end. It is held in leash by a hippopotamus-goddess, who often has a crocodile on her back, but her hand rests on Menat, the Mooring-Peg, and this is the straight line from Arcturus to Spica, the original measuring-point of the zodiac.

The other northerly constellations include a lion and also Selket the scorpion-goddess, who is not, however, in the place of our Scorpio. And it is odd that on the oblong zodiac of Denderah the Foreleg and the Hippo-goddess are figured between the southerly constellations Sagittarius and Capricorn, whereas at Edfu they appear just to the right of Sirius and Orion, apparently on the opposite side of the sky. This shows how Egyptian diagrams cannot be taken literally and applied to the sky like transfers.

The oblong zodiac of Denderah was carved on the ceiling of the portico. It is over sixty feet long, and each half is twelve feet wide. There are two registers, running one above the other along the body of Nût the sky-goddess, who is dressed in a design of ripples. The lower register shows the decans as human and animal-headed figures in boats (since the Egyptian gods always used boats to cross the sky), and beside them are written their names and a rough design of two or three stars to help recognition. The upper register gives the signs of the zodiac and various other constellations, the planets, and the hours of the day, each drawn as a woman with a star over her head.

When it became possible to read the inscriptions on the walls of the temple of Denderah, it turned out to have been built in the reign of the Roman emperor Tiberius. The actual date has been computed by Mr Fagan to be the evening of April 16th Julian, A.D. 17, and the oblong zodiac contains, according to him, four different New Year's Days. The new moon of April 17th is shown on the back of the Bull, and this is the Babylonian 1st Nisan. The Sothic New Year occurred on July 19th, the year of the Wandering Calendar began on August 19th, and finally the 'New Year's Day of the Ancients' with the heliacal rising of Spica on October 5th. The vernal equinox is shown by the baboon of Thoth following the Ram. The planets on the circular zodiac are rather small and in the signs of their exaltations, which gives no clue to the date, but in the oblong diagram they are in their zodiacal positions.

The two zodiacs of Esna have been dated by Professor Parker to A.D. 175–6, but this is unsuitable because they are for New Year's Day and show the heliacal rising of the constellation Virgo, just as the Denderah zodiacs show that of Leo. The Egyptians considered the first sign of the zodiac to be that which rose heliacally on New

Year's Day, hence the 'first' sign changed about every 112 years, and in a retrograde direction. The 'first' sign actually changed from Virgo to Leo in the first century B.C., and the Esna zodiacs must be within 117 years previous to that change. Mr Fagan has given their exact date as September 26th, 137 B.C.[11]

Thus by Egyptian standards none of these four zodiacs is at all old. And the same applies to the two horoscopes found on the ceiling of a tomb at Athribis, and shown in Plate 15. They were dated originally by Knobel to May 20th, A.D. 52 and January 25th, 59, on the assumption that the horned hawk was Mars.[12] But the horns must surely be those with which the name of Jupiter is written, and Mars should be the hawk with the head of the beast of Setekh; and in that case the dates will be April 26th, A.D. 141 and February 14th, 177.[13]

Another Egyptian astronomical picture which is often quoted comes from the coffin of Heter;[14] but the date of that is A.D. 93. In fact not one of the zodiacal diagrams found in Egypt is as old as the Thirtieth Dynasty, which ended with Cleopatra. And this makes it extremely unlikely that the zodiac was known to the Egyptians of dynastic times; for no culture has left more abundant monuments in record of its beliefs.

The zodiac may have a connection with Egyptian astronomy none the less.

(iii) *The Decans*

There is a tradition, both in India and the West, that each sign of the zodiac may be divided into three segments of 10° each called decanates or decans. To astrologers, this subdivision was useless unless the decans could be distinguished in character, and there were devised several methods of doing this. One was to allot the first decanate of a sign to the pure influence of that sign, and the other two to the two other signs of the same element, earth, air, fire, or water. This system was used by Varaha Mihira, but cannot be older than Claudius Ptolemy because he first regularized the allocation of the elements to the signs. It never became very popular, indeed Hindu astrologers were so little impressed by it that they invented subdivisions of signs by 9 and 12, called *navamsas* and *dwadashamshas*.

Manilius allotted the decans to the signs in straightforward order, so that the three decans of Aries were ruled by Aries, Taurus, and

Gemini, those of Taurus by Cancer, Leo, and Virgo, and so forth. Another attempt to control the decanates gave them ruling planets, beginning with Mars for the first decanate of Aries and continuing in the 'Chaldean' order, which is not that preferred by the Babylonians, but is the order of speed of movement—Saturn Jupiter Mars Sun Venus Mercury Moon—until Mars again ruled the last decanate of Pisces. This arrangement was traditionally called (for instance by Lilly in the seventeenth century) the 'Egyptian' system, and indeed it is found in Teucros; but the name only shows a last faint realization that there ought to be an Egyptian system; for the decans are of Egyptian origin.

The arrangement whereby the first and last of them are ruled by Mars is obviously factitious, but Wilhelm Gundel put forward an ingenious explanation for it.[15] The third part of a sign is also called its 'face', and these faces were originally actual portraits of the ruling gods, as can be seen for instance on the marble tablet of Bianchini.[16] After Ptolemy III had inserted the sixth epagomenal day, the cycle of the year consisted of 36 decans plus 6 extra days, a total of 42 phases—in leap-years only, however. Since 42 is divisible by 7, this leap-year count could be allotted to the 7 planets; but the notion of starting it with Mars and Aries, which is the ruling sign of Rome, was probably invented by Sosigenes once he had moved to Rome, where the year began in March. For the Egyptians the beginning and end of the cycle was the first decan of Cancer, because this was the meridian longitude of Sirius. Originally, however, the decans were not divisions of the zodiac at all. That is what they later became, and as such they can be seen arranged round the edge of the circular zodiac of Denderah. But they go back to the third millennium.

It is not possible to draw up a single authentic list of the 36 decans, for the Egyptian lists vary, and over thirty are known, from the Tenth Dynasty to Roman times. Some of the older asterisms either went out of use or were renamed, which was natural enough; not all the lists were copied accurately; and since the celestial equator is not constant it is even possible for decans to change their order of rising over a long enough period.[17] They were evidently selected from constellations already formulated all over the sky, and it was likely that in different parts of the country different stars would be chosen. This explains why so many decans are named as the beginning, middle, or end of various larger constellations. The list of them printed on Table 21, facing page 200, gives a conflated order of their sequence on the monuments, and runs to a total of over forty. It could be extended considerably by taking account of all the variants found in and out of Egypt; for as Gundel showed, the lore of the decans survived into far more recent times than we should expect and in doing so developed all kinds of fantasies and divagations.

One of the least fantastic of these is probably the catalogue of barbarous names found in Harleian MS. 3731, where the presiding genii of the three decans of Aries are named Aulathamas, Sabaoth and Disornafais. The occurrence of Sabaoth, a Hebrew word, shows that we are in the Gnostic world of Alexandria in the early centuries A.D., the melting-pot of religions and mythologies; but most of the other names are Greek attempts to spell Egyptian words: Zathor, for instance, is the son, man, or some part of Hat-hor; Seneptois may be similarly related to Ptah, Psineus to Neith, and Rempsois suggests Re' in some situation or other.

The Byzantine list of Johannes Kamaterôs (eleventh century) is that of Hephaistion (fourth century) in a corrupted form; an even more altered version occurs in one of the books attributed to Hermes Trismegistos.[18] Rationalization, bad handwriting, and sheer guesswork had already done a good deal by the time Cosmas Indicopleustes came to write in the sixth century. He was an India merchant from Alexandria who later turned monk and wrote an account of his travels. He attributes each decan to some Greek divinity, beginning with Hades, Persephone, and Eros for the Ram, and ending with Ocean, Wile, and Hope for the Fishes. One or two of his attributions seem to have some shadow of reason, in that Libra, the sign of justice, is divided between the Pursuing Fury (Erinys), Opportunity, and Nemesis; and Hestia comes at the end of Virgo, which is tolerable, though Plato put her in Capricorn. But it is not so clear why the Nymphs should rule the first decan of Scorpio, nor why Aquarius should be divided between Justice, Terror, and Osiris, with evident reference to the Last Judgment.[19]

Yet so late as the seventeenth century Athanasius Kircher[20] was still summing up the tradition, and allows himself more freedom even than Cosmas, for he includes not only Greek and Egyptian deities, but also the Persian Arimanius, the Cyclops, Typhon, and a few possibly Semitic names such as Nephan and Sourut. But these later developments appear frequently capricious and not always genuinely connected with the zodiac.

Firmicus quotes an interesting passage from the famous textbook of Nechepso and Petosiris:

> In each sign there are three decans which occupy certain degrees and leave others void. The degrees in which decans were found are called 'full' degrees (*plenae*), and 'void' (*vacuae*) those which have never borne the number of a decan. So whoever has in his horoscope the sun and moon and five planets in full degrees will be like a god and raised to the height of majesty. But this can never happen. Those who have one planet as well as the sun and moon in full degrees will be moderately well off, those who have two will attain to every kind of happiness, those who have three will receive extraordinarily numerous blessings of fortune, and those who have four will attain to the power of royal felicity.

Naturally those who have no planets in full degrees will be always poor and destitute, and Firmicus gives the alleged names and longitudes of the decans, with the extent of the void spaces between them. The names Senator and Romanae look highly suspicious, but at least Sothis appears in the right place; the other names should be compared to the decan-lists on Table 21.

TABLE 18   *Full and Empty Degrees*

	void	full	void	full	void	full	TOTALS void	void	full
Aries	3	senator 5	9	senacher 4	5	sentacher 4	0	17	13
Taurus	3	suo 7	2	aryo 8	5	romanae 5	0	10	20
Gemini	0	thesogar 7	2	ver 5	3	tepis 6	7	12	18
Cancer	7	Sothis 6	2	sith 4	2	thiumis 9	1	11	19=31
Leo	0	craumonis 7	4	sic 3	6	futile 10	0	10	20
Virgo	5	thumis 4	2	tophicus 6	6	afut 6	3	16	14
Libra	0	seuichut 5	6	sepisent 8	3	senta 6	3	12	19=31
Scorpio	3	sentacher 5	6	tepisen 6	2	sentineu 5	3	14	16
Sagitt.	0	eregbuo 9	3	sagon 7	4	chenene 7	0	7	23
Capri.	7	themeso 3	5	epiemu 4	5	omot 6	0	17	13
Aquarius	4	oro 5	4	cratero 6	3	tepis 8	0	11	19
Pisces	6	acha 6	3	tepibui 5	6	uiu 2	2	17	13

185

If now we turn back to the original Egyptian list, as written in hieroglyphs, we notice three water-pots in a rack, a pair of fishes, and a sheep. They occur in that order, and roughly the same distance apart. Can they have anything to do with the Urn, the Fishes, and the Ram, three successive signs of the Hellenistic zodiac? It is usually thought not. In that zodiac, where the decans were 10 segments of the ecliptic, the apparent water-pots (which may be simply a phonetic sign for spelling the syllable *khent*) fall in Libra, the two fish in Scorpio, and the sheep in Capricorn—but we have no reason to suppose that the Egyptians, like the Chinese, failed to distinguish sheep from goats.

Not only were the decans in late times 10°-segments of the ecliptic; so early as the Eleventh Dynasty, about 2000 B.C., on the coffins of Tefabi and Khiti,[21] we find the first decan, Kenmut, following the last, which is Sirius, so that they appear to form a complete circle. But it does not follow that they were already at that date arranged along the ecliptic, nor that they represented equal divisions of space. Before jumping to conclusions we have to explain the standard form of Egyptian celestial diagram, which occurs at all periods from the Eleventh Dynasty to Roman times, and of which nearly twenty examples are now known.[22]

There is also a key diagram in the cenotaph at Abydos of the king usually called Sety I, but sometimes Sethos or Setekhy (Plate 18). Now we have to remember constantly that Egyptian celestial diagrams are neither scientific observation nor literal-minded representational art. Comparisons make it plain that the figures were often arranged to suit the artist, and not in the style of a map; discrepancies must be regarded as normal, nor is there any difficulty in finding definite mistakes. It is therefore essential to realize what the Egyptians were about in making these diagrams. They were never intended for use on earth in any case: they were designed to help the deceased in finding his way to the sky after death, when he would join the Sun in His boat as He crosses heaven and the underworld. The standard diagram has therefore quite justly been called 'The Horoscope of Eternity'. Sety's example of it is shown in Plate 16.

(ii) *The Standard Diagram* (given in part in Plate 16)

In the middle of this diagram Sirius appears in a boat, sometimes in the form of a resting cow, but more often as Isis standing. To her right Orion may appear in another boat, in the form of a king running; but since he is always included among the decans his boat may be omitted. Sometimes he lies in it,[23] face up or face down, because that was the attitude in which he rose, and for that matter still rises. His name in Egyptian is Sahh, apparently meaning The Toe, and the name of Sirius is Sopdet, which the Greeks pronounced as Sôthis, and it means something like Sharp One, Arrow-head, or Pointer. From here to the right the picture lists the names of the decans, sometimes with a rough diagram of their appearance.

More importantly, we find to the left of Sirius two or three of the planets, which will always be Saturn, Jupiter, and Mars, next Two Turtles, then about five names of obscure meaning called Meta-decans, then Mercury, and finally a large heron, which is 'Venus the bennu-bird of Osiris'.

One must not imagine that because Sirius is enthroned in the middle of the diagram she is on the midheaven; quite the contrary, she is on the eastern horizon. And the decans to her right, as well as the planets and meta-decans on her left, are not a chart so much as simply a catalogue.

Why then did the diagram take this form? Why is Venus always represented so large, and on the extreme left? What are the meta-decans? And why are the directions of Mars, Saturn, and Jupiter usually but not always stated? For the answer to the first of these questions we are indebted to Mr Fagan; some of the others will be answered here for the first time.

The importance of Sirius is well known: its rising marked the New Year. Hence the original of all these diagrams must have represented the sky at dawn on New Year's Day, and therefore most probably at the inauguration of the Sothic calendar. Having realized this, Mr Fagan calculated that the only possible date was 2767 B.C.[24] As can be seen from Plate 23, the appearance of the sky at that moment was extraordinary. It showed a close conjunction of no less than four planets all within 7° of each other, rising on the eastern horizon at the same moment as Sirius, while the Moon, just past the full, was declining in the south-west. Such a close quadruple conjunction on the Ascendant on the day of Sirius' rising may never have occurred since. And furthermore the date was that of the summer solstice.

This very striking combination of phenomena cannot have failed to impress the Egyptians of the time of Zoser. Not only was it memorable in itself, falling on the one day of perfect harmony in the Wandering Calendar; dawn is also the natural opportunity for the deceased to catch the Sun's boat and sail to heaven. So it is not surprising that the event should have been perpetuated, both as the fixed point of the calendar and also as the beginning of life in the world to come.

This explains why the planets are all grouped together at the left of Sirius; indeed the repeated mention in the Pyramid texts[25] of 'those four youths who sit on the eastern side of the sky' may be a reminiscence of this event. The Pyramid texts make Horus the ferryman of the sky, and that is why the planets, sometimes including Venus, are identified with him. There is also the oft-repeated statement: 'He ascends to heaven among the imperishable stars, his sister is Sothis, his guide is the Morning Star.'

The Morning Star is feminine in the Pyramid texts, except when identified with Horus, and Professor Mercer thinks that it was whichever asterism rose just before the sun — there is no mention of the decans. This, however, does not agree too well with the enormous importance attached to Venus in these diagrams. She is always drawn very large, and on the extreme left, probably because on that morning in Heliopolis she rose last, at the same moment as Sirius. She takes the form of a heron because that is the bird of the inundation; when the Nile begins to flood, the herons leave the restricted bed and fly all over the country fishing in the canals and fields.

Accepting this, we can explain the meta-decans. They are so called because they come after the decans, in the left upper corner of the diagram. Various suggestions have been made to account for them. Dr Chatley, for instance, thought they might be the constellations visible on winter nights to the south of the equatorial zone; and this would be possible, since the Egyptian artist placed his data where it suited him, and not where they belonged.[26] The thirty-six decans are usually crowded into about twenty-seven columns; the pictures of constellations resemble each other about as much as do medieval pictures of the Lion or Crab; and the rising-times of star-groups are inserted on Plate 18 wherever space allows, those on the goddess's arms belonging next to those on the ground.

Mr Fagan took the meta-decans to be the stars in the Sickle of Leo, which rose in the north-east about the same time as Sirius in the south-east, and this is not far off the mark. In fact, however, Sirius and Venus in 2767 were on the horizon simultaneously, and their distance apart in azimuth, that is to say along the horizon, was no less than 55°. The planets Mars, Saturn, and Jupiter were, as we already know, included in this space, so the meta-decans also would most naturally belong to it.

The first of them is the Two Turtles. The Turtle was a symbol of drought and an enemy of the Sun-god; it is sometimes shown being speared by one of the gods in the solar barque. The two must therefore represent some pair of stars which rise when the Nile is at its lowest, in the last month before the rising of Sirius. They might be Castor and Pollux, which in −2800 rose respectively forty and thirty-four days before Sirius; but Castor and Pollux are quite likely to be the Twin Stars of the Ramesside hour-tables. The Two Turtles are always represented exactly the same size, so it seems less suitable that they should be Procyon and its companion; Procyon in −2800 rose thirteen days before Sirius. The third possibility is the two Aselli, which lie very close together in the constellation of the Crab, and in those times rose nineteen and fifteen days before Sirius. These Turtles are then probably the first hard-shelled creatures to be associated with what later became the constellation of the Crab.

After the Two Turtles the second meta-decan is called *nesru*. It is hard to give the meaning of Egyptian star-names because the determinative is almost always omitted; in the commonest form of Egyptian spelling the vowels are not given, only a framework of consonants, and then an unpronounced ideogram which determines the range of meaning. Thus SH S P followed by the sun means 'light', but if followed by a picture of a house it means a room or courtyard. If it be followed by neither, one is left in some doubt; a rectangle is not uncommon in the sky, but so is light. *Nesru* is said to be an island where the sun is born, but its standard determinative is a picture of a fire. As a meta-decan, therefore, it most probably means 'the glow of dawn', and in that case it is not an asterism.

The third meta-decan is called *shesep* or *shespet*, and this can mean either a rectangle or light, more probably the latter, for we shall meet this word again in a mysterious text from Abydos.

The fourth is variously spelt as *'Abesh, 'Abshes, Ipsedj* or *Ipdjes,* and is followed by a fifth called *Sobshosen.* Both of them appear in the Greek decan lists as *Aposot* and *Sobkhos,* but there they occupy the last decanate of Virgo and the first of Libra; so what are they doing here on the eastern horizon? We shall see later.

The last meta-decan is called *wash-neter,* which ought to mean 'divine power and glory'; and perhaps this is just what it does mean, alluding to the approach of the sun. In Greek times the word meant a palanquin, which has somewhat the same suggestion: 'Here comes the king.'

(v) *The Hour-Stars*

On Plate 17 may be seen an amusing picture of a priest sitting cross-legged on a temple roof in order to help a colleague to observe the stars. His ears are drawn double-sized because they are supposed to mark the midpoint between shoulder and eye. Over his head are drawn seven vertical lines, to show how the stars were supposed to be observed descending in the south-west over his eye, ear, or shoulder, and over his 'heart', meaning his middle line; the thirteen horizontal lines indicate an hour of twilight, and the twelve seasonal 'hours' of the night. To exemplify this supposed observation here is a translation of the table for the first day of the month of Paophi:

> Second month of the season of inundation, beginning of
>   night, neck of the Giant exactly central.
> 1st hour, his dagger exactly over the left eye.
> 2nd hour, his thigh exactly central.
> 3rd hour, his knee exactly central.
> 4th hour, 'Aryt exactly central.
> 5th hour, the Goose's Head over the left eye, obliquely.
> 6th hour, its Tail exactly central.
> 7th hour, Thousands exactly central.
> 8th hour, Sa'r over the right eye, obliquely.
> 9th hour, the beginning of Orion over the right eye.
> 10th hour, the star of Orion over the right eye, obliquely.
> 11th hour, the star of Sothis over the left eye.
> 12th hour, beginning of the Two Stars exactly central.

The instrument tucked into the priest's girdle is an astronomer's staff (called in Egyptian *merkhet*), consisting of two small sticks or a small split palm-branch, with a plummet hung in the middle. The Star of Sothis is of course Sirius, the star of Orion is Betelgeuze, and Thousands are the Pleiades. To identify the other stars, though it might seem difficult, is not impossible, because they are not mentioned in a haphazard way, but in twenty-four dated catalogues similar to the three shown in Plate 17; and thus we can say with reasonable assurance that 'the start of Orion' is Betelgeuze and not Bellatrix or Rigel; and also make various other identifications.

But it also turns out that the practice so picturesquely illustrated can never have taken place exactly as one might suppose, for the simple reason that, if so southerly a star as Sirius was marked by a man's right shoulder, as we are told that it was, than a more northerly star such as Spica, which also appears on the list, would not have been marked by his left shoulder; it would never have come near him at all.

This makes it plain that these lists of hour-stars have not come down to us in their original form. Like most Egyptian monuments, these twenty-four lists of apparent hour-stars have been 'traditionalized'. Almost half the circle of the heavens is taken up by two enormous constellations, The Hippopotamus and The Giant. In the other half various identifications are possible, once one has realized that these stars were not originally chosen as hour-stars at all but, like the Indian *yogataras*, were markers along the path of the moon. Here then is a list of the Egyptian hour-stars in their original form as Moon-markers:

TABLE 19   *Egyptian Moon-markers*

The Goose's Head	Sharatain (β Arietis)
Its Tail	Menkar (α Ceti)
Thousands	Pleiades
Jawbone ('Aryt)	PrimaHyadum (θ Tauri)
Sa'r	Aldebaran (α Tauri)
Beginning of Orion	Bellatrix (γ Orionis)
Orion	Betelgeuze (α Orionis)
Beginning of The Twins	Alhena (γ Geminorum)
The Two Stars	Castor and Pollux

Stars of the Water	Praesepe, Aselli, Cancer
Lion's Head	Regulus (α Leonis)
His Tail	Zosma (δ Leonis)
Numerous	Coma Berenices
Beautiful Boy	Vindemiatrix (ϵ Virginis)
Mooring-Peg	Spica

It will be noticed from this, which is a direct translation of the ancient document shown in Plate 17, that the Egyptians had a constellation of the Lion somewhere between Sirius (Sothis) and Spica, and also another not far away, between Sirius and the Pleiades, called the Two Stars, which therefore might possibly be our Gemini—Gemini at this date consisted of a group in which the two principal stars were of much the same brightness—and also between the Lion and the Two Stars a constellation called Stars of the Water, which might be the origin of our constellation Cancer, more especially as there exist various Egyptian pictures of this constellation in the form of the Two Turtles; and a river-turtle, which does occur in the Nile and also in Asia Minor, is a hard-shelled water-creature just as a crab is.

Apart from these three constellations, and the Ram (illustrated in Plate 19), there are two other signs of the zodiac which may have an Egyptian origin, as we shall see later on. But it is also worth mentioning that there do exist various inscriptions which state the directions of the planets. Naturally there is no reference to the zodiac, but we do get a notion of how the Egyptians thought about the stars. In all these inscriptions we are always told that Mars is retrograde, which is ridiculous, since of the five planets which the Egyptians knew, Mars is the one which is least often retrograde. Mercury was obviously never observed, since his direction is never given. The inscriptions tell us whether Saturn, Jupiter, and Mars, were in the south, east, or west, leaving us to infer that a planet mentioned without any direction stated had been seen but had now set and was therefore in the north, whereas a planet not mentioned at all was in conjunction with the sun and therefore invisible. Since the directions of the planets are simply given by stating 'east', 'south', or 'west', the notion of classifying a planet as being 'in' a constellation had obviously not yet become common practice.

The Nût Diagram

In none of these diagrams is the moon so much as mentioned, although they were all diagrams, or horoscopes, for the rising of Sirius, and in three of the six she was visible. The reason is that the diagrams were all for New Year's Day, and the Egyptian year effectively began not on the date of Sirius' heliacal rising, which would have given slightly different dates for different parts of the country, but at the following new moon. Actually there is an inconspicuous moon on the haunch of Nût in the key diagram from Abydos, shown in Plate 18. No inscription is attached to it, but close by is the brief notice: ⊙ ✳ 'eastern horizon', and not far away is the decan of Orion's foot. The moon therefore should be rising. In shape she looks like a new ☽, but this is impossible, since a new moon does not cross the eastern horizon until the sun is already up. Besides, if the moon by Orion's foot were new, Sirius would be invisible.

No planets are shown in the diagram, which therefore does not apply to any particular year. As usual, Nût the sky-goddess is seen bending over the earth. She is upheld by Shu, the god of space, and near his toes is written the word 'sand'. The columns of writing on either side of Shu are computations to the effect that if a star culminates at dusk on a certain day (and the dates given are all at intervals of ten days), then it will set at dusk 90 days later, and its heliacal rising will occur 70 days later again. These computations are not for different stars, as might be expected; the intervals being the same in every case, in theory all should apply to Sirius, and constitute a key whereby its rising, southing, and setting could be roughly computed throughout the cycle of the Wandering Calendar. But as it happens, they are astronomically impossible, or at any rate highly schematic.

The sun in Plate 18 is represented four times. Touching Nût's lips he folds his wings to set, for she eats the stars as they set, and they are born from her in the east. We are even told in one of the accompanying texts that Shu quarrelled with Nût and told her that she ought not to eat her children in this manner, but she replied that it was quite all right, they would be born again in due course. The two hieroglyphs on Nût's cheek read 'western horizon', corresponding to the eastern horizon on her groin.

Down on her foot the sun is shown again, and the inscription beside him declares: 'The majesty of this god comes forth from her hinder parts.' Another on her thigh announces that he 'opens the thighs of his mother Nût'. Beside her thigh he is shown in the form of a scarab with wings outspread flying up towards the eastern horizon. The fourth sun is quietly reposing in the underworld.

Since the sun appears three or four times, this must be a composite diagram, like the circular zodiac of Denderah. To which sun, then, is the moon to be related? If to the setting sun, which seems most important from its enormous wing, then it becomes a full moon, as Lange and Neugebauer propose; but the full moon is not of outstanding importance in Egyptian astronomy, not more so than the new. And the inscription over Shu's head reads: 'This happens in the 1st month of Akhet at the time of the rising of Sirius.' The sun therefore is at the beginning of the constellation Leo, near Regulus, and the full moon will fall in Aquarius; it cannot therefore be near Orion's foot.

This interpretation is, however, usually accepted. It is thought that the decans are each 10° long and extend all round the sky, hence the fact that all 36 are represented on Nût's body cannot mean that all of them were visible simultaneously. And this appears to be sound, since a sun setting in Leo cannot be opposite to Orion, although his foot is drawn near the eastern horizon. If sunset is the hour of the chart, we are using the temple calendar in which the day began in the evening, and neither Sirius nor Orion is visible. But in view of the inscription over Shu's head for Sirius to be invisible would be distinctly odd.

If, on the other hand, we relate the moon to the unrisen sun in the form of the scarab flying up Nût's thigh, then this is also partly (being composite) a dawn chart for New Year's Day, and in that case the decans of Orion and Sirius were indeed seen above the eastern horizon where they are drawn. The decans next to the setting sun are unimportant, being invisible.

In the horoscopes dawn was the operative hour, and the date was the day of the moon's invisibility. But the old moon is never seen in the evening, hence the day for this purpose must have begun at dawn, and the last day of the old year was the last day on which the old crescent was seen before sunrise. The day on which it failed to appear was New Year's Day. Hence the importance of observing the crescent moon in the east, and hence the crescent ☽ on Nût's haunch. In drawing it as a new ☽ the artist has strictly perpetrated something impossible; but had he drawn it as an old ☾ the diagram would have represented the last day of the old year and not the first of the new. This explains why he turned it round and drew the impossible; and after all the invisible moon is a 'new moon' and used as such, so there was some reason for drawing it that way round. Possibly the importance of the setting sun is because the day in the temple calendar, as opposed to the civil calendar, began at sunset.

If this be the true explanation of the Abydos diagram, and it contains elements of both dawn and sunset, then it cannot quite so well be used as evidence that the decans were only five degrees in extent, although all thirty-six of them appear between the two horizons.

(vi) *Planetary Dates computed from the Heliacal Rising of Sirius*

Various ancient Egyptian monuments give a version of what has here been called the Horoscope of Eternity, but with indications of the directions in which the soul of the deceased should expect to find the planets. Rather naturally, these have not been taken seriously by Egyptologists. There can, however, be little doubt that they were seriously meant, so it has seemed worth while to calculate the dates to which they refer. But in order not to bore the reader with a long and learned disquisition, and at the same time not to waste a good many hours of study, it has been decided to include here (without further explanation, which would only interest the few experts) a table summarizing the results. It should be borne in mind that, if these computed dates are for any reason rejected, there is no saying whether others could be found or not; it might so happen that another date which would fit the planetary positions stated could be found in the very next year, but it might also happen that no other suitable date could be found within a hundred years.

TABLE 20 *Egyptian Planetary Dates Computed from the Heliacal Rising of Sirius*

monument	date expected	date computed	New Year's Day	SATURN stated	SATURN found	JUPITER stated	JUPITER found	MARS stated	MARS found	VENUS stated	VENUS found
tomb of Senmut	1503–1481	1501	Aug. 13th	east	east	south	east	omitted	combust	rising	rising
Karnak clepsydra	1415–1380	1407	July 25th	not given	north	south	north	omitted	combust	rising	rising
tomb of Seti I	1310–1290	1306	July 18th	west	west	omitted	west	east	east	rising	rising
Ramesseum	about 1281	1295	Aug. 15th	east	east	not stated	east	west	west	rising	rising
right-hand diagram in tomb of Ramesses VI	1158–1143	1236	July 24th	east	east	omitted	east	east	east	OMITTED!	combust
left-hand diagram in tomb of Ramesses VI / Ramesses VI	1158–1143	1156	Aug. 12th	west	west	uncertain	west	east	east	rising	rising

(combust = invisible under the sun's rays)
Computed with Schoch's tables (margin of error 1° bzw. 1 day)
The formula for computing meridian longitudes is: cot long. (tropical) = cos obliquity cot R.A.

(vii) *Decans or Pentads?*

In late times the thirty-six decans were a complete circle of asterisms, each 10° long; Sirius headed the list in the first decanate of Cancer, the forefeet of Sagittarius were placed 'in the middle of the boat', and the last decan, at the end of Gemini, was called '*phuhor*', meaning 'end of the sky'. Even so early as the Eleventh Dynasty the 'diagonal calendars' on coffins show the decans making a complete circle of 360°. On the coffins of Khiti and Tefabi the columns are headed 'first ten days', 'middle ten days', and 'last ten days', and after Sirius, normally at that period the last decan, the circle continues directly with Kenmut, which is the usual beginning.

Now we have already seen that three constellations of the zodiac may have had an Egyptian origin, namely Gemini, Leo, and Cancer; the Egyptian names of these constellations were the Two Stars, the Lion, and Stars of the Water, also known as the two Turtles; but their Babylonian names were the Great Twins, the Great Dog, and Allul (an unidentified water-creature). The question now arises, may any other constellations of the zodiac have had an Egyptian origin? Among the Egyptian constellations are three names which make one wonder, but the problem remains, do they occur in the right positions? These names are the Fish, the Sheep, and the Water-pots or Jar-stand. If we accept the placing of these constellations according to the Greco-Roman scheme whereby the decans are all 10° long, agreeing with the opinion of most modern astronomers and Indian astrologers, then these constellations cannot have anything to do with the zodiac, for the Fish fall in Scorpio, the Sheep in Capricorn, and the Water-pots in Libra (*see* Table 21). But if we take it that the so-called decans were originally divisions of the ecliptic 5° long, then the sheep falls on Aries the Ram, the Fish on our modern Fishes, and the Water-pots or Jar-stand on what the Greeks called the Urn, and we call Aquarius.

We ought therefore to consider whether the decans should be regarded as 10° spaces, as the Greeks and Romans took them to be, or simply 5° spaces. For this latter possibility, revolutionary though it may sound, nine arguments have been advanced by Mr Cyril Fagan, and to these nine, three more can now be added. The arguments are as follows:

1. On the Nût diagram (Plate 18) the whole of the 36 decans

197

are represented on the body of the sky-goddess, as if they were all above the horizon at the same time. The first decan, 'beginning of Kenmut', is at the base of her neck, quite close to the inscription 'Western horizon', and near the last an inscription expressly states 'Eastern horizon'. We know that the Egyptians always had 36 decans; any semi-circle measures 180°, and 36 divided into 180° gives 5°.

2. This list of decans is divided in the middle by the inscription over the head of Shu, which ought to indicate the south point. Seventeen decans are shown east of his head and twenty to the west, and allowing 5° per decan this accurately corresponds to the obliquity of the arc of the zodiac visible when Sirius rose.

3. The Pleiades and Hyades are placed 9 and 11 decans distant from Sirius, making respectively 90° and 110°, but their actual distances in meridian longitude in 2767 were 47° and 59°, almost exactly half as much.

4. Orion is not infrequently allotted four decans, or 40° of space, and yet the maximum extent of this constellation is little over 20°.

5. In the Ramesseum the whole of the 36 decans are allotted to the last $5\frac{1}{2}$ months of the Sothic year, making 6 to each month instead of 3. (Part of this allocation can be seen in Plate 19.)

6. On the Denderah zodiac (Plate 14), under the constellation Pisces is found a disk with a human figure holding a pig by its hind foot. The same picture has been found on a Mesopotamian clay tablet of the third century, where it falls between the Pleiades and the Bull.* It does not therefore refer to the region of Pisces, but to the decan Akhui, the Two Spirits, which is seen below it and corresponds, as a pentad, to some part of Taurus.

7. The disk containing eight captives, which is so conspicuous in the Denderah circle, has no explanation if it falls at the end of Capricorn, but by the pentad arrangement belongs to Aries and marks the eighth degree, which was the equinox of the Hellenistic zodiac.

8. Still on the same zodiac, the decan 'Heads of the Two Souls', marking one of the cardinal points, is placed underneath Pisces, where it has no particular significance; but in 2767 B.C. this pentad marked the Spring Point.

* Illustrated in Langdon, *Semitic Mythology*, Fig. 92 on p. 305.

9. The Egyptian word for 'five' was drawn with a picture of a five-pointed star, which was also the ideogram for 'star'.

To these nine arguments, of which the first four are fairly solid and the fifth very difficult to ignore, three more can be added.

10. The conspicuous absence from the decan-list of the Lion's head and tail, the Beautiful Boy, Spica, the Hippopotamus, and the Giant is easily explained by supposing that the Egyptians used different stars, or the same stars under different names. But that is a mere guess, and an equally good guess would be that the half of the sky which the decans cover did not include those constellations—in fact they were under the earth when Sirius rose.

11. The Nût diagram gives the dates in the Egyptian calendar for the evening southing and setting, and the heliacal rising, of several decans. Since these dates are astronomically impossible, it does not much matter that they fill a whole circle instead of a half, but the one point where they may touch reality is at their beginning. The first of the list of decans in point of time is not Sobshosen, whose name is written on Nût's breast, nor yet Ipsedj and the Pregnant One, which appear on her forearms, but 'Under the Foreleg of Kenmut', which is placed behind the heels of Shu. Its culmination at dusk is given for the 6th day of the fourth month of inundation, which then fell about October 11th Gregorian, so the sidereal longitude of Kenmut would be near the beginning of Aquarius. Its evening setting, 90 days later, falls at the same sidereal time as the rising of Sirius, which puts it close to the end of Capricorn. Its heliacal rising, of course, does not fit, but none the less we have two further pieces of evidence that Kenmut sets when Sirius rises, and hence the decans only occupy 180°. Kenmut, in fact, takes the place of our constellation of the Eagle, and may mean Vulture or, since it has a foreleg, the Ape.

12. The Egyptians paid considerable attention to the constellations of the Ram and the Boat, both of which are made especially conspicuous in several of the diagrams. In Greek times the Ram fell in Capricorn, and the Boat under the forefeet of Sagittarius; but when Sirius rises Sagittarius is under the earth, so it seems odd to draw an especially handsome picture of it!

The Ram is several times drawn with five stars along its back and four on its belly, and this does partly agree with Capricorn, whose back has a straight line of stars. But Senmut makes the Pleiades egg-shaped and gives the Hyades twice too many stars, and both of them can be seen at the right of Plate 18, in the shape of a lop-sided V and a cow's ear. The Ramesseum schematizes Gemini and the upper half of Orion as two stars, then many, then two, then three; also it turns the Boat into something only a firework display could equal (Plate 19). I never expected, therefore, to identify the Boat, when suddenly I saw it staring up at me from the precessional globe in the Science Museum (Plate 20).

The boat in which a god crossed the sky or processed through a town would have a high straight prow and an equally high but bent stern, with a rectangular cabin or shrine amidships. And a very conspicuous rectangular constellation for which the Egyptians must surely have had a name was the Square of Pegasus. The resemblance is so striking that it is hard to doubt.

But if the Boat is the Square of Pegasus, then the Egyptian Two Fishes, just underneath it, fall on our Pisces; the Egyptian Sheep on Aries the Ram, which in any case, as we know, was not a Babylonian constellation; and the Egyptian Water-pots coincide with Aquarius, which the Greeks and Romans simply called the Urn. The Babylonian names of the constellations Pisces, Aquarius, and Aries were not by any means those to which we are accustomed, but were GU.LA (name of a goddess); Kun (the tail) and Anunitum (female dweller in heaven); and The Hireling.

(viii) *The Mysterious Text from Abydos*

A final point on the Nût diagram is the two inscriptions running from the sun's wing towards the wrists of the goddess. The upper one reads in Dr Frankfort's translation: 'The majesty of this god enters into her mouth in the Netherworld. The Netherworld is opened when he sails in it. The stars enter after him and they come forth after him and they hasten to their places.' But when the cenotaph was first published by the Egypt Exploration Society no attempt was made to translate the lower inscription, which seemed very obscure. I suggest translating it as follows:

'The majesty of this god enters at the hour [which is called] 'her time of twilight', he shines and is beautiful for the waters within, which Osiris gave him and in which he washed him. The majesty of this god sets in life at her 2nd hour as 'The Pregnant One'. Then the majesty of this god gives prosperous words to the westerners and issues orders in the Netherworld. The majesty of this god comes forth upon the lower earth, becoming a ... [break in text] ... his might like the Goose's head on the horizons. Then he becomes a great god in Edfu ... [break in text] ... to the iron limits of heaven, she causes him to enter, she makes it night at the hour of dusk when he sleeps in the waters within.'

This translation may not be entirely certain, but it mentions the Goose's Head, which to us is the Head of Aries, and tells us that the second hour of night is called the Pregnant One.

But if the decans are only 5° each, the problem remains, what happens in the other half of the sky? The Ramesseum implies that it merely had no decans. Mr Fagan suggests that those six months were omitted in order to avoid bad weather in the afterlife. This is conceivable, but not very likely, since it would mean a year with no harvest time. There remains another possibility.

The mysterious text from Abydos contains the expression, literally translated: 'As the time Head-of-Goose its two horizons.' And once again we must realize that in a non-materialist culture the apparent effects of forces receive far more attention than the shape of objects, just as the impact of an actor or speaker is far more important than the shape of his face. The magical influence of the hour called the Goose's Head would not lie on one horizon to the exclusion of the other, but would be characteristic of that moment, at which when a certain star rises another certain star necessarily sets. From the magical point of view, therefore, the hour of the Goose's Head could well control both horizons at once.

But at that rate the hour of Kenmut would always follow the hour of Sirius, and we need not feel puzzled because half of the circle has been omitted. Or we might choose to suppose instead—though this is far less likely—that the decans had pairs of opposing stars of similar declination, chosen because each rose as the other set, like Scorpio and Orion.

Further, the Pregnant One is sometimes spelt in the dual, as the Two Pregnant Ones; why does it not matter whether she is one or two? And whenever the 'sons' of any asterism are mentioned, they are always put in the dual as 'the two sons'. It is easy enough to fancy that this may simply refer to two small stars near a bigger one, but it is not likely that the smaller stars would always be two, and never one or three. Why do we find 'The Two Spirits', 'The Two Souls', 'The Two Sons of the Sheep', 'The Two Sons of Kenmut', and the two pairs of two men fraternizing?

This argument will seem far-fetched in a culture where material objects are thought more important than the living powers which use them. But there is another reason why no more decans were needed to fill out the other half of the sky, and that is that in Dynastic times the Egyptians already knew what happened under the earth; there was a subterranean landscape through which the sun passed and which was described in the Book of Gates. Hence the stars passed through it too, and the presence of stars beneath the earth never became a living idea to the Egyptians until the Alexandrian period, when the function of the decans had been forgotten and they were inflated to cover 360° and allotted to the zodiac at the rate of 10° each. Since all Egyptian charts were drawn for the rising of Sothis, the lower half of the celestial circle was never shown and there was no call to devise decans for it.

The Goose's Head, however, is of particular importance because throughout Dynastic times it culminated when Sirius rose. Hence *Smed-sert*, the Divider of the Sheep, which occurs among the decans, must originally have occupied the meridan, the halfway point, just as the similar word *Smedet* means the halfway point of the moon, Full Moon Day.

Not infrequently the decans have the names of presiding gods attached to them. It is not clear on what principle these rulerships were allotted, but certainly this is the root of Plato's doctrine that each sign had its ruling god, and thus, of the later astrological doctrine, that each sign has its ruling planet. It also explains the alternation of the Ram and Goose in the constellation Aries, and reveals the fallacy of supposing that the only origin of the names of the constellations was a fancied resemblance to a physical object.[27] The Egyptians did not believe that kickable objects were the only reality; indeed they would have called that notion not just a fallacy, but a demonstrable untruth. For to them, as to all peoples for whom the reality of experience has not been killed by argument, both gods and men were powers which act in a characteristic way, and the purpose of understanding either was to cope with whatever kind of force each one of them could bring to bear. For in every one of us still dwells, under the conscious surface, the savagery of Mars, the justice of Ma'et, and the elemental terrors and joys of Hat-hor.

If the decans had ever in dynastic times covered the whole circle, it would have been a constant sight for the Egyptians to see only half of them at any one time, and at least one monument might have survived showing only half the decans. But this has not happened, and before Roman times no such possibility is even hinted at. At Abydos (Plate 18) the decans stretch from Nût's head to her hind-quarters, and all thirty-six of them are shown as if comprised in this space. Since the rising of Sothis seems to have been to the Egyptians the only important astronomical moment, this will doubtless have been the origin of the astrological notion that certain celestial moments are more important than others, and also that the decans represent the condition of the sky at the particular moment of the 'horoscope of eternity', that is to say, of taking up residence in eternity.

It must not be supposed that each decan comprised two opposite spaces of 5° each; that would be to attribute to the Egyptians modern notions of accuracy and literal-mindedness. In dynastic times the invisible stars would not be important. Just as Horus, and later Mars, was called 'Horus of the Two Horizons', and as is shown by the constant use of the dual in such phrases as 'the two sons of the Sheep', so each asterism would have its two moments when it was 'lord of the horizon' and therefore lord of the hour, and this would make it unnecessary to have 36 more asterisms to fill up the other half of the sky. For with 180° allotted to pentads there would always be some known asterism on one horizon or the other, just as, in a horoscope, if one knows the Ascendant, one does not need to be told the Descendant as well.

As shapes, a ram and a goose are not alike, but Goose and Ram were the two sacred animals of the god Amun of Thebes, hence they represented to the Egyptians the same divine Power; and so, if the Egyptians had invented the zodiac, the ruling Power of Aries would not have been Mars, but Amun, the Hidden One, the Unknown God to whom St Paul found an altar in Athens and whom the Egyptians had known two thousand years before Moses.

Since all Egyptian horoscope-charts are diagrams of the heliacal rising of Sirius, it seems that the large heron drawn on them is not just traditional decoration, but represents an actual observation of Venus rising. Thus Sirius represents Isis, and Venus, which is always represented as a *bennu*-bird or heron, represents Osiris, who incidentally is also represented by the constellation Orion. So these astronomical diagrams with planets may justly be called horoscopes because they are observed celestial moments, which is what a horoscope is. Nothing was predicted from them either in this world or the next, but each one was the moment of a Sacred Marriage of Isis and Osiris; and this, in the simultaneous rising every eight years of Sirius and Venus, was the moment when the ideal touched the real.

Much more could be said, of course, about Egyptian astronomy. Three hundred and sixty-three years before the invention of the Sothic calendar there may have been a Horakhti calendar, and the date of its inauguration would be September 15th, 3130 B.C.[28] At that period the traditional ideogram of a cow in a boat, with a star between its horns, would have meant the heliacal rising of Spica, not of Sirius, and drawings of it have been found from the reign of King Djer early in the First Dynasty.[29] Again, the remarkable orientation of various pyramids would not have been possible without accurate observation of the transits of the stars, and this probably began with another king of the First Dynasty, Semerkhet, whose name apparently means 'the man with the astronomer's staff'.

But in the zodiac it seems certain that Aries was originally an Egyptian constellation, possibly Gemini, and probably also Aquarius, Pisces, and Leo. Egyptian bottles and jars were frequently made with a pointed base suitable for thrusting into the sand, hence any house built on solid ground needed a jar-stand to hold them upright; and this, rather than the Nile-god or the 'god with streams', will be the origin of what the Greeks and Romans called The Urn.

It only remains to confront the Egyptian evidence with the Babylonian.

TABLE 22   *Planetary Positions at the Inauguration of the Sothic Calendar*

Sirius (magnitude −1·58°) rose at Heliopolis (30° 08' north, 31° 18' east) on July 16th (Julian) 2767 B.C. (=−2766) at 4·01 a.m. L.M.T., which gives the following positions (Spica=29° 0' Virgo):

	Latitude	Longitude	R.A.	Declination
Midheaven	—	10° 43' Aries	331° 41'	—
Hamal (αϓ)	+9° 55'	13° 24' Aries	330° 39'	− 1° 42'
Mars	+0° 53'	19° 07' Cancer	65° 50'	+23°01'
Jupiter	+0°18'	21° 41' Cancer	68° 42'	+22° 50'
Saturn	nil	25° 04' Cancer	72° 23'	+23° 00'
Venus	+0° 29'	25° 48' Cancer	73° 07'	+23° 35'
Sirius	−38° 30'	20° 10' Gemini	49° 05'	−21° 42'
Zodiacal				
Ascendant	nil	28° 58' Cancer	—	—
Sun	nil	10° 40' Leo	89° 22'	+24° 00'
Mercury	+0° 50'	29° 00' Leo	109° 27'	+23° 38'
Moon	+3° 25'	19° 08' Aquarius	278° 24'	−20° 22'

Obliquity of the ecliptic 24° 00'. It was the day of the summer solstice. (From C. Fagan, *The Symbolism of the Constellations*, London, 1962, pp. 52–3.)
Gregorian date: June 23rd.
Distance from Sirius to Venus in azimuth (round the horizon) 55°.

13. *The Naming of the Constellations*

THE origin of an idea is naturally hard to trace; it appears to spring full-grown like Athena from the head of Zeus. But when Athena was called on to create she produced an olive-tree out of the earth; and the study of human intuition shows that there is normally some soil in which the idea has grown. Its genesis, like that of anything else, is by conflation: the meeting and mating of two old and known ideas produces one which is new.

The zodiac grew up, and must have grown up, as a device for measuring time. Only later did it come to be used for divination, and later still for the analysis of character. But divination is not and never has been based on cause and effect. The principle, which has been best explained by Jung and Pauli,[1] is synchronicity, or the interpretation of signs occurring simultaneously. Divination is a matter of signs, not causes, and the ancients did not suppose there to be any mysterious causative influence of the stars. It is therefore a waste of time for either astrologers or their enemies to try to establish or disprove the existence of such an influence.

The Babylonians were deeply addicted to taking omens, and in particular to observing them in the sky. This is one half of astrological practice. But their method was basically empirical; they expected a similar sign in heaven to be followed by a similar event on earth in virtue of correspondence between heaven and earth, not in consequence of any cause. And, most important, they did not time their omens closely. The occurrence of a halo round the moon and enclosing Venus would have two different significations according as it appeared in the west or east, and possibly according to the width of the conjunction; but it was only expected to foretell one event in the near but not precise future, and it was not taken as a significant moment from which the future should be counted. This, which is the other half of astrological practice, was unknown to the Babylonians in the second millennium.

The Egyptians, on the other hand, were not given to celestial divination. Next to telling the time at night and the seasons of the year, their chief interest in the stars was in learning how the soul could ascend to heaven and join the Sun in His boat. They did, however, believe in lucky and unlucky days, and each hour of the day or night had its tutelary spirit, whose name was known. It was inevitable that eventually some hours, and later some ruling spirits or some groups of stars, should be regarded as more favourable than others. The same idea could have arisen equally well in Babylon.

In addition, the Egyptians possessed two calendars which were far superior to anything known to the Babylonians; and because one of them rotated through the seasons there occurred once in fifteen centuries an epochal beginning-point when the first day of the Wandering Calendar returned to its ideal position in the Sothic Calendar. Thus the recurrence of epochal dates was part of Egyptian culture in a way that it could not be in Babylon. Furthermore, the Egyptians had a traditional celestial diagram which they copied from century to century, and although it was more traditional than contemporary it did represent a particular moment from which time was counted. Thus it is not unfair to say that the first horoscope ever drawn was, so far as we know, that of the Phoenix Era of 2767 B.C.

The Egyptians will not have made any predictions from this horoscope, nor was it drawn in terms of the zodiac; but when the Assyrians conquered Egypt in 671 B.C., or even through cultural contact in the previous century, there was likely to occur a conflation of influences from which both the zodiac and the notion of astrological prediction could arise. The evidence for this is in the timing.

Of the Babylonian zodiac, with 18 irregular signs, various copies have been found dating from the sixth to the third centuries. This does not prove, however, that the zodiac of 12 signs was still un-invented; the Babylonians and Assyrians, like the Egyptians, were great copiers of traditional documents, and in the less organized world of those days the regular zodiac will not have superseded the older systems in a week or even a century. We should expect to find texts from the transition period, when the zodiac was not yet used as it later came to be used. And such texts exist.

As late as the first century A.D. the technique of prediction was still undecided. A Coptic horoscope published by Griffith[2] divides the life of man into periods ruled by different planets. Two of the few complete sentences in it read as follows: 'The third period, which is that of Jupiter, is from 28 years 2 months 15 days to 34 years 5 months 24 days ... Jupiter became a hostile star on the day of his birth, perhaps he will desert his wife or be hostile to her or towards his children.'

This system of prediction, though normal in India, has never had a vogue in Europe. Ptolemy, writing about A.D. 135, makes no mention of it, but gives the totally different method usual in the West. And the fragments of Nechepso and Petosiris, which ought to enshrine the ancient teaching if anything does, reflect the political conditions of Egypt and Syria in the third century B.C., while their techniques differ again. They speak of 'full' and 'empty' degrees, the lore of the Part of Fortune, and the 'progression' of the Ascendant, but lay the chief emphasis on the actual condition of the sky, including the direction of the wind (quite in the Babylonian manner) at the rising of Sothis on the Egyptian New Year's Day.

Other transitional documents are the moon-staircases of the second century B.C.[3] They represent the moon's progress from new up to full, when the Eye of Horus is enthroned under the guardianship of Thoth. In one of these the Ram appears on the 4th day, the Bull on the 7th, Hapi the Nile-god (the later Aquarius) on the 11th, and the Bow, which suggests Sagittarius, on the 13th. Another list shows Aries 1st, Taurus 4th, and a scorpion 6th. Yet another puts Aries 2nd, Taurus 5th, and Hapi-Aquarius 9th. At first sight it looks as though the zodiac had been at this date still unorganized. But the constant interval of 3 days between Aries and Taurus implies that these two are signs of the zodiac, though the rest are not. Hapi is followed by Sothis, which puts him at the end of Gemini and enables him to introduce the inundation by his heliacal rising. The Bow then falls in the middle of Cancer, not Sagittarius, and the Scorpion is the Egyptian constellation and not zodiacal.

Then again, early horoscopes do not always mark the meridian and ascendant. The two horoscopes from a tomb at Athribis, shown in Plate 15, show only which signs were above the horizon and which below. No aspects between the planets can be measured since only the sign-position is given.

Finally, there are the two different circles of animals, the annual circle which became the zodiac with its ruling planets, and the hour-circle, which has a completely different set of animals and no ruling planets.

All these uncertainties do suggest that as late as the beginning of the Christian era the zodiac was not yet an old and tried tradition, nor were the techniques of astrology generally agreed upon, any more than they are now.

After all, when Babylonian priests were brought to Egypt in the train of Esarhaddon, and after some years discovered the unchanging Sothic calendar and the Horoscope of Eternity, their first question would naturally have been: 'And what did you predict from that celestial event?' The Egyptian priest would have blinked before answering: 'We did not predict anything.' At which the Assyrian priest's jaw would have dropped. Fancy missing such a wonderful opportunity! I do not suggest that this little romance at Heliopolis actually occurred; but it could have done: place, time, and climate of thought converged.

That was in the seventh century B.C. No direct evidence has survived for the use of the zodiac in prediction before the fifth century, and in Egypt before the third.[4] But Proclus, writing of the philosopher Theophrastus, Aristotle's immediate successor who died about 288 B.C., says that 'the most extraordinary thing of his age was the lore of the Chaldeans, who foretold not only events of public interest but even the lives and deaths of individuals.'[5] So astrology as an effective technique invaded Greece in the latter half of the fourth century. To have reached such a stage of development there must already have been behind it a hundred years of practice. This suggests that the first notion of astrology as we know it was begotten on Babylon by Egypt between the seventh and fifth centuries, and the zodiac itself, as a calendrical device, was of similar origin but may be a little older.

Plato, writing about 365 B.C., still has the signs of the zodiac ruled by gods and goddesses, and doubtless two or three centuries were required to establish the transition from divine powers to mechanical planets. The earliest known personal horoscope has a date of 410 B.C.,[6] in Plato's youth, so the well-known passage in the Timaeus[7] may be the first reference to horoscopy in literature; but little or no interpretation is found attached to early horoscopes. An equinox in 15° of the constellation Aries was used by some Hellen-istic astrologers,[8] but this was sheer guesswork, for it was only correct in the ninth century, long before their time; but an equinox in 10° Aries was quite correctly established about 500.[9]

Thus the zodiac certainly existed before 500 B.C. But the con-flation of Egyptian and Babylonian astronomy need not have waited until the Persian occupation of Egypt, which lasted from 525, under Cambyses, to 405. Nor is it likely to be the result of the brief occupa-tion by Nebuchadnezzar II of Babylon in 567. The Assyrian con-quest and occupation lasted from 671 till 610, and the astronomical library of Nabu was transferred from Calah to Nineveh by Asshurbanipal, who reigned from 668 to 626. Astronomy was a great interest at the Assyrian court, and at the same time the fashion ran strongly towards Egyptian art, which was imitated and sold in great quantity to the Assyrians by Phoenician artists.[10]

This takes us back as far as the seventh century B.C. To carry the argument further we shall have to look to the exaltations of the planets. Traditionally each planet is 'exalted' in a certain degree of the zodiac, and has its fall in the opposite degree. Astrologers have naturally assumed that each was especially strong or weak in those degrees or in the signs containing them. Their origin, however, remained a mystery, since they cannot be explained by juggling with the planets' nodes, aphelions, or epicycles, or their proximity to the zenith.

The word translated 'exaltations' means in fact 'hiding-places', and the hiding-places of a planet are obviously those parts of the zodiac in which it is invisible, and especially the degree in which it disappears from view into the sun's rays at heliacal setting and the degree of its reappearance at heliacal rising. The same is true of the moon, and is proved by the distance of the moon's 'hiding-place' from the sun's, 14°, which is a typical elongation for a new crescent. Since these phenomena change their positions every time they occur, we are evidently faced by an historical date, and there can be no doubt whatever that this date is 786–785 B.C. As for the sun having a hiding-place, it emerges from darkness at dawn on New Year's Day.

Until the zodiac drew attention to the position of planets in con-stellations, the chief focus of interest in them was their heliacal disappearances and reappearances, and in 786 all the planets had

heliacal phenomena in or very near the degrees of their exaltations —
an event so improbable that it cannot plausibly be ascribed to chance.
The list of these phenomena and the exaltations which they fit is as
follows:

TABLE 23   *Exaltations of the Planets*

Exaltation

1 Nisan=April 4th, 786= New Year's Day.

May 10th	Venus	heliacally set in the east in		9° Cancer.
June 22nd	Jupiter	„	„	15° Cancer. 15° Cancer.
July 24th	Venus	„	rose in the west in 18° Virgo.	
July 30th	Jupiter	„	„	„ „ 21° Cancer.
August 25th	Mars	„	set	„ 11° Pisces.
September 14th	Mercury	„	„ in the east „	16° Virgo. 15° Virgo.
September 23rd	Saturn	„	„ west	21° Libra. 19° Libra.
October 27th	Saturn	„	rose east	26° Libra.
February 4th, 785	Mars	„	„	„ „ 1° Aquari. 27° Capri.

The positions of Sun, Moon, and Venus are for New Year's day: Sun 19° Aries. 19° Aries.

Moon 29° Aries. 3° Taurus.

Venus 26° Pisces, 27° Pisces

(Mercury's 13 other phenomena omitted)

The year 786 B.C. saw the opening in Calah of the new temple of
Nabu (Nebo), the god of writing associated with the planet Mercury.
This is the origin of Mercury's connection with writing, wisdom,
commerce, and all similar subjects. The Egyptian god of writing and
wisdom, Thoth-Tahuti or Hermes Trismegistos, was not associated
with the planet Mercury until astrology was in full sail across the
Hellenistic world; for Thoth as god of time-measurement was a
moon-god. He readily became director-general of celestial happenings, as he was of the weighing of the soul before Osiris, but there was
no Egyptian reason to associate him with Mercury.

There are two slight weaknesses in this argument. The heliacal
risings and settings are not as close together as they might have been;
and also some are risings and others settings. This apparently
haphazard selection may leave us unconvinced that the coincidence
is not an accident.

But the exaltations are not and cannot be the horoscope for the
foundation or opening of the temple of Nabu, for Mercury cannot be
in Virgo while the Sun is in Aries. They are simply heliacal
phenomena recorded in that year; and since they are not those
closest to a given date, and since they include an arbitrary mixture

211

of settings and risings, it becomes probable that they were not observed and catalogued at the time, but were looked up in the temple records when the priesthood conceived the notion that they might be especially important. But what could have given them that idea?

It is a curious thing about Egyptian astronomy that we often find the year treated as of 360 days, the 5 epagomenae being ignored. If we could believe that by 'days' the Egyptians meant 'degrees' they would be using our system. And there is an extant text which says: 'A temple day is $\frac{1}{360}$ of a temple year.'[11] This is not an astronomical text at all; on the contrary, by 'a day' it means a day's rations. But it exemplifies once more the Egyptian habit of dividing the circle of the year into 360 parts.

When Assyrian priests came to Egypt and compared notes with their Egyptian colleagues, as they would naturally do, not being monotheists, they might easily think, if the esoteric lore were not full explained to them, that the Egyptians divided the circle into 360 equal parts. Thus the ideal circle of days invented by the Egyptians for use in the afterlife would have become a real circle of new and convenient degrees. This is possible even if a year of 360 days was used in the ^{mul}APIN tablets.

And similarly when the Assyrians met the Horoscope of Eternity and realized that it was drawn for the beginning of an era, they would be likely to return home and look up the records to see what they could do in the same line. They could not choose a more significant epoch than the foundation of the temple of their own god of astronomy. And because the Egyptians mentioned planets in the west and south as well as the east, they would think it natural to make a mixture of heliacal settings and risings. If this hypothesis be correct, then the exaltations were an Assyrian imitation of the Horoscope of Eternity, not observed at the time but looked up in the records, and thus perhaps a century or more later than 786 B.C. For almost a century scholars have said that the zodiac was of Babylonian origin and left it at that; it now seems more probable that it was the product of interaction between Babylon, Egypt, and Assyria.

For the Ram, to begin with, is definitely not a Babylonian constellation. It was also thought not to be Egyptian because on the later system of decans it fell in Capricorn. But the Ram and Boat were both extremely important in Egypt, and this cannot be explained if both were invisible at the rising of Sothis. It has of course nothing to do with the later position of Aries as the first sign of the 12. The Ram was important because it culminated when Sirius rose, and the Boat as a particularly obvious sacred emblem which stood on the same occasion conspicuously high in the sky. If we accept the identity of the Boat with our own Pegasus (Plates 19 and 20), then the Ram was an Egyptian and not a Babylonian constellation.

The Bull on the other hand is not Egyptian. Had it been so, then its ruler, when ruling planets were allotted, should have been Saturn and not Venus, just as Mars would have been the ruler of Leo. The Egyptians called Saturn 'Horus the Bull of Heaven', and bulls are not uncommon in Egyptian astronomy, but they are not attached, like the Babylonian Gud.anna, to this part of the sky.

The Twins are the Babylonian Great Twins, Maštabba.galgal. It is not quite so certain, but very likely, that they were the Two Stars of Egypt. This is one of the few constellations which is named from its shape, the others being the Boat, the Lion or Dog, and the Scorpion, or at least its tail.

As a Crab, Cancer is Babylonian, but it derives nevertheless from both countries, since the Egyptian Two Turtles were also hard-shelled aquatic creatures, the origin of the Tortoise which was put here by both the Greeks and the Chinese. And Hermes ruled this constellation because his Egyptian correspondence was Thoth, who as god of astronomy ruled the time of Sirius' rising, in his name of Tekhi the Accurate.

The Lion again is Egyptian, and goes back to the third millennium, like the Ram; its Babylonian name was the Great Dog.

The next five signs are all Babylonian, and a possible reason is that in this part of the sky the Egyptians had their enormous constellations of the Hippopotamus and the Giant, which could not be cut down to fit. In Gemini, Cancer, and Leo, the Assyrian priests who standardized the zodiac had had no difficulty in combining Babylonian and Egyptian ideas, but from Virgo to Capricorn they used the constellations of Mesopotamia.

Virgo originally was the Great Mother as corn-goddess, hence the title of Spica, the Ear of Corn, and hence also Demeter, corn-goddess of Eleusis, placed by Plato to rule this constellation. From a

213

corn-mother to a pretty maid is not a contradiction but simply a different stage of evolution: at Eleusis the harvest-goddess Demeter was always associated with her daughter Korè, The Maid, who is the seed-corn and springing wheat. And the Virgin Mother, of course, is still worshipped.

The position of Virgo has obviously nothing to do with shapes imagined among the stars. The corn-goddess belongs to her proper season, and the full moon in Virgo, which happens nowadays in April, occurred two thousand years ago at the beginning of March, and earlier still in February. This does not fit the Babylonian harvest, which began in May, nor the Assyrian, which happened in June, but it fits the first appearance of the spring corn, for the fields become green in February, and that is why we have the Virgin rather than the Earth-Mother. The Babylonian title is the Furrow, which clearly does not refer to harvest; but in Egypt the harvest began at the evening rising of Spica, when the moon was full in Virgo, and this fits in with the Ear of Corn even if not the Virgin. The goddess who holds the Ear was original to Babylon, and can be found centuries earlier than our Plate 13.[12]

Zibanitu, the Scales, is a well-known Babylonian constellation and corresponds to the myth of the Last Judgment in the autumn and the weighing of souls. It happens also to be seasonally suitable to Egypt, for the harvest would be weighed, and taxes assessed, when the moon was full in Libra.

Selket the scorpion-goddess does appear in the Egyptian heavens, but in the northern sky, far from the constellation Scorpio. She is drawn sometimes as a scorpion and sometimes as a woman, so there is no question there of fanciful resemblances. Mr Fagan makes this constellation seasonal in Egypt on account of the Khamsin wind, when scorpions are common, but its real origin doubtless is the scorpion-man of the Babylonian boundary-stones.

The Centaur with his bow has no precedent in Egypt, and the Goat-fish is a well-known Babylonian monster. Since the goat does not require lush pasture, the obvious implication of this hybrid symbol is 'end of the dry season'. This, however, does not suit the climate of Babylonia, where the Tigris is in flood from early March until the middle of June (Gregorian), and the Euphrates from mid-March until September; but the first rain, putting an end to the dry season, falls in the month of Tishri, which was October–November. The full moon of Capricorn, however, occurs now between July 27th and August 16th Gregorian, but about 700 B.C. it occurred between June 27th and July 18th Julian. Although these dates do not fit the Babylonian seasons, July 18th Julian is the day after the rising of Sirius in dynastic Egypt, so that the dry season ended when the moon was full in conjunction with the star Denéb Algédi, or Delta Capricorni, the Goat's Tail. This close piece of timing, coupled with the seasonal suitability to Egypt of the full moon in Aquarius and Pisces during the inundation, suggests that the traditional Babylonian Goat-fish was employed by Assyrian astronomers resident in Egypt in the train of Esarhaddon and Asshurbanipal to indicate the Egyptian end of the dry season.

This may seem slightly improbable. But the Assyrians were a parvenu people, always imitating the Babylonians because they had little creative ability of their own. They must have been amazed by the Egyptians, who boasted readily of their superior knowledge and justified their boast by having a better calendar than the Babylonians. Indeed, as we saw, the Assyrians were so impressed that they went home and invented the exaltations of the planets in imitation of the Horoscope of Eternity. Can it have been they who put the Goat-fish into the sky, about 650 B.C.?

There is no question of this emblem having been invented in Assyrian times or for this purpose; it is far older. But its occurrence on monuments does not prove that it had any reference to the sky, the more so since it belonged to the god of the waters under the earth. It is quite simply 'The Antelope of the Subterranean Ocean', a symbol of the god Ea. It occurs in the zodiac of 18 signs, and is not absent from the mulAPIN tablets of about 700 B.C. But these tablets may represent a tradition as old as the ninth century, when the equinox really was about 15° of Aries, where Eudoxus was taught to put it before he came to visit Plato. So it seems rather more probable that the Assyrian astronomers, who marked the season of ploughing by the full moon in Taurus (Gud.anna, the Bull of Heaven), and the springing of the green corn by the moon's repletion in Virgo (Ab.sin, the Furrow), were much struck by the fact that she was, by pure chance, full in the tail of Sukhur-mashu the Goat-fish when the Nile began to rise. Hence when they wanted to regularize the last two

215

signs of the zodiac they abandoned their goddess GU.LA in favour of their 'god with streams', who could carry the Egyptian urns, and adopted the Egyptian Two Fishes in the place of The Tails and the Great Swallow.

It is legitimate to wonder whether anyone in Egypt still knew that this was the longitude of the Two Fishes, since the late system of decans omitted them, apparently from the region of Scorpio. But, against this, whence did the Babylonians and Assyrians obtain their Ram, if not from Egypt, where the Ram was of special importance? It is hard to believe, when one studies Plates 19 and 20 and the sky itself, that the Egyptians can ever have forgotten the constellation of the Boat, which we can still see so plainly. And in that case both Ram and Fishes will still have been known because they were next to the Boat.

This first zodiac, of course, cannot have been tropical. It was not supposed to be either tropical or sidereal, but was simply assumed to be both at once. When this turned out to be untrue, no one could claim to have been using the moving equinox without knowing that it moved; for astrologers had been using the fixed stars without realizing that the equinox was no longer where it used to be. That the first zodiac can only have been measured from the stars was not only inevitable but also a fact[13] — although, of course, it was no sooner invented than it was thought to be tropical and used as such.

The animals of the hour-circles found from Egypt to China are certainly less ancient than the signs of the zodiac, for they do not go back to Babylonian and Egyptian constellations. When it was found that the twelve regular signs take roughly the same time to cross the meridian (but not the horizon), it must have seemed convenient to use their names for the twelve double-hours of day and night. This, however, would not work because their positions change once a month. Hence a different circle was devised to name the hours, regardless of the stars, and the animals of this circle, not being traditional, vary from country to country, and were also used for numbering years, months, and days. This fits in with the twelve-year cycle of predictions for the prospects of harvests, found in various lands.[14]

This second circle of animals did not originally run in the opposite direction to the zodiac, but, as we learn from a text published by Gundel, its animals were selected from paranatellonta of the zodiac, that is, from small asterisms rising with particular degrees at a particular latitude[15] — in this case, of course, Alexandria. These asterisms, together with various versions of the hour-circle or dodecaoros, are given in a table at the end of this chapter, and the Cat which figures under Aries is the same Cat as, according to Teucros, 'makes designing cowards'.

If the far eastern cycle is compared with the lists given by Teucros and in the Papyrus of Paris, more than half the animals are seen to be the same, but the order seems confused. There is, in fact, only one way in which they will fit together. For if we equate the Chinese sheep with Teucros' goat, or the dog with the dog, the ox with the bull, or the dragon with the crocodile, we get no other suitable correspondence; and if we equate the ape with the ape we get only one other, the hawk with the cock. But if we equate Nos. 3, 4, 5, and 6 in each cycle, we get tiger corresponding to lion, hare for ass (and both have long ears), dragon (or the Kirghiz crab) for scarab, and snake for snake, besides cock for ibis, and dog for dog-faced baboon (which is the kind of ape intended).

Hence the Twelve Branches of the far eastern hour-circle are derived from the Greco-Egyptian animal circle given by Teucros, but naturally in reverse order because they were needed to measure time instead of space. The twenty-eight animals of the Chinese show nothing more in common with Teucros' list than do the Twelve Branches, but they do pair off in couples, with four added to make up the number of lunar days, so we can say that we have here the origin of both Chinese circles of animals, and the origin is the same, although they run in opposed directions.

It would be useful, perhaps, to end with a brief history of the twelve glyphs or sigla commonly used as abbreviations for the signs. This is only partly possible because not enough work on the subject has been done. In medieval manuscripts the sun is represented by ♂, so our modern ⊙ cannot claim to be derived directly from the ancient Egyptian ⊙. In Greek manuscripts the constellations are frequently spelt out in full or referred to by numbers. On demotic Egyptian ostraca and papyri of the early centuries A.D. the abbreviation is either the first letter of the name, as in Berlin Papyrus P.8279, or the determinative which follows it, as in the Stobart Tablets. Thus there is in most cases a traceable derivation from hieroglyphic.

The last table (Plate 22) is derived from three publications of Professor Neugebauer.[16] The hieroglyph for Aries is an animal's pelt and tail, and for Taurus a phallus. In neither case is the modern glyph derived from it. There is a hieroglyph resembling ♈, but it has nothing to do with the case, and the Egyptian 𐤀 is the origin of the letter A but not so far as we know of ♉ . ♋ is suggested by the abbreviated scarab in column S, but Leo is drawn in demotic as a knife, and Pisces likewise has no great resemblance. Of the rest, Scorpio, Sagittarius and Aquarius, are clear, and Virgo may be seen in the glyph of the seated woman if it be turned on one side. Capricorn comes from the symbol for 'face' because it was drawn either as 'goat' or 'face' to represent 'goat-face'. (The word for 'goat' was spelt with the same consonants as the word for 'life', hence the appearance of the well-known 'ankh', which was pronounced something like *onekh* or *anehh*.) Libra came to be written with the hieroglyph for 'horizon' some time after 250 B.C., when it began to rise heliacally on New Year's Day and thus became for the time being the first of the signs.

Finally perhaps one might suggest that the meaning of the zodiac for the human race is not to be found merely outside ourselves, with radio telescopes and statistics, but by looking into the source of all meaning, which is referred to as 'God' in the following quotation from Plotinus:[17]

> Now the Supreme, because within it are no differences, is eternally present; but we achieve such presence only when our differences are lost ... We have at all times our centre There, though we do not at all times look Thither. We are like a company of singing dancers, who may turn their gaze outward and away, notwithstanding they have the choirmaster for centre; but when they are turned towards him, then they sing true and are truly centred upon him. Even so we encircle the Supreme always, and when we break the circle, it shall be to our utter dissolution and cessation of being; but our eyes are not at all times fixed upon the Centre. Yet in the vision thereof is our attainment and our repose and the end of all discord, God in his dancers and God the true Centre of the dance.

TABLE 24 *The Hour-circle or Dodecaoros*

original asterism	Teucros and Plate 22	Egyptian god	Country	Bianchini tablet	Pagoda at Trichinopoly	Magic Papyrus of Paris	Mimaut Papyrus	Kirghiz cycle	Far Eastern cycle	Numbers in the Chinese 12 Branches	28 asterisms
26–27° Aries	Cat	Bast	Persia	Cat	Lion	Cat	Ape	Sheep	Goat	8	23
14° Taurus	Dog	Anubis	Babylon	Dog	Tiger	Dog	Unicorn	Horse	Horse	7	25
6–7° / 19–20° / 22–27° Gemini	Snake	Uto	Cappadocia	Snake		Snake	Cat	Snake	Snake	6	27–28
24–26° Cancer	Scarab	Khepra	Armenia	Crab	Boar	Scarab	Bull	Crab	Dragon	5	1–2
? Leo	Ass	Setekh	Asia	Ass	Ass	Ass	Lion	Hare	Hare	4	4
? Virgo	Lion	Re	Ionia	Lion	Elephant	Lion	Ass	Panther	Tiger	3	6–7
20–30° Libra	He-goat	Goat of Mendes	Libya	Goat	Bull	Goat	Camel	Cow	Ox	2	9
12–18° Scorpio	Bull	Apis	Italy	Ox	Cock or Hen Hawk	Bull	—	Mouse	Rat	1	11
27–30° Sagitt.	Hawk	Horus	Crete	Hawk	Dog	Hawk	Ibis(?)	Pig	Pig	12	13
2–4(?) Capri.	Ape	Thoth	Syria	—	Snake	Baboon	—	Dog	Dog	11	15–16
4–30° Aquar.	Ibis	Thoth	Egypt	—	—	Ibis	—	Cock	Bird	10	17–19
4–30° Pisces	Crocodile	Sobek	India	—	Rat	Crocodile	—	Rat	Ape	9	20–21
W. Gundel, F. Boll, *Sphaera*, Footnote 15 above, p. 296.	Paulus Alexandrinus ch. 7.			See Chap. XII, Note 16.	F. Boll, *Sphaera*, P. 344.	C. Wessely, *Denkschr. Akad.* Wien, 1888.	R. Reitzenstein, *Poimandres*, Leipzig, 1904.	F. Roeck, *Kalender der Tolteken*, Wien, 1922 (in reversed order).			

Notes and References

THE references, numbered serially by chapter and collected here for convenience, have been deliberately kept as few as possible: to the general reader a superfluous display of learning is not attractive. This explains the absence of references to a number of well-known books which, though good in themselves, are not or are no longer directly useful. Examples of these are T. L. Heath's work on Greek mathematics, Duhem's *Système du Monde*, the *Phainomena* of Aratos, Daressy's *L'Égypte Céleste*, the *Mandaean Book of the Zodiac*, the works of Kepler, Bouché-Leclerc, Sir Norman Lockyer, Emmeline Plunkett, and numerous Arab astronomers and astrologers, besides a large number of outdated Sitzungsberichte. Finally, I am not convinced of the zodiacal reference of the well-known Gezer Tablet published by Macalister in *Palestine Exploration Fund*, Oct. 1902, p. 262.

CHAPTER 4: MEDIEVAL MAGIC AND PSYCHOLOGY

1 See for example Franz Cumont, *L'Égypte des Astrologues* (1937), and the picture of Sicilian society in the fourth century given by Firmicus Maternus.
2 Cardan's *Aphorisms*, etc. trans. Lilly (London, 1676).
3 When not otherwise stated, authority for statements in this chapter can usually be found in Lynn Thorndike, *History of Magic and Experimental Science* (Macmillan, 1923).
4 *Confessions* VII, cap. 6 (Loeb edition p. 356, but not the Loeb translation!).
5 xxv, 5.
6 Luke xxi 25.
7 H. de La Ville de Mirmont, *L'Astrologie chez les Gallo-romains* (Montpellier, 1904).
8 *Mineralium*, II, iii, 3.
9 P. E. M. Berthelot, *Collection des alchimistes grecs*, I, 88–92.
10 Cp. also Hugh Ross Williamson, *The Arrow and the Sword* (Faber, 1947).
11 Latin in Migne, P.L. 171, 1446. Juno is the planet Venus.
12 This tradition goes back to Berossos, a priest of Bel who settled in Cos about 290 B.C. (Seneca, *Nat. Quaest*. iii, 29).
13 *Autobiography of a Yogi*, by Yogananda (Rider, London, 1950).
14 *Opera Omnia* (Basel, 1550), cols. 2037–42.
15 *Opera* 27, 249, ed. J. de Vercellis.

16 *Secretum Secretorum*, ed. R. Steele (Oxford, 1920), p. 15.
For a good collection of medieval zodiacal illustrations see Henri Stern, *Le Calendrier de 345* (Paris, 1953).

CHAPTER 5: THE TWELVE GODS: PLATO AND AUGUSTUS

1 *De Caelo* II, xii, 292a.
2 41–2.
3 *Journ. Near Eastern Studies*, IV (1) (Jan. 1945), pp. 21–2.
4 II. 34 Kroll.
5 *Vita Augusti, c.* 94, transl. Rolfe. On Augustus's coins, cp. Deonna in *Journ. Warburg*, XVII 47–86.
6 *Suet. Tib.* lxix. Cp. F. H. Cramer, *Astrology in Roman Law and Politics* (Amer. Philos. Soc., 1954).
7 *Nat. Quaest.* vii, 30.
8 id. ii, 32.
9 *De Natura Deorum* ii, 21 ; *De Div.* ii, 88–99.
10 IV, 773 and Housman *ad loc.* Laurentius Lydus p. 8, 1.8 Teubner. Ginzel in *Sitzb. Berlin Akad. 1887*, 1122 ff.
11 Longitudes of the planets, April 6th, 753 B.C., about noon L.M.T.
12 *Starlore* vol. III, no. 23 (Sept. 1899), p. 43, where the date is erroneously given as July 15th, 481. The Greek in *CCAG* (*Catalogus Codicum Astrologorum Graecorum*) vol. I, pp. 103–4.
13 *CCAG* I, 107. Cp. O. Neugebauer and Van Hoesen, *Greek Horoscopes*, p. 147 *Trans. Amer. Philos. Soc., 1959*). Other fragments of Palchus in *CCAG* I. 80–107, VI, 63, etc.
14 *Fragment* 2, col. A.
15 ii, 77–82.
16 III *ad fin.*
17 ix, 14.
18 Pliny, *Nat. Hist.* xviii, 59 ; Achilles Tatius, *Isagoge* 23.
19 *Works and Days*, 385.
20 *Georgic* IV, 231–5.
21 A. Rehm, *Parapegmastudien* (*Abh. Bayr. Akad. d. Wiss., phil-hist. Kl.*, neue Folge, vol. 19, 1941). The illustration is from H. Diels and A. Rehm in *Sitzber. Berlin Akad. 1904*, pp. 92 ff., 752 ff. Another pegged calendar, found at Coligny near the Franco-Swiss border, is illustrated in T. D. Kendrick, *The Druids* (London, 1927), p. 116.
22 *De Div.* II, 87.
23 *Phaedrus*, 246e *ad fin.* All the quotations from Plato are given in Jowett's translation, which seems the best at present.
24 *Timaeus*, 38.
25 252c.
26 *Phaedrus*, 246 c 6; *Timaeus*, 40 a 3, 41 a 3.
27 II 439 foll. Variant lists in W. H. Roscher, *Ausf. Lexikon d.gr.u.röm. Mythologie*, VI, 786.

28 H. Stuart Jones, *Catalogue of the Sculptures in the Museo Capitolino*, Pl. 29;
    Roscher's *Lexikon*, VI, 798.
29 *Laws* V 745, VIII 848.
30 *Laws* VIII, 828.
31 *Laws* VIII, 767 c.
32 246 e.
33 *Od.* xiii, 96–112.
34 Symposium, 188.

CHAPTER 6: THE ZODIAC IN CHINA

1   L. de Saussure, *Origines de l'astronomie chinoise* (Paris, 1926–31), p. 523;
    but see also Needham (note 13 below) vol. III, 260.
2   id. p. 185.
3   *Uranographie chinoise* (The Hague & Leyden, 1875) esp. pp. 583, 585.
4   *Ostasiatische Zeitschrift* (Berlin, 1919–20), vol. 8, pp. 42–48.
5   J. Edkins in *China Review* (Hongkong), vol. 14 (1885), p. 345 ff.
6   E. Chavannes, *T'oung Pao* (Leyden, 1906), p. 71.
7   Id. p. 87.
8   Saussure, op. cit., p. 134.
9   id. pp. 124, 127.
10 This is explained in Li-ki xi, 1, 3 (Legge), see following note.
11 Translated by James Legge in *Sacred Books of the East*, vol. 3 (Oxford,
    1879).
12 P. V. Neugebauer, *Hilfstafeln zur astronomischen Chronologie* (Berlin and
    Leipzig, 1912–25).
13 The standard work on this subject is now J. Needham, *Science and
    Civilisation in China*, esp. vol. II, pp. 346–95 (divination), and vol. III,
    pp. 210–82 and 390–408. There is an illustration of a Chinese horo-
    scope in vol. II, Plate XVII (p. 352).
14 Spring and Autumn, viii, 1; Li-ki, second month of autumn; id.
    iv, 12.
15 Derk Bodde, *Statesman, Patriot and General in Ancient China* (New Haven
    1940). Richard Wilhelm, *Frühling u. Herbst des Lü-Bu-We* (Jena,
    1928).
16 Needham, op. cit., III, 259–61; also III, 182–282, 436, esp. pp. 218,
    402.
17 *De Die Natali* 18.
18 W. Eberhard, *Beiträge zur kosmologischen Spekulation Chinas* (Bässler
    Archiv, Heft 16), esp. pp. 58, 63, 67.
19 Giles, *Chinese Dictionary*, vol. I; W. Eberhard, in *Sitzber. Preuss. Akad.*
    1933, ii, 937.
20 M. Cantor, *Vorlesungen über Geschichte der Mathematik*, I, 27–8;
    Ideler, *Mémoire sur la chronologie chinoise*, *Abh. Berlin Akad.* Feb. 16th,
    1837.

21 Ebenezer Burgess, translation of Surya Siddhanta, ed. Sengupta, Calcutta, 1935. (Beware of misprints in this edition.)

22 See above; notes 13 and 18.

23 *Asiatic Review*, Jan. 1938 (with bibliography); other articles by this author in *Journal of Royal Asiatic Society*, Oct. 1938, *Occasional Notes of Roy. Astron. Soc.*, June 1939, no. 5.

24 xix, 58. I am grateful to Mr E. D. Grinstead of the British Museum for this reference.

25 Boll, *Sphaera*, p. 320 gives these equations for other far-eastern countries.

CHAPTER 7: FROM MEXICO TO TIBET

1 Vol. II (1816), p. 3.

2 C. P. Bowditch, *Maya Numeration* (Cambridge, Mass., 1910), pp. 287–289.

3 Berard Haile, *Starlore Among the Navaho* (Sante Fé, 1947).

4 Fritz Roeck, *Kalender der Tolteken* (Vienna, 1922).

5 F. K. Ginzel, *Handbuch d. math. u. techn. Chronologie* (Leipzig 1906), I, 434.

6 For a desperate effort to maintain the contrary, E. J. Webb, *The Names of the Stars* (Nisbet, London, 1952).

CHAPTER 8: PERSIA AND THE FOUR ELEMENTS

1 *The Sacred Books of the East*, ed. Max Müller (Oxford, 1880 onwards), vol. 5, *The Bundahish*, transl. E. W. West, Chap. 2. Vol. 23, *The Sirozahs and Yashts*, transl. Darmesteter. Vol. 31, *The Avesta*, transl. L. H. Mills.

2 Tishtrya is the Persian name of Mercury in Budge, *History of Alexander* (1889), p. 9.

3 The ninth asterism, towards the end of Cancer.

4 West, op. cit., pp. 397–400.

5 F. Cumont, *Textes et Monuments figures relatifs aux Mystères de Mithra* (Brussels, 1896), Vol. II, 244–5, fig. 77.

6 id. Vol. II, p. 389, fig. 304, and p. 395, fig. 315. Cp. Vol. I, p. 300.

7 On Mithraism in general see S. Dill, *Roman Society from Nero to Marcus Aurelius* (1904); W. J. Phythian-Adams, *Mithraism* (1915).

CHAPTER 9: THE BIBLE AND BIRTHSTONES

1 Kalt, *Biblisches Reallexikon* (Paderborn, 1931).

2 Sigmund Mowinckel, *Die Sternnamen im alten Testament* (Oslo, 1928).

3 J. J. Hess, 'Die Sternnamen in Hiob 9^9 und 38^{31} (Festschrift Jacob).

4 D. Feuchtwang, 'Der Tierkreis in der Tradition und im Synago-
genritus' (Breslau, *Monatsschrift f. Geschichte u. Wissenschaft d.
Judentums*, Nov.–Dec. 1915).

5 G. A. Cooke, 'The Book of Ezekiel' (*Internat. Crit. Comm.*, Edinburgh
1936), p. 14.

6 Schrader, *Die Keilinschriften u. das alte Testament*, ed. Zimmern &
Winckler, pp. 631 ff. (1903).

7 F. J. Boll, 'Aus der Offenbarung Johannis', Stoicheia I (1914); cp.
J. Freundorfer, 'Die Apokalypse d. Apostel Johannes' (*Bibl. Studien*
Vol. 23, 1930).

8 Josephus, Bell. Jud. v. 5.5; Philo, *Quis rer. div. haer.*, ed. Cohn, 221 ff.

9 Gunkel, *Schöpfung und Chaos* (Göttingen, 1885), pp. 302–8; but see
Charles, *infra* note 11.

10 ii. 31.

11 R. H. Charles, *The Book of Revelation* (Edinburgh 1920), I, 130–2.

12 Daniel vii, 7 and 24.

13 Bundahish iii, 11.

14 Dieterich, *Abraxas*, p. 120, n. 4.

15 As note 6 above, Vol. 3, p. 360, n. 3.

16 *De Nupt. Philol. et Merc.* i. 75 (Teubner, p. 34).

17 Genesis xxxvii 9.

18 Jubilees II 9 and VI 36–8. Ed. R. H. Charles (S.P.C.K., 1917).

19 Enoch VIII 3.

20 Enoch XXXIII 3, cp. XXXVI 3.

21 *Oedipus Aegyptiacus* (1653) II, ii, 177; Charles, op. cit. I, 315.

22 Cooke, op. cit., pp. 26 near top, 317, 323.

23 Charles, op. cit., II, 166.

24 *Ant.* iii, 7, 7, transl. W. Whiston (1928). Cp. id. iii, 6, 7; Bell. Jud. v,
5, 5, and 7.

25 G. F. Kunz, *The Curious Lore of Precious Stones* (Philadelphia, 1913),
p. 299.

26 Kunz, pp. 124, 316–17, 342.

27 Nothing much can be learnt from the magical properties attributed
to gems, see for instance *Mani Mala*, by S. M. Tagore (Calcutta,
1879).

28 Jerome, Epist. ad Fabiolam=Migne PL XXII 616; agrees with
Revised Verson except for exchange of Nos. 3 and 4, jasper instead
of diamond, and chrysolite before beryl and onyx.

CHAPTER 10: INDIA AND THE ASTERISMS

1 Brihat Samhita, Chapter 2, transl. H. Kern (1913), in his collected
works, Vol. I, 173.

2 Transl. Ebenezer Burgess, introduction by P. C. Sengupta (Calcutta,
1935), p. viii.

3 Muhammad ibn Ahmad Al-Biruni's *India*, English transl. by Edw. C. Sachau (London, 1910).

4 Ujjain lies 23° 13′ N, 75° 52′ E; Alexandria 31° 10′ N, 30° 0′ E. Models of the astronomical buildings at Ujjain may be seen in the Science Museum, London.

5 By for instance Das and B. G. Tilak; see Needham, *Science and Civilisation in China*, III, 86, and G. R. Kaye, *Hindu Astronomy* (Calcutta, 1924).

6 Sengupta, op. cit., p. xxxi.

7 Adi, Chap. 3, cp. Sengupta, ibid.

8 Bangalore, 1919, chap. XXVII.

9 *Surya Siddh.*, Chap. III, 12.

10 id. II, 1–2.

11 Kaye, op. cit., pp. 30 ff.

12 Sengupta, op. cit., p. xxx.

13 G. Thibaut in *Grundriss d. indo-arischen Philologie* (Strasbourg, 1899), Vol. III, Part 9, p. 7.

14 Sengupta, notes. 12 and 2, *Supra*.

15 *The Poona Orientalist*, Jan., Apr., and July 1941; *Hindu Heritage*, Feb. 1942; see also the astronomical section in Vedic Bibliography by R. N. Dandekar (Bombay, 1946).

16 Šalya 34, 3.

17 Atharva Veda XIX, 7, and 8 ad init.

18 Kaye, op. cit., p. 98.

19 Thibaut, op. cit., p. 14 ff.

20 Needham, op. cit., III, 82.

21 A. Weber in *Abh. Akad., Berlin, 1862*.

22 'Mémoire présentée à l'Acad. des Inscriptions et Belles-Lettres.'

23 cit. Kaye, op. cit., pp. 61–2.

24 O. Neugebauer, 'Tamil Astronomy', in *Osiris X* (1952), 252–76.

25 Atharva Veda VI, 110.

26 Laws of Manu IX, 258, and VI, 50. Cp. *Baudhayana II*, 1, 2, 16 and *Vasishtha X*, 21 (in same volume of *Sacred Books of the East*, ed. Max Müller).

27 As Note 1 above, but p. 178 and Chap. II, 17.
    B. L. Van der Waerden finds that Pap. Rylands 27 (Kgl. Dansk Vidensk. Selskab, hist.-vil. Meddeler xxxii) bridges the gap between the last cuneiform texts and Varaha Mihira.

CHAPTER II: BABYLONIAN MYTHS AND OMENS

1 'The reader who is unable to control the ancient Mesopotamian and Egyptian sources is hereby warned against using R. Eisler, *The Royal Art of Astrology* (London, 1946). The author writes with an air of authority, but virtually everything he says about Mesopotamian

astrology is either hopelessly muddled or incorrect.' (Prof. A. Sachs in *Journal of Cuneiform Studies*, Vol. VI, No. 2, 1952).

2 Otto Neugebauer, *The Exact Sciences in Antiquity* (First edition, Copenhagen, 1951), p. 132.

3 Cornelius' dates, in B. L. van der Waerden, *Jaarboek Ex Oriente Lux* (Leyden, 1952), Vol. III, pp. 414, 419.

4 S. Langdon, *Babylonian Menologies* (London, 1935), p. 1.

5 id. 68, 107; *The Epic of Creation* (Oxford, 1923), p. 27; *Semitic Mythology* (Boston, 1931), p. 307.

6 O. Neugebauer in *Journal of Near Eastern Studies*, IV (1945), p. 15, §11.

7 *Menologies*, p. 11.

8 P. V. Neugebauer and E. F. Weidner in *Sitzber. Sächs. Akad. Leipzig, 1915*, pp. 82–5.

9 F. X. Kugler, *Sternkunde und Sterndienst in Babel*, II, 474.

10 id. II, 71.

11 *Menologies*, pp. 48, 54, 73, 77, 84–9.

12 A. Ungnad in *Archiv für Orientforschung*, XIV, 278.

13 R. Campbell Thompson, *Reports of the Magicians and Astrologers* (London, 1900), No. 186.

14 id. No. 183.

15 Carl Bezold in *Sitzber. Heidelberg Akad., phil.-hist. Kl., 1911*, pp. 22–3. Cp. Ungnad, op. cit.

16 van der Waerden in J.N.E.S. (as Note 6 above), VIII (1949), p. 21, cp. X (1951), p. 20 ff.

17 Schaumberger in Kugler, op. cit., *Ergänz*. III, 322.

18 Langdon, *Epic*, 149 ff.

19 id. 152; E. F. Weidner, *Handbuch der bab. Astron.* (Leipzig, 1915), 41, 62; van der Waerden, J.N.E.S., 1949 § VIII, and pp. 22 to end.

20 p. 495.

21 *Menologies*, p. 10.

22 id. p. 20.

23 A. Sachs, 'Babylonian Horoscopes', in *Journal of Cuneiform Studies* VI, No. 2, 54–7.

24 Kugler, op. cit., Erg. I, 130–5.

25 *Menologies*, pp. 107, 64.

26 B. L. van der Waerden's 'History of the Zodiac' in *Archiv für Orientforschung* XVI (1952–3), 216–30 and references there.

27 ibid. 218–19; *Amer. Journ. Sem. Lang.* XL (1923), 192; Kugler, op. cit., Erg. I, 70; S. Weinstock in *Journ. Hellenic Studies* LXIX (1949), p. 54.

28 van der Waerden, ibid., note 13; Thureau-Dangin, *Tablettes d'Uruk* (Paris, 1922), No. 14; E. F. Weidner, *Handbuch der Bab. Astron.*, p. 121.

29 *Journ. Roy. Asiat. Soc.*, 1925, pp. 37–60.

30 Langdon, *Sem. Myth.*, pp. 105–6; *Epic.*, p. 10.

31   id. *Epic*, Tablet I, 140–2.
32   *Epic*, p. 88, footnote 4; Wm. J. Hinke, *A New Boundary-Stone* (Philadelphia, 1907), pp. 98–103 and 231; *Arch. f. Or.* (see Note 26 above), XVI, 227.
33   E. D. Van Buren, *The Flowing Vase and The God With Streams* (Berlin, 1933), Plates VIII 30, XIII 43, et passim. M. Joachim Menant, *Recherches sur la Glyptique Orientale* (Paris, 1883), I, 111–12, figs. 60–65.
34   *Sem. Myth.*, p. 236.
35   P. F. Goessmann, *Planetarium Babylonicum* (Vatican, 1950), p. 176; BM. 86378, II, 19; *Menologies*, p. 99.
36   The full story is in *Sem. Myth.* 29 and illustration there.
37   *Georgics* I, 217.
38   *Arch. für Orientf.*, I, 69–78; *Menologies*, p. 12.
39   *Zodiacs Old and New* (Anscombe, London, 1951), p. 21, cp. *Menologies*, p. 2.
40   *Sem. Myth.*, pp. 158–60; *Menologies*, ibid.
41   Goessmann, op. cit., No. 126 (VAT 9428; cp. Thureau-Dangin, op. cit., No. 12).
42   *Sem. Myth.* Figs. 96, 97.
43   Goessmann, op. cit., No. 14; contrast van der Waerden, *Journ. Near Eastern Studies*, 1949, p. 13, Note 17 and 31; *Arch. f. Or.* (above), p. 226.
44   *Sem. Myth.*, p. 159.

CHAPTER 12: THE HOROSCOPE OF ETERNITY

1   Richard A. Parker, *The Calendars of Ancient Egypt* (Chicago, 1950) p. 32, and R. Weill, *Revue d'Egyptologie* V (1946), 255–6 and VI (1951), 224–5; Parker and Neugebauer, *Egyptian Astronomical Texts* (1964).
2   Karl Schoch, 'Planetentafeln für Jedermann', *Spalte* XLIV, Tafeln A and A² (Berlin, 1927).
3   Maurice Burton, *Phoenix Reborn* (London, 1959); R. T. Rundle Clark in *University of Birmingham Historical Journal* II (1949–50), 1–29 and 105–40.
4   *Wisdom of the Egyptians* (London, 1940), pp. 4 ff.
5   id. p. 5.
6   P. E. Newberry, *Beni Hasan I* (Egypt Explor. Soc., 1893), p. 61.
7   L. Borchardt in *Zeitschrift für Aeg. Sprache* 37 (1899), 89–103.
8   H. E. Winlock, 'Origin of the Anc. Eg. Calendar' (*Proc. Amer. Philos. Soc., 1940*), p. 463; Parker, op. cit., p. 151.
9   H. Frankfort, *The Cenotaph of Seti I at Abydos* (Egypt Explor. Soc., London, 1933), p. 84.
10   *Ant.* i, Plates, 79, 80, 87; iv, 18–22.
11   *The Astrological Magazine* (Bangalore, January 1954), p. 82.

12 W. M. Flinders Petrie, *Athribis* (British School of Arch. in Egypt), pp. 23–4.

13 First given in Duncan Macnaughten's not generally accepted *Scheme of Egyptian Chronology* (1932), pp. 327–8.

14 H. Brugsch, *Recueil*, I, 30–35 and Pl. XVII; O. Neugebauer in *Journ. Amer. Or. Soc. 1943*, p. 115.

15 W. Gundel, *Dekane u. Dekansternbilder* (Warburg Studies, Vol. 19, Hamburg, 1936), p. 252.

16 Illustrated in Gundel, op. cit., Plates 16, 17; Henri Stern, *Le Calendrier de 354* (Paris, 1953), Pl. XXXIII.

17 cp. L. de Saussure, *Origines de l'Astronomie Chinoise* (Paris, n.d.), pp. 144–5.

18 Gundel, op. cit., pp. 77–81.

19 id. p. 81 =*CCAG* viii (3) 120–1.

20 *Oedipus Aegyptiacus* (Rome, 1653), II (2), 182–6, quoting Abenragel (eleventh cent.).

21 A. Pogo in *Isis*, xvii (Bruges), pp. 6–34, also *Osiris*, i (1936), 500–9; P. Lacau, *Sarcophages antérieurs*, ii, 107.

22 H. Chatley in *The Observatory*, Vol. 63 (March 1940), No. 790; O. Neugebauer in *Journ. Near Eastern Studies* IV, 1 (1945), p. 5, n. 11.

23 e.g. at Edfu (*Descr. Eg.* i. 58).

24 As Note 11 above, pp. 81–90.

25 Nos. 1104, 1708, 360, and cp. 1123. Ed. K. Sethe (Leipzig, 1908 foll.); S. B. Mercer (New York, 1952).

26 *Journ. Egyp. Archaeol.* 26 (1940), pp. 120–6.

27 e.g. E. J. Webb, *The Names of the Stars* (London, 1952).

28 Note 11 above, pp. 81–2.

29 Petrie, *Royal Tombs*, II, Plates V, 1 and VIa, 2.

CHAPTER 13: THE NAMING OF THE CONSTELLATIONS

1 C. G. Jung, *The I Ching or Book of Changes* (English translation, 1951), introduction; Jung and Pauli, *The Interpretation of Nature and the Psyche* (London, 1955).

2 *Zeitschr. f. aeg. Sprache* (1900), pp. 71 ff.

3 J. Duemichen, *Kalenderinschriften* (Leipzig, 1866), Plates cxvii, cvii, xcviii–xcix.

4 O. Neugebauer, *Journ. Amer. Or. Soc.* I (1943), 122.

5 *In Timaeum*, 285 F.

6 Above, Chap. X, n. 23.

7 40 C–D.

8 C. Fagan, *Zodiacs Old and New* (Anscombe, London, 1951), pp. 17–25 and references there.

9 Ibid.

10 *Illustrated London News*, January 17th, 1959, Plates II–IV and pp. 99–100.

11   F. L. Griffith, *Siut* (London, 1889), Plates 7, 11.285, 300; S. Schott, in *Abh. Akad. Mainz* (Wiesbaden, 1952), ad init.

12   E. D. Van Buren in *Analecta Orientalia* XII (1935), 327–35.

13   Kugler, *SSB* II, 582; *Erg.* I, 130–35; id. *SSB* I 163; Fagan, op. cit.; v.d. Waerden in *Archiv für Orientforschung*, XVI 222, para. 5.

14   e.g. *Geoponica* I, 12 (Jupiter in the 12 signs); Censorinus, *De Die Natali*, 18; and the *Chi Ni Tzu* (Needham, op. cit., III, 123 n.).

15   *Neue Texte des Hermes Trismegistos* (Munich, 1936), p. 229 ff.; F. Boll, *Sphaera*, pp. 296–346.

16   *Trans. Amer. Philos. Soc.*, 1942, p. 246, and 1959, p. 1; *Journ. Amer. Or. Soc.*, 1943, p. 124, n. 38.

17   *Enneads* VI, ix, 8, tr. Dodds; cit. E. Wind, *Pagan Mysteries in the Renaissance*, p. 171 (Faber, 1958).

Index

ABANO, PETER, 55, 57, 111
Abelard, Peter, 45
Abhijit, 145
Accadians, 152
acronychal rising, 74
Adad-nirari III, 171
administrators, 145
Adonis gardens, 161
after death, Egyptian astronomy for use, 186
after life, 212; bad weather in the, 201
agricultural writers, 75
agricultural year, Egyptian, 176
Agrippa, 64
Albert the Great, 47, 51, 53, 57
Albiruni, 138, 146
Albumasar, 52
Alcandrus, 52
Aldebaràn, 55, 126, 171, 191
Alexander the Great, 58–9, 97, 118, 153
Alexandria(n), 139, 140–41, 146, 149
Alphard, 96, 106
Alphonso the Wise, 111
Amun (God), 203
ancient physics, 63
Antares, 89, 92, 96, 106, 116, 126
'Antelope of the subterranean ocean', 166, 215
'anting' of birds, 177
Antoninus Pius, 177
Anu, Way of, 160
aposot, 190
Apotelesmatica, 73
Aquarian Age, 44, 55, 171
Aquarius, constellation of, 162, 167, 168
Aquinas, Saint Thomas, 58
Arabs, 101, 123
Arab way of counting nakshatras, 144, 149
Arborius, C. A., 48
Argoun (Mongol chieftain), 89
Ariean Age, 171

Aries, constellation of, 76, 173
Aristophanes, 84
Aristotle, 58–9, 62–3, 66
Arnald of Villanova, 57
Aryabhata, 139, 140
'Aryt, 191
Ascendant, 162
Asclation, 66
Aselli, 189
'aspects', 36
Asshur, 153
Asshurbanipal, 90, 153, 210, 215
Assyria, 152–74 passim
asterisms (hsiu, nakshatras):
    Chinese, 87, 89, 93, 96–7, 99, 101, 103–9
    Chinese main list of, 104–5
    Egyptian, 183, 188, 197, 203
    Indian, 144–6, 149
    Indian main list of, 150–51
    the 28 collectively, 55, 103
Astraea, 42
astrologers expelled from Rome, 45, 66
astronomer's staff, 190–91
astronomical era, 96
Asvins (or Açvini), 116
Athanasius, Saint, 126
Atharva Veda, 144, 148
Augustine, Saint, 45, 46, 48, 51, 59, 126
Augustus, Emperor, 30, 64–6
Ausonius, 48
Avesta, 118
'ayanamsha', 19, 147

BAAL OR BEL, 153
Babylon, 88, 101, 144, 152–74
Babylonian(s), 90, 123, 126, 144, 148
Bacon, Roger, 47, 57–8
Balance of Justice, 25
Basil, Saint, 59
Bayeux Tapestry, 51

Beautiful Boy, 192, 199
Bede, Venerable, 51
Bellatrix, 191
'benefics', 35
Betelgeuze, 191
Bezold, Carl, 90, 91, 99
Billi the magician, 157
Biot, J.-B., 103
Blake, William, 83
Boat, constellation of the, 200, 212–13
Bonatti, Guido, 44, 49, 50
Boniface VIII, Pope, 57
boundary-stones, 127, 164–5, 167, 170
Bradley, Donald A., 29, 30
Brahmagupta, 139
Brahmanas, 142, 144
Breastplate, High Priest's, 135
Brihat Jataka, 140
Brihat Samhita, 148
Buddhist influence, 98
Buddhists, 64
Buddhist text, 91
Bull: as symbol of fertility, 118; constellation of the, 213
'Burning of the Books', 94, 98

CALAMITIES OF THE PIG, 91
Calendar:
    asterisms the basis of, 101
    Babylonian, 154, 160, 181, 207
    based on observation, 20
    Coptic, 179
    Egyptian, 175–8, 207
    found to be wrong, 93
    Greek, 77, 93
    Gregorian, 175, 179
    Hebrew, 131
    lunar, 75, 92, 178
    Muslim, 75, 176, 179
    solar, 92
    Sothic, 178, 187
    Wandering, 175, 178, 187, 188
Caligula, 66
Caliph, of Baghdad, 52, 56
Campanus, 38
Cancer, constellation of, 82, 173, 192, 197, 213; ruled by Mercury, 80–83
Canon of Yao, 92–3, 95–6

Canopus, Decree of, 178
Capricorn, constellation of, 82, 155, 162, 165–8
Cardan, Jerome, 49
'cardinal' signs, 41
Cassite period, 152, 165
casting a horoscope, 37
Castor and Pollux, 74, 189, 191
Catherine de' Medici, 131
Cecco d'Ascoli, 47–8
Censorinus, 99
centaur, 167, 214
Chaldeans, 78
Charles, Dr, 129–30
Chatley, Dr, 106, 188
Cheng, 98
Chigi, Agostino, 59, 61
Ch'in Dynasty, 97–8
China, Chinese, 87–109, 145, 149, 157, 171
Chinese year, 93
chong-ki, 93
Chou, 93
Chou-kong, 93, 103
Christians should believe in astrology, 47
Chrysostom, St John, 46
Cicero, 67, 78
Circle of Animals, 87, 217, 219
circumpolar stars, 88, 96, 102
Cleostratos of Tenedos, 64
clepsydra, Karnak, 196
climatic explanations, 21, 160, cp. 161
clockwise movement, 87
collective mind, 23
Columella, 73, 75
Coma Berenices, 192
'common' signs, 41
conception, horoscope of, 63–4
constellations: stars located in, 154; unequal, 55, 60
Cooke, Dr, 135
correspondences, law of, 132, 206
Cosmas Indicopleustes, 184
'cusps', 37

DARIUS I, 175

'day for a year' method, 37
day-names, Mexican, 113
decan(ate)s, 181–8, 199, 202–3, 216
decimal point, 138
declination, 17
decumbiture, 50
Demeter, 83, 213
Democritos, 77
demons, 156, 162, 165, 172
Denderah, zodiac of, 167, 180–81, 198
Denéb algèdi, 215
Denebola, 169
determinism, 45
Deuteronomy XVIII, 124
Deuteronomy XXXIII, 123–4
'diagonal calendars', 197
Diodorus Siculus, 127
dipper, the big, 180
diviners, divination, 21, 25, 84, 148–9,
    157–8, 206–7
dodecaoros, 217–19
Dodeka Theoi, 80
double-bodied signs, 70
Dragon's Head (Rahu), 40, 56
druids, 48
dwadashamshas, 182

EA, 153, 160, 162, 166, 168
Eagle, constellation of, 199
Ear of Corn, constellation of, 213
eclipses, 155, 162
ecliptic, 17, 88–9, 101, 139, 158
Egypt, 164, 174, Chapter 12
Egyptian lucky days, 156
eighteen signs, 165–6
eight 'houses', 38
'elections', 71–2
elements, the four, 41, 119
Elohim, 153
Enkidu, 168–9
Enlil, or Ellil, earth-god, 153, 160
Enoch, Book of, 129
Enuma Anu Enlil series, 152, 174
epact, 162–3
epagomenae, 176, 178, 183, 212
Epic of Creation, 158
epicycles, 142

Epinomis of Plato, 85
equal signs of zodiac, 163–4
equator, 17, 18, 89, 101, 139, 163
equinox, 18, 27, 51, 73, 142, 147, 162,
    181
Esarhaddon, 173–4, 209, 215
Esna, zodiac of, 167, 172
Eudoxus, 74, 78, 215
Euphrates, River, 152, 172
Evangelists, 112, 126
exaltations of the planets, 169, 170–71,
    210–12
Exodus, Book of, 130, 135
Ezekiel, Book of, 126, 130

FABULOUS ANIMAL, 107, cp. 166, 214
'face', 50
Fagan, Mr, 27, 55, 170–71, 182, 187,
    189, 197, 201
faith, 48
Farnesina Palace, 59
ferryman of the sky, 188
fiducial of the zodiac, 179
Firmicus Maternus, 52, 111, 185
First Point of Aries, 19
Fishes, constellation of the Two, 172,
    216
'fixed' signs in astrology, 41, 125–6, 172
flowers of the signs, 85–6
'forgeries', Chinese, 94
Forlì, 49, 50
Fortune of a city, 153
'fortune-telling', 21–2
four calendars at same time, 179
Four Holy Creatures, 112, 126
freemasonry, 120
free will, 45
full moon not important in Egypt, 194

GALATEA, SALA DI, 59
Gates, Book of, 202
Gauricus, 48
Gemini, constellation of, 20, 197
'general prognostication', 63
Genesis, Book of, 123, 130

Gilgamish, 167–9
Goat-Fish, constellation of, 160, 165, 214–15
god, Plato on following one's, 78–9
God-with-streams, 167–8
Goose, constellation of, 202–3
Goose's Head, constellation of, 201–2
gout in the knees, spell against, 58
gravitational pull, 24, 32
Great Twins, constellation of, 213
Greco-Roman world, 54, 63
Greece, 147, 164
Gregory the Great, 51
Gundel, Wilhelm, 183–4, 217

HALLEY'S COMET, 51
Hammurabi, 152, 156–7, 159
Han period, 89, 94, 101
Hapi (Nile-god), 167, 208
Hare, constellation of, 87
harmony of the Many and the One, 85
Harpocrates, 180
healing on the Sabbath, objection to, 156
heliacal rising, what it is, 176–7
heliacal risings, 140, 159, 162–3, 177, 181, 208
Heliopolis, 177
Hellenistic zodiac, 39, 75
Helpericus, 53
Henry VII, 49
Hephaistion, 184
Hermaphrodite's horoscope, 52–3
Hermes, 83
Hermes Trismegistos, 53, 184, 211
Hestia (hearth-goddess), 81–2
Heter, coffin of, 182
'hiding-places', 210
Hildegard of Bingen, Saint, 47
Hindu zodiac, 141
Hipparchus, 19, 32, 64, 74–5, 139
Hippolytus (Church Father), 47–8
Hireling, constellation of, 173–4
holy living creatures, 126
Horakhti calendar, 204
horary astrology, 69
horoscope, 34, 38–9, 162; the first, 207; the earliest personal, 209

Horoscope of Eternity, 175, Chapter 12 esp. pp. 195, 205
horoscope of Jesus Christ, 46
Horus, 188
hour-circle, 87–8, 102, 108–9, 217
hour-stars, 191
houses of the horoscope, 37–8
hsiu, 99, 102, 104–6, 109; see also asterisms
Hugh of St Victor, 45, 53
Humboldt, Alexander von, 110
Hynek, Dr, 30

ILLEGAL DIVINATION, 66
images, magical, 56–7
Imhotep, 178
imperialism, Roman, 68
India, 54, 55, 98, 101, 109, 119, 137–51, 157
Indian astrology, 40
indoor workman, 173
instinct, 25
intuition, 21, 22
inundation of Nile, 176, 208
ipsedj, 190
Ishtar, 152, 161, 165, 169
Isidore of Seville, 53
Isis, 204

JAMDET NASR, 152
John's Day, Saint, 161
Jones, Sir William, 138
Josephus, Flavius, 127, 130–31
Jubilees, Book of, 129
Julius Caesar, 75, 175
Junctinus, 49
Jung, Dr C. G., 21, 24, 25, 39
Jung and Pauli, 206

KABBALISM, 120
Kali Yuga, 138, 143
kalpa, 138
Kamaterôs, Johannes, 184

Khiti, coffin of, 186, 197
Kidinnu, 64, 74, 154
Kircher, Athanasius, 129, 130, 184
Kish, 152, 166
Kugler, 162

LANGDON, PROFESSOR, 156, 160–61, 167, 169, 171, 173, 198
Lao-tse, 98
Latitude, 17
law, Roman, 67–8
Laws of Manu, 148
Leo, constellation of, 20, 43, 197, 213
Leonardi, Camillo, 132
Leontios, 72
Libra, constellation of, 169, 214; as Scorpio's claws, 78; thought to rule China, 145
Li-ki, 99
Lilly, William, 43–4, 183
Lion, constellation of, 213
Louis, XI, 57
Louis XIII, 48
lucky days, Roman and Egyptian, 156, 207
lunar returns, 37
lunar year, 18
Lü-pu-wey, 97–8
Luther, Martin, 48
lyre, 81

MAD DOGS, SPELL AGAINST, 58
Mahabhārata, 140, 144
'malefics', 35
Manetho, Pseudo-, 73, 75
Manilius, 27, 67, 73, 75, 80, 182
manvantara, 98
Marduk, 158, 166
Mars, attributions of, 43–4
Martianus Capella, 128
Martin IV, Pope, 48
matter, materialist, 83
Maunder, Mr and Mrs, 160
meaning, 33, 138
measurement by length of shadows, 119
measuring the zodiac, 59, 73

Melanchthon, 49
Menophres, Era of, 178
Mercury, 35–6, 171, 211
Mesopotamia, 152–74
meta-decans, 187–9
Meton, 74, 77
Metonic cycle, 67
Michigan, Papyrus, 73, 75
milestone of Athens, central, 80
Mithraism, 118, 120
Mithridates, 120
monotheism, 153
monotheists, 212
Montefeltro, Guido da, 49, 50
month began, 156
moon, 152, 153, 164, 170
moon's sidereal revolution, 101
moon's synodical revolution, 93, 154
moon-staircases, 208
moon-stations, 109
Morin de Villefranche, 48
Moslem calendar, 54
mulAPIN series of tablets, 158, 160, 164, 170, 212, 215
'mutable' signs, 41
mystery religions, 175

NABU (NEBO), 165, 171–2, 211
Naburiannu, 64, 74
Nagual religion, 111–14
nakshatras, 109, 144–5, 149, 150–51; see also asterisms
navamsas, 182
Nebuchadnezzar II, 210
Nechepso and Petosiris, textbook of, 185, 208
Nectanebus, 59
Needham, Professor, 102
Neptune, 36, 82
Nero, 66
nesru, 189
Neugebauer, Professor Otto, 63
Nidaba, 171
Nigidius Figulus, 65
Nile, rise of, 167, 177, 188
Nineveh, 90
Nippur, 154, 161

Nisan, first of, 181
Numbers, Book of, 130
number twelve, 18
Nût diagram, 193, 197–9, 200
Nût, sky-goddess, 181, 194

OMENS, 63, 154, 206
opposition, Babylonian explanation of,
    159
Orion:
    in Bible, 122–3
    in China used to give date, 20, 180,
        191, 204
    in the eighteen signs, 163
    in India, 142
    near Moon's exaltation, 170
    as Osiris, 204
    as Tammuz, 161, 163
Osiris, 200, 204, 211
outdoor workman, 173

PALACES, THE FOUR, 89, 96
Palchus, 69, 70–73
Pamprepios, 72
Pança Siddhantika, 146
parallax, 24
parapegma(ta), 76, 155
Parsees, 101, 119
Part of Fortune, 40, 69, 208
Paul III, Pope, 48
Paulus of Alexandria, 139
Pegasus, 163, 174, 200, 213
Persia, 115–21, 175
Peruzzi, Baldassare, 59, 60, frontispiece
Peter of Abano, 55, 111
Phaedrus of Plato, 23, 79, 82
Phanes, 121
Philip of Macedon, 59
Philippe le Bel, 89
Philo of Alexandria, 127, 131
phoenix, legend of, 177
Phoenix Era, 177–8, 207
Piscean Age, 171
Pisces, constellation of, 172, 216
Placidus, 38

planets:
    all wicked in Persia, 118
    Chinese names of, 91
    directions of, in Egypt, 192
    not stated to be 'in' constellations,
        192
    not used in early India, 145
    plants of the signs and planets, 85–6
Plato, 23, 46, 58, 62–3, 78–9, 80, 85,
    209, 213, 215
Pleiades and Aldebaràn, 171
    and asterisms, 144, 146
    in Babylon, 163
    in Bible, 122–3
    in China, 90, 98
    in Egypt, 191
    in Hesiod, 75
    as markers, 96, 106
    and Moon's exaltation, 170–71
    variously, 150, 155, 165
Plotinus, 218
Plough Star, 158, 169
Plutarch, 67
Pluto, god of Hades, 82
Pluto the planet, 36, 82
poisonous beasts, spell against, 58
polar longitude, 139
pole of the equator, 139
Posidonius of Apamea, 65
possible but wicked, astrology held, 47
Praesepe, 163
precession of the equinoxes:
    and Aquarian age, 171
    Babylonian estimate of, 162
    Canon of Yao and, 96
    and Great Year, 55
    Surya Siddhanta estimate of, 140
        146
    time to discover, 74, 78
    two zodiacs and, 147
    in Vedic times, 142
    what it is, 19
predicting: death of emperor, 66; the
    future, 16, 22–3, 36–7; length of
    month, 154
prediction(s), 90, 158, 162, 171
Pregnant One(s), 201
'primary directions', 37
Proclus, 63, 209

Procyon, 189
'progressed horoscope', 37
prohibitions, ritual, 156
Ptolemy, Claudius:
  and constants, 139-40
  and longest day at Babylon, 101
  and schematization of zodiac, 41, 42,
    44, 65, 164, 167, 172, 182
  and technique of prediction, 208
  thought to have lived before Hermes,
    53
  and tropical zodiac, 31-2
  southern hemisphere unknown to, 32
Pyramid Texts, 188

QABALAH, 125, 133
Qualities, the three, 41
Querolus (Latin play), 48
Quetzalcoatl, 111
Quiché, 111

RAHU AND KETU, 40
Ram, constellation of, 164, 166, 172-4,
  192, 199, 202-3, 212
Ram's head, constellation of, 165
Ramesses I, 178
Regiomontanus, 38
Regulus, 126, 169, 192
reincarnation, 83
retrogradation, 142
Revati, 98, 147
Revelation of St John, 127-31
Ricci, Matteo, 88
Rigel, 191
right ascension, 17
Robson, Vivian, 42
Rome, Roman Empire, 120, 147-8, 183
Rome: astrologers expelled from, 45,
  66; horoscope of, 67-8
Romulus, birth and conception of, 68

SABAOTH, 184
Sabbath, origin of, 156
Sagittarius, constellation of, 167
Sardinia, 161
Saturn, 73, 166, 169

Saussure, L. de, 92, 99
Scales, constellation of, 214
Schlegel, Gustave, 90
science, 83, 138
Scorpio, constellation of, 20, 43, 72, 74,
  92, 165
  claws, 78, 87, 169
scorpion-man, 167
scorpion-goddess, 181, 214
scorpions, 167
seasonal element in zodiac, 160; see
  climatic explanations
Selket, goddess, 189, 214
Semerkhet, 204
Semites, 153
semnopithecus schistosus, 90
Sengupta, 142
shadow, measurement by length of, 119
Shamash the sun, wheel of, 152, 165
Shang period, 96, 99
Shapur II, 118
shespet, 189
Shih King, 96
Shi-ki, 90
Shu King, 93
Sibzianna, 161
sidereal zodiac, 19
sin: astrology a, 129; planets and, 45-6
Sin (Moon-god), 152, 157, 165
Sirius or Sothis, 116, Chapter 12
  passim, 208-9, 213
sobkos, 190
sobshosen, 190, 199
solar entries, 31
solar returns, 36-7
solar year, 18
solstices, 20
Sosigenes of Alexandria, 175, 183
Spica:
  in Babylon, and The Furrow, 172
  in China, chief asterism, 87, 92, 98-9
  in Egypt, 191-2, 204, 213, 215
  in Greece, connected to Virgo,
    213-14
  and Horakhti calendar, 204
  original marker of zodiac, 99, 180-81
Star of the Tablet, 171
Stars of the Water, 192, 197
Suetonius, 64-5

sun, the, 152–3
Surya Siddhanta, 137, 139, 140, 142, 146
Sylvester, Bernard, 46
Symposium, Plato's, 84
synchronicity, 24, 206
'synetic' zodiac, 30–31

TABLET, STAR OF THE, 171
Tail(s), constellation of the, 164, 172
Tammuz, 161
tapir, 107
Tarot, the, 22, 125–6
Tarrutius, 67–8
Taurean Age, 171
Taurus, constellation of, 169, 170–71
Tefabi, coffin of, 186, 197
'term', 50
Tertullian, 45
Tetrabiblos, 32, 63, 75
Teucros, 183
Thabit ibn Kurrah, 56
Theogenes, 39, 64–5
Theophrastus, 209
Thomas à Becket, 52
Thoth-Tahuti, 211, 213
Thrasyllus, 65–6
Tiâmat, 162, 165–6
Tiberius, Emperor, 65–6
Tigris, River, 152, 172
Timaeus, Plato's, 62–3, 209
Tishtar, 116–18
tithi, 146
Toltec astronomy, 112–14
Triangulum, constellation of, 158, 169
triplicity, 50
tropical zodiac, 19, 32, 60, 75, 147
tropics, 20
Turtles, the Two, 189, 192, 197, 213
twelve, number, 18, 131
twelvefold division, 99
Twelve Gods, 80–82
Two Sons of the Sheep, etc., 202–3
Two Stars, the, 191

UNCONSCIOUS, THE, 21–3
unequal constellations, 55, 60
unicorn, 107

Ur, 152, 166
Uranus, 36–7, 82

VARAHA MIHIRA, 137, 139, 140, 146–8, 182
Vedas, 101
Vedic Era, 143
Vedic sacrifices, 142
Vega, 145
Venus:
    as Anahita, 115
    in Babylon, 152, 169
    in Egypt, 187–9, 204
    period of, in Mexico, 110
    in Persia, 115
vernal equinox, 18, 32, 181
Vesta, 80–81
Vindemiatrix, 192
Virgil, 170
Virgo, constellation of, 42–3, 172, 213–14
Vues des Cordillères, 110

WAIN, THE, 180
Wandering Calendar, 178, 181, 188
wash-neter, 190
Ways of Anu, Ea, and Enlil, 158
widdershins, why zodiac numbered, 87
William the Conqueror's chaplain, 51
winged bulls, 172

YAO-TIEN (Canon of Yao), 92–3, 95–6
Yellow Emperor, 91, 98
yogataras, 145, 147, 191
York, archbishop of, 52
'younger gods', 62–3
Yueh Ling, 96
Yukteswar, Sri, 57

ZADKIEL, 44
Zechariah, Book of, 127
Zeno, Byzantine Emperor, 69, 72
Zervan, 121
Zoroastrianism, 119
Zoser, 178, 188

Rupert Gleadow

Born in Leicester, England, in 1909, Rupert Gleadow was educated at Winchester and at Trinity College, Oxford, gaining first-class honors in both classics and Oriental languages. For some years he lived in Paris; then, during the war, he was engaged in secret work for Britain's Foreign Office and Air Force Intelligence. *The Origin of the Zodiac* took him seven years to write. Among his other books are *Magic and Divination*, *The Unclouded Eye*, and *Astrology in Everyday Life*.

NO SURRENDER

THE LIFE & TIMES OF IAN BOTHAM

Also by Dave Bowler

SHANKS
The Authorised Biography of Bill Shankly

NO SURRENDER

THE LIFE & TIMES OF IAN BOTHAM

Dave Bowler

ORION

Copyright © 1997 Dave Bowler

All rights reserved

The moral right of Dave Bowler to be identified as the author of this
work has been asserted by him in accordance with the
Copyright, Designs and Patents Act 1988

First published in Great Britain in 1997 by
Orion
An imprint of Orion Books Ltd
Orion House, 5 Upper St Martin's Lane, London WC2H 9EA

A CIP catalogue record for this book is available
from the British Library

ISBN 0 75280 803 6

Filmset by Selwood Systems, Midsomer Norton

Printed in Great Britain by
Butler & Tanner Ltd, Frome and London

To Mom and Dad
My best friends

And for Denise
A mountain moving deep within
Always
David

CONTENTS

Acknowledgements

Author's Note

Introduction

ONE May You Live in Interesting Times   7

TWO Storms   41

THREE Reconstruction of the Fables   72

FOUR What Do I Do Now?   92

FIVE Whom Lord's Would Destroy They First

     Drive Mad   126

SIX I Read the News Today. Oh Boy.   149

SEVEN Grace and Danger   171

EIGHT Angels in the Architecture   201

NINE Out of Time   217

POSTSCRIPT Walk This Way   227

Chronology   233

Test Match Statistics   245

Test Match Batting & Bowling Records   263

Bibliography   264

Index   267

ACKNOWLEDGEMENTS

There are a number of people without whom this book could not have been written. Chief among them are Tanja Howarth and Mark Hayward and everyone at Orion Books. Thanks too to Bryan Dray. And Carrie – show them this at school.

I'd also like to thank David Frith for his help and encouragement both with this book and in the past. Thanks also to Phil Neale, Tom Graveney, Dennis Breakwell and Ted Dexter for their offers of assistance.

Finally thanks to Denise who had to put up with me while I wrote this, and to Mom and Dad for introducing me to Edgbaston a long time ago.

AUTHOR'S NOTE

The following is not strict biography, nor does it follow any obvious chronological pattern. More than enough such books are already available about Ian Botham, and in the wake of his own autobiography it is impossible to justify such a narrow reading of his life through the simple facts and figures.

Instead, *No Surrender* is an attempt to look at Botham as he is revealed by his relationships with other people and agencies. In studying his reaction to the county game, his contacts with the media, his arguments with the TCCB, I believe that it is possible to learn more about this surprisingly complex individual than it is by simply reliving the events of the Oval in 1982. Ian Botham is the most important cricketer of the post-Packer years. In understanding his story, perhaps we can better understand the way the game has developed over the last twenty years.

This thematic approach means that there must inevitably be a degree of cross-over from one chapter to another. Every effort has been made to reduce any such repetition to the bare minimum.

A LITTLE REBELLION NOW AND THEN
IS A GOOD THING.

THOMAS JEFFERSON, 1787

THE ART OF THE IMPOSSIBLE

To the end of the English season in 1996, more than 2000 individuals had represented one or more countries at Test match level since play began in the inaugural Test at the Melbourne Cricket Ground in March 1877. From Old Trafford to the SCG, from Basin Reserve to Sabina Park, a galaxy of talent has registered a catalogue of mighty deeds. Their memory has been handed down through the generations via the pages of *Wisden Cricketers' Almanack*, yet their achievements raise barely a flicker of interest among those not committed to the game. Among those hundreds of fine cricketers, few have done more than graze the consciousness of the outside world. W.G., Jack Hobbs, the Don, Denis Compton, Garfield Sobers, Fred Trueman, Dennis Lillee, Brian Lara, these are among the select handful who have managed to thrill even those who otherwise have no understanding of, nor interest in, the game of cricket. To that elite group must be added the name of Ian Terence Botham.

In his prime, year in, year out, it was Ian Botham who provided the most memorable moments of the season: a stunning spell of swing bowling at Lord's to unhinge the Pakistanis in 1978; an explosive acceleration towards the Test match double in 1979; *his* summer of 1981; a murderous double hundred against the overwhelmed Indians in 1982; bludgeoning the punch-drunk Aussies into submission in 1985 with a fusillade of boundaries and bouncers. These, rather than the staggering facts and figures that he amassed along the way, are the enduring images of one of the most remarkable careers the game has witnessed.

Yet there has always been more to Botham than just cricket. No sporting field, however huge, could contain so generous or mighty a spirit and it was surely inevitable that his larger than life personality would spill from the game and out into the real world. To become an icon, as Botham most assuredly has, you have to be much more than just a highly gifted sporting superstar. The majority of those giants already listed were more than mere players. Grace was as much a grand Victorian impresario and showman as a cricketer; likewise there was Compton the Brylcreem boy, epitomising ideals of post-war elegance and joie de vivre, Sobers the smiling, happy-go-lucky gambler, the face of the sunshine islands, Trueman the bluff caricature of Yorkshire bloody-mindedness, Lillee the perennial rebel without a cause. In those cases, forces beyond the individual's control took a guiding hand, irresistibly dragging them to a position where what they did became somehow less important than what they represented. It's not unique to cricket, of course, for you could say much the same about Chaplin, Valentino, Presley, Monroe, Lennon, Warhol, Madonna, Gascoigne, Cobain, Cantona, though those unfortunates have had to deal with far greater fame on a far wider scale. Among cricket's greats, perhaps only Bradman and now, to a lesser extent, the record-breaking Lara achieved their international renown thanks solely to their efforts on the field, cricketing equivalents of Pele, Babe Ruth or Jack Nicklaus.

As the media has grown since the war, so has the public's demand for the extraordinary, the legendary. It is an appetite that mere sporting prowess cannot satisfy, an appetite increasingly fed by controversy, scandal and salacious gossip. A hundred before lunch at Lord's may get you into the papers, but it won't keep you there. To stay in the limelight, and thereby maximise your earning potential, you need to be able to do a bit more than handle a slab of willow. To maintain a high profile in the face of fierce and constantly renewing competition, you must become a 'celebrity', a 'personality'. It's not a new phenomenon but it's an increasingly important one as the press fights to keep its hold on the audience's ever dwindling attention. Today's celebrities are like buses. Missed one? Never mind, there'll be another one along in a minute. It's good for newspaper sales, bad for the individuals who are used, discarded and sometimes destroyed in the process.

Football has always been ahead of cricket in that respect, simply because it is the national game with a far stronger hold on the hearts of the population. In modern terms, George Best was probably the first sporting superstar. Utterly uncalculating, Best became an icon by accident rather than via the Machiavellian scheming of some shadowy agent. He was one of the most potent symbols of the 1960s not simply because he was a footballing genius, but because he caught the popular mood. Freed from the slavery of the maximum wage, footballers suddenly became wealthy, at least in comparison with the working man. George enjoyed that new financial freedom to the full, while taller and taller tales saw him surrounded by booze, birds and boutiques. Best's legend is still far stronger than that of comparable team-mates Denis Law and Bobby Charlton because he was seen as more than a young man who could do extravagant things with a football. Where Charlton was a nice but dull, archetypal 'I know my place' 1950s man, Best was the footballing Beatle, the long-haired maverick who bought his gear in Carnaby Street, the flawed genius who had the world at his feet but kicked it into touch. Best provided the stories and the excitement that the public wanted and his reward was to become inextricably linked with his decade – think of the 1960s in England, and Georgie's there. History will show that Ian Botham caught the public mood equally well in the 1980s.

Much of the Botham legend has been a function of his immaculate timing. He arrived on the scene just as England's premier all-rounder Tony Greig was being turned into the pantomime villain and lured away by Packer's lucre. The Packer schism allowed Botham to make his mark on the international scene against relatively poor opposition, gobbling cheap runs and wickets on the way. His post-captaincy rehabilitation in 1981 coincided with the royal wedding, a time when British flag-waving was at its height. His brash rampage through the 1980s provided personification of the laddish loadsamoney culture, Porsche-driving city boys and buttock-baring brickies alike enshrining him as some kind of patron saint. The later, often lean, years saw him maintain his place in the England side long after he should have been dropped, an automatic

3

selection simply because there was no other viable alternative for the all-rounder berth.

Ian Botham is such a huge character that everyone can take something from him that he or she can enjoy or admire, be it a thumping drive back over the bowler's head, a cheeky aside to Bill Beaumont on *A Question of Sport*, the generosity he's consistently shown to leukaemia sufferers or his refusal to be ground down by the wheels of the Establishment. It is equally inevitable that everyone finds something in him that drives them to distraction – a boorishness that has occasionally bordered on thuggery, the inanities of his media persona, the stubborn refusal to accept the passing of time and the dimming of his powers, the inability to turn the other cheek in the face of insults, imagined or real.

To trawl through Botham's life day by day is a futile exercise. More than enough ink has already been spilt on that score – the dozens of filing cabinets currently buckling beneath the weight of Beefy-related clippings in assorted newspaper libraries across the country testify to that. What needs to be established are his claims to greatness, his place among the quartet of superb all-rounders that dominated the 1980s, the uses to which he put his huge abilities, the legacy he left to English cricket, and the way in which his rise and fall has mirrored that of the English game as a whole. Equally, his treatment at the hands of the media needs to be assessed for Botham represents the bridge between the relatively deferential treatment meted out to Best in the 1960s and the vilification of Gazza in the 1990s. Did Botham manipulate the media or was he controlled by it? How did living his life in the glare of the media spotlight affect other members of the England team? Ian Botham's story needs to be looked at from a different angle than the merely chronological.

Simon Hughes, his colleague at Durham, best summed up the dilemma that faces anyone attempting to write about Ian Botham in his book *From Minor To Major*: 'It is hard for anyone else really to relate to him. He has such a powerful aura that sweeps past, leaving everything else in its wake. Pressmen who privately ridicule him daren't do so in print. Rightly so too. They are wary of writs arriving on their desk and mindful also, perhaps, of a remark of Dr Johnson: "A fly, Sir, may sting a stately horse, and make him wince; but one is but an insect, and the other is a horse still." ' To some, including perhaps Botham himself if his autobiography is any guide, Ian Botham is at the very least the greatest *English* cricketer that ever drew breath and almost certainly the world's finest all-rounder bar none. For his supporters, any hint of criticism of the great man is heresy, vindictive claptrap that is rooted solely in jealousy. Elsewhere, revisionists are making the case that Botham was, as E.W. Swanton remarked, at best 'a mixed blessing', that his greatest performances were reserved for inferior opposition, that he was never the colossus he was portrayed as being, and that his off the field exploits damaged the game.

From a personal standpoint, the arrival of Ian Botham at the crease, with either bat or ball, was a source of great pleasure and no little excitement. Having followed cricket for twenty-five years, I can think of no player who provided greater value for money, none who has played the game with such visible enjoyment, nor one who has had the capacity to thrill and disappoint in equally dramatic measure. To see Botham seize a game at whatever level and bend its course according to his whim was a regular, but nonetheless remarkable, feature of the sporting life. As David Frith, founding editor of *Wisden Cricket Monthly*, points out, 'for force of personality, he ranks with only one other all-rounder since the war, and that's Keith Miller'. To see Botham at his peak was to see the game of cricket come alive, to enjoy it at its vibrant best. Even so, so haphazard were his performances post-1982, it is hard to rate Botham accurately and there are a number of other players who can lay claim to his crown as the premier all-rounder of the modern era. Domestically, too, players such as Gooch, Gatting, Brearley, Willis and Gower would have their supporters in any election to find England's most valuable player of the Botham years. What none can rival is the relationship that Botham enjoyed with the British public: Botham put more bums on seats than anyone else, and for that achievement alone English cricket should be eternally grateful.

What follows is a look at the key elements of Botham's life. It is ordered thematically though for those that require a jog to the memory, a chronology is included in the appendix. The facts and fictions of Botham's life are already a matter of public record, but they provide just a part of the tale, showering us with conflicting evidence. It seems that what is now required is a degree of objectivity and a wider perspective on the man's life and times. I hope that the following chapters will contribute towards a better understanding of England's most famous cricketer.

CHAPTER ONE

MAY YOU LIVE IN INTERESTING TIMES

The County Game

Cricketers achieve greatness in the Test arena. International matches are the be all and end all of the game. A ground like Edgbaston can be packed to overflowing for a dull, one-sided Test match occasion, yet the following week a far more absorbing duel in the County Championship can be played out before a couple of hundred spectators. One of the great Championship games of modern times between Warwickshire and Northamptonshire in 1995 struggled to attract more than a couple of thousand paying spectators to Edgbaston over its four see-sawing days.

Whatever the differences in profile between county and international matches county cricket is the bedrock of the English game. Future Test talents are forged in its arenas, and valuable experience gained in what is still, despite claims to the contrary, a competitive environment for most of the season. This is where a player grows towards greatness. If a young man cannot make his mark domestically, the call will never come from the English selectors. Naturally, some people make a bigger and quicker impact; most build gradually over three or four years, registering 1000 runs in a season, then 1200, 1600, 2000, accompanied by a slowly increasing average and an 'A' tour or two, before graduating to full honours. This is the path followed by the likes of Graham Thorpe and Dominic Cork in the last few years. Some explode onto the domestic scene, demanding a place in the England side – Graham Gooch had played fewer than twenty first class games before representing his country. Surprisingly, although Ian Botham made a big splash in his first full season with Somerset, he belongs to the former category, a player who built incrementally on his strengths over three seasons.

Botham was always likely to end up with Somerset. Born in Heswall, Cheshire on 24 November 1955, he had a peripatetic childhood. His father Les was serving in the Fleet Air Arm and so Botham the toddler spent his time in Londonderry before the family returned to his native county. Within a year or so Ian, Les, mother Marie and younger sister Dale had moved to Yeovil and put down some roots. Botham senior was working for Westland Helicopters and the family were happy to settle in the very heart of the West Country. Ian went to a small private school before moving on to Milford Juniors for the autumn term of 1962, where he was introduced to football and cricket. An enthusiastic child, he made the school teams well in advance of his age, holding his own among the older boys. It was clear that Ian Botham was something a little out of the ordinary. A love of sport ran in the family: his father played most games during his stint in the Fleet Air Arm and his mother was a keen cricketer, captaining the VAD nursing service during 1946.

For some kids, the prospect of going to a larger secondary school is a daunting one. Not for Botham, who approached his transfer to Buckler's Mead with relish, admitting in his autobiography that 'my sheer bloody-mindedness about getting my own way was well established'. He already knew what he wanted to do with his life and nothing was going to stop him. Big for his age, he was able to dominate his classmates on the sports field, while his monumental desire to win helped him compete against older boys. This was all the proof he needed to show that a life in professional sport was waiting for him. The only choice was between football and cricket. Crystal Palace had offered him terms and several other clubs were carefully monitoring his development. His father counselled that he was a far better cricketer than footballer, and so the die was cast.

Nowadays, the call is to catch our kids at a young age and instil the basics of a sport in them before they can develop bad habits. The success of Australia's cricket academy suggests that there's a lot in this, as does the Ajax philosophy in football, where promising seven–year–olds are invited to play for the club's numerous junior sides. Even so, vast amounts of coaching can drive promising youngsters away from their love of sport. Turn the sports field into an extension of the classroom and enthusiasm quickly wanes. Kids want to play sport, not learn about it – Botham was the prime example. He worked on his game by playing matches anywhere and everywhere, be it a representative game for the school or an impromptu net in the back garden with his sisters bowling to him.

Already he was a big character. At home, his sisters lived in fear of being the butt of another of his practical jokes, and at school he was the centre of attention, at least where games were concerned. He was the best sportsman of his year and was very popular with his classmates as a consequence. Some of his teachers were harder to win over, driven to distraction by his refusal to knuckle down to school work. A precocious child, Botham couldn't see the need for diplomas and certificates. He'd make his mark on life with a cricket bat and ball. Having a Geography 'O' level wasn't much help when you wanted to get into a county cricket side. Though not a disruptive influence on his school, his absolute sense of assurance was unnerving for those who represented the education system, teachers who had seen many like him fail to make the sporting grade with no qualifications to fall back on. Botham continued to follow his own particular path. As he developed physically, his sporting prowess grew at a commensurate rate. Sport was all that interested him, winning all that mattered, his interest in girls first pricked only when he found one who could actually run faster than him.

Before he was fifteen, he suffered his first real cricketing set-back. Having won selection for the South West in the English Schools Under Fifteen Festival to be held in Liverpool, and having bowled well to a meticulously set field, Botham felt sure that the five wickets he'd claimed would merit selection for the England Schools side that would go on to play the Public Schools XI. Instead, his father told him that he'd overheard one selector commenting that 'it was a fluke'. This first injustice was perhaps a pivotal moment in his career. It still burned brightly enough for him to write twenty-three years later that 'whenever I managed to achieve anything on the cricket field, it gave me the greatest satisfaction to remember those blinkered observers and wonder what they were doing with their lives at that moment'. Just as important was the selectors' conclusion that Botham was primarily a batsman, not

9

an all-rounder, reasoning that his bowling wasn't up to scratch. While this desire to prove himself was a vibrant part of the young Botham who made his mark in international cricket, it became a handicap later on when he was determined to show that he was a great bowler long after those days had passed.

That failure in Liverpool was swiftly consigned to the history books when later that same year he was accepted on to the groundstaff at Lord's. On the recommendation of Somerset he had a trial there in August 1971 and was invited back the following year. With his confidence still intact despite the snub he'd received from the Schools selectors, Botham went about his new job with relish. At Lord's he got to bowl at members of the MCC in the nets, something that helped build his formidable stamina. Given that he found some MCC members supercilious and full of airs – as well as being poor tippers – it also helped feed the fires of his hostility towards batsmen. Cricket aside, Botham had a riotous time now that he was unleashed on the big city, away from home for the first time. He shared digs with the young South African Rodney Ontong, who went on to play county cricket for Glamorgan. The two worked hard at Lord's, but away from the ground they made up for time lost during the day with most evenings spent wrapped around a pint or two.

A second year at Lord's was planned for 1973, but Botham had broken into Somerset's Second XI by then. In the under twenty-five county competition, he made a name for himself by taking three Glamorgan wickets in the final over when they'd required just eight to win. Participating in the Minor Counties Championship, Somerset Seconds came in second behind Shropshire. Botham averaged almost thirty-one from his ten innings, though his bowling was unremarkable at this stage – nine wickets at thirty-two. Based on those performances, few had much faith in his talent; many of his Somerset contemporaries felt that he was a useful cricketer but hardly an explosive one. Writing in *It Sort Of Clicks*, Peter Roebuck noted that 'at the age of sixteen [in 1972], no one I know predicted that Botham would break through ... he might be a useful belter down the order but you couldn't play that way in county cricket'. Having said that, given Somerset's slender resources, it was seemingly just a matter of time before he made the leap into the first team. He even managed to get into their one day side at the end of 1973.

However, it was in 1974 that Botham made his breakthrough, under the wing of Brian Close. Botham, once again, timed his arrival to perfection. After years as a backwoods side, as a team that enjoyed its cricket but was never competing for honours, Brian Close had begun to forge a club that played good aggressive cricket and was acquiring the winning habit. Though Close never managed to lead the county to a trophy, he was the pivotal figure in helping the club land its first ever trophies in 1979 when Somerset clinched both the John Player League and the Gillette Cup. Somerset were clearly a maturing side when Botham joined their ranks. They had old stagers such as Close, Graham Burgess and Derek Taylor on hand to provide experience and discipline on the field for youngsters like Botham who were making their claims to the future of the county.

Just as Botham had lived life to the full in the company of Rodney Ontong at Lord's, he was soon adopting a similar attitude with spinner Dennis Breakwell. In 1973, the two shared a flat that seemed little better than a squat. So dismal were their surroundings, they spent most of their spare time in the local pubs and clubs, putting off the inevitable moment when they had to return home to a sleeping bag on the floor and a couple of cockroaches for company. As the two moved up the pecking order at Somerset, Botham's salary increasing to £500 for 1974, the pair moved out to share a flat next door to the county ground with the club's newest import, Vivian Richards. Richards was no slouch as a socialiser either and the three enjoyed one another's company. The bond between Botham and Richards was especially strong. The two were inseparable mates at county level, sharing a similar passionate belief in their cricketing destinies. Within a few years both were thrust towards superstardom by their efforts on the field; away from the game they could talk and share each other's problems, knowing that they were two of the few men in the world who could really understand the pressures involved. As the two most famous cricketers of their generation, it was probably as well for them both that they were able to spend so much time in each other's presence.

It was Richards who first made his mark on the world scene, his

11

batting in England in 1976 verging on the Bradmanesque. Scoring two double hundreds in the four Tests he played, he established himself as the greatest batsman in the world with extraordinary ease. With an arrogant demeanour on the field, off it he took the plaudits modestly but with a sense that they were his due, the reward for a lot of hard work. Richards had grown up playing cricket on the beaches of Antigua without the inherent advantages of comparative wealth that Botham, like the vast majority of his fellow countrymen, took for granted. Richards took little for granted, and though he was always willing to go out for a drink with the boys, he always looked after himself physically and mentally. Botham was a little less circumspect, noting that while Richards slept with his bat by his side, he slept with a bottle of gin.

Brian Close instilled a Yorkshire-style professionalism in the side. In addition, he was a part of the staff who had groomed a new generation of players, men like Botham, Roebuck, Rose, Slocombe and Marks. The talents of these young men were complemented and enhanced by the phenomenal batting skills and absolute confidence of Vivian Richards, probably *the* county cricketer of the 1970s. Yet, as *Wisden* pointed out, in 1974 it was Botham who 'showed star quality ... his successful fight to win the Benson & Hedges quarter final at Taunton showed technical abilities underlined by courage and temperament of the highest order'. It was that game on 12 June that established Botham in the minds of the cricketing public. Hampshire had scored a moderate 182 (Botham two for thirty-three from his eleven overs) but Somerset collapsed to 113 for 8 with fifteen overs left. Botham, coming in at number nine, had just Hallam Moseley and Bob Clapp for company, neither of whom could rank among the adequates with a bat. With Somerset scarcely any closer to their target, West Indian paceman Andy Roberts, one of the quickest bowlers in the world, came on, ostensibly to finish the game. Within moments, Botham took a fierce blow in the mouth from a Roberts bouncer. The all-rounder spat out a couple of broken teeth, had a glass of water, and then proceeded to thrash the living daylights out of an astonished Hampshire attack. Victory came when Botham hammered yet another boundary to clinch the game by one wicket with an over to spare, finishing with forty-five not out and the Gold Award as man of the match. That sort of display was headline news across the country, though as he was firmly informed by some seasoned Somerset pros, he was famous today, nobody again tomorrow. That was good advice, for the rest of the season was a comparative anti-climax, although he did enough to catch the eye of *Wisden* editor Norman Preston. In his notes to the 1975 almanack, he took the unusual step of commending him to the selectors: 'I would particularly like to see Botham given a chance while he is young and enthusiastic.'

Botham returned for 1975 as an established player but failed to make such a powerful impact. He suffered from second season syndrome: players who are an unknown quantity in their debut season are soon worked out by their fellow professionals. Botham's bowling was solid if unspectacular – 'a useful seam bowler of increasing pace', according to *Wisden* – and his batting was intermittently brilliant but largely disappointing. At this stage, Botham was all promise with little delivery. Of that season, Close felt that 'he tried to make things happen and things don't always happen in cricket'.

Botham would never agree with what he would see as defeatism. He would play county cricket the way he played Schools cricket, hurling the ball down, staring out opposing batsmen and belting the leather off the ball. That was what had worked in Yeovil, it would work at Lord's, Taunton and Headingley too. That blinding confidence carried him through two fairly ordinary years, statistically speaking. What *did* make its mark was his competitive spirit, his willingness to bowl all day, his desire to win every individual battle, every game in which he took part. Brian Close was a wily enough captain to recognise that such a temperament was rare indeed. Cricket is a mind game as much as a physical one and many have failed simply because they cannot cope with the pressure out on the pitch – Mark Ramprakash, for example, was summarily dismissed from the England scene by Ray Illingworth since he believed that here was another fine player who couldn't handle the Test match spotlight. Close saw that Botham would never be lacking in confidence or faith in his ability and that the only danger was of overestimating his own talents. Writing in his 1978 autobiography, Close also pointed out that 'he is the ideal type for the present-day game, a natural all-rounder ... experience and time will teach him to temper his aggression with a little patience: an exciting prospect for the future'.

In spite of Close's belief in him, had Somerset had more players on call, perhaps it might have taken Botham a little longer to win a regular place in the side. Part of Botham's problem as well as his attraction was that his game was built largely on belligerence in those early days. As a nineteen-year-old he was fit, but against older men he was not always strong enough to get away with some of his more extravagant play. By 1976 he had matured physically and was starting to look more like the man mountain that terrorised opponents for the next few years. His figures reflect this passage from strapping adolescent to full manhood. Bowling a yard or two quicker, he took sixty Championship wickets at twenty-seven. More significantly, with Viv Richards touring with the West Indians, Botham seized the opportunity his absence offered. Underlining a lesson that few learned in his career, Botham was at his best when accepting responsibility for the team. Taking the burden of replacing Viv's runs on himself, he began to bat at number four, passed 1000 first class runs for the season, and scored his maiden hundred, a blistering 167 not out at Trent Bridge where he hammered the Nottinghamshire attack into the ground, hitting six sixes and twenty fours. Thanks to that knock, Somerset successfully chased what had seemed a stiff target of 301 to win with plenty of time to spare. Unlike the Benson & Hedges game with Hampshire two years before, this was no false dawn. Ian Botham had arrived. *Wisden* felt that over the season he 'played a large number of exciting attacking innings, and if many subsided in over-ambition, he frequently showed the ability to harness his enormous talent to building a large innings'. Their summary closed with one of the great understatements: 'at twenty, he will surely get many further chances to advance in the game'.

Although he managed a place in the England side for the one day internationals at the end of 1976, he was disappointed to miss out on the chance of touring India under Tony Greig in 1976/77. Perhaps that was a blessing in disguise, for instead he wintered in Australia under a Whitbread sponsorship scheme, though he admitted to sulking for days on end when the chance to visit India had been denied him. That Australian trip broadened his experience, though his actual playing returns were quite meagre; because of the way the scholarship was organised, he spent more time surfing than playing cricket on his visit.

Off the field he was able to make a name for himself, in typical Botham fashion, via an unedifying brawl with Ian Chappell in a Sydney bar.

When he got back to Taunton for the 1977 season, he was hotly tipped as the coming man in English cricket, his new popularity following the Chappell incident doing him no harm with a press always on the look out for someone to provide stories. Once Tony Greig's involvement with Packer was announced in the first weeks of the season, all eyes turned to Botham as his natural successor in the England team. Raising his game to meet these new circumstances, he proceeded to demonstrate that he had the temperament to withstand any sporting pressures. His early season performances were impressive: five wickets in a rain-ruined game against Glamorgan; a half century against Nottinghamshire; and five wickets and scores of fifty-nine and thirty-nine not out against the touring Australians. Although he wasted a week carrying the drinks during the one day internationals, when the call finally came from the England selectors for him to join the party at Trent Bridge for the Third Test, Botham was ready. Unrecognisable from the bucolic character who had first got his chance under Brian Close, his all round game had responded to the disciplines of county cricket while his aggressive character and utter faith in his abilities remained undimmed. They were the classic components of the Test match temperament.

For a lot of players, once they've broken into the England side county cricket can seem like a chore. Often there's a lot of discontent among county members that their England star seems unable to put the same effort into his bread and butter job – Bob Willis and David Gower often stood accused of that failing. Initially, at least, Botham had no trouble putting everything into his game at Somerset. Perhaps he was fortunate that Somerset were living through exciting times, always in the running for trophies. Even so, his regular absences from the side over the next few years meant that Somerset were never really in any position to challenge for the County Championship. In 1977, he managed to play in twelve of the twenty-two fixtures, in 1978 he played ten matches, eleven in 1979. Given that Somerset were never in the running for the three-day crown, it was hard for Botham, now used to the adrenalin that flowed during a Test match, to respond to the challenge of a cold day in Taunton in front of 150 people. The more Test cricket he played, the less enticing the Championship games became. Nevertheless, he continued to be an important member of the side, particularly in their quest for a one day title, their best chance of success. With the addition of the mighty Joel Garner, one of the finest of the limited overs bowlers, Somerset were a formidable team.

Ironically, Botham was not always the master of the one day situation. As an attacking cricketer it might seem he was ideally suited to its peculiar demands, but as the game evolved domestically it was often the more cautious, canny cricketers who came out on top. As a bowler, the young Botham was so determined to take wickets, so keen to experiment, that he could be costly; in limited overs cricket, eleven overs bowled for twenty without taking a wicket is eminently preferable to eleven overs bowled for sixty, even if the latter spell contains two or three scalps. That was anathema to his way of thinking. Though he did manage to bowl some miserly spells, he was fortunate that his profligacy at one end was balanced by the economy of Garner at the other. The fact that Garner would rarely concede more than a couple of runs per over gave Botham a little extra licence to bowl aggressively and look to pick up wickets, leeway he rarely got with England.

Somerset, a county without any trophy, came astonishingly close to breaking their duck throughout the 1970s. In 1978 they cruised to the Gillette Cup Final where they met unfancied Sussex, a side they'd trounced by 102 runs in the Benson & Hedges Cup earlier in the year. Having seen Brian Rose take fourteen off Imran's opening over, Somerset collapsed. Richards reached forty-four, a comparative failure by his standards, and it was left to Botham to nurse the side to a reasonable total of 207, another example of his willingness to take on responsibility. His eighty was the Somerset mainstay but no one was able to offer him enough assistance. When he bowled, his twelve overs cost sixty-five, and though he got rid of Imran and Barclay, Sussex romped home. The following day Somerset had the chance to atone. Back at Taunton, they needed only a tie (or a no result) from their game against Essex to take the John Player League. Set 190 to win, they batted with unaccustomed indecision. Botham top scored with forty-five as his team fell short by just two runs. Somerset had paid for their caution at the death, their determination to win – or rather, their fear of defeat –

overcoming their natural inclination to excite and entertain. Botham was to remember the pain of those defeats for a long time. His resolve that he would not lose sheepishly again in future surely contributed to his downfall as England captain, notably in his dismissal at the hands of Viv Richards in Trinidad. The utter determination to take the fight to the opposition, recklessly on occasion, was a trait he rarely managed to subdue.

Richards and Botham reaped the benefits from playing in a side and in a location that offered them a kind of relaxation away from the pressures of playing for a side like Surrey, Yorkshire or Middlesex, where expectation was high. Though they still put on some good displays in the Championship, their efforts were concentrated on one day cricket, a format in which Somerset could be expected to compete with the best. If the crowd and committee indulged their occasional three-day failings because of this, they also revelled in the marketable nature of their two superstars. There were Botham T-shirts, Richards posters, Somerset hats and the like providing a lucrative sideline for a county that had never had any financial clout in the past. In addition, by 1980 membership subscriptions alone raised £100,000 surpassing the 1978 record of £45,000. Such records continued to fall for a number of years. The club found itself presented with a commercially sustainable future, no longer dictated to by the penny-pinching needs of the pre-Botham and Richards era.

Their two West Indian stars were wholly committed to the club, and it showed in 1979 when they returned to make amends for the failures of the previous year. This time around there was to be no mistake. Although their assault on the Benson & Hedges Cup ended in ignominy – they were disqualified when captain Brian Rose declared their innings closed after one over in a group match in order to protect their run rate, within the laws of the game but outside its spirit – they moved serenely on to the Gillette Cup Final. Botham took three for fifteen and Garner five for eleven to brush Kent aside in the quarter-finals, while four more Garner wickets and a powerful ninety from Peter Denning beat Middlesex in the semis. Against Northamptonshire in the final Somerset were in complete control from the outset, winning by forty-five runs. Richards scored a peerless hundred and Botham came in to

17

bludgeon twenty-seven in a partnership of forty-one that lasted just seven overs, to take their score out of reach. The following day, Somerset travelled to Trent Bridge needing to beat Nottinghamshire to take the John Player League. With just 185 to defend, Botham nipped out Hassan early on and returned to finish the game by trapping Mike Bore lbw. After 104 years without a trophy, the club had won two in two days. Having finally broken their duck, Somerset looked poised to dominate the one day domestic agenda for the next five years and more. Their side was a nice balance of the explosive – Botham and Richards – the thoughtful – Roebuck, Marks and Rose – and the experienced – Burgess and Taylor. As players like Botham continued to mature, the side could only get better.

That disqualification from the Benson & Hedges Cup was a defining moment, for it showed just how desperately Somerset wanted to win, how much it now mattered to them. As Peter Roebuck noted in *It Sort Of Clicks*, 'like Viv and Vic [Marks], perhaps even Joel, Ian is more emotionally committed to the county than he'd care to admit'. Yet being England's brightest star meant that Botham had to lead a schizophrenic existence: most of his thoughts inevitably focused on the national side. This was never more true than in 1980 when he was elevated to the England captaincy. Often his performances for the county seemed to be little more than reactions to his troubles elsewhere. Heaving that mighty sledgehammer bat, he set out his credentials for the captaincy by flaying Warwickshire for 126 in 109 minutes and then celebrated his new status by taking 228 off Gloucestershire in four minutes over three hours with ten sixes and twenty-seven fours. As the season progressed and the level of criticism grew, Somerset's opponents felt the weight of his frustration. His innings were often brief, but always furious – ninety-four in eighty minutes against Worcestershire, for example. Even so, he topped Somerset's Championship averages with 875 runs at 62.5, but there were no new trophies as the side lost Richards and Garner to the touring West Indians and Rose and Botham to England. Even when Botham did play for the county, he was so hampered by a serious back injury that he rarely bowled in anger.

The next year, 1981, was another season of reaction for the all-rounder. By now, the writing was on the wall as far as the England captaincy was concerned. The Chinese water torture dripped on until after the Second Test at Lord's in the first week of July. In the game before that inevitable demotion, having all but decided to relinquish the captaincy, Botham had plundered 123 in 137 minutes from Glamorgan. Once he had announced his intentions after his pair at the Lord's Test, he relaxed by picking up three for twenty-three in the Benson & Hedges semi-final against Kent and then took six for ninety and played what *Wisden* called 'a dazzling innings' of seventy-two against Sussex. The rest of the summer was his in England colours, but with Somerset it was anti-climactic once the Benson & Hedges Cup was won. Understandably drained by his efforts in the Tests, he fired only intermittently. When he did, it was glorious, but mentally he often seemed to be elsewhere.

The next couple of seasons followed the same pattern. In 1982, the Benson & Hedges Cup was retained with ease, Botham taking two for nineteen as Somerset restricted Nottinghamshire to 130, but consistency eluded them. He cracked 131 in sixty-five minutes to clinch an unlikely win against Warwickshire – his hundred came off fifty-six balls – but sixth was all they could manage in the Championship. The following summer, Botham captained the side intelligently in Rose's absence, playing a match-winning innings in the NatWest semi-final win over Middlesex, guiding his side home with disciplined strokeplay, then repeating his excellent leadership in victory in the final. Still he seemed reluctant to bowl – 119 overs in ten games wasn't hard labour. By now, Somerset were looking purely to the one day game for success, apparently dismissing any hopes of a serious tilt at the title. There was a suspicion that Somerset were beginning a transitional phase. Perhaps some members of the trophy-winning teams weren't as hungry as they had been and needed fresh challenges. Certainly County Championship encounters no longer lit as bright a fire of ambition as once they had; though racked by injury, tenth place was the poorest result for some time. Over a couple of seasons, some of the senior players had begun to look jaded, exhausted by the sheer volume of cricket they had played around the world. By1985, Botham for one was tiring of the daily grind of the game and was in need of fresh momentum. As he demonstrated with his eighty sixes in that summer the county game did not stretch him; he no longer needed it as his power base and he often treated it with a withering contempt.

Much has been made in recent times of the frailty of the Championship game while there have been many recommendations that our top performers should be rested from them at the behest of the England management – Graeme Hick and Mike Atherton were involved in minor skirmishes on that point in 1996. It's significant that the only time a side can guarantee to field a full-strength outfit is in the Benson & Hedges and NatWest games. These are scheduled specifically so that they do not clash with Test matches, an indication of the priorities within the English game: money comes before quality.

It has to be accepted that the County Championship is economically unviable. It's unlikely that it ever will be again, for any game that unfolds during the day in the midst of the working week is doomed to failure, though more adventurous pricing could attract pensioners, children and those not currently working. Even so, any such increases in revenue would inevitably be minimal. It is the one day games, great occasions such as a NatWest semi-final, that get the punters through the gates. The Sunday League has become something of an institution, a regular family day out for many. One day cricket is a vital part of the programme and it can help the overall development of some players; good players can succeed in any form of cricket. Any batsman that can hit powerfully and selectively will do well. A bowler that can maintain a good length and line under pressure will prove invaluable. Even so, the conventional wisdom is that the one day game can stunt professional growth and lead to technical problems when under the microscope of the five-day game. Certainly the 1996 Indian tourists, starved of Test cricket, seemed at sea in the first of the three Test series. If that is so, then perhaps our top players need to play more Championship cricket and fewer one day games. One day matches would continue to thrive with or without their presence simply because they offer the package people require: like a good play, a limited overs game has a beginning, middle and an end, all in one day. In contrast, if you can only spare the time to see one day of a county game, you will hopefully see some good cricket but not in its full context. Without context, a dogged defensive innings or a spell of express pace bowling is interesting but largely meaningless.

Nevertheless, this is the form of the game in which players must excel if they want to make a go of Test cricket. Botham had to make his runs and take his wickets all over the country before he made the Test side. Perhaps once a player reaches the England team, he should be excused the exhausting one day duties instead of Championship chores, for a tight one day game is infinitely more taxing.

Botham was close to burn-out on a number of occasions. If he'd been spared the hurly burly of a Sunday afternoon, perhaps he would have stayed fitter for longer. There are adverse financial implications for the individuals involved which would have to be addressed, but this is not an insurmountable problem given the substantial rewards available to an England regular. In addition, for those players who replace the England star there is the chance to play in matches which often mean more to the club, certainly in terms of pressure. This would help selectors to see whether an up and coming individual can cope with the tension that is the very stuff of Test matches. The down side to this is that young talents who are attempting to find their way in the game can find it hard dealing with the changing requirements of first class and one day cricket. Yet good players – the ones who are going to become top quality Test stars – can cope with either. Ian Botham did.

However, this does not address the central problem. Should these England players be excused county commitments? Net practice is still considered a vital part of honing skills. If that's true, the corollary to good practice is better match play. Therefore, should not Test players be required to play *more* County Championship cricket? The difficulty there lies in motivation. If a player has just scored a hundred to win a Test at the Oval, where's the attraction in returning to an unimportant Championship game against Glamorgan in Cardiff? If you happen to be an Ian Botham, that doesn't necessarily matter. As Phil Neale, his captain at Worcester, pointed out, 'Ian always wanted to win, whether it was a big game or not. He just wanted to win.' Some of his international colleagues have shown less commitment to their respective counties, and had Botham not been reinvigorated by his move to Worcester, perhaps he too would have lost interest in the domestic scene.

One argument against county cricket, and a strong one too, is that a player needs to be fresh in order to give full expression to his ability.

There is a lot to be said for this, but it ignores the fact that quick bowlers like Allan Donald and Courtney Walsh seem to manage the trick. Similarly, if a batsman makes nought in his only innings of a Test and then goes two weeks before playing another innings, again in a Test match, he could justifiably complain of feeling rusty and out of touch. What the experience of players like Ian Botham teaches us is that good players will take what they want from the county game and that no one can prevent them from doing so. If a good cricketer has a point to prove – Botham post-captaincy, Gower in 1992 – he will do so conclusively. If he is secure in the England team, he will treat county opposition accordingly. If the mood takes him, he'll hammer the bowling to all four corners of the ground in a masterly exhibition of strokeplay. On another day, there'll be a few quick runs and a swift return to the dressing room. Some, those from the Boycott school of thought, will treat each county game as though their lives, or at least their averages, depend on it. Others, on the eve of a Test for example, might look for a confidence-boosting net out in the middle, or might spend the afternoon studiously trying to avoid the captain's eye and an exhausting spell of bowling into the wind. This is not to say that these players are not committed to their county, but rather that no individual can be a world-beater every day. It is impossible for some to maintain the necessary level of intensity away from the Test match arena.

There's a belief that English cricket is now too soft – certainly Botham believes that to be the case. Since the days of Botham's prime, the international schedule has become more punishing. Tours last longer, there are more matches crammed in, and, with the growth in satellite television, players are under the microscope more than ever. That must put a lot of mental as well as physical pressure upon a Test team, particularly its captain, more even than when Botham was under attack through the 1980s. That's not going to change. If anything, the pressure to win will intensify. Mark Taylor has been a very successful leader and yet, having won the first two Tests of the 1996/97 series against the West Indies, once he ceased to score his customary heap of runs and Australia lost out in the one day games and the Third Test, his position was apparently under on-going threat. To grasp the rewards that are on offer, a professional cricketer will have to harden himself to these pressures, be they rightly or wrongly applied. Some suggest that to instil such steel we split the Championship into two divisions, playing just eight four-day games a year. Though that is a model similar to the Sheffield Shield in Australia, which has been producing top class Test cricketers in abundance recently, it's one that would have significant drawbacks here. The theory is that if there are only eight games to be played, that's a maximum of sixteen innings in which to bat or bowl, and each opportunity is therefore precious. In the current domestic format, it is argued, an up and coming player is less focused as he knows he'll get another chance tomorrow. But does that hold true? No player actually likes getting out or being hammered all round the ground to take one for eighty from twenty overs. Each player has a high level of pride – if they don't, they don't last long in the county game.

Even if we agree that a reduction to eight games might help players physically, will it improve their game? A prerequisite is decent surfaces on which to play and there are precious few of those around the country. So many games are finishing well inside three days because of pitches that favour the bowlers that the players aren't getting the opportunity to play properly. Another problem is the English weather. In Australia, the chances are a four-day game won't be too badly affected by rain or poor light. In a wet summer with just eight first class games, a top order batsman might be lucky to play nine or ten innings, while a front-line bowler might manage just 200 overs. This is scarcely enough for them to hone their skills. Botham became a top flight bowler by sending down 2126 overs in his first four seasons; given his aversion to what he saw as meaningless net practice, it was vital that he got through so much work out in the middle. Bowlers learn how to bowl by bowling. And pity the poor spinners in damp weather on seaming pitches.

Combative cricket makes for combative cricketers; the improvement seen in both Nick Knight and Ashley Giles after moving to Warwickshire is proof of that. Although Ian Botham had enough competitive spirit for a whole team, it was sharpened by the dressing room environment in which he developed and by the level of cricket he played. If Brian Close was the foremost of the Somerset personalities, Botham also learned much from Vivian Richards. In his book *The Enemy Within*, Alastair McLellan makes the telling point that 'if Vic Marks and Peter

Roebuck were the brains of Somerset's impressive late 1970s and early 1980s team, and Ian Botham was the sinew, then Viv Richards was the heart'. Perhaps this is where English cricket has lost its edge in recent years. Since the number of overseas players per county was reduced to just one (in most cases) from 1987, English cricket has hardly been awash with wonderful new talent. Yet overseas cricketers were, supposedly, inhibiting Englishmen. Just look at some of the Englishmen who came through between 1968, when the overseas contingent first made their mark, and 1987, when change was effected. Among the batsmen there are players such as Gooch, Randall, Gatting and Gower, among the bowlers the likes of Willis, Hendrick, Emburey, Edmonds and Dilley. Then, of course, there is Ian Botham. Any one of those players would walk into the current England side, selectoral eccentricity excepted.

These were the players who came through when the competition from the foreign players was at its stiffest. Rather than stifling the development of English talent, the presence of great players from around the world seems to have provided an incentive. Only the very best English talent broke through, and then went on to do well on the international stage. They had to be determined, bloody-minded, confident and, more than anything else, good. Very good. If the English game is weak now, it is because a couple of places that could be filled by talented Australians, Pakistanis or South Africans are being filled by mediocre Englishmen. In addition, how could any potential Test match cricketer be harmed by spending a year or two playing with and against Wasim Akram, Dean Jones, Allan Border, Viv Richards, Michael Holding, Richard Hadlee, Waqar Younis, Allan Donald or David Boon? Didn't Botham come to prominence by taking on and beating Andy Roberts? If a youngster is good enough, he'll get into the side. The best way to improve the quality of county cricket is to make it fiercely competitive by the reintroduction of another overseas player per team, always providing that said player is of top Test match standard – quality thresholds would need to be introduced. We need to produce more young Bothams, Gowers and Gattings, cricketers with the hunger, the desire and the determination to do well, men who are not awestruck when they come across Courtney Walsh in Kingston or Shane Warne in Sydney.

It was the presence, or rather the sacking, of the overseas players that brought Botham's time with Somerset to a close, though it was a parting of the ways that was always coming. Captain in 1984 and 1985, Botham was determined to maintain Somerset's glory years as a springboard for another assault on the England captaincy, yet so often was he away on England duty, he managed to play just twenty-two of Somerset's forty-eight Championship games. Without the necessary continuity, it was almost impossible for him to lead the side in any coherent fashion. In 1984, Martin Crowe, replacement for the touring Richards, was a huge success and Marks, Roebuck and Popplewell showed marked improvements, but Somerset came seventh in the Championship, thirteenth in the Sunday League, and were quarter-finalists in the Benson & Hedges and NatWest competitions. These were miserable performances for a county used to success. The following year, Rose, Roebuck, Wyatt, Felton and Garner all suffered serious injuries; twenty-four men represented the team in the Championship. The club slumped to bottom of the Championship, tenth in the John Player League, fell at the first hurdle in the Benson & Hedges, and made the quarter-finals of the NatWest. Unable to turn the tide, Botham seemed more interested in hitting a record number of sixes than in galvanising his team to better things. Perhaps the presence of Richards inhibited him as captain, possibly he felt that his six-hitting translated into leadership from the front – he did average one hundred in the Championship after all. More likely he was simply taking out his anger on the opposing bowlers in the absence of the communication skills necessary to motivate youngsters who were in awe of him.

Botham's spell as captain ended in failure and he relinquished the captaincy for 1986, Peter Roebuck taking over. Tellingly, Botham then accepted a one-, rather than two-year playing contract. In their joint book, *It Sorts Of Clicks*, Roebuck pointed out that

he had a vision of a beautiful world at Somerset, where he and his mates, arriving in eccentric clothes to upset the fuddy-duddies, would laugh and drink the nights away, and then storm around defeating all the conventional types with their managers and their serious faces. He wanted his team to play by his own lights, with an anarchic, daredevil spirit. Above all, he wanted Somerset to do well . . . but Ian could not communicate his vision, he wanted it simply to happen. Nor did he show his younger team-mates that he wanted his team to do well . . . they saw his anarchism not as hilarious but as destructive.

He missed much of the 1986 season because of the ban which followed his *Mail on Sunday* revelations that he had smoked pot. Once he returned with form that was 'thunderous even by his standards', according to *Wisden*, it was clear that things were not as they once were. In his 'County Cricket' column in *Wisden Cricket Monthly*, David Foot, that seasoned observer of the West Country cricketing scene who had collaborated with Viv Richards on his autobiography, had been hinting that a time of reckoning was coming for the club. In his summary of the season in the October 1986 issue, he noted, 'ordinary players, lesser mortals, have confided that there have been too many disruptive elements. The cult of the personality has worked rather cruelly against them.' A small club by county standards, Somerset was no longer big enough to handle men who had become internationally famous. Had he played for Surrey, Botham might have had some anonymity in the capital city, but in Taunton he was a whale in a garden pond.

The events that cloaked Somerset in darkness for some months differ according to which side is doing the telling. They were brought to a head by the thorny issue of the overseas player. A change in the rules for domestic cricket meant that each county would be able to field only one overseas player, an exception was made if a player was contracted prior to 1979. That meant that both Richards and Garner could still play in the same Somerset team for as long as they wished. So far, so good. However, Somerset's fortunes, so buoyant in the early 1980s, had taken a tumble over the previous couple of years. Garner had fallen foul of the stresses and strains to which all quick bowlers are prey and had missed a lot of games. Richards, though still the world's leading batsman – the fastest ever Test hundred in Antigua in April 1986 was proof of that – seemed stale with Somerset, and could not raise himself to the heights with such regularity, though perhaps he too was affected by events off the field. Certainly the Somerset chairman had asked him earlier in the season whether or not he might feel it was time to give county cricket a rest. In the background there was New Zealander Martin Crowe, who had made such an impact in his year with the county in 1984 scoring 1900 runs and taking forty-four wickets, positively Bothamesque. In addition, *Wisden* noted that 'his mature influence and general deportment rounded out a wonderful introduction to county cricket'.

David Foot revealed further disquiet in his November 1986 column in *Wisden Cricket Monthly*: 'Somerset ended the season one from the bottom. It was a wretched season. A summer which opened with a vibrant enthusiasm under a new captain became distorted by controversy. The media's attention for Botham must have been disruptive for many of the young pros. One told me, "All I want to do is play cricket in a normal atmosphere. I'm sick of this personality cult."' Inevitably Botham's return to the side after his drugs ban caught the headlines. TV, radio and newspapers swamped Somerset's games to report on the rehabilitation of England's all-rounder; the attention was more intense since England were in the process of losing to India and then New Zealand on home soil. For Botham, the publicity was a mixed blessing. He revelled in the limelight but resented the intrusion. And the Somerset dressing room was no longer the haven it had been. Five years earlier it was full of men with whom he had grown up. Now there was just Roebuck – with whom he was soon to fall out – Marks, Garner and Richards. Somerset were rebuilding and the new boys were understandably cowed by sharing a dressing room with these legends whose great abilities allowed them to cruise through the county games. Many suggest that a divide grew between Botham's gang and the newer players, players not used to his idiosyncrasies, his disdain for practice, and so on. For his part, Botham found it hard to understand anyone who was not as robust as himself, who could not burn the candle at both ends and still clatter a century before lunch the following day.

In *It Sort Of Clicks*, there's a revealing passage that shows the gulf between Botham and mere mortals. Roebuck writes: 'In 1985, he gambled ... with Somerset plagued by injuries he summoned a lager-drinking friend of his to play against Glamorgan. Luck did not smile upon this gamble, for the friend (one of the best players in club cricket) tore a muscle before or during the game – it was not clear which, though he had been lying on the physiotherapist's table before taking to the field – and was a virtual passenger in a match which was lost on its last ball. [This was] a devastating blow to Ian's standing in the team.' As Roebuck added, had this typical gamble worked, Botham would have been hailed a genius, yet they seldom did. As a county captain he was willing to take a chance, but these so often relied on others to pull off the kind of audacious stunt of which only he was capable. Brian Close's axiom that he wouldn't ask any player to do something that he wouldn't do did not work for Botham – his whole career had been built around doing things that nobody else could. Ironically, by now he was better suited to the demands of captaining England where experienced players could, or were at least more likely to be able to, do the extra-ordinary. At Somerset, younger players in the team apparently felt his leadership was at best insensitive to their particular needs, at worst simply wilful; these new talents, lesser players perhaps than colleagues such as Marks or Roebuck, needed discipline, not maverick leadership. Given the pressure that Botham was under following the drug stories emanating from the 1983/84 New Zealand tour, it was understandable if sub-consciously he did not always concentrate fully on the plight of his youthful charges. The fact that he lived in North Yorkshire during his tenure as captain could hardly have helped – as Bob Willis had pointed out in his 1978 *Diary Of A Cricket Season*, 'My only fear for him is that his interminable chasing up and down the country may eventually get him down. I could do it at twenty-two, but I couldn't now.' Willis was twenty-nine when he wrote those words. In 1984 when he ascended to the Somerset captaincy, Botham was twenty-eight. Even he must have been prey to fatigue.

When the Somerset crown passed to Roebuck and Botham then had to sit on the sidelines because of suspension, his authority dwindled still further, yet as far as the press were concerned, Somerset was still Bothamshire. In the dressing room things were a little different. As Botham's position weakened, so too did that of Viv Richards. The two had long been inseparable, forming the most potent of cricketing double acts. The first rumours of Botham's possible defection from Somerset apparently arose in the middle of the summer as soon as he had returned from his ban – Roebuck's official history of Somerset, *From Sammy To*

Jimmy, bears that out. That can only have undermined Richards further; if Botham left, he would lose his closest, most powerful ally as well as his loyal friend. While Joel Garner was fit and firing, Somerset would employ both him and Richards, but Garner was approaching the end of the road, leaving Viv exposed to the winds of change. As Botham pointed out in his autobiography, Garner only wanted to play for one more season. Effectively, that meant the committee had a straight choice between Crowe and Richards for the overseas berth, a position further complicated by Richards' inevitable absence in 1988 when he would be with the West Indian tourists.

The matter was brought to a head when Martin Crowe was approached by Essex to replace Allan Border as their overseas player for 1987. If Somerset did not act now, they would lose Crowe and still have to cast around to replace Richards in 1988. Although Botham confirms in his book that Richards had already been told he was to be offered a contract for 1987, he was called into the Somerset offices – while Botham was away and becoming the greatest wicket taker in Test history at the Oval – to be told his services were no longer required. It is this that is the most damaging reflection on the club, that they should renege on their promise. In cricketing terms, the decision between Richards and Crowe was a hairline one given Richards' forthcoming international commitments and the contrast between the club's rejuvenation in 1984 and the decline in 1985 and 1986. In Crowe's favour was his rapport with the youngsters at the club. Roebuck writes of him forming 'the youngsters into a club which met every Thursday at the Nag's Head in Taunton, wore blazers to matches and worked hard in the nets. Crowe is a magnificent coach because he has built his own game as an architect builds a house. To the apprentices he was an example and a help. Without his influence in 1985 they were much less successful.' It helped that Crowe was not a legend when he first arrived in Somerset, thus making it easier for him to fit in. Giant personalities such as Richards and Botham are often unaware of the fact that their very presence makes others feel uneasy. On the field, that gives them an edge; off it, it can make life awkward. Players like these need to make an effort to relax their team-mates, particularly if they are new to the dressing room. All too frequently older heads and the new men form separate cliques. With

Somerset needing fresh direction to clamber up the Championship table, Crowe seemed the sort of player who might break down the barriers that existed. As a cricketer he was on the threshold of a glittering career. At the start of the 1987 season, he would be just twenty-four while Richards would be thirty-five. Clearly Richards had more left to offer, but how much more? After a gruelling tour with West Indies in 1988, would he fancy another season of county cricket in 1989 when he'd be thirty-seven? With Crowe, Somerset looked assured of having available for the next three years a top class batsman who could also bowl a few useful overs. With Richards, there would be some uncertainty. On those grounds, Martin Crowe looked the better option, hard though it would be to dispense with the services of a man who had done so much to turn Somerset into a successful county. As Richards pointed out, it had been his runs that had built the new pavilion at Taunton.

Botham's stance was a little melodramatic. Certainly loyalty is to be valued and one can hardly criticise a man for the admirable trait of standing by his friends through thick and thin, but Botham and Richards were both experienced enough to know that professional sport is a ruthless business where the cliché that you're only as good as your last game holds true. As international captains, each knew that he had to have the very best side for the job out on the field. Once a player has reached the end of his useful life or is out of form he has to be replaced, otherwise the side is lost by dint of loyalty to one particular individual. That is the nature of the game, survival of the fittest. Those rational considerations went out the window as Botham blustered. It was natural that he should be desperately upset that his close friend had been let down by the club after they had offered him assurances of his retention. That was appalling behaviour, undeserving of any sympathy. Since both Richards and Botham are highly principled figures, perennial believers in the value of a handshake, both would be angered and wounded by Somerset's duplicity. Nevertheless, Botham's decision to pin a 'Judas' note above Roebuck's peg in the dressing room was pathetically juvenile, although he still states that he was proud of his actions. He followed that up with the bitter statement that 'I hope Somerset don't win anything for another hundred years. For what they did to Viv that would be fair.'

Roebuck's part in the drama is, like that of most others, clouded in mystery. Certainly as an incoming captain he would have wanted to stamp his authority on the side, not easy if the dressing room was packed with superstars. As Botham argues in his book, perhaps Roebuck was at the root of it all, keen to get Richards and Garner out of the way, happy to work with Crowe and determined to isolate himself from criticism within the side. Perhaps, too, Roebuck was a poor choice to replace Botham given that in his book *It Never Rains . . .* he had portrayed himself as mildly depressive and extremely introspective, not ideal captaincy credentials. In *From Sammy to Jimmy*, he admits that he might have handled the situation better, but insists that the breach was between the committee and the players concerned. He had no real sympathy for either.

The rights and wrongs of the affair could fill a book of their own. It is Botham's part in it all which should concern us here. If we accept the declamations of all concerned at face value, Botham emerges as an extremely loyal man given to childish demonstrations of that devotion. We might also ask whether he should have been more loyal to the club as a whole, the people who paid his wages and who had given him his break, rather than to two of his colleagues. Given his relationship with the authorities in every form, that was always unlikely. Botham's persuasive riposte would be that Somerset's actions meant they had forfeited the right to his support. They had breached the code of ethics by which he lived, a code which meant he acted first in defence of his friends and thought of the consequences much later. As later chapters will show, this was not the first example of such conduct. Such rash disregard for self interest allowed him to prosper at the crease; it did not always benefit him in life beyond the boundary.

Further questions remain unanswered. Did Botham really make threats in 1985 to leave after the 1986 season and, as some stories suggest, promise to take Richards with him? If that is the case, Somerset's actions were justifiable – they were acting to safeguard the future of the club. Was the Richards affair part of a wider agenda to rid the club of the triumvirate that was too big for some of their colleagues? The cricket committee must have known where Botham stood in relation to his friend, must have known he would quit if Richards was pushed out. Botham was so close to Richards that, even had he not been generally unsettled anyway, he would certainly have followed him out the door. In that case, why did Somerset want rid of him? The sad truth is that a personality like Botham is so big that in the media age he's simply too large for a county like Somerset to accommodate. In the West Country there is no top flight football team to deflect attention away from the cricket. The cricket is the focus of local sporting life. Botham, by definition, had to be at the very centre of it all. Initially, that was a bonus, helping the county shed its unfashionable image and capture some silverware. As time wore on and Botham became as renowned for his off the field activities, the media spotlight went from being tiresome to embarrassing, and finally to disruptive. This was not all the fault of Botham himself, but neither could he dismiss it. Whatever happened on the field, all the tabloid media saw was what Botham had done.

It was sad to hear that this great team man had been involved in the irrevocable breakdown of team spirit. At the special general meeting called by the club to discuss the Richards departure, Nigel Popplewell, speaking for the club, won the day. Popplewell had retired after 1985 and his speech was a devastating critique of the dressing room atmosphere. He told the gathered throng that through his final season the atmosphere in the side had been 'dreadful', while the commitment of Richards and Garner 'was different to everybody else's', adding that they expected maximum effort from everyone else but only contributed when it suited them. Given that Richards managed to average 76.5 in 1985 and scored 322 against Warwickshire that seems harsh, but it does reflect the breakdown between the two factions in the dressing room.

Botham's indignation was real, there's no question of that. At the same time, the turn of events acted in his favour. By now, it was obvious that for all concerned it would be better if a change were made; Botham had already intimated that much after the leadership passed to Roebuck. Without the captaincy to sustain him, he needed fresh momentum. Ian Botham was the archetypal Somerset cricketer. He played the game with a smile on his face, looked like he was enjoying his work. With those powerful shoulders and mighty forearms, he could swing the bat like the most agricultural of belters, though he was clearly no mere slogger. Botham was in the line of Woods, Wellard and Gimblett, huge hitters who entertained the Somerset public and became a vibrant part of the local folklore. In the long term that probably did Botham a disservice, for it made it easy to characterise him as just another yokel. For journalists not disposed to him, it was a short step from yokel to yob, and he was often portrayed as a thick hooligan with a bat. He might not have shown a lot of common sense on occasion, but Botham is anything but stupid. Nor is he without his cultural interests. The brash beerboy was a nice 1980s cartoon, but it hid much of what was real about Botham. By now, such idle journalism was becoming a pain in the neck and, on occasion, was threatening to turn his life upside down. Had he had a different public image, one more like that of David Gower for example, the scandal sheets would have been hard put to hang anything on him. As it was, Botham's public persona suggested he was capable of anything.

That he wanted to turn things around in both his personal and professional life was clear. He allowed his 1986 joint venture with Peter Roebuck, the book *It Sorts Of Clicks*, to be described as 'part of Ian's campaign to rebuild his reputation'. Having tried to draw a line under the drug allegations with his *Mail on Sunday* confessions, perhaps it was time for a new cricketing start too. He'd decided that the England tour in 1986/87 would be his last, choosing thereafter to winter in Queensland instead. Maybe this was the right time to pull up the roots on the domestic front. His hand was forced by Richards' sacking, but for Botham, it was all for the best. Had Richards stayed at Somerset, however, Botham might have too. Although he needed a change of scene and relished the chance to sign a more lucrative contract than that on offer at Taunton, he was comfortable there, the more so when he could exchange stories with Richards. The two men were a team and a powerful one, even if their best days were behind them. The two greats of their generation, they were a mutual support group. As the eye dimmed, each could reassure the other that he was still a giant; while neither was capable of the regular destruction of old, in each other's company they were still the greatest and would prove it. In spite of the threats, it's hard to imagine that Botham would have gone if Richards had not been torn away from Somerset.

Botham's passionate defence of his colleague did his image no harm either. As the wheels of the Somerset establishment tried to grind these free spirits into the dust, Botham was staunch in his support. That was his natural stance, he could do nothing but respond to Richards' plight, but it certainly played well to the cameras. In addition, it gave him the opportunity to leave Somerset as a hero rather than being branded as a traitor for walking out, a charge he would otherwise have found hard to refute having received a club record benefit of £90,822 from the 1984 season. Botham did not engineer these circumstances, nor did he deliberately look to profit from them, but for the first time in a while, events happened to fall in his favour.

Even so, had he imagined that every county in the country was desperate for his signature, he would have been wrong. A number of clubs were put off by his reputation, with Warwickshire pulling out of the hunt following a lot of unrest among the membership. His eventual employers, Worcestershire, were equally troubled by the prospect of having Botham on board, though the fears were soothed by the presence of Duncan Fearnley. Fearnley was Botham's bat manufacturer and had had a cordial relationship with him for a number of years. As chairman of the club, he was in a position to allay some of the more outlandish concerns that were expressed about Botham. In the final analysis, though, Phil Neale was the Worcestershire captain and, consequently, the man whose opinion was most important. It was he that would need to integrate Botham into the dressing room, he that would have to get the best from him. He never had any doubts that Botham could play a huge part in the development of Worcestershire's cricket: 'We'd been developing well as a side from the early 1980s when we'd become a young side very quickly, right through to 1985, 1986 when we were a decent side but kept losing semi-finals. We didn't quite have the final ingredient to make us winners. The ability was there, it was more a question of self belief and knowing how to win. When it became clear that Ian might be available, I was very definite that he was right for us.' Neale and his Worcestershire team had already had the proof that Botham was still a considerable county cricketer if the motivation was there:

We were the first team to play Somerset after his ban had finished, so we had two months to contemplate his comeback! He duly came back at Weston-Super-Mare, scored 104 not out in sixty-six balls, and he smacked us all around the ground and then that evening he received a cheque for about £900,000 for his John o'Groats to Land's End walk! It was around then that we first picked up the vibes that he might be available, that he wasn't happy at Somerset. I came back to Worcestershire and told everyone we should go for him. There was some anti feeling initially. Some supporters felt that Ian would be a disruptive element in a settled dressing room, and eighty or so people signed a petition against him; another twenty would have meant a special general meeting which costs the club a fortune. I put something in the local paper saying that as far as the players were concerned, we were looking forward to having him, we didn't think there'd be a problem and we wanted a top player in our midst. Duncan Fearnley and Mike Jones went off to Australia to complete the signing and came back with Graham Dilley as well which was a real coup. So for the 1987 season, we were raring to go with top quality men in the side.

The Worcestershire deal was made public in Australia on 10 January during the final Test of the Ashes tour. Though no details were revealed, it's fair to say that Botham's financial package was far better at Worcestershire than it had ever been at Somerset. And so it should have been. He was the greatest crowd pleaser of the age and deserved to share in the profits that were made off his back. Worcestershire's membership went up and, in a move not unrelated to his arrival, they announced a £100,000 sponsorship agreement with the Carphone Group and another 'lucrative' deal with the Midlands Electricity Board. Without Botham, it's unlikely that that would have happened. Some have complained that men like Botham, Gower and Gooch were too well rewarded and that it dulled their hunger. This is surely a fallacious argument. As the rewards escalate, the motivation to stay at the very top becomes greater. Are Clint Eastwood and Martin Scorsese making poorer movies now that they're wealthy men? Great sportsmen want to stay at the top for egotistical as much as financial reasons. They need to prove that they're the best, not merely the wealthiest. If their youthful tunnel-visioned approach to the sport changes, it's more to do with a widening range of interests than the cash, something that is true of most of us as we get older. *Wisden* made it clear that it felt Botham was worth every penny Worcestershire had invested in him:

> A new era dawned at New Road in 1987 as Worcestershire, inspired almost inevitably by Ian Botham, captured their first trophy for thirteen years by becoming the first winners of the Refuge Assurance League. Much of their improvement on the previous season in the Sunday competition, when they finished sixteenth, could be credited to the England all-rounder. His arrival from Somerset amid a blaze of publicity, had not met with the approval of all the members, nor with the unanimous backing of the committee. But come the final Sunday of the season when for the first time since the days of Bradman the County Ground gates were locked behind a capacity crowd, there was no longer any doubting the wisdom of luring Botham to Worcester.

Although the side slipped to ninth in the Championship, Botham having an ordinary season with bat and ball, that summer was all about utilising the new optimism around the ground and winning that first trophy. A brilliant knock by Surrey's David Smith defeated them in the Benson & Hedges quarter-finals and good bowling from Lever and Topley saw Essex through in the NatWest second round on a seamer's paradise, so Worcestershire placed all their eggs in the Sunday basket. Needing to win the last game at home to Northamptonshire to take the trophy, they obliged, romping home by nine wickets as Botham scored sixty-one and took two wickets. It was a fairytale ending to the season, but no more than one had come to expect from Botham. Interestingly, Neale had encouraged Botham to try a new role on Sundays:

> Ian opened the innings for us. He didn't play outrageously, Tim Curtis often kept pace with him, but the two of them and Graeme Hick all got 500 runs on a Sunday. In the last four games when we needed to go out and win the trophy, Ian and Tim kept putting on century partnerships to see us through. Ian's form once we got close was very consistent and that was what we needed as a side, someone to show us how to win trophies. We'd brought Ian here as a move to prove to the players that we meant business. With a player of his stature at the

club, they started to believe in themselves and in the club. Winning the first trophy is always the hardest, you have to acquire that winning habit. His role on Sundays was huge and it provided the breakthrough.

Botham was a revelation for many. It wasn't simply his form that was crucial, it was also his presence in the team. Young players at Worcestershire were delighted to see him join them. Where at Somerset the deeds of the recent past weighed heavy on the up and coming professionals, Worcester had little to live up to. They wanted to win and Botham showed them how to do that. Keen to build on the efforts of the previous year, it was especially sad when his 1988 season ended almost before it had begun. On 20 May, that eight-year-old back injury finally needed proper treatment. Botham entered hospital for an operation to fuse two vertebrae. Even so, such was the belief engendered by the previous year's exploits, Worcestershire managed to retain the Refuge Assurance title, finished beaten finalists in the NatWest, and then took the County Championship, beating Kent by one point. Neale recalls that 'Ian gave his County Championship medal away. I don't know whether it was because he felt he hadn't played enough games because of his injury or whether it was just a mark of respect for Jack Turner, the pavilion attendant, but he gave it to him, and Jack was absolutely thrilled, over the moon about that.' Having never won a Championship medal and with no guarantee of doing so in the future, that was a mighty gesture. It was indicative of Botham's commitment to his newly adopted home, where he spent some of his happiest and most productive years as a county cricketer.

Having been out of the game for twelve months, 1989 was a crucial year for him, as Neale recalls: 'He came back and he wanted to stamp his presence on another Championship-winning side. He also had to prove that he was fully fit. He had slightly limited mobility but he used his experience instead and bowled in a different fashion. He still hit the wicket hard because he had a good action and he was so strong, but he became a very good bowler on our wickets which were good for seamers at the time.' That season was his best with the ball for some years: he claimed fifty-one victims at twenty-two. His batting was poor, seemingly affected by an injury sustained in June when a delivery from Glamorgan's

Steve Barwick left him with a depressed fracture of the right cheekbone. As *Wisden* noted, his 'modest 357 runs at an average of 18.78 ... must have counted against him when the selectors were choosing the England team for the West Indies'. Nevertheless, Botham fulfilled an ambition by playing an active part in wrapping up the County Championship with a game to spare. Interestingly, crucial parts had been played by men such as Stuart Lampitt and Martin Weston who had seemed most under threat from Botham's arrival at New Road. Instead, they had drawn inspiration from him and had become very good county cricketers. Botham took particular delight in this, using it as ample evidence that the effect of his presence in a dressing room was not as malign as his detractors would suggest.

Once Botham had missed the trip to West Indies in 1989/90, his career gradually began to wind down as it became clear he would never again dominate the international stage. Injury restricted him and a number of team-mates throughout a less successful campaign in 1990. It's a theme that recurs, but Botham has a very low boredom threshold. So great are his gifts that he treats them too lightly, takes them for granted, and if they are not stretched to the utmost he cannot function, cannot lay his hands on his genius; that is why he and he alone of the cricketers from his era could have rescued England at Headingley in 1981. It was a nice challenge, something to be faced. By 1990, life at Worcestershire had become cosy. He'd done what he went there to do. They were now a formidable county, yet without the adrenalin rush of regular Test cricket, that was not enough for Botham. An excellent season with both bat and ball in 1991 helped see Worcestershire home in the Benson & Hedges Cup and the Refuge Assurance Cup, but that was that. An irresistible challenge was waiting in the wings. Having been less than warm in their welcome in 1987, Worcestershire's members were disappointed that he was now ready to leave before the end of his contract. Phil Neale was realistic however:

> We had him for five years and I think he'd always given his best for Worcestershire. He'd changed a lot of people's opinions about him – yes, there's a lively side to him, but in his commitment to his cricket and to Worcestershire, he showed there was a lot more to him than

what you read in the papers. I think by 1991 he felt the international scene had gone, and he always wanted fresh challenges. Durham seemed interesting to him. It was taking him closer to his home and it was very exciting to launch a new county, the first time it'd been done in seventy years or so. We couldn't stand in his way – he'd given us five good years and it was time for the next stage of his career. We had players like Stuart Lampitt who were ready to play regularly and so it was right for all concerned.

Leaving without acrimony was the right way for his Worcestershire odyssey to end. Sadly, as he conceded, going to Durham was one of the worst decisions he ever made. Perhaps in his 1981 splendour Botham might have arrived at Chester-le-Street, galvanised the ragbag of seasoned professionals and utter novices with his own brilliance, and propelled Durham to the summit single-handed. Well though Botham played at times – a blistering century off ninety-eight balls on his first class debut – he couldn't turn the tide. Even that hundred came in a losing cause and Durham, predictably, finished bottom of the table. Early season promise degenerated into injury and the latter stages of the season saw Botham absent – he didn't play in any of the final four games. Wearied and battle-scarred, it was sad to see him in a team going nowhere, unable to change its course as he had so easily in his youth. His disenchantment was increased by the fact that he thought he was going to Durham to captain the side, only to find that David Graveney had already been appointed. Botham also felt that Director of Cricket Geoff Cook did not want him on board, though whether this was an example of Botham's deeply rooted establishment-related paranoia is hard to tell.

In *It Sort Of Clicks*, Roebuck avers that Botham 'is a man with a life to lead, believing that it is better to burn out than to fade away. Nothing would be more horrible to him than playing as a grumpy old professional of thirty-eight.' At thirty-seven years and eight months, grumpy or not, Ian Botham finally drew stumps. It had been his intention to retire at the end of the 1993 season, but with the Australians touring he'd hoped for one final fling at the old enemy. Once it became clear that he had no hope of breaking into the England team, the fragility of the ambition that had kept him going was exposed. When Australia played Durham at the university in July, Botham's resolve finally collapsed and he announced his retirement. It was fitting that he bowed out against the Australians, sad that perhaps he had continued beyond his useful sporting life. In his autobiography, Botham complained that his glorious finale was turned into a damp squib. On the field, there was no one to blame but himself. His self belief had been his trump card a decade earlier, now it made him look rather ridiculous. A public slanging match with England chairman of selectors Ted Dexter was unedifying, his final performance for Durham described in *Wisden* as 'flippant'. Better by far to forget those final days and recall the days when Botham was such a giant he was the unanimous choice of the people as England captain.

CHAPTER TWO

STORMS

The Captaincy

L ives, careers, history can turn on just one incident. For Botham, that legendary 149 not out at Headingley in 1981 changed his life for ever. Among the many implications, it ensured that he would never again receive the call to captain his country. Having taken a mere thirty-five wickets to add to just 276 runs in a dozen games as captain, the Establishment came to the understandable, if possibly flawed, conclusion that it was no coincidence this first match without the burdens of leadership produced his first match-winning display since Bombay in 1980. Never again would Botham be considered for the captain's job for conventional wisdom had it that that would be tantamount to dropping him as a player. It's interesting, if fruitless, to speculate on the possible reaction had Botham holed out early on in that innings with one of those extravagant hoicks, or if Dilley, Old and Willis had perished quickly leaving him high and dry on forty-seven. The 1981 series might have gone begging, Botham might not have enjoyed his most famous hour, but he might have been deemed worthy of a second chance as England captain just as Gower was given further opportunities after his first stint in the job had ended in failure.

It is impossible to defend Botham's captaincy without belittling the events of Headingley, but facts have to be faced. However enormous the feat, it was achieved against very average opponents and with an enormous degree of luck – certainly it wasn't remotely in the same class as his peerless hundred at Old Trafford or his ton in Melbourne in 1979/80. Botham entered the 1981 series under a cloud of comparative failure. The previous eighteen months had been nightmarish: ten Tests without a win and none of the customary individual fireworks with bat or ball, though it is true to say that very few players produced consistently good performances against the West Indies, such was their domination of world cricket. In comparison with Clive Lloyd's men, Australia, robbed of the likes of Greg Chappell, were a poor side, further enfeebled by the internal disputes over Kim Hughes' role. Lillee and Alderman aside, the 1981 Australians were little better than the Indian and Pakistani sides Botham had trounced in previous years. It was only to be expected that a player of his stature would knock the stuffing out of them at some stage in the summer; the weaker the opposition, the more likely any player is to produce average-enhancing displays. If you are willing to accept that view, then the Australians had Headingley coming to them. If he hadn't destroyed them at Leeds, he'd have done it elsewhere sooner or later.

Once that argument is accepted, it must be conceded that, rather than the captaincy itself holding him back in the first two games of 1981, it had been selectoral uncertainty which had finally felled the giant. For the first time in years, by appointing him on a game by game basis those at the top were questioning his ability. Worse still, they were following a policy that had failed and has continued to fail time and again: Denness was given one Test in 1975 against Australia and lost it; Gower was given one game against India in 1986 and lost that; Emburey and Cowdrey suffered similar indignities against the West Indies in 1988. Selecting on a game by game basis is simply an unintelligent approach in an age when cricketers are under external scrutiny to a far greater extent than in the playing days of selectors like Bedser, May, Illingworth and Dexter. Under that spotlight, players need greater security to help their talents flourish. It was *that* intolerable pressure rather than the cares of leadership that took the edge off Botham's game, those external suspicions that required him to question his ability, technique and temperament and forced him into the agony of self doubt in the throes of which one's best form must always be elusive.

The legend of Mike Brearley is almost as potent as that which surrounds Ian Botham himself. He was the captain with 'the degree in people', as Rodney Hogg termed him, the man who could inspire

England's cricketers to play above and beyond their own abilities, the shrewd tactician who could pressurise his opponents into playing false shots or bowling loosely. Even now, almost sixteen years after his last Test, England's captains are still judged against the yardstick he provided and he is being tempted back into the England set up in some kind of counselling role. There's little doubt that Brearley was the finest English skipper of his generation. Keith Fletcher was his only real rival, and that was purely at county level. However, Brearley's primacy among all England's leaders must be questioned.

He came into the job at the right time. Having been thoroughly beaten by Lillee and Thomson in 1974/75 and then outclassed at home by the West Indies in 1976, there was an ongoing post-mortem into the state of English cricket. The national team was at its lowest ebb in years and not even an impressive win in India in 1976/77 altered that assessment, the parochial view which dismissed the Indians as a minor cricketing nation still holding sway. Nevertheless it is always hard to beat India in their own backyard and those hard won victories, followed by a strong performance albeit in defeat at the Centenary Test in Melbourne, indicated that England were on the way back. Tony Greig had taken up the captaincy in 1975, after Mike Denness bowed to the inevitable following another massive defeat against Australia in the first of the summer's four Tests at Edgbaston. Greig has become a much maligned figure, understandably so since many felt he betrayed his position as England captain by signing for Kerry Packer and becoming one of the chief disciples of his World Series empire. That simplistic dismissal ignores the good work that he did as England skipper, rebuilding a team that had had its confidence shattered by express pace bowling. Greig instilled his own colossal self belief into the side, leading it from the front. Some of his oratory was self defeating – his avowed desire to make the West Indians grovel in 1976 was the prime example – but by the time he was stripped of the captaincy in 1977 for his role in the Packer schism, he had created a team that believed in its own abilities again, leaving Brearley to inherit a dressing room buoyed by the strongest team spirit. When set alongside the crumbling authority Greg Chappell held over the visiting Aussies riven by the Packer dispute, the relative harmony in the English camp was all the more valuable.

Once Brearley's men had steamrollered Australia into submission and regained the Ashes, he was feted as a tactical and motivational genius, for English supporters prized that victory far more highly than the rather more worthy Indian success. The credit for the improvement in fortunes was laid squarely at Brearley's door and subsequent series victories over Pakistan, New Zealand, Australia and India merely enhanced that view. In truth, England were rarely stretched by the opposition over this period, thanks largely to Packer's circus which robbed Australia and Pakistan of their finest and most experienced performers while leaving England relatively unscathed: Amiss was replaced by the returning Boycott, Knott by Taylor, Woolmer by Gower, and Greig by Botham. It was not until peace broke out that Brearley's men were sorely tested. Easily beaten by the West Indies in the 1979 World Cup Final, India then pushed England hard in the subsequent home series before they flew out to contest a three-match series with a full strength Australia, a series in which England were comprehensively defeated by 138 runs, then by six and eight wickets. Not even a fine captain like Brearley could reverse the ultimate cricketing truism: when one side outclasses the other in every department, they will generally win. It was a lesson Ian Botham would have to learn the hard way.

A few commentators had begun to question Brearley's apparent invincibility even before the visit to Australia. In a prescient piece in *Wisden Cricket Monthly*, for example, Jim Laker had asked whether Brearley's decision to take the England side there was his first real error of judgement. Certainly he had required some persuasion before agreeing to go since he was now looking deeper into his post-cricketing career in psychoanalysis. Initially he had planned to winter in England so that he could study for this vocation but the Australian challenge was too great a temptation, the more so since there appeared to be no obvious replacement captain on the horizon. Inevitably, the technical shortcomings among England's younger players were brutally exposed and thoroughly exploited by the battle hardened Australians who looked on the matches against England as a little light relief after the mauling they had just received at the hands of the West Indies. In the face of such a yawning gulf in quality, Brearley was left to watch Canutelike as the irresistible Australian tide overwhelmed his men. Somehow, despite the reverse, Brearley's reputation remained intact. Lord's had refused to put the Ashes up for grabs since the three-game series had been slotted in at short notice as part of the peace settlement to appease Packer. The atmosphere was further soured by incidents such as Lillee's aluminium bat fiasco and the extremely hostile attitude of sections of the Australian crowd, whipped up into an anti-Pom frenzy by the aggressive new marketing of cricket instigated by Packer's Channel 9 TV station. Domestic reaction to England's defeat was generally sympathetic, and any gloomy reflections on Australia's superiority were quickly dispelled by England's emphatic victory over India in the Jubilee game in Bombay where Botham scored a century and took thirteen wickets in a virtuoso display. Normal service had been resumed.

Still regarded as one of England's greats, Brearley chose the side's return to confirm that he was to take his leave of the international stage, announcing that he was no longer available for touring duties. The selectors were then confronted with the choice of either persisting with him through the 1980 English summer or blooding a new captain. A tough decision was made harder by virtue of the fact that England were heading into the most taxing two years they'd ever faced: back to back series home and away with the West Indies, the undisputed world champions, then an Ashes summer, and finally a visit to India, resurgent since the arrival of their own great all-rounder Kapil Dev. Faced with such a daunting itinerary, it might have been sensible to invite an experienced hand such as Keith Fletcher or Roger Knight to take charge as an interim candidate, allowing the likes of Botham, Gooch, Gower and Gatting to mature and stake a claim for the role when India and Pakistan visited in 1982. If Fletcher had taken a beating as captain, there'd have been no longer term psychological damage. Fletcher or Knight, at the end of their respective careers, were expendable. Botham was not.

The one real controversy of Brearley's reign had centred around his own form. Without a Test century to his name, Brearley was one of the many English players of recent years just short of international class. Had it not been for his excellent record as captain, it's unlikely he would have won more than a few caps. Even as he racked up the victories, there were still those who felt he was not worth his place in the team.

With that uppermost in their minds, the selectors concluded that they had no desire to travel down that road again. Following the Australian model, they wanted to pick the optimum eleven and find a captain from among them. In essence, that meant the captain had to come from within the party that had gone to Australia and India. The decision then effectively made itself, particularly in the light of that Test match in Bombay. Ian Botham was the only option. The succession was decided, the heir anointed. Indeed, Boycott aside, he was probably the only player that could be relied upon to hold down his place throughout the summer.

In hindsight, the decision to hand the job to Botham in 1980 was fatally flawed from the outset. His selection was supposed to herald a bold new era, the great new superstar taking the fight to all and sundry, leading his men over the top in a glorious charge to the summit of world cricket. Those observers who detached themselves from the hype were a little more sceptical. Realistically, whoever captained England against the West Indies could only lead them to defeat. They might go down fighting, but they would go down all the same. The only question was the scale of that defeat. The West Indies were an awesome combination: a batting line up of Greenidge, Haynes, Kallicharran, Clive Lloyd and the mighty Vivian Richards, then at his brilliant best, backed up by the four-man pace quartet of Roberts, Holding, Garner and Marshall (or Croft), a combination that was virtually unplayable. Even if the batsmen could preserve their wickets, the West Indies bowled their overs so slowly and delivered so many short-pitched balls, from which it was all but impossible to score, that no side could amass sufficient runs quickly enough to put them under any pressure.

One of the England selectors was Brian Close, Botham's mentor at Somerset. He made it perfectly clear that he didn't feel his erstwhile charge should be exposed to the ordeal of captaincy, particularly when he was the only England player who could be expected to withstand the Caribbean blast and give as good as he got. Ironically, that very pugnacity was the quality that made some feel Botham might be cap-taincy material at the tender age of twenty-four, and with no experience of running a side. The theory was that his up-and-at-'em approach and his vibrant, attacking personality might inspire England to beat Lloyd's men at their own game. Without such an attitude, many felt that England would simply lie down and die. That view failed to learn the lessons of Tony Greig's humiliation in 1976. Greig was every bit as combative as Botham. He was always looking to carry the fight to the West Indians, but he and his team were just not good enough. If anything, by the time they arrived in 1980 Lloyd's team was even stronger and an even greater threat than it had been. England, on the other hand, were anything but a robust unit for while Brearley had been successful in papering over the cracks, the side remained desperately short of real quality. Boycott, Underwood, Taylor, Knott and Willis were all nearing the end of distinguished careers, Randall's idiosyncratic batting was enough to remove the fingernails of the most equable of captains, the Test careers of Gatting and Gooch were in their infancy, and Gower was suffering an inevitable slump in form now that international bowlers had had a chance to probe for weaknesses in his technique. As far as the bowling went, Dilley was promising but raw, Edmonds, Miller and Emburey never threatened to dismantle the best batting sides, and Lever, Hendrick and Old were solid support players who were regularly beset by injury. The belief that people had had in Brearley left them with the idea that he was handing over a very good side which could hold its own in the best company. That erroneous impression merely added to the weight that already lay upon his young successor's shoulders.

Time and again throughout Brearley's reign, the difference between English victory and defeat had not been the captain but Ian Botham. Certainly Brearley handled his star player well, better than anyone else ever did, but it was Botham's ability that turned matches England's way. Brian Close was right to argue that Botham was too inexperienced to captain the side. He was also right when he insisted that England's most potent weapon should not be shackled by added responsibility at a time when the team would need him at his very best. Close had been recalled to the national colours to withstand the 1976 onslaught and had first hand knowledge of the threat that Holding *et al* would pose. Given his almost paternal pride in Botham's exploits, it's fair to assume that he was equally keen to shield him from the media backlash that would accompany the slightest fall-off in his performance. Even had Botham been allowed to do battle with the West Indians from the ranks, his figures would surely have taken a battering. Their batsmen were formidable, but facing their bowlers was akin to standing in the path of a juggernaut. Allied to that, Botham was not the greatest player of pace bowling. The slack over rate automatically meant that he couldn't keep the scoreboard rattling along, and his macho temperament meant that he could always be baited into taking on the leg trap, hooking with abandon however many men might be stationed in the deep. Botham's instinct was always to fight fire with fire, however foolhardy that might be. It was a characteristic that Joel Garner and Viv Richards knew only too well from their close association with him at Somerset. They knew it was the source of his strength but they felt it could also be a weakness, as was proved over the course of the summer.

A more serious problem was looming for Botham. Just at the point when he needed to be at his very best, he was laid low with the first serious injury of his career, an ailment so debilitating that at times it threatened his future in the game. Playing against Oxford University for Somerset on a bitterly cold April day he strained his back, X-rays eventually indicating a spinal deformity. With the rigorous schedule lying ahead of England's foremost cricketer, there was no way he could risk an operation which would put him out of action for a year and which might even do more harm than good. Any kind of back pain can have repercussions, seriously limiting mobility and requiring changes in lifestyle. When an athlete is struck down by the problem, its impact can be catastrophic. Botham made changes to his action which robbed him of much of his effectiveness, and he also ran up to the crease more gingerly than in the past, the consequent reduction in pace giving his opponents extra time to deal with any movement off the pitch. When he was routinely routing opponents on his way to the fastest 100 Test wickets in history, he'd often been bowling at a pace that was just fractionally short of genuinely quick while still retaining the ability to move the ball extravagantly. Now, he was more often than not confined to almost military medium, which was never seriously going to incon-venience the likes of Viv Richards. The intermittent nature of the injury made it all the harder to bear since for the duration of the summer Botham never knew just when it might flare up again, and so could never trust himself to bowl the long and incisive spells on which he'd built his reputation. He was unable to bowl more than a few overs throughout May, and when June and July were wet his workload was further reduced; inevitably, he put on weight and his back problem intensified.

Though the weather prevented him doing as much bowling as he would have liked, it would not have been impossible for him to take other forms of exercise to keep the weight off, thereby easing the pressure on his spine. Dennis Lillee survived a serious back injury that put his whole career in jeopardy thanks to a single-minded devotion to regaining fitness. If colleagues such as Bob Willis could fight off injuries by embracing a punishing schedule of road and gym work, Botham should really have been able to do likewise, the more so now that he'd been given the extra responsibility of leading the England team, but there are times when Botham can be his own worst enemy, driven along by his compulsion that he always knows best. As the summer wore on, his weight went up to around sixteen stone, fully a stone and a half more than his optimum cricketing weight. So serious were the implications that by the tail end of the season the England selectors were demanding that he got back into shape before they would even consider taking him on tour. Botham could and should have tried harder to stay in shape, whether he was fit to bowl or not. After all, as England captain he should not have found it difficult to find sufficient expert medical advice and have an appropriate fitness regime set up for him. That said, the whispering campaign against him, one that grew in intensity over the course of the summer, verged on the hysterical and did little for his state of mind. He had to withstand the most vituperative criticism of his weight and his family were subjected to some disgusting examples of press intrusion – members of the Fourth Estate, desperate to make stories out of Botham's tubbiness, stooped so low as to ask his four-year-old son Liam what his father had been eating! Faced by this awful behaviour from the media and with Botham's own stubborn refusal to discuss his problems, his family were placed under an intolerable strain. All that can be said, and it's pretty cold comfort, is that at least it made them, Kath in particular, strong enough to cope with the vicious blasts of scandal and innuendo that were to come their way in future.

His relationship with the press will be examined elsewhere, but it would be disingenuous to discuss his performance as captain without occasional reference to the treatment meted out to him in 1980, for it had a serious effect on him, his family and his form. Things had started happily enough. Bestowing the captaincy on Botham was viewed as a surprisingly enterprising move which boded well for the future, though there were early indications that not everyone was so confident when he was appointed only for the two one day internationals that preceded the Test series, scarcely time to prove anything to anyone. Once he had responded with a match-winning knock of forty-two in the second one day international at Lord's, smiting the winning runs off Joel Garner and avenging the defeat in the World Cup Final on the same ground a year earlier, it looked as though he was accepting another challenge with his customary relish. England approached the First Test at Trent Bridge in good heart, Botham having been re-appointed as leader.

Between the 1973/74 tour of the West Indies and the visit in 1989/90, England failed to win a solitary Test against the West Indies in twenty-nine attempts. Over that entire period, they never got as close as they did in that first Test match in Nottingham. Setting the West Indians 208 to win, England took wickets with sufficient regularity to suggest they might pull off a famous victory, Willis bowling with the fervour that would find its fulfilment in his glorious hour at Headingley a year later. Only opener Desmond Haynes stood firm among the West Indians, but at 180 for 7 he was joined by Andy Roberts with just Garner and Holding to come. They inched the score forward, but with twelve wanted, Roberts skied a delivery to cover. The swirling ball was tracked by David Gower, the finest outfielder in the England team. Suffering his own crisis in confidence following a battering in Australia, Gower got both hands to the ball but dropped the catch. A few moments later, the West Indies were home by two wickets, Haynes guiding them most of the way with a five-hour sixty-two. It was the first intimation that Botham's luck had deserted him. If Gower had held that catch, the likelihood is that England would have won the Test match, Botham would have maintained his status as the man with the Midas touch, and with the confidence booster that such an impressive early victory would have provided he might well have gone on to be a successful England captain for many years. Certainly he would have dispelled any doubts that captaincy would ruin him, the more so since he'd top scored with fifty-seven in the first innings in spite of having his batting helmet split by Garner, and had bowled intelligently throughout. As it was, England left Nottingham one down and with their backs turned to the wall. As the series unfolded, the West Indians hit their stride. The difference between the two sides became more apparent, but thanks to a combination of a powerful never-say-die attitude and some very wet weather, England managed to salvage each game, eventually losing the series by one match to nil, even holding the upper hand in the ruined Old Trafford Test.

Since Australia had been hammered at home the previous winter by the same combination, Botham could take much satisfaction from the fact that his England side had held on to the West Indians, comfortably avoiding the blackwashes which David Gower endured as captain. Admittedly Botham was fortunate when it came to the weather, for in a fine year at least one more game might have been lost. Even so, it is to Botham's credit that his men were not disgraced by clearly superior forces. Sadly, he was given little chance to experience any such glow of satisfaction at a job reasonably well done. After years of being feted by the media and public alike, he suddenly became public enemy number one. The reasons why the press turned on him so quickly were many and varied, some understandable, some ludicrous, some a result of Botham's own stubbornness and some the outcome of the vindictiveness which is apparently required to sell newspapers. In that regard, Botham contributed to his own downfall by writing a ghosted column for the *Sun*, a red rag to the rest of the Fleet Street bulls who were only too happy to discredit their rival's star reporter. Being a Test cricketer was still no passport to fortune in Botham's early career. In that light, one can hardly blame him for agreeing a lucrative contract with a newspaper, one which provided good money for little work. Once you enter the belly of the beast, however, it's hard to complain about tabloid excesses without looking like a hypocrite.

That said, no one should be forced to endure the ridicule that Botham had to put up with and, more particularly, no one's family should be caught in the crossfire. By the end of the year, England's inability to beat the West Indians had been portrayed as a national disaster rather than the honourable defeat that was more accurately the case. Many writers ascribed England's failings to the weight problems of the captain and his poor performances with bat and ball, John Arlott looking at both sides of the coin for *Wisden Cricket Monthly*: 'He has brought immense enthusiasm to the office of captain; he has motivated his players, won their confidence and introduced considerable enthusiasm and counter-attacking drive. It must, though, be asked if the responsibilities have affected his play.' Few journalists were as sympathetic, attacking his tactical shortcomings when compared with Grandmaster Brearley. The public took its lead from the media. By September, England's hero of the previous three years was subjected to jeers and cat-calls wherever he went. On the final Sunday of the 1980 season, John Player League champions Warwickshire played host to Botham's Somerset. Success-starved supporters packed Edgbaston to see Warwickshire skipper Bob Willis parade the trophy, but very quickly the afternoon degenerated into a Botham-baiting competition which was quite shameful in its intensity. Early the following summer, his wife Kath was driven from cricket grounds, close to tears at the malevolent abuse hurled at her husband. According to Botham's book *The Incredible Tests*, she lost a stone in weight, such were the anxieties of the time.

What was Botham to make of all this? A year earlier, he could do no wrong. He was the people's champion, everyone wanted to talk about him, praise him, congratulate him. By September 1980 the selectors were openly criticising him and threatening to leave him out of the team for the West Indies, the newspapers were writing off his career, and the public were enjoying the rare privilege of having ringside seats at a public execution. His crime was the simple one of losing form. Those that touch genuine greatness are expected to set up camp on the Olympian heights. Should they ever descend from those peaks, they are never forgiven, for in their fall from grace they remind us all of our own mortality. Gods should be above the fray, they should be invulnerable. In reality, those who can wield a bat or racquet with distinction are mere mortals, often encumbered by feet of clay. It is a rare cricketer indeed who has not tasted failure. Criticism on this scale was something new and it inevitably had an effect on his form and on his frame of mind. There's no question that the scale of the attacks was every bit as over the top as the praise that had been heaped upon him when he was at the peak of the game, but a Kiplingesque acceptance of and disregard for those two impostors were not part of Botham's character. The verbal assaults made their mark just as they would on any but the most thick-skinned individual. At this distance, the question is whether or not that degree of criticism was justified. Was Botham a good captain, was he promoted above his abilities, was he laid low by the cares of office?

The domestic series against the West Indies gave some grounds for optimism in spite of his relatively subdued performances. Prior to that series, he'd picked up 139 victims at just over eighteen each, a sharp contrast to the thirteen more he took in that series at a cost of thirty. Even so, his lack of prowess with the ball could largely be excused. There is nothing that restricts a quick bowler more than doubts over the durability of his back, so it's unsurprising that he bowled fewer overs at reduced pace and with less conviction than in the past. When you then remember that the West Indies' batting was stronger than that of any other country, it's clear that reports of his demise as an international bowler were premature. As a batsman he fared even less well. Starting brightly with a solid half century in the first Test at Trent Bridge, an innings which almost turned that game England's way, he lost his way subsequently, scoring just 112 more runs in his next eight innings. A series average of nineteen did not compare well with a career average of forty on his return from India. True, some colleagues such as Gower did not even survive the series, but others such as Gooch and Willey showed the necessary application and technique required to stand up to the most hostile of attacks. All too often Botham seemed to lack the patience to occupy the crease: his 169 runs came from just 270 balls, a healthy striking rate against that kind of attack. However, as Phil Edmonds wrote in *The Cricketer* during the 1985/86 tour to the West Indies, 'there can be no long-term capital in trying to hook the world's quickest bowlers consistently … I am sure we will be far better off trying to occupy the crease and attack within a restricted framework'.

Unwilling to try to wear down the fast bowlers and accumulate runs, Botham regularly fell victim to his instinctive desire to take the fight back to Holding or Roberts, a brave but foolish approach that was destined to have sporadic success, especially on some of the unreliable pitches he was to encounter in the West Indies. In part, this was a failing in his technique, for though the quickest bowling had never held any physical fears for Botham, his game was not suited to combating it. His belligerent and whole-hearted strokeplay allowed him to destroy spinners or medium pacers and to hold his own even against those bowlers like the ageing Dennis Lillee or Geoff Lawson who were just that bit short of express pace. Botham's game was one built on domination of his opponents, not a plan suited to the West Indian attack where the ball was constantly speared in at the rib cage at 80 or 90 mph, and where there might be fewer than a dozen genuinely hittable deliveries in an hour, most of which could be delivered while Botham was at the non-striker's end. To graft for a two-hour session and return to the pavilion with just an extra sixteen or twenty runs to your name was not an approach which appealed to the young tiger, and consequently he was often frustrated into an error. He admitted as much in the book he wrote with Peter Roebuck, *It Sort Of Clicks*. Discussing his crucial innings at Sydney on the 1978/79 tour, when he scored six in an hour and a half to allow England's Derek Randall to build a match-winning total at the other end, he admitted, 'I'll never play another innings like that ... I didn't enjoy it ... I was told to stay in. It was vital. It was more a matter of time than runs. But I went too far.'

In Botham's defence, little has been made over the years of the systematic way in which the West Indians targeted the opposing captain. After his own humiliation in Australia in 1975/76, Clive Lloyd turned his men into a side that hunted together in packs, one which was quick to scent blood and devastatingly efficient going in for the kill. Lloyd was a shrewd tactician too, one who knew the value of undermining his opposite number: if the captain was worried about his own form, he was less likely to be able to give his full concentration to the well-being of the side as a whole. In turn, that could have a psychologically detrimental effect on the side as a whole – Mike Atherton's trials in Zimbabwe on the 1996/97 tour are testimony to that. Throughout their ascendancy under Lloyd, it's instructive to see how often West Indian armoury was deployed in this way. Back in 1976, though he still managed a couple of performances of note, Tony Greig was eventually brought to his knees by the uncompromising pace of Michael Holding, who defeated him and, subsequently, his team. One defiant performance at Headingley apart, Greig managed fifty-one runs in seven innings. He also picked up a mere five wickets at a cost of almost seventy each. In Australia in 1979/80, Greg Chappell withstood the initial barrage but was eventually overcome and, had it been a five- rather than three-Test series, he too might have been destroyed in the end, as he was in the three-Test rubber of 1981/82. His replacement, the much maligned Kim Hughes, was also given the full treatment over two series in 1983/84 and 1984/85 when he amassed just 294 runs in fourteen innings and was forced into tearful resignation by the pressures they exerted. It's a pattern that's been repeated time and again down the years, with captain after captain offered up as a sacrificial lamb every time the West Indies arrive.

Picking through the carnage the West Indies left strewn in their wake all over the world throughout the 1980s, it's clear they weren't always given the credit their awesome power deserved; writing a summary of England's 1980/81 tour in *Wisden*, Michael Melford claimed that 'this was not a great West Indies side'. Certainly their strength was often built on the sheer brutality of their bowling attack, and purists railed against that and their dismal over rates, yet that should not have disguised the fact that Clive Lloyd assembled a cricketing side that came closer to being genuinely invincible than any other – even Bradman's Australia lost sometimes. The West Indies became a fighting machine, one that was willing to win at all costs. The consequence of that was that opponents would lose in all circumstances until the Caribbean conveyor belt no longer produced sufficient players of the highest quality. Spectators from the boundary and in the press box seemed to believe that playing lightning quick, short-pitched bowling was, if not easy, then straightforward. Just apply the principles: get on the back foot, get into line, punish the short ball square of the wicket. That was the dictum, yet not even the finest players of the time such as Greg Chappell, Mohammad Azharuddin and Javed Miandad were able to prosper with regularity. The West Indian attack posed problems that were insurmountable, the equivalent of surviving fifteen rounds against Muhammad Ali only to find yourself immediately confronted by a fresh Joe

Frazier. Viewed in that light, all their opponents could do was their best. It was never likely to be good enough, certainly not on a consistent basis.

Leading a team at home is a very different proposition from leading one overseas. At home, the job revolves solely around cricket and the eleven men selected to take the field. There are external pressures, largely media based, but essentially the job is straightforward. On tour, cricket can often be the least of the captain's worries. The England captain is seen as something akin to an ambassador for the nation. There are functions to attend, hands to shake, dignitaries to meet and greet. A captain must also be ready to deal with the local media as well as the travelling press corps, keep his eye on practice facilities, ensure that everyone is in good health, that they all know their jobs, and that everyone is pulling together. Away from home for months on end, team spirit is especially important, particularly among the two or three players who are quickly identified as the travelling reserves, those who aren't in line for the Test matches and who will consequently play little cricket. Their response to their personal disappointment is crucial, for unhappy, even jealous, tourists can quickly sour the atmosphere. It's a captain's job to keep these players content, remind them that there's always a chance they'll get back into the side, that they are an integral part of the party and share equally in its successes and failures. In short, the touring captain's job is a huge one. The only consolation for Botham was that the media scrutiny on tour was less intense than at home – at least, that was the case in 1981.

Momentum is all important in professional sport. A side that has won a game is filled with confidence, ready to win again. Particularly in a contest as short as a Test series, decided over three or five games, once one team has an ascendancy, things can easily run away from the other side. Gallant losers at the start of a series can easily become bedraggled and vanquished a couple of months later – David Gower's teams gave just that impression against the West Indies. In England, Botham's men had held on to the West Indies and had never capitulated as thoroughly as Australia had done the winter before. Yet even that was not enough for his critics. The pressures were built up off the field: he was surrounded by innuendo, battered with suggestions that he was tactically naive, that he wasn't up to the job. Even before England set off for the West Indies, they were written off as no-hopers.

Comments from beyond the dressing room can often undermine a team's spirit. In adversity, a side can either pull together or tear itself apart. The situation never quite reached that level of drama, but Botham's authority was called into question throughout the tour, with both Viv Richards and Clive Lloyd making the point that he did not always get the respect he deserved from senior professionals in the side. The finger was often pointed at Geoff Boycott in particular, the more so since the rebel tour to South Africa that took place in 1982 was first mooted in the West Indies. Boycott was a key figure in the organisation of that tour and any talk of deserting English cricket *à la* the Packer rebels would probably have emanated from his corner, doing little for morale. In fairness, Boycott still did his best on the field, averaging more than forty in the Test matches, but the 1977 Australians had shown just how dangerous it was for a touring party to divide into distinct camps; great player and fine leader though he was, Greg Chappell couldn't hold on to a team that was at war with itself. In his book *Opening Up*, Boycott reflected on Botham's captaincy: 'I would have preferred to see him groomed for a couple of years before being given the job. I would have liked him to have sown his wild oats while he could, but now he has it, I want him to succeed.' Never one to hide his lack of respect for Mike Brearley's ability as a Test batsman, Boycott added, 'Ian has the enormous advantage of being able to lead from the front; when the chips are down, players naturally look to a captain to pull them through by the strength of his performance. They like to feel they can lean on the skipper's ability and he won't let them down.' Even so, the relationship between Boycott and Botham was not the warmest, Boycott making the point that Botham rarely asked for his opinion on anything, on or off the field.

Early on in the West Indian tour, it looked as if Boycott's point about leading from the front was well made. In the first one day international which preceded the Test series, Botham had been impressive, top scoring in St Vincent with sixty from 125 all out as England lost by two runs. The fragility of England's batting was clearly a major worry, a situation worsened by the poor weather the side encountered in the first seven weeks of the tour, when they managed just seventeen days of cricket. The rain had an impact on the quality and frequency of practice, and on the mood of Botham's troops. Bored by the enforced inactivity, the tension in the camp began to grow almost from day one. In such circumstances, Botham was anything but the ideal leader. Trying to distance himself from the rest of the side in order to preserve his authority, he found it hard to lighten the atmosphere with the usual practical jokes that had been his stock in trade when he was one of the lads, while his efforts to cheer everyone up by getting his round in merely confused the issue. He was equally frustrated by those who found the tour hard going. He confessed in his autobiography that man management was not his strong suit. Some players in losing sides need a shoulder to cry on, need to be built up and told they're the best. Botham freely admitted that he could not understand why anyone should need motivating before going out to play for England. Playing for your country should be all that any sportsman desired. Botham failed to accept that each individual needed to be handled differently, something at which Brearley had been so adept. For the players, this shift in emphasis was something of a culture shock, and Chris Old suffered particularly from the change in leadership.

Botham had his differences of opinion with Graham Gooch too. Gooch was then in the early stages of the strict fitness regime which helped him stay at the top for so long. Botham's disregard for long training runs and net practice was already legendary. He felt that Gooch's dedication to physical preparation was taking the edge off his performances on the field, though according to Gooch, Botham tried to ban his jogging on the grounds that it left him too tired to socialise in the evenings. The irony was that a dozen years later, Botham would complain that Gooch was too inflexible as a captain and treated all his players in the same way, something of which he was equally guilty. Where Gooch was a disciplinarian, Botham was anything but, Gooch making the point that 'Ian's lifestyle did not sit easily with setting an example to his players ... when you are captain, you have to be able to detach yourself a bit, take a step back, not be aloof of course, but not be 110 per cent "one of the lads". Being the latter for a captain is almost impossible when, next morning, you might have to crack the whip.'

Had Botham been leading a winning side, questions would not have been asked. As it was, things on tour lurched from bad to worse, most of the problems originating in areas beyond the captain's control. Early on, Bob Willis, his main strike bowler, and then Brian Rose, one of the batting successes of the previous summer, were forced out of the tour through injury. Though replacements were called for – Robin Jackman and Bill Athey – this still left Botham with a threadbare side. The loss of Willis was particularly serious for he was an experienced and conscientious vice captain who could have been an extremely valuable contributor to the tour off the field as well as on. Writing in *Wisden* in 1982, Mike Brearley reflected that 'in Australia, Bob Willis helped me, as vice-captain, by being prepared to take a tough line with players on occasion, to share the responsibility for an unpopular decision or a critical attitude'. If someone as experienced as Brearley found Willis's presence invaluable, how useful could he have been to Botham, a man still learning the ropes?

Heading into the First Test in Port of Spain, England were already looking in poor shape. The problems were compounded by reckless selection: England took just four front-line batsmen – Boycott, Gooch, Gower and the ailing Rose – into the game. Having lost more than a day to the weather, a draw should not have been beyond their powers, allowing them to rethink their strategy for the remainder of the tour. Putting the opposition in to bat on an uncertain pitch, Botham had the dubious pleasure of watching Greenidge and Haynes amass 168 for the first wicket, but excellent bowling from Emburey saw England fight their way back into the game. Lloyd was still able to declare on an unassailable 426, but with almost half the allotted time gone England had given themselves hope. It was left to the batsmen to avoid the follow on and save the game. The defeat that followed was described by *Wisden Cricket Monthly*'s Paul Weaver as 'without honour, humiliation beyond redemption'. Henry Blofeld was equally scathing in the *Sunday Express*, asserting that Botham 'captains the side like a great big baby. His attitude is astonishingly naive and he is letting his country down.' Blofeld later complained that Botham had jostled him at Bermuda airport at the end of the tour, the captain understandably annoyed at this less than constructive critique. Even so, his willingness to meet antipathy with volatility called into question his judgement and placed a further question mark against his being the right man to lead England, given the prestige of that position.

The English resistance in Trinidad started promisingly, the first three wickets posting 110, with Gower undefeated and confident. From those heights England collapsed to 178 all out, Colin Croft picking up five wickets as the folly of packing the side with 'bits and pieces' players was exposed. Even so, with the intervention of the weather, they entered the final day with eight second innings wickets in hand, Rose and Gooch having gone early on. Even before England had started batting, Botham had pronounced the pitch a good one and had told a press conference that if England should lose the game, 'heads will roll'. With that exhortation ringing in their ears, his batsmen proceeded to fall apart again, Boycott and Gower once more trying to postpone the inevitable with scant support. Botham himself entered the fray with the score on 103 for 4. After scoring sixteen runs to follow his first innings duck, he holed out to mid-off, attempting to hit Viv Richards out of the ground. In a match where England had been put to the sword by the fastest bowling on earth, losing your wicket to a gentle off-spinner with no pretensions as a bowler was carelessness bordering on the suicidal. With that one stroke, Botham effectively ended his spell as captain. In his autobiography he tried to defend his actions, arguing that 'the ball was there to be hit'. In truth, the shot was indefensible. If it had gone for six, it wouldn't have mattered, wouldn't have loosened the West Indian grip on the game. At that stage, with England still more than a hundred short of the West Indian total, runs were irrelevant. Occupation of the crease was all that mattered. The captain above all others should have tried to resist such obvious temptation and knuckle down to the task in hand, however alien that was to his nature. As it was, England were just an hour short of saving the game when the final wicket fell, the rest of the side collapsing in the wake of their captain's wantonness.

The tour could easily have degenerated into utter disaster from there on in but, to give credit to Botham, he held things together in the face of awful, then tragic, circumstances, all of which was accompanied by a complete collapse in his own form. The first matter on the agenda was the replacement of Bob Willis who had to fly home for surgery on his knee. Robbed of his vice captain, Botham wanted Gooch to step into the vacancy but was ordered by Lord's to give the position to Geoff Miller. As a pragmatic move this was faintly ridiculous since, following his poor performance in Trinidad, Miller's chances of playing an active part in the remainder of the series were poor. Conversely, Graham Gooch was an integral part of the side. More importantly, Lord's had undermined Botham's position in his own eyes and in the eyes of the team, since he had already offered the position to Gooch and was forced to retract. This was a significant and very embarrassing episode, indicating that Botham was on borrowed time, a curt reminder for the uppity youngster of just who was in charge of English cricket. This was Botham's first really serious brush with the game's establishment, and it left a lingering taste of bitterness and mistrust that was to cloud the rest of his career, and often his judgement.

Willis had to be replaced as a bowler, too, so Surrey's Robin Jackman was summoned to the Caribbean, arriving in Guyana on 23 February. Jackman had close ties with South Africa, having wintered either there or in Zimbabwe for the previous decade. With the sporting boycott against South Africa at its height, the Guyanese government, among the fiercest critics of the apartheid regime, decided that Jackman was persona non grata, reasoning that his regular presence in South Africa constituted tacit support of Botha's policies. The England team was instructed to leave the island and Jackman was served with deportation papers on the twenty-sixth. For the next week, the future of the entire tour was in the balance with many of the tourists openly expressing their preference for a swift return home. In those circumstances, Botham and the tour management of A.C. Smith and Ken Barrington did an excellent job in keeping the players focused on the job in hand. Smith was the team's ambassador, dealing confidently and competently with government and cricketing officials, while Botham and Barrington tried to keep the players occupied. By 4 March, with the team in Barbados, the go–ahead finally arrived and the tour was saved. Having suffered vilification on a scale unseen since Jardine's Bodyline tour, spirits in the camp were unavoidably low. Botham was yet to grasp the basics of man management, which didn't help matters, but Jardine himself would have struggled to maintain discipline in the face of such insurmountable odds.

The Jackman affair was the most significant event of its kind since Basil d'Oliveira had been refused entry to South Africa in 1968. Since then, South Africa's isolation had increased and official cricketing ties between it and the rest of the world were non-existent. Even so, there had been some unease within the cricketing family for some time, centred around the many English professionals who worked in South Africa during the British winter. Given that a professional's salary pre-Kerry Packer might be little more than £4000, it was hardly surprising that many felt the need to augment their income in the off season. Few employers were willing to grant an employee a five-month sabbatical in the summer to play county cricket, so work in this country was hard to find. A winter in South Africa provided a financially vital lifeline to many cricketers. Though some nations disliked what they saw as fraternising with the enemy, they were generally willing to turn a blind eye to it in the interests of world sport. The rationale was that as long as these players were acting as individuals, they had the right to ply their trade wherever they chose. In the 1980s, many predominantly black nations came to see that as a hypocritical stance, understandably so. The more militant governments wanted to see such associations actively discouraged and were willing to cause splits in the sporting world to further their cause. Sporting boycotts, for all sorts of political reasons, were becoming widespread – the Moscow Olympics, for example, was cheapened by the absence of the Americans. Other regimes were as keen to flex their diplomatic muscle in an attempt to force every nation to sever its ties with nations such as South Africa. In that sense, the Jackman affair was an accident waiting to happen – it might have happened a year earlier or a year later and it might have involved a different cricketer, but it had to happen. The issue had been festering beneath the surface for too long; it needed to come out into the open and a workable solution needed to be found.

Jackman was unfortunate that he was the victim of world politics; any sportsman who 'colluded' with the South Africans at that time was asking for trouble. From a cricketer's point of view the whole sorry mess reeked of double standards. Barclays Bank continued to have the strongest links with South Africa, businessmen of every kind could buy and sell their goods with impunity, but sportsmen weren't supposed to take the rand. That much was true, but then aping the indefensible is scarcely a valid response. Even so, South Africa was a highly emotive issue within the game, particularly among those cricketers who were just short of Test standard. A contract to coach in South Africa enabled them to keep their heads above water; if that were to be taken away from them, many might have to leave the game. Indeed, some genuinely felt that they were helping racial integration by insisting that they coach black and coloured children as well as whites. Yet how can there be normal sport in an abnormal society?

The attack on the commercial activities of the English players touched a nerve. In the wake of the Jackman affair there were genuine fears for the future of Test cricket: a real possibility had arisen that it would split on the lines of black and white nations. Ironically, the actions of the Guyanese government made South Africa all the more attractive to a number of English cricketers who were tired of the game's politics, concerned for their financial futures, and annoyed at the restrictions placed upon them. Such emotions provided a fertile breeding ground for the first rebel tour to South Africa which took place a year later. As noted, Geoffrey Boycott was actively involved in recruiting, and tentative discussions filled the idle moments of the Caribbean odyssey. Such intrigue did little for team spirit, the more so since anyone tempted to join the touring party was effectively putting money before their England career – understandable, perhaps, but hardly conducive to giving of one's best for the national side, nor to inspiring confidence in others.

Amid the Guyanese trials, perhaps the key figure in the camp had been Ken Barrington, the assistant manager. Loved and respected by all the players, he was instrumental in keeping things on an even keel and providing the support that the inexperienced skipper required. Botham apart, few realised the strain he was under, but the pervading tension was taking its toll. On the second night of the Barbados Test, 14 March, Botham received a call from A.C. Smith at around eleven o'clock to inform him that Barrington had suffered a fatal heart attack. Initially unwilling to carry on with the game, Botham and the players elected to continue since that would be in the very nature of Barrington's bulldog spirit. Unsurprisingly, they were unable to win or even save the game for him. Already in a poor position, England were brushed aside by the

West Indians, Viv Richards atoning for a first innings duck with an imperious 182. England lost by 298 runs, but the game was remarkable for a couple of cameos. The best remembered is the over Michael Holding bowled to Geoff Boycott at the beginning of England's first innings. That most dependable of England's batsmen had his technique thoroughly unhinged by an over of bewildering speed on a lightning fast track. Holding tormented him with a series of perfect deliveries before Boycott swiftly departed for the sanctuary of the pavilion having failed to trouble the scorers. England were dismissed for just 122, Botham following a determined performance with the ball – he took four for seventy-seven in the West Indian total of 265 – with a defiant innings of twenty-six amid some of the most disciplined intimidation seen on a cricket field. David Frith described Botham's innings in *Wisden Cricket Monthly*: 'Botham managed a juicy cover-drive off Garner, the retort a bouncer which removed his helmet as he ducked. Garner sent down a high ration of lifters and Croft set a 7–2 off-side field for Botham who hooked him fine and then drove him royally. Soon he was hurling his bat away as a Holding bouncer almost sliced his chin open, and when he was caught behind he kicked the pitch in disgust and left with a face dark with anger.' Hard though Botham tried, his best form had deserted him at a time when even that might not have been sufficient to stem the tide. At Bridgetown, the wicket was prepared specifically for the West Indian quicks and they responded with glee. Just as he had beaten Boycott in the opening over, so Holding tortured Ian Botham. Watching from the dressing room, the colour drained from the faces of the English tail-enders. Seeing their captain, a man rightly described as the world's greatest all-rounder, floundering at the crease was a painful sight. As Botham threw his bat away, as if to say that it was impossible to bat against bowling of such hostility, they were beaten men before they got to the middle. Once Botham fell, the tail was annihilated, Bairstow, Emburey, Jackman and Dilley managing just seven runs between them.

The attacks on Botham were becoming increasingly personal, though he was fortunate to be as far from the British newspapers as he was, unable to read much of what was written. Even so, he knew the pressure was mounting. His greatest problem was the very quality that had been perceived as his greatest asset – the ability to lead from the front. With his prodigious form of the past now a fast fading memory, Botham could not inspire his troops in the way Boycott had forecast. Picking up a few tail-end wickets rather than scything through the top order, struggling for a dozen or so runs before getting out, even dropping catches in the field, this was not the great man England had come to rely on. Again, it must be emphasised that few players tasted success against the West Indians, but Botham's fall from grace was the more marked since it was so steep, so sudden, and so unexpected. Drained of his own powerful self belief, he was struggling for the first time in his career, and with the loss of Barrington he now had no one to whom he could turn for advice or reassurance.

His troubles badly affected his authority on the field. Where Brearley had been able to detach himself from his failings with the bat and retreat into the captaincy as an intellectual diversion, a refuge from personal adversity, Botham did not see cricket in the same way. Where to Brearley it was a strategic game, chess played with human pieces, for the young Botham it was more akin to a game of space invaders where the opposition was there to be blitzed. Where Brearley had planned with the scientific brain of a Montgomery, Botham simply ran straight into trouble like the reckless Custer. Temporarily robbed of his attacking powers, he found his side shorn of its most potent weapon in the field – himself. Without Botham pounding in and swinging the ball at will, England's shortcomings were exposed. Jackman was a willing workhorse but unlikely to prosper in the West Indies. Dilley had little experience and Emburey was tight, but rarely a threat on pitches that offered little turn. The fact was that if Botham played well, England might just be able to conjure a win from somewhere. If he didn't, they couldn't. Where Brearley could throw the ball to Botham to win him a game, Botham had no such luxury.

Since Botham's time as captain, England have regularly capitulated once behind – Gower's sides were particularly prone to that. Botham should receive praise for inspiring his side to fight back in the final two games, salvaging some pride with a couple of hard-fought draws. In Antigua he saved England from oblivion when, with the West Indies at 268 for 3 in response to England's 271, he suddenly plucked out three wickets in five balls, while it was left to Gooch and Gower to secure an honourable draw at Sabina Park in the final game. Thus ended Botham's first, and only, tour as England captain, having lost two Tests from four. The tour was treated as disastrous and Botham dismissed as a five-minute wonder. Certainly his batting was poor: he registered just seventy-three runs, coming seventh in the averages, and never threatened to come to terms with the West Indians. However, it was only by his own lofty standards that he failed with the ball. He was England's top wicket taker with fifteen topping the averages too; remember that Greig had a truly appalling series with both bat and ball in 1976 yet few questions were asked about his position in the side. With the bowling attack lacking penetration once Willis departed, Botham often had to operate as a stock, rather than strike, bowler, mounting a damage limitation exercise by blocking up one end; Botham later suggested that that compromised his effectiveness with the bat, the hot sun taking its toll, leaving him physically spent by the time he got to the crease. As Jack Bannister noted, it was a role for which he was unsuited, having 'neither the technique nor the temperament to bowl long spells of containment'. Had Willis been there to help from the other end, perhaps Botham might have been the attacking first change he had been in the past; coming on with the West Indies 18 for 2 would have offered him the luxury of bowling with his characteristic aggression and his figures might have been better yet. Viewed dispassionately, the tour might have been regarded as part of a longer rehabilitation from his back problems and an encouraging sign that he was returning to fitness and form. Instead, his failure in the series to take five wickets in an innings was seen as evidence that he wasn't the man he'd been built up to be.

That contention was inextricably linked with concern over his future role as England's captain. Subsequent events were to suggest that his days were already numbered and that the match by match trial he had to undergo was just so much window dressing. Assailed by adverse press comment, embarrassed by his innocent yet potentially damaging role in the Joe Neenan incident in Scunthorpe, and maddened by his responsibility with the bat in Trinidad, Lord's could withstand the pressure no longer. Botham was to be made the scapegoat for a damaging, though scarcely disastrous, defeat at the hands of a far better team. Had the selectors had any real desire to see Botham continue as England skipper, maturing and growing into the role, they would have appointed him for the whole summer of 1981. That seal of approval would have allowed him and the team to attack a comparatively weak Australian line up knowing they had a full six Tests in which to secure victory. On the basis of a game by game appointment, Botham never had the time to reassert his authority over his shell-shocked players. Such a move was never even considered, for short termism rules all in England. The real problem was that had Botham been given that opportunity and had England lost the first couple of Tests, the criticism would have moved away from the skipper to be trained on the selectors and the TCCB instead. Fearful of losing their comfortable place in the scheme of things, administrators tend to look for a sacrificial lamb rather than try to identify the underlying reasons for failure. (The same propensity is obvious in football. When the crowd calls for the manager's head, he goes, because if he doesn't the next chant is 'Sack the board'.) Defeat against the West Indies was not Botham's fault. England were simply outclassed, and sacrificing him was a case of blaming the messenger for the message, complaining that a general armed with a peashooter had been defeated by one packing four nuclear warheads.

Almost inevitably, the changes in leadership did little long term good: Keith Fletcher, appointed eighteen months too late, led England to a one-nil defeat in India the following winter, in a sense a worse result than that experienced in the West Indies. If nothing else, it highlighted and drummed home the deficiencies in the English team and provided proof positive that Botham was not the root of all evil. Fletcher's appointment was yet another example of short termism. If Botham had to go, then a comparatively sedate tour away from the public eye in India would have been the ideal time to give the likes of Gower or Gatting a chance to prove themselves in the job, growing into it away from the pressure cooker atmosphere of a home series or a series against vastly superior opposition. With relatively low profile home series against India and Pakistan to come in 1982, the selection of Fletcher and then of Willis to replace him was a retrograde step.

Returning to the start of 1981, Botham now had ten Tests under his belt – England had achieved a solid draw in the Lord's Centenary Test against Australia the previous year. Surely this was the time to take advantage of that accumulated experience and look to the future. Give him another six Tests in charge against more manageable opposition and then look at his record as both captain and player to see if he was starting to come good, especially with less formidable opponents on the horizon for the forthcoming year. No one at Lord's or among the selection panel showed the necessary will in the face of media pressure to stand up and say, 'This is our man, we'll stand by him.' So it was that England lost a potentially impressive skipper. With hindsight, Botham would have been best advised to decline the invitation to lead the Ashes side from the outset, but the England captaincy is not a job anyone turns down or relinquishes lightly, especially when the incumbent concerned is a fervent patriot, the coming foe is the Australians, and the odds are so heavily weighted against victory; if nothing else, Botham proved that he was not one to hide when things got tough. David Frith argued in a *Wisden Cricket Monthly* editorial that 'England's enchantingly bull-headed leader, Ian Botham, cricket's hellraising Hemingway ... needs the support of the press and public though not necessarily in respect of the captaincy ... it came not only too early but in the wrong sequence. Had Mike Brearley been retained, even his previously successful record would have been shredded by Lloyd's lancers.'

It was an argument few others were willing to accept. Botham had been written off, the selectors had made their lack of faith in him very clear, and his confidence evaporated. By the end, at Lord's in the Second Test, he cut a lonely figure, shuffling around the field he had once commanded. Morose and remote, incapable of inspiring himself, he and his colleagues spilled chance after chance in the First Test in Nottingham, handing the game to Australia, while Botham seemed reluctant to bowl on a pitch seemingly made for him. Bagging a pair at Lord's when in search of quick runs following Boycott's stultifying sixty was the final straw. Custer's last stand ended in ignominious failure. The fallen idol returned to the Long Room to stunned silence, the members writhing in paralysed English embarrassment, unable even to offer him a consoling hand; ironically, a year earlier he'd written in *The Cricketer* that 'Lord's is my favourite [ground] ... something always seems to happen there ... my love affair with Lord's will always bring out the best in me.' It seems to bring out the worst in some of its members, and Botham, who can hold grudges as tightly as ever he held slip catches, has yet to forgive them for what he felt was a callous betrayal. Deciding to stand down as captain, he was then stripped of his final shred of dignity when chairman of selectors Alec Bedser told the press that if he hadn't jumped, he'd have been pushed anyway – a barbed and unnecessary remark which nevertheless seemed to provide a fitting conclusion to this most fraught and, at times, bitter affair.

What are we to make of Ian Botham, cricketing captain? The accusation that the captaincy ruined him as a cricketer is palpable nonsense, a myth which needs to be dispelled once and for all. It was the might of the West Indies that brought him to his knees. The comparative figures against the West Indies tell the story: as captain, he scored 242 runs at an average of fifteen, while in the ranks he managed 550 at twenty-six; with the ball, the skipper took twenty-eight wickets at thirty-one, the player thirty-three at nearly thirty-nine apiece. In essence, his performances against the West Indies were decidedly ordinary whether he was leading the side or not. In terms of his wider-raging responsibilities, however, there were many errors. As a member of the selection committee he has to take a share of the blame for poor selections and wrong headed policy. There was a reliance on bits and pieces players at the expense of specialists, folly in the face of a West Indian onslaught. He often appeared unsure about how best to use himself as a bowler. He mistook leading from the front for taking too much upon himself, becoming stock and strike bowler and consequently doing neither well. He could be insensitive of the needs and intolerant of the idiosyncrasies of some of his players. He rarely had any net practice himself and saw little use for it; he wanted to motivate the side in the bar by relaxing, while some players needed to get in another hour at the crease, something he had trouble understanding. Off the field, he sometimes seemed unaware of the importance of his office and reacted to pressure with an unappealing belligerence, though he was not alone in that among England captains of the 1980s. Yet on the positive side, it's apparent that for the most part the players did do their utmost, working at least as hard for him as for any other contemporary leader. In England in 1980, following the disappointment of losing the first game of the series, his side fought back well with the aid of the weather to keep the margin of defeat down to one game. In the West Indies, his team withstood the Jackman affair and the death of Ken Barrington to regain lost pride during the last two Tests of the series. In that regard, he was able to keep a tighter rein on events than David Gower managed.

Leading Somerset in the 1983 NatWest semi-final against Middlesex at Lord's, Botham proved beyond all doubt to the arrayed MCC members that he had the tactical acumen to make a good captain. It was his cool, calculating brain that took the club into the final: he scored a brilliant ninety-six and showed a rare appreciation of the unfolding situation, stonewalling through the final over to see Somerset home on fewer wickets lost. He led them to the trophy in the final too, defending a low total of 193 with ease. Though his prolonged absences from Taunton on England duty hampered him when he captained Somerset in 1984 and 1985, he led the side astutely at times and even managed to average a hundred with the bat in Championship matches in 1985 – no sign of captaincy affecting his form there. Sadly it soon became obvious that no one in authority was watching and that the England captaincy would never come his way again; this was in part due to the blinkered attitude of the Establishment, but it was also a result of his penchant for attracting unsavoury headlines. His response was to devote himself instead to other goals, such as maximising his earning potential away from the game, at the expense of making any sustained bid to win the role once more.

Perhaps the fundamental mistake Botham made is one which still haunts English cricket. His leadership was dogged by internal dispute, a few of the old stagers becoming increasingly hostile to him as time went on. Botham was unable to assert sufficient authority to rid himself of these turbulent influences, so they eventually ground him down. It was a lesson Kim Hughes failed to take on board but one to which Allan Border paid assiduous attention. Like other successful captains such as Frank Worrell or Clive Lloyd, over a period of time Border constructed *his* team filled with *his* players. He removed any disruptive influence, dispensed with the need for the time-honoured senior pro, and created a team built solely in his image. Gritty, aggressive, strong, taking no prisoners, they were ready to follow the captain to the hilt wherever he took them. Border took risks, losing plenty of games early in his reign, but once he had established that side with players like David Boon, Geoff Marsh, Mark Taylor, Mark and Steve Waugh, Craig McDermott, Merv Hughes and Ian Healy, he reaped the benefits. Had Botham been able to do the same, the 1980s might have been a golden period. As it was, the opportunity slipped by, the recurrent story of English cricket.

CHAPTER THREE

RECONSTRUCTION OF THE FABLES

The Summer of 1981

It was the strangest of times, the English summer of 1981. Two years into its term, the Thatcher government's hermetic monetarist squeeze was decimating Britain's manufacturing industry. Unemployment was shooting up at an exponential rate, racing beyond the previously intolerable level of two and a half million and showing no signs of slowing. There were riots all over inner-city Britain, the most serious in Liverpool's economically ravaged Toxteth district. Meanwhile, in London, the heir to the throne married the fairy-tale princess in St Paul's Cathedral attended by all the pomp and circumstance the nation could muster. And in the midst of all that was the cricket.

Sport has a central role to play in any developed nation, yet commentators are often very slow to recognise the fact. In South Africa, for example, the various sporting boycotts played a crucial role in forming both world and domestic opinion and were a vital tool in the final dismantling of the odious apartheid regime. The Warsaw Pact countries were only too well aware of the propaganda value of successful athletes, bringing prestige to political systems reviled by the rest of the world. Hitler had his showcase Olympic games in 1936, Mussolini left no stone unturned in his determined pursuit of football's World Cup in 1938, and the Argentinian junta recognised that a World Cup win in 1978 would divert the populace's attention from the country's appalling economic plight, if only for a short time (the Falklands invasion fulfilled that role four years later, just as it did here). A high profile and thoroughly successful national sporting side can paper over cracks in the social fabric more effectively than almost any political measure could ever hope to do. The people at large are far more interested in the fortunes of their football, cricket or basketball team than in any remote and convoluted political ideology.

The above rank among the more extreme examples, of course. Nonetheless, even in a country as inherently conservative as Britain, sport's role is an important, if altogether more subtle one. There is little which is as good for the collective morale as a national victory – reflect on the lessons of Euro '96 or Tim Henmania if you need to be convinced of that. Orwell's dictum that serious sport is 'war minus the shooting' still rings true, in this country as much as in any other. Indeed, there are few countries for whom sporting victory is as important as it is for England, few where the fate of the national teams is of such consequence, few where the press is so obnoxious in victory and so pitilessly vindictive in defeat. There are far fewer still which take winning and losing seriously without ever making any real effort to assist their athletes. Just as the communist bloc used sport as an image building tool in the propaganda war they waged, England has looked on sporting success as confirmation that she is still a force in the world. East Germany and the Soviet Union had far greater success in that respect, for the communists at least had the good sense to channel resources properly to fund their performers, something which we, locked in our time-warped romance with the amateur ideal, remain extremely loath to do. With its role on the world stage ever declining, England is a nation with a perpetual identity crisis. Entering this century with an empire, we look set to leave it without influence, perhaps even without our economic sovereignty. The sporting stage acts as a palliative, providing us with the opportunity to prove our worth and, on rare occasions, to beat the world once again.

In the 1970s, our national sense of self worth was at its lowest ebb. Our manufacturing industry was thrown into turmoil by the global oil crisis and we were then humiliated by the bankers at the International Monetary Fund who ordered the decimation of the nation's infrastructure before they would provide financial assistance. The UK, the nation that had stood almost alone in the cause of freedom in the early years of the last war, was now forced to go cap in hand to anonymous financiers and was subsequently brought to its knees as a result of their strictures. By the end of the decade the country was in decay and, apparently, terminal decline. Ironically, of course, such conditions provide the perfect breeding ground for renewed nationalism: the Silver Jubilee in 1977 offered a brief respite from the grim realities, eliciting a huge popular response. On a more sinister level, the National Front reported significant growth at the time – economic deprivation breeds nothing as quickly as isolationism and xenophobia. Thankfully, the more intelligent majority sought their patriotic refuge on the sports field.

If ever a feelgood factor were needed, it was in 1981. The 1979 Conservative election promises of revitalising the nation were already ringing hollow in the ears of their victims, those thrown out of work and on to an ever-expanding dole queue. An unemployment figure of 2.5 million was regarded as a national disgrace and it prompted the People's March For Jobs, a huge outpouring of anger at the situation and a final 'legitimate' expression of the majority's frustration with Britain's apparently irreversible decline. Callaghan's Labour government had failed to manage the country in 1978/79 following its refusal to confront the IMF. Now Thatcher's golden vision of a future where wealth cascaded down from the top of society to the bottom was proving stubbornly elusive. In early July the disenfranchised took to the streets in the worst outbreaks of rioting seen in Britain in living memory, the rioters' fury fuelled further by the impending royal wedding, a display of wealth and privilege that could only breed resentment among those who were being so comprehensively turned aside. Yet even then, the wedding was marketed as a unifying force. Union Jacks were peaceably unfurled for just about the first time since the Silver Jubilee four years earlier.

Spurred on by Margaret Thatcher's instinctive national chauvinism, through the 1980s Britain in general and England in particular lived through its most fiercely patriotic, some might say jingoistic, decade since the end of the war. Newspaper editors jumped on to the band-wagon, pumping their readers with stories of 'Great Britain', of a country apparently still fighting World War Two, the rest of Europe and the iniquities of the Common Market, of a nation still among the most important and influential on the world stage. It was palpable nonsense, but so keen were people to escape from the realities that surrounded them, the nation bought into the dream in a big way. The New Right were perfectly positioned to take full advantage of the situation, and the idea of Britain, and especially England, as a superpower and a nation of which we could still be proud was relentlessly promoted.

A figurehead was required to satisfy these circumstances, a hero who could rally the nation behind this new-found devotion to the flag. Charles and Diana were busily doing their bit, lending a warm, if brief, glow to the ideal of Queen and country, yet no one could ignore the obvious parallels with happenings in the real world. Labour MP Tony Benn, for instance, remembers that 'just before the wedding, there was a huge fireworks display in London, a reaffirmation of the position of the Establishment, the way it had become entrenched again with Margaret Thatcher in power. It was televised and I remember watching that and then turning over to another channel and there were pictures of riots in Liverpool. The contradiction was so powerful, so vivid. Here was a country that seemed as socially advanced as the French before the revolution!'

Sport remained the most effective force for social cohesion and Ian Botham was the ideal saviour, a working class hero who was getting on through his own efforts. The timing could scarcely have been more propitious for the arrival of a natural born hero. Demonstrably proud of playing for his country, Ian Botham was a latter-day St George come to slay the Foreign dragons. When he had first begun to smite the Australians in 1977, the national football team was about to miss out on qualification for the 1978 World Cup, there were no signs of any new top class golfers ready to replace Tony Jacklin, and as the careers of Virginia Wade, Sue Barker and Mark Cox wound down we were soon to be without a tennis player who could survive the first two days of Wimbledon. In Botham's early years, the greater part of England's sporting hopes and fears rested squarely on the shoulders of the national cricket team.

Timing is a theme that crops up again and again in relation to Ian Botham. No sportsman better represented the spirit of the times, the decade's zeitgeist, than Botham. That was why he transcended his sport and became a national figure of real importance, a legend that would endure. Timing is all in the propagation of a legend. It was wholly appropriate that England should regain the Ashes in 1953, Coronation year, and that Denis Compton should be there at the death. England's World Cup win would have been less satisfactory had it come in any year other than 1966 and at any venue other than Wembley and under any other captain than Bobby Moore – London was the centre of the universe, the swinging sixties was our gift to the world, the suave Moore the embodiment of English cool. If we'd taken the Jules Rimet trophy in 1962 or 1970 instead, the story would have lost some of its magic. In the same way, it seemed right that England should revive the Dunkirk spirit and take victory from the jaws of defeat in the royal year of 1981 – the script could not have been more dramatic had it come from Hollywood.

As is described elsewhere, Botham had suffered his own crushing defeat earlier in the summer. Shorn of confidence and with support from Lord's that was faint-hearted at best, he was forced into retreat and resigned the captaincy with England one down after two Test matches, a comparatively weak Australian side looking increasingly comfortable and dominant. Having been appointed on a game by game basis, Botham rightly and bravely concluded that such indecision was anathema to a side in sore need of decisive and dynamic leadership. His resignation was the action of an honourable, if bewildered, man, one who could be forgiven for wondering where all his friends had gone.

With Botham removed from their deliberations, the selectors were free to recall Mike Brearley. They had long since come to regret replacing him in such haste a year earlier. Having lost the role as captain when he reaffirmed his refusal to tour again, bringing him back was scarcely the most logical of moves, yet it was probably the only avenue open to the panel. Certainly, there's nothing to suggest they looked too hard for alternatives. The competition was decidedly thin: Bob Willis seemed, yet again, to be coming to the end of his Test career; Boycott was never seriously considered; Gooch, Gower and Gatting were every bit as inexperienced as Botham had been when he took on the job a year before and Willey was viewed as a staunch sergeant-major type rather than a leader. Ignoring Brearley would almost inevitably mean the new captain would still have to come from outside the team, which in itself would be potentially disruptive and would, by definition, further weaken the playing strength. Perhaps if the next Test hadn't been at Headingley Keith Fletcher might have been given the job, one he was awarded for that winter's tour of India. Certainly Fletcher was a better bet with the bat than Brearley, an important consideration given England's fragile middle order. His captaincy record at county level was at least the equal of Brearley's, inspiring Essex to the trophies that had eluded them throughout a hundred years of history. Unfortunately, the Headingley crowd were renowned for giving him a hard time and since it was a game England just had to win, or at the very least not lose, it would hardly be fair to have Fletcher battling with both the Aussies who had tortured him in 1974/75 and a packed crowd of unimpressed Yorkshiremen. When to that equation was added the fact that he hadn't played for England in more than four years, the case against him became overwhelming.

So Brearley was charged with the rehabilitation of England's cricketing superstar. That was his task, for if Botham could be made to fire on all cylinders once more the Australians were clearly vulnerable. A revitalised Botham, picking up his customary five wickets in an innings with the odd fifty or hundred added for good measure, would surely be too much for a side who were not the strongest of visitors. Once it had been determined that Botham would be playing at Headingley – and whatever his disappointments, at this stage of his career there was no way he would voluntarily miss out on a Test cap – the nation was waiting for his rebirth, though perhaps more in hope than in expectation. Following his agonising fall from grace, many had been quick to suggest that he was not quite the colossus in which the country had been led to believe. His runs and wickets had come against weak opposition, the West Indians had exposed his flaws, he wasn't the new Messiah after all – so ran the general opinion. In part this was undeniably accurate. His awesome figures *had* been bolstered by powerful performances against tepid opponents, but then all the greats have helped themselves to cheap runs and wickets when the opportunity has presented itself. The West Indians had reduced him to the ranks of the mere mortals, but as the 1980s were to show, no one could consistently thrive against such a fierce attack. This new wisdom also conveniently disregarded such displays that few others could match: he'd savaged a strong Australian attack spearheaded by Dennis Lillee at Melbourne with a thrilling hundred in a losing cause; he'd dismantled the Indians in their own backyard in Bombay. To be more realistic, Botham was going to Headingley on the back of two poor games against the Australians when he could be forgiven for having his eye on anything other than the ball. For the first time since his arrival on the scene he had something to prove, but his overall reputation still remained in good shape in the eyes of objective viewers. The question marks now were against his mental, rather than physical, strength.

The most telling observation about the 1981 series, the 'Incredible Tests' as Botham's book termed them, was that the two teams were very evenly matched and were enduring similar internal problems. In terms of captaincy, Australia's Kim Hughes was as bedevilled as Botham. Just as the latter had been thrust into the breach when Mike Brearley declined to tour, the former had been elevated to the captaincy once Greg Chappell refused to visit England for a fifth time. As Botham had clinched the job with a virtuoso performance in a celebration Test – the Golden Jubilee match in Bombay – Hughes had pushed his claims with a scintillating display in the Centenary game at Lord's the previous summer. It had been his graceful and spectacular strokeplay that had enlivened a disappointing game that was otherwise best forgotten. And where Botham was undermined by those in the dressing room and beyond who felt the crown should have passed to Boycott, Hughes was put on trial and ultimately undone by similar elements who believed that Rodney Marsh would have done a better job. To compound his difficulties, the absence of Chappell's technique and experience from the most brittle of batting orders was to prove crucial. In a sense, that was akin to the loss England endured in the Caribbean when Ken Barrington passed away, a loss that exposed all the side's mental and technical frailties.

Leading an average side to success on the field requires a talented captain. With due respect to Clive Lloyd's part in formulating tactics and creating a formidable team spirit in a previously volatile dressing room, most experienced Test players could have made a fist of leading the West Indies through the 1980s. With Holding, Croft, Roberts, Garner, Marshall, Richards, Haynes, Greenidge and Lloyd himself in the side, it was almost as difficult to lose a Test series as it was to win one. It's hard to judge Lloyd as a skipper because great captains are marked out not so much by the frequency and regularity of victories as by their ability to inspire a team match after match to play *above* its collective abilities. In recent years Dermot Reeve has shown himself to be such a leader at county level; Hansie Cronje promises to reveal similar qualities on a consistent basis on the international stage. Mike Brearley has been seen as one of England's foremost leaders simply because he turned a losing team into a winning one, while it has passed into folklore that Botham was an extremely lucky cricketer, picking up wickets with bad balls and mishooking sixes. Yet Brearley was as fortunate, getting the rub of the green when he needed it most. There was so little to choose between England and Australia in 1981 that any slight improvement in England's form or a little dip in that of the Aussies would be enough to turn the tables. Brearley was inheriting a team that was being attacked out of all proportion to its defects. Written off as losers, in the first game at Trent Bridge England had actually come within a couple of dropped catches of being one up rather than one down. If any of those had stuck, Botham might well have gone to Headingley as captain. England were not fighting superior forces but a side on a par with their own and with the added disadvantage of playing away from home. Brearley wasn't taking charge of a team without hope; his job was to restore belief, not perform alchemy.

There were other aspects to this series in his favour too. Dennis Lillee, though still a potent threat, had been hit by viral pneumonia early on in the tour. Obliged to marshal his reserves of energy, he operated at a fraction of his customary pace, though he continued to bowl beautifully throughout the series. A fully fit Lillee might have proved an insurmountable obstacle. His pace bowling partners, Alderman excepted, also had their share of ill health: Rodney Hogg appeared in just two Tests, his performance at Trent Bridge as back-up to Lillee and Alderman proving vital, before his tour was ruined by injury, and Geoff Lawson missed the last three Tests. So low were their bowling reserves, Australia had to call up Mike Whitney from league cricket where he'd been playing with Fleetwood. Remember too that Botham had rarely had the luxury of a fighting fit Bob Willis with whom to attack the opposition.

Brearley's miracle was carried out with Willis right in the vanguard. In retrospect, prospects could scarcely have looked more promising for an English fightback.

From the moment Mike Brearley lost the Headingley toss on Thursday morning through to the fall of Bob Taylor's wicket midway through the Monday afternoon, with England still ninety-two short of avoiding an innings defeat with just three wickets intact, the tide had flowed remorselessly in Australia's favour. The only crumb of comfort to be gained by English supporters was the fact that Botham had top scored with fifty in the first innings and, as he'd promised his captain, had taken six wickets for ninety-five runs in Australia's 401. At last, he was beginning to recapture some of the self belief that had deserted him in the previous couple of months. By the fourth day, though, not even Botham thought the game could be saved unless the weather intervened. When he was joined by Graham Dilley with the score on 135 for 7, the game was up. Australia were two ahead with three to play, the myth of Brearley's miraculous captaincy would finally be laid to rest, and Botham himself might have been facing a lay off from the Test team. Over the weekend, the cricket correspondents were outspoken in their condemnation of the team and stalwarts such as Willis, Boycott, Willey, Old and Taylor were apparently about to contest the final moments of their Test match careers while others such as Botham, Gatting and Gower might well have been heading back to their counties for an extended break. Had Botham still been leading the team, the burden of responsibility might have forced him to try to play out time, stonewalling *à la* Trevor Bailey in the forlorn hope that a cloudburst might offer a reprieve. The game would almost inevitably have been lost, but it would have been seen as 'doing the right thing', particularly in the aftermath of Trinidad. With the vultures of the press pack hovering, he would have been unwilling to provide another hostage to fortune by swinging irresponsibly even in a hopelessly lost cause. Finally allowed the freedom that had made him so dangerous in previous years, Botham was able to enjoy his cricket again, and he treated that Monday afternoon as an excuse to amuse himself. Even before Dilley came to the wicket, he had swung himself almost off his feet in abortive attempts to hit the Australian quicks out of the ground. Had any of those deliveries which shaved the stumps induced a snick to the slip cordon, Kim Hughes would have been the hero of the hour, a touring captain on the verge of recapturing the Ashes. As it was, Botham survived and prospered.

And how he prospered! Time and again he opened those massive shoulders to unleash another uncomplicated swing of the bat, striking the bowling to some of the most unlikely parts of the ground. So spectacular, so spontaneous and so unrepeatable were some of his shots, it was impossible to set a field for him, though Hughes clearly blundered in his refusal to use the spinner Ray Bright earlier. While historians thought back to the turn of the century and the destructiveness of Gilbert Jessop, Botham himself regarded the whole innings as something of a joke, a wild slog where everything came off. The spectators also realised that this was not the controlled play of a batsman utterly in charge of the bowling, but rather a cartoon, intended to lift the spirits, entertain briefly and perish gloriously. Yet as each boundary boosted the score, Botham seemed to grow in stature; it was as if at lunch Popeye had finally got his hands on the keys to the spinach cupboard and had tucked in to the heartiest of meals, gorging himself after a year-long famine. Biceps bulging, Botham chuckled away as he enjoyed some extravagant good fortune, playing and missing, mishitting wide of the fielders – more slices of good luck in that one afternoon than he had had in the previous dozen Tests put together. Imperceptibly at first, but then more and more obviously, he wrested the initiative from the beleaguered Hughes whose tactical uncertainty, along with the vulnerability of his position within the side, left him paralysed, incapable of acting. Persisting with the tiring Lillee and Alderman for far too long, he was seemingly oblivious to the fact that the faster they bowled, the harder the ball was hit. As the Aussies began to fall apart long before England had posted anything like a threatening score, so the smile grew wider on Botham's face.

Even then, with his hundred reached and with Chris Old now at the other end with just Willis to come, Botham didn't envisage victory. It was Brearley who, signalling wildly from the balcony, urged him to stay at the crease after he'd posted three figures. The chancier moments were generally confined to the early part of his innings, and though he often dismisses the 149 he scored at Headingley as being as much luck as judgement, the longer he stayed in, the better he looked. Despite playing like a millionaire, he somehow had an air of Boycott-like invulnerability about his play, such that the Aussies might have bowled at him for another full day without getting him out. When the players trooped off at the close of that remarkable Monday, England were 124 runs in the lead with Bob Willis, the perennial number eleven, lunging forward bravely and keeping Botham company. Interviewed by Peter West for the BBC, Botham boldly suggested that another thirty or forty runs might make it an interesting finish, but sanity returned, albeit briefly, when Alderman had Willis caught with just five added on the final morning.

One hundred and thirty to get for a two-nil lead seemed like a formality, especially when Australia reached 56 for 1, accumulating the necessary runs steadily. Yet the game had already been won and lost. No other sport is played in the mind as much as cricket and each Englishman knew that just one breakthrough could open the door. Botham himself recalled that the previous evening the Australians had sat slumped in their dressing room, unable to believe this new course of events, staring emptily around them in stunned silence, beaten men. With a number of the team lacking confidence in him as a leader, Hughes could not raise their spirits, and the spectre of a humiliating defeat hung in the air. Studying a batting order that lacked the calming influence of men like Greg Chappell, Doug Walters and David Hookes, and instead featured the promising but rather inexperienced skills of Hughes, Wood, Dyson and Border and precious little else, it was clear that England were anything but out of it. Once Willis, labouring ineffectively, had changed ends to bowl with the wind behind him, he was transformed. A vicious lifter undid Trevor Chappell, a smart catch from Botham removed Hughes, and once Chris Old bowled Border with a delivery that went through the pitch, the game was over. Bob Willis, pounding in and blazing away at the shell-shocked Australian batsmen, conducted the last rites, seemingly unaware of the drama that was unfolding around him until, the last wicket taken, he finally whirled away in relief as much as delight.

In the 1982 edition of *Wisden*, Mike Brearley wrote:

Sometimes the need is to rediscover the expectation of winning. Last summer, England had gone twelve Tests without a win. They were dropping as many catches as they were holding; the bowlers were looking, at times, slightly half-hearted. Spirits sagged if a fielding session yielded no tangible successes. Not long after, virtually the same team was catching everything and fielding with a new vitality. This transformation, I hasten to add, was achieved almost entirely by inspiring individual performances.

As Brearley was generous enough to concede, it was Botham that proved the catalyst for this upturn in their fortunes, just as it was he who had been the fount of their collective self doubt in the first two matches of the summer. As good a captain as Brearley was, he was unable to turn the tide alone. Instead, Botham once again became England's talisman, a freak display of hitting blasting away the dark clouds that had surrounded him and his team-mates. Had those runs not come, the game would have been lost, and much of Brearley's reputation with it. In turn, Willis, pensioned off a day earlier, was possessed by the idea of a famous victory, Graham Dilley, astonishingly sure of foot, ran backwards and held a steepling catch on the boundary to remove Australia's last real hope, Rodney Marsh, and Mike Gatting, never the most lithe of men, sprinted yards to take a vital, tumbling catch to dismiss Lillee. All of these feats would have been almost inconceivable on the Thursday when Dyson ground out a dour but important hundred and England were continuing their aimless drift towards the next defeat. Botham alone was the inspiration. In the midst of riotous national celebration, he had eclipsed the forthcoming wedding of the heir to the throne.

With that one innings, the series was turned. Though England contrived to get themselves into trouble on numerous occasions, Australia were fresh out of self belief and purpose and, Border apart, had no batsman consistently capable of holding things together when under heavy fire. Indeed, the impact of Headingley 1981 is something that Australian cricket is trying to deal with even now, strong as they are. On a number of recent occasions Mark Taylor has refused to enforce the follow on, determined to shut the game up instead by batting again, closing the opposition out at the risk of turning victory into a draw. If

Headingley still has antipodean repercussions sixteen years on, just imagine how hard it must have been to deal with as the series unfolded.

The Fourth Test was held at Edgbaston, in the golden afterglow of the royal wedding. The ground was festooned with union flags, the crowd vocal in their support for the home nation, just the kind of atmosphere designed to fuel England and strike fear into the downbeat tourists. Hard though Kim Hughes had tried to play down Headingley as some kind of freak storm, he and his team must have feared that Botham might be back to his consistently destructive best. Australia struck the first blow, bowling well on a difficult track, and it was only some dogged defensive batting from Brearley that enabled England to post a moderate score of 189. Botham struggled with the ball in Australia's reply, the main thrust coming from Old and Emburey who bowled beautifully. Batting again in response to a deficit of sixty-nine England were just ninety-eight ahead with two wickets remaining before Old and Emburey again turned things around with a perky stand of fifty. Faced with 151 to get, the echoes of Headingley were sounding in the ears of even the most detached observer.

Sunday play in a Test match was a new feature of this 1981 summer, and here it came to England's aid. Under a baking sun Edgbaston was packed, that vast concrete bowl a seething cauldron as the fiercely partisan crowd backed their cricketers as if it were an international football match at Wembley stadium. The home crowd's favourite, Bob Willis, stormed in to bowl backed by raucous chants more reminiscent of the hill at Sydney – for Willis, Old and Taylor, survivors of the 1974/75 tour, it must have been rewarding to hear English crowds baying for blood as the Aussies had done in the days of Lillee and Thomson, even if the physical threat was not quite the same. There's little doubt that the participation of that packed house was vital in inspiring England and forcing the Australians back on the defensive and into a cocoon of introspective indecision. Had the fourth day – one which dawned with Australia needing 142 with only Wood out – been played out on a Monday before a couple of thousand spectators instead of this full house, no such emotion could have been generated and the result might have been in greater doubt. As it was, following the events of a fortnight earlier, Australian morale was fragile. The fervour of the

84

English crowd was enough to make some of them look as if they wished they were back home in Melbourne, Adelaide or Perth.

Allan Border made it apparent that his was a very considerable talent, batting with resolution to post forty runs as Australia inched their way in single, agonised steps towards their goal. At 105 for 4 it was his dismissal that again signalled the end, just as it had in Leeds. It took another unplayable delivery to get him this time, the ball from Emburey fizzing from a good length, catching the glove and flying to Gatting who held the crucial catch. The door open, Brearley acted with the decision that had often eluded his predecessor, calling Botham into action from the City End. With Border gone, England were suddenly favourites despite the small target. With the psychological hold Botham had established over the tourists in Leeds, the sight of this gargantuan hero marking out his run up must have seemed like the coming of Armageddon for poor Kim Hughes, now helpless in the pavilion. As part of his ongoing rehabilitation, Botham had returned to Lord's, the scene of his cricketing nadir, and picked up a winner's medal in the Benson & Hedges final a week before the Edgbaston game, but thus far he'd done comparatively little of note in this Test. Now, just as the script demanded, he swept through the Australian tail, capturing five wickets for just one run. Bursting through the crease with a vigour that hadn't been seen since the onset of his back trouble, Botham was the irresistible force once more, tempting Dennis Lillee into one of the most horrible strokes he could ever have played, and wrapping up the game by the reasonably comfortable margin of twenty-nine runs. This was Botham at his intimidating best, threatening opponents with his size, his aggression and the prodigiousness of his gifts. Daring them to compete with him, he brushed them away from his sight with the same contemptuous disinterest with which a man might flick an insect off his sleeve. Brearley remarked that 'Ian is bowling without complications now which is the main difference to the way he bowled last summer'. The real difference was one of pace, for Botham was bowling with a will and at the kind of velocity that had regularly embarrassed tail-enders in the past. Australia's stunned cricketers had no answer to the speed and movement he generated.

It was to nobody's surprise that Botham dominated the Fifth Test at

Old Trafford, the game that clinched the series. This time England were in a healthier position, 205 ahead with five wickets in hand. Botham then proceeded to play one of the finest Test match innings of all time. His 118 came off 123 balls and was as forensic a display of calculated aggression as his Headingley knock had been an example of simple exuberance gone mad. In 1982's *Wisden*, John Thicknesse described the carnage: 'His innings included six 6s – a record for Anglo-Australian Tests – and thirteen 4s, all but one of which, an inside edge that narrowly missed the off stump on its way to fine leg, exploded off as near the middle of the bat as makes no odds. . . . Alderman and Lillee took the second new ball and Botham erupted, smashing 66 off eight overs.' It was an innings that any of the great masters of the game – from Grace to Trumper, Hobbs to Hammond, Bradman to Compton – would have been proud to call their own. It had a tempo and a fury that only the likes of Jessop or, compliment of compliments for Botham, Viv Richards could have matched. Where other English batsmen had been tentative, Botham was decisive and confident, handing Dennis Lillee the greatest pasting of his long career, the great Australian magnanimous in defeat, admitting that 'you couldn't do anything to stop him'. Jim Laker, commentating, called it the most spectacular Test hundred he'd ever seen, *Wisden*'s editor John Woodcock echoing the assessment in print, saying 'no-one, I believe, can ever have played a finer Test innings *of its type* than Botham's'.

For once, Botham's mastery seemed to inspire the Australians too, for despite being set more than 500 to win they fought long and hard. In this summer of the inexplicable, they even seemed to be in with a chance of victory on occasion. Border and Yallop made differing but equally valuable centuries, and England seemed drained by the dramas of the series. Finally, Bob Willis had Mike Whitney caught to seal a 103-run victory and the retention of the Ashes, 'Botham's Ashes', as the series became known. When the Sixth Test at the Oval ended in comparative anti-climax – the resurgent England unable to motivate themselves fully in the wake of their strength-sapping and mentally draining efforts, the punch drunk Australians putting up a creditable display before a defiant partnership between Brearley and Knott denied them victory – thoughts turned back to the incredible events of the series as a whole. Botham's thoughts turned to sleep: twenty-six of the next thirty-four hours were spent with his eyes tightly shut. In the wider, waking world, questions were asked as to how the Botham who bagged a pair at Lord's could demoralise the same foe with such ease just a few days later.

The answer was Botham's astonishing belief in himself and his own abilities. The captaincy had become a burden by nature of his temporary hold on the job. Always looking over his shoulder, trying to do the 'right' thing instead of what came naturally, he was shackled. Even then he never questioned his own ability; every set-back was the fault of some outside agency, be it a change in luck, press harassment, an injury – nothing was the fault of Ian Botham. Stated brutally, that implies he was a churlish, childish character; more accurately, it describes the armour-plated bubble of confidence in which the real greats live. One of cricket's glories is its allowance of a collective ethos, alongside the most highly self absorbed of individual battles to be housed in the same team. To have consistent success of the order of a Richards, a Waugh, a Warne or a Botham, you have to be utterly self reliant, willing to back yourself in every situation simply because you believe you are the best and that no one can beat you without the assistance of some outside agency such as extreme good fortune. Deep down such players may know that's not strictly true, but it is that very ego which denies the existence of a superior force which drives them on to their remarkable feats. If Viv Richards seemed arrogant and unconcerned as he strode to the crease, it was merely affirmation of the fact that he expected to give the fielders a hard time for a few hours. Some bowlers were beaten before they'd sent down a delivery – his complete demoralisation of Bob Willis in 1984 is a case in point. Botham possessed that same sense of certainty. Ultimately, as his physical powers began to wane, that bull-headedness became a failing. In 1981, it was a great strength.

In Patrick Eagar's 1985 photographic study of Botham, John Arlott wrote:

If he never scores another run, takes another wicket nor makes another catch, he must stand at the peak of cricket history. In 1981 he did what no-one else has ever done or is ever likely to do. He took up a

Test series his country was losing and, reshaping it in those mighty hands, decided it by his own efforts from at least one virtually imposs- ible and another quite precarious position; performed outstandingly in a third, and took ten wickets in the drawn sixth of a six-match series.

To achieve that from the unpromising raw material of Lord's was every bit as incredible as Arlott suggested. The only parallel is Bradman's performance in 1936/37 when, leading Australia for the first time against England, his side fought back from two down to clinch the series 3–2. Bradman, without a hundred in the first four innings of the series, scored 690 runs in his final five efforts. Like Botham, Bradman had no understanding of failure, believed that he would come out on top if all other things were equal. Botham's series was a triumph of his own powerful imagination. Nobody at Headingley felt that the game could be turned around, less still by the ailing superstar. Nobody could see this giant recapturing his bowling form at the precise moment that the doors had to be kicked down at Edgbaston. Nobody but Botham could have envisaged the blitzkrieg that finished the Aussies at Old Trafford as England's second innings had slowed to a crawl. For Botham, it was just a question of making up for lost time, time when external worries – largely the press and the Establishment at Lord's – had reduced him to the level of mortals.

The closing weeks of that summer must have been a bittersweet period for Botham. He was thrilled by the reaction of the people at Headingley, Edgbaston and Old Trafford, as well as the other grounds he visited with Somerset between Tests. The recapturing of their affection meant a lot to him, but surely he must have dwelt on the fickle nature of the general public. Those who lauded him now were the self same people who had reviled him, barracked him, inflicted such misery on his wife and family just months earlier. A more reflective individual might have taken the praise with a pinch of salt, preparing himself for the day when the wheel turned full circle again. With Botham that was never an option, for he simply believed that those days would not come again. It would have been difficult for anyone not to get swept along by the public mood, the more so if you were at the very centre of events.

The sporting public took to Ian Botham in 1981 in a way that no one individual has emulated since. There was delight in his cricket, relief in his return to fitness and form, pleasure in his rebuttal of astronomical odds. Once more Botham was a lightning conductor, a barometer of the public mood. The previous year had been grey and depressing with unemployment a frightening prospect for one and all, inflation racing ahead, the government seemingly in tatters. Botham, accordingly, was in his grey period, defeated, depressed, lacking in his customary spirit. By 1981, the press had tired of such despair. We had a royal occasion in the offing, the word spread that it was good news year, and Botham responded, not simply by winning games, but by winning them in style, acting not just as a cricketer but as a force for the social good. Writing of Headingley, David Frith was moved to call it 'a symbol and reminder of the fighting spirit which not only won a famous Test match but which can win much larger social and economic battles'.

Once you've rescued an entire nation from the grip of doom, gloom and despondency, what do you do for an encore? That was the question that now faced Ian Botham, one which he rarely looked able to answer. Once someone has achieved something incredible, the rest of his or her life is judged by that yardstick. Understandably, it was a challenge to which Botham could only occasionally rise, and never quite so spectacularly. The rest of his cricketing career was built largely upon myth, on fables. The events of 1981 were so remarkable because they were unrepeatable, unique. So many chance elements came together at the right time to create an environment in which a legend could thrive that it's highly unlikely the same thing could happen again. If Greg Chappell had toured, Australia would have batted better, would have been led better, would almost certainly have gone two up at Headingley. If Bob Willis had broken down again, the Australians would have sailed to their target. If Kim Hughes hadn't been under such internal pressure, his captaincy might have been more assured. If Botham had fancied a Test match off to clear his head after the events of Lord's, or if the selectors had deemed it wise for him to have a rest, he'd have missed Headingley altogether. If the country hadn't been living through such a patriotic year, the emotional crowd scenes which spurred England on might not have been possible, the results would not have had such resonance. If India had been touring, such fightbacks would have been shrugged off as impressive but irrelevant. If the weather had been as it was in 1980, none of the Tests would have finished. If Botham had had the same ill luck at Headingley as he'd had in Trinidad, the game would have been over in four days. If Australia had had a consistently fit pace attack, England would have had to fight harder for their runs. If Botham had made his Headingley runs in the first innings, it would have been a spectacular knock in a drawn game, just like his innings on the same ground against India in 1979, enjoyable but insignificant. The list of imponderables goes on, but if any one of those listed above had been the case, everything could, surely would, have been different.

Yet Botham never seemed to doubt his ability to replicate such moments of genius. That, more than anything else, dogged the rest of his career. Every innings had to be as good as the one at Old Trafford, every spell as incisive as that at Edgbaston. Viv Richards, one of his closest friends, summed him up well in Trevor McDonald's authorised biography:

> The main point about his play is that he plays cricket the way people like to see the game played. Ian Botham is with the public's thinking about cricket and you better believe it. They need the spirit and the enthusiasm he brings to the game. On his day, playing well, he is magnificent. There is never a dull moment when he's batting . . . Ian has the ability to be a class batsman, but he believes that there is probably something equally important or perhaps even more important. He is an entertainer.

McDonald himself has long held that view. In an interview in the *Daily Telegraph* in 1992, he noted: 'I support the West Indies but I love to see Ian Botham do well . . . to my mind, Botham is flashily brilliant and the English don't like him because they prefer the honest tryer.' There is an element of truth in that assessment, for Botham's style of play is naturally Caribbean. By the same token, you don't achieve greatness just by being flashily brilliant. Sobers – 'head and shoulders above all the all-rounders' according to Tom Graveney – was consistently brilliant, in a variety of styles. His view on Botham, as expressed in *The Changing Face Of Cricket*, is instructive: 'A very good player, yes, who could have become a great one. But he didn't ... if Ian had applied his talents, he could perhaps have ranked with the all-time greats.' Had Botham applied himself more, his figures might have avoided the hammering they took in the latter part of his career, but then he would not have been quite the crowd pleaser he was, nor would he have achieved cult status.

Having done what no others have ever done in 1981, there was an inevitable sense of anti-climax about the remainder of his career. Although he relished pulling on his England sweater, even Botham found it hard to inspire himself for the fray on a regular basis. It was only the sight of a baggy green cap from 22 yards that could get the blood flowing as it once had at Old Trafford and much of his most memorable cricket came against Australia. Had Botham still had Mike Brearley, Brian Close or Ken Barrington around him on a day to day basis, his career might have been very different. As it was, there was no one who could stand up to him, none who could persuade him that his way wasn't always the best, none who could get the ball out of his hand when he was taking punishment, none who could make him take his batting more seriously.

From 1981 onwards, Botham behaved like a man who had sleep-walked through the bloodiest of battles, emerging on the other side completely unscathed, and who was thereafter possessed by a sense of his own immortality. His tale became one of a man who had seen it, done it, and would not be deflected from his chosen course.

CHAPTER FOUR

WHAT DO I DO NOW?

Mentors & Miscreants

For the sake of Botham's equanimity, it might have been better had the Australians sailed comfortably to their small target at Headingley in 1981 and gone two up in the series. Botham's 149 would then have been remembered for what it really was, a great, mischievous talent sticking two fingers up at the thought of defeat in a glorious, ultimately futile, blaze of rebellion. That it became such an epochal moment was unfair to the man, for he was expected to repeat the feat time and again, something beyond any cricketer who ever picked up a bat.

Despite his obvious self absorption, Botham was a genuinely committed team man, a player who always wanted victory for his side even if the plaudits went elsewhere. He knew well enough that his efforts in the summer of 1981 had been underwritten by the team, notably by Brearley's captaincy, by Willis and by Emburey, surely the real man of the match at Edgbaston. Even so, according to the orgy of publicity that followed it was Botham who had won each game single handed, he who could have played the Aussies on his own, he who needed no assistance from anyone. However much he knew in his heart of hearts that that was just so much hot air, rubbish used to fill newspapers and TV retrospectives, the more times the myth was repeated, the harder it became to discount. Such adulation almost certainly impaired Botham's future. For one who always thought he knew best, this was proof positive that he had been right all along. Here was a real superhero, Popeye, Batman and Superman rolled into one; had the Gang of Four installed him as the new leader of the SDP, the Alliance really could have prepared for government. When someone possesses such overwhelming self belief, the greater is the need for sensible advice. With no one on whom he felt he could lean once Brearley left the England scene at the end of 1981, there was little to temper the wilder flights of fancy to which he was prone. His wife Kath might have been able to do so but such was Botham's outlook of macho bravado that he rarely took her into his confidence.

In his formative years, Botham had given due warning that he was a child apart, one who knew his own mind and refused to apply himself to anything that held no interest for him. He wore down his local careers master with his utter determination to play sport for a living, while simultaneously deciding that he had no need to gather a crop of 'O' levels, since that didn't get you into a cricket team. Had he embraced a slightly more academic range of interests, perhaps he might have had less trouble dealing with the man management side of captaincy. Nevertheless, here was a bullish, headstrong individual, the sort of child who had to win, had to get his own way and never for a moment felt there might be a different path forward. Twenty-five years later as his first class career was winding down, there was little to suggest that he'd ever really changed. He was still just a big daft lad who ignored advice and was generally proved right. Talking to Pat Murphy, he confirmed that 'I just knew instinctively what to do. In my life, I think I've only had about six hours' coaching and the only ones I've listened to have been Tom Cartwright, Kenny Barrington and Viv Richards.'

A physically strong child, one who is bigger and tougher than the rest, can get away with a lack of subtlety, even a lack of quality, on the playing field. A superior frame will carry them through, pure brute force riding tackles, clobbering forwards, clubbing sixes or knocking down wickets. At professional level, well though Botham disguised the fact, a player needs to have a little more intelligence than that, needs to employ a wider variety of skills. By the age of twenty-something, size isn't everything. For Botham, the chance to join the Lord's groundstaff was a crucial part of his development as a cricketer; without that experience he might not have risen to prominence with quite such speed. Deputed to handle him at cricket's HQ were chief coach Len

Muncer and his assistant Harry Sharp, seasoned coaches who had seen countless young boys pass through the Grace Gates full of dreams of cricketing glory. Muncer and Sharp were both highly professional individuals who knew the game inside out. However, like many coaches of the old school, they were reluctant to alter long formed opinions, with Muncer in particular slow to warm to Botham's unorthodox approach to the game. A child of his times, Botham had little interest in the age-old maxim that appearances counted, that the means were more important than the ends. Although he conformed to some text book teachings – his action was admirably side-on early in his career; he generally looked to hit the ball straight – he viewed the game as more than just a scientific discipline. Cricket was a source of fun, of entertainment. Having grown up in the Beatle years, having taken Chelsea as his favourite football team at a time when Osgood, Cooke and Hudson were in full flight, Botham knew the value of flair, of excitement, of the extraordinary. He'd seen how these people had romanced their very different crowds and he wanted to be a part of that. Dull conformity had no interest for him. Muncer, on the other hand, had no time for flights of fancy. He wanted players to wear the right clothes, play the right way, do the right thing. It was inevitable that he and the irrepressible young Botham would be on a collision course from the outset. The more Muncer tried to make him conform, the less Botham did, turning his training into a classic battle of wills.

Muncer and Sharp were in a tough position in many ways. Not only was cricket changing at that time with the introduction of the limited overs game and the gradual increase in media coverage, but society was transforming itself too. For years boys had been turning up at Lord's with a naturally deferential temperament instilled in them: know your place, do the right thing, wear the proper clothes, don't speak unless you're spoken to. The 1960s and the arrival of cocky 'working class' heroes such as the Beatles and the Rolling Stones, Michael Caine and Joe Orton, George Best and Jackie Stewart, meant that those social rules were breaking down. Botham was in the vanguard of youngsters turning up at Lord's knowing what they wanted to do and how they wanted to do it. Lads like him wanted some of the fame, some of the glamour they'd seen others grabbing; it no longer seemed such a pipe dream that ordinary kids could become extraordinary adults. Cricket was lagging behind a little in the glamour stakes, but Botham believed he could change all that and do himself some good into the bargain. Faced with such an attitude, one they'd rarely encountered before, it's not too surprising that coaches like Muncer were taken aback.

The position was made far worse since Muncer didn't rate Botham as a bowler, continuing the general opinion that the Schools selectors had formed of him in Liverpool. Muncer knew his trade and so his views held some weight, and in fairness to the staff at Lord's, they were in the majority, for many good judges failed to recognise that this was a great cricketer in the making, labelling him instead as potentially a useful county cricketer but no more. Like so many, they felt that if he were to make anything of himself, it would be as a batsman, a feeling that persisted among most of his colleagues until he forced his way into the Somerset side. In the long term that might have been a good call, for Botham could have been an even more successful batsman than he was had he applied himself more.

Botham, then just sixteen, ignored the opinions of his seniors and determined to play the game exactly as he wanted to. Most kids, turning up to learn about the game at the home of cricket, would have been cowed by this received wisdom handed down from on high. The reaction of most would have been to accept these exhortations as expressions of harsh reality, working on the basis that Lord's didn't employ coaches who didn't know the game inside out. If Muncer and Sharp reckoned you couldn't bowl, they must have a good reason for saying so.

However cocksure Botham might be, it is still amazing that away from the security of his home and at such a tender age he should have been able to ignore the advice of those who ruled his life, who had it within their power to make it a misery should they so choose. Such a lack of confidence was not a part of the Botham character. Nor was the idea of standing around in the field while others took the glory particularly appealing. Botham had to be part of the action, the centre of attention at all times. It didn't make things easy for him, for Muncer ruled the lives of the groundstaff boys. Many would have given in to him but Botham's spirit could not be broken. Making his point in the only way he could, he bowled tirelessly in the nets, an activity which did him a great deal of good, building up his stamina and tightening up his action. He was also a good listener if he felt it was worth his while, and for all his run-ins with the chief coach, Botham learned a lot about the basics from him and his staff. He left Lord's a much better player than when he'd arrived. Muncer gradually warmed to him, telling his parents that he felt Botham could have done well in the Somerset Second XI in that summer of 1972. If nothing else, his time there had reaffirmed the value of standing up for himself. Harry Sharp was something of an ally in this for while he disapproved of Botham's occasionally loose technique, he understood that if the method worked for him, he was best to stick with it rather than trying to change. Sharp recognised the gifts of a 'natural' and allowed them to flourish, admitting that if what looked like a terrible shot ended up with the ball sailing to the boundary, there might be something in it after all. That said, even Sharp had reservations as to Botham's ability to carve out a successful career for himself.

Again in fairness to the staff at Lord's and many of his contemporaries at Taunton, Botham never really looked the part with the ball until Tom Cartwright and Brian Close got hold of him. Cartwright was the archetypal niggardly English seam bowler, capable of bowling length and line for hour after hour, nagging away at the batsmen, always probing and asking questions, rarely bowling a four ball. Unlucky that he was one of a crop of excellent English seamers, he managed just a handful of Test caps, but that didn't diminish the quality of his play – 1536 first class wickets at a cost of just nineteen each pay eloquent testimony to his skill. If Cartwright was bowling on a good wicket, batsmen knew they'd have to graft for their runs. If there was a little moisture in the pitch, a hint of green on top, then he could be lethal, running through the best sides in short order. Playing out the latter stages of his career at Somerset, Cartwright was delighted to see such an extrovert character as Botham coming into the game. Though he had played in an age when the game was treated with a siege mentality, often grinding out results in dour struggles, he was quick to realise that the game had to move on in the 1970s if it were to survive. The pace of life had quickened and cricket had to mirror that. It also needed personalities, striking individuals who would give the public what they wanted to see, keeping the game in the public eye. He saw that Botham could be very good news for the game.

As the two were on the same wavelength, Botham warmed to Cartwright and was eager to listen to his opinions. Never one to respect stories of how the game was 'better in my day' – he had had his fill of that attitude at Lord's – what struck him about Cartwright was the older man's acceptance that cricket was changing, that good players were good players whether they conformed or not. He wasn't mired in past glories but looking to the future. Once the two became friends, it was easy for Botham to listen to what Cartwright had to say. He admired, even envied, Cartwright's remarkable control, recognising that that was a skill he could use. His legacy to Botham was a structured, economical run up, an ability to pitch the ball precisely where he wanted, and an action that maximised the value of his powerful upper body. Cartwright pointed out to Pat Murphy that 'Ian worked very hard indeed at the nets. He didn't show the dedication of a Boycott, but it was there.' The lesson from this alliance is simple. If Botham responded well to someone's personality and felt they had something worthwhile to impart, he would listen and take the advice – though not necessarily right away. To avoid giving ground and to protect his macho status, he would often go away and implement the latest recommendations in his own good time. He admitted as much in *Wisden* when discussing another great mentor, Kim Barrington: 'he would get me a cup of tea, suggest something which I'd reject probably because I was tired, but then I'd do it and usually it worked'. Similarly, his antipathy to nets has long been a badge of pride – the kid who can pass exams without revision. Practice was for swots and cissies in Botham's book.

Though Cartwright was of immeasurable value to Botham on the technical side, it was his Somerset captain Brian Close who can be credited with turning him into an international class performer by forcing him to increase his pace with the ball; he told David Frith after that famous Benson & Hedges game in 1974, 'I'm going to make this lad into a fast bowler.' If Cartwright had helped teach him how to move the ball through the air and off the pitch seemingly at will, Close's need for a quick bowler, a shock weapon to get him wickets quickly, meant that Botham had another role to fill. Close was also lucky to get Botham at the peak of his physical development; once that frame gained the maturity it had lacked at Lord's, Botham became an altogether different proposition. With all the aggression a fast bowler could ever need, Botham was ideally suited to the job. Most impressive of all, the increase in pace had no discernible impact on his ability to gain movement for he'd already mastered those subtle arts under Cartwright's tutelage. Opponents now had no time to check a shot once they'd spotted the deviation because the ball – and the bowler – was already on them. As a result, Botham reaped a mighty harvest of wickets almost from the outset.

Close and Botham were made for each other, the latter admitting that 'starting out with Closey was vital for me because he taught me so much about attitude ... Closey had taught me there was no point in going out on the field with any other attitude than that I was the best cricketer alive'. There have been few more curmudgeonly or committed cricketers than Brian Close in the recent history of the game. Seemingly constructed from bits of granite and scrap metal, Close was as disputatious a man as you could hope to find, a cricketer who would never willingly give way to any opponent, a man, in short, cast from the same mould as Ian Botham. Perhaps the enduring image of this gifted all-round sportsman came in 1976 when, recalled to England's colours at the age of forty-five, he and John Edrich were subjected to a remorseless diet of fast bowling from the West Indies. Repeatedly struck about the chest, Close would not give ground but stuck to the task for which he'd been recalled – attempting to dull the edge of Holding's fierce pace by dogged occupation of the crease.

Perhaps that's an unfair and inaccurate memory of him. Close was a better player than his oft-recalled status as a punchbag suggests. England's youngest Test player when he made his debut in 1949, he was very unfortunate not to play more than his twenty-two Tests, particularly since he managed to make a fine reputation for himself as a Test match captain. That honour was taken away from him amid a welter of controversy when flagrant time wasting by Yorkshire at Edgbaston helped them save a game they'd apparently lost, a further example of Close's belief that you play sport hard, you play to win, and if you can't win you make damned sure you don't lose. As he got older, Close surely must have regretted some of the disaccord that seemed to follow his every move and which cost him so many Test caps and even the captaincy of his country (it might well have been him rather than Ray Illingworth recapturing the Ashes in Australia in 1970/71 had he taken more time over his public image). Recognising much of himself in his new young charge, he made strenuous attempts to save Botham from himself, trying to ensure that he was fully focused on his cricket. When his engagement to Kathryn Waller was announced in September 1974, Close was horrified. Young cricketers didn't get married! On this Close's opinion was duly noted and ultimately ignored. Nevertheless, his characteristic aggression and attacking attitude to cricket became ingrained in Botham; more accurately, Botham saw a successful cricketer who had just the same attitude to the game as he did and drew from that further confidence to play things his way.

Attack was the one thing they agreed upon, defence used as a last resort when absolutely necessary, Botham saying, 'I loved his attitude that you were better off losing a good game than boring everyone to death with a dull draw.' Botham was lucky that Close was his captain early on for although he owed much to Tom Cartwright, his view of bowling as a war of attrition held little fascination; indeed, had Cartwright possessed Botham's attitude he might well have been a more successful international cricketer. To the new all-rounder, every ball should be a potential wicket taker, not just a dot ball on the long road towards frustrating a batsman into error, a tactic that might work at county level but which would be less successful on the Test match stage. He wanted to experiment, to try new ideas, to attack, attack and attack again. In his first season of first class cricket, Botham was still in the Cartwright mould, conceding 2.4 runs an over, picking up a wicket every sixty-two balls, taking just thirty over the course of the season. By 1977, his breakthrough year, he was giving away three runs an over but was now striking every forty-five balls, his tally of wickets rocketing to eighty-eight. Some less adventurous county skippers would have taken more note of the runs per over statistic, but Close was wise enough to recognise that the strike rate was the crucial factor. If one end could be bottled up by a stock bowler, Botham might rattle through twenty overs and pick up four wickets for sixty-five where Cartwright might have taken one for thirty. To win games, the opposition generally has to be bowled out twice – that's certainly the case at Test level. Bowlers who can get their wickets quickly are a rarity, and they are real match winners.

By allowing Botham his head, Close helped him become one of the most incisive seam and swing bowlers in the country. Free of the containing mentality that reduced many of his contemporaries such as Mike Hendrick to the status of accountants, fretting over singles pushed backward of point, Botham had licence to try anything and everything. Consequently he could look very ordinary if things weren't going his way, and yet that was all part of his menace. A juicy half volley would be despatched to the boundary only to be followed a few balls later by an almost identical delivery. This, though, would be a fraction quicker, might be pitched up a shade further, might swing just a little more, might even go the other way. Botham would have another wicket from a seemingly innocuous ball. That type of cricket contributed to his reputation as a 'golden arm', a man who could bowl a lot of rubbish and still pick up a hatful of victims. Certainly he did have luck on his side from time to time: his first Test wicket, Greg Chappell, came from a ball Bob Willis described as 'the worst ever bowled in Test cricket'! Later on in his career, though, Botham made his own luck. It wasn't just what he bowled, but the way he bowled it. Every ball was fired down with such venomous belligerence and with such expectation of success that many batsmen were out before they knew what had happened. Always looking to unsettle a batsman with an unorthodox delivery, a stream of observations about how well he was bowling or how lucky the batsman was, or an extremely optimistic appeal, no one had an easy time while Botham was in the field, precisely the kind of attitude Close appreciated. Peter Roebuck wrote in *The Cricketer* that 'Close used to rail against cricketers with lazy minds', and certainly Botham was a first class product of the Close academy – alert, intelligent, instinctive, always looking for an advantage to seize, and with a solid understanding of the game to fall back on.

After two full seasons in the Somerset side, Botham was coming to the attention of the England selectors, finally winning a Test place in 1977. This gave him his first chance to work alongside Mike Brearley, the captain who was to have such an enormous effect on his career. Brearley was a nice contrast to Close, though both were excellent readers of the game who spoke a great deal of sense in a way to which Botham could relate. Neither was interested in overblown theories but simply cut through the jargon, motivating his players in his own way. It was extremely important for his well-being that just as Brian Close was announcing his retirement from the county game, Botham got into the Test team and so had Mike Brearley on hand to replace Close as his central adviser.

None could dispute that the partnership between Brearley and Botham was highly productive for both parties. Where Close had given Botham the confidence, the framework and the encouragement simply to let rip against county opposition, Brearley's use of him was altogether more calculated, as indeed it had to be in the international arena. It's interesting to reflect that in their early days together, Brearley saw Chris Old as his main all-rounder once Greig had left for Packer's circus. Botham got little cricket on the tour of Pakistan in 1977/78, his first senior overseas tour, having gone down with a stomach bug early on. Perhaps this was a blessing in disguise for Botham would have derived little movement from the baked Pakistani wickets that ensured the tour comprised three extremely tedious drawn Test matches. The only moment of excitement came in unfortunate style when Brearley was injured on a poor pitch, breaking his arm and leaving the captaincy open for Geoffrey Boycott on the second leg of the tour in New Zealand. If Boycott was not an ideal captain, few could fault his judgement of players. His frank, often highly critical assessments and a marked reluctance to accept simple human error as an excuse for getting out have won him few friends over the years, but there are still few shrewder judges of cricketing ability. Boycott's erstwhile Yorkshire colleague Brian Close had said of Botham that he was such a good batsman he should never get out; it was the central tenet of the Boycott faith that no one should get themselves out. Botham's ability was one of the few matters on which Close and Boycott could agree and Boycott quickly installed Botham in the side, letting him bat at six and giving him the responsibility and prestige on which he thrived. Botham reciprocated by running him out on vice captain Bob Willis's instructions in

Christchurch after Botham had registered his maiden Test hundred in the first innings. It was in these games that Brearley, watching as a journalist, first saw how valuable a player Botham could be to him.

Back in England for the 1978 summer, Brearley quickly resumed the captaincy. That was the beginning of a relationship which oversaw most of Botham's best Test cricket. Within a matter of weeks he came to be the player on whom Bearley leant most often, the England captain recognising his astonishing aptitude for raising his game to the necessary heights, seemingly at will. Time and again, when a wicket was required to break a threatening or stubborn partnership, Botham did the trick with a swinging half volley or a blinding slip catch. Similarly, if England were struggling at the crease as at Lord's against Pakistan in 1978 when they were 134 for 5, Botham could stride out and take the bowling to pieces; in that Lord's match he did just that, clubbing a hundred in 104 balls to wrest the initiative. He then pocketed eight wickets for just thirty-four runs to complete an innings victory.

Brearley has to take some credit for getting the very best out of Botham, something subsequent captains often failed to do. If he was struggling to get to the crease, Brearley would give the nod to Willis at mid–on. Willis would meet Botham on his way back to his mark and advise him that he was bowling like an old woman. Once the inevitable flurry of bouncers had been hurled down, a couple of overs later Botham would, likely as not, have two more scalps to his name. Brearley was also wise enough not to overtax the willing tyro. Many of his later captains have said how hard it could be to get the ball out of his hand for Botham was always sure that another wicket was just around the corner if only they'd let him bowl (the events of 1984 against the West Indies and Sri Lanka, both at Lord's, proved conclusively that that wasn't always so, Botham taking some fearful stick with Gower unable to prise the ball from his grasp). Brearley was strong enough to tell him when he'd had enough and was intelligent enough to use him in a shock bowling role, his strongest suit when he was in his pomp. Under Brearley's leadership, Botham was used almost exclusively as an attacking weapon, with bat and ball.

Although Botham was obviously a far better cricketer than Brearley, the captain was the first among these equals. Like Close before him,

Brearley was happy to give Botham responsibility. He understood that Botham needed to be in the thick of the action as much as possible but he also saw that Botham was a great team man. By ensuring he had a specific job to do, a fully articulated goal for which to aim, and by relating that to the overall success of the England team, Brearley ensured that his all-rounder was fully focused on the job in hand. He made it clear that Botham should only bowl at the right moment and that that moment was not every minute of the day. Botham had complete respect for Brearley because the captain was too sensible to be authoritarian in his approach to the players. His actions were taken for a reason, and his strategy evolved in team meetings that gave everyone a chance to have his say before Bearley had the last word. Having been denied a voice by coaches in the past, Botham responded well to this quasi-democracy.

Just as Brearley was intrigued by Botham's talent, his natural aptitude for the game and his general enthusiasm for life, so Botham was fascinated by Brearley's intellectual take on cricket. Each had the greatest respect for the other, each had things they could learn from the other, and each was willing to listen. They became firm friends off the pitch but that was a relationship that did not harm their work on the field; there was no playing of favourites under Brearley. If Botham needed a rollicking, he got one, but he only got one when it was deserved. Praise came when it was merited, consolation when necessary. That was the key to their partnership and the reason Botham was willing to accede to Brearley's wishes, accepting that he 'could read me through and through'. Quite simply, he respected his judgement as a cricketer who could do something he could not yet do himself.

When Brearley left the scene in 1980, Botham was exposed to and beaten by West Indian might. Had Mike Brearley been captain, England would still have been second best for much of those two series, but even Botham would have to concede that he would probably have returned better individual figures. Where Brearley had employed his bowling gifts sympathetically, Botham flogged himself mercilessly or gave other less deserving and penetrative bowlers first use of a helpful pitch. Asked to make the decisions, Botham took all his side's considerable failings about his broad shoulders and tried to fight the good fight alone. Troubled by his back, he inflicted an excessive workload on himself and was never really effective. With Brearley in command, Botham might have bowled as many as overs, but he'd have bowled them in shorter spells and at times when wickets were likely to fall; as skipper he seemed to put himself on mainly when the likes of Lloyd and Richards were on top – brave, but ultimately foolish. Captain Botham was always looking to take on extra responsibility, an instinct Brearley had kept in check, recognising that he needed to stay fresh to be a threat.

Brearley had also provided a shoulder to cry on. Although Botham would never break down in that way, Brearley was always on hand to keep him going when things were going against him. Without him in the side, Botham had nowhere else to turn for advice on the field of play. In his early days, Botham seemed to have some kind of guardian angel looking over him, for he was lucky to be taken under the wings of some impressive men who could offer a steadying influence. It's probably no coincidence that, with both Close and Brearley off the scene in 1980, he first got himself into trouble with the Joe Neenan incident in Scunthorpe. Though Botham was acquitted of all charges when the jury could not provide a unanimous decision, it suggested that here was a man who might be lacking in judgement and who needed some authority figure to keep him in check. Like it or not, as England captain and sporting hero Botham was a sitting target for any local toughs who wanted to make a name for themselves. Able to turn the other cheek most times, it was inevitable that Botham would snap on occasion, just as any other man would do under intense provocation. The sensible course would have been to avoid nightclubs and pubs where things can always get out of hand, but the sensible course never appealed to him. Botham was his own man who did his own thing, but had he known he would have incurred the wrath of Close or the displeasure of Brearley for such an ill advised escapade, he might have stayed at home more.

Going to the Caribbean as captain in 1980/81, he was again fortunate in his advisers, accompanied this time by the TCCB's Alan Smith and, more importantly, Ken Barrington, who had not been included in the original touring party. That was a surprising omission since Barrington had become an integral part of England's management and coaching set up, especially abroad. Just as when he was playing, having Barrington aboard as a coach was a distinct plus for England; certainly he was one of the few people to whom Ian Botham ever listened. Graham Gooch felt the same way about him, noting that 'his influence on me was massive. An uncle, a friend, a wise counsellor.' For his part, Botham respected the fact that Barrington was as fierce a patriot as he himself was, that he would give every ounce of effort for his country and would never accept defeat until the stumps were drawn. Like Cartwright, Barrington was not one of the old school who felt the game was going downhill and that today's players couldn't hold a candle to those of yesteryear. He understood that the game had changed, that different demands were placed on players, and that good players now would have been good players in the past. He also accepted that the West Indian attack was more formidable than anything he'd had to face, endearing himself to Botham and his players in the process.

As a coach he was excellent. Having been forced to reconstruct his own game early on in his career when his profligacy with the bat had found him out, he had an encyclopaedic grasp of the game's technicalities coupled with an ability to put it across in the simplest of terms. A straightforward bloke who was extremely popular with everyone in the touring party, Barrington made a huge contribution to English cricket, Jim Laker averring that 'he upset no-one and did not make a single enemy on the way'. He was especially helpful on that tour to West Indies, advising Botham on practice facilities, giving him pointers on his own game, and so on. While England's hero was under fire from every quarter, he could always rely on Barrington to give him support as well as any of the unpalatable truths he would refuse to hear elsewhere. It was impossible to take offence at any criticism Barrington might make for he would offer it simply and genuinely while always trying to stress any positive moves that had been made. Most engaging of all, he regularly put the needs of others before himself.

The nervous energy this born worrier expended on behalf of others must surely have hurried his untimely demise. When he died during the Third Test in Barbados, the saddest outcome of the strains placed on everyone by the Jackman affair in Guyana, he left a void no manager or coach has subsequently filled. A partnership featuring Botham and Barrington might have gone on to great things through the 1980s. His premature death robbed the game of a great character and stripped Botham of perhaps his last great adviser. In a short space of time, Close, Brearley and Barrington had passed out of his day to day life, leaving him with nobody on whom he could, or would, rely. Had Brearley continued as captain, had Barrington lived, had Close been six or seven years younger, the remainder of Botham's story might have been very different. As it was he was left to sort things out for himself, not always in the best manner. In his tribute to Barrington in 1982's *Wisden*, Robin Marlar pointed out his worth to players such as Botham: 'To the generation that is coming to full maturity Ken Barrington had become as important as the maypole; something solid. He was the "Colonel" around whom a team of cricketers could revolve.' More importantly perhaps, given the respect in which Botham held him, was his attitude to practice:

> [Barrington] was brought up in a generation which believed as an act of faith that once a cricketer had played at Test level he knew it all. How else could he have been selected? Furthermore, and this is still a more prevalent attitude than Barrington liked, a player who makes as much of a fetish about practising as Boycott is regarded as a freak. *As one who had to work out his technique, to subordinate under a layer of discipline the stroke-making ability he had acquired in his early days* ... he was ideally suited to the task of developing younger talent and skills.

The words in my italics are crucial, for if Botham ever wanted to come to terms with West Indian bowling, he would have had to make changes in his game. Viv Richards has suggested that since Botham was such a born entertainer it would have been quite impossible for him to do so. Perhaps Barrington might have persuaded him otherwise. At the very least, he might have managed to get him to net practice more often and to work more assiduously at his game. Barrington was ahead of his time in coaching terms, never decrying practice and always ready to point out the virtues of application and the study of technique, attributes that today's top coaches such as Bob Woolmer are utilising to the full with excellent results.

Barrington was a very down to earth man. Had he been around to enjoy Botham's successes of 1981 and then to work with him in India, he'd have been the first to congratulate him and the first to remind him that the hard work started all over again in this new series. Barrington had absolute conviction in the ability of Botham, Gooch and Gatting, but the other two had fewer conflicts in their lives, were better able to focus on their cricket. Someone who lived the chaotic, kinetic lifestyle of Ian Botham could not always keep his eye on every ball he was juggling. He needed regular reminders of the right path. Tellingly in Barrington's obituary in *Wisden Cricket Monthly*, David Frith wrote that 'all the fighters in Test cricket – Bailey, Edrich, Lawry, Burke et al – could belt away like one-day cricketers if they chose. Their exceptional common gift was self-denial. Certain other batsmen, touched with genius, could bat forever if endowed with this discipline.' Perhaps the art of self denial must be inbuilt into a person's character, perhaps it cannot be taught like the forward defensive. Even Barrington might not have been able to tame Botham's wilder flights, though it should be recalled that one of Botham's most heroic efforts, his dogged innings of just six in ninety minutes at Sydney in 1978/79, came under the watchful eye of Barrington and Brearley. What must be certain is that Botham would not have wanted to do anything to disappoint the genial Barrington, for he had become family. That determination alone might have saved him from a lot of trouble in subsequent years. Of all the losses Botham had to endure, it was that of Ken Barrington that was the most grievous.

One of the problems inherent in replacing any of those figures was the generation factor. Close, Brearley, Barrington and Cartwright were elder statesmen as far as Botham was concerned; though they didn't automatically command his respect because of their seniority, it was easier to listen to them since they were not his exact contemporaries chasing the same goals. In 1982, the main players in the England set up were all around the same age as Botham. Inevitably they were as competitive with one another as with the opposition, for the England captaincy would eventually pass to Gower, Gooch, Gatting or Botham again, though Gooch quickly ruled himself out of the running by going on the rebel South African tour. Keith Fletcher might have been helpful to him, but his role as England leader was over in a matter of months following a disappointing tour of India. Fletcher's case wasn't helped by a show of dissent, knocking over his stumps when given out – frustrated displays of temper were clearly not the sole preserve of young lions. Bob Willis stepped into the breach at England level and, as a close friend of Botham's, their relationship was a healthy one, Botham returning to the role of court jester within the dressing room, maintaining morale with his range of practical jokes. His respect for Willis kept his natural exuberance in check and his performances for the gangly fast bowler were generally solid. Notably, under Willis, he managed to maintain the consistent improvement that was being seen in his batting. Following on from his Ashes successes, Botham had been superb on Fletcher's tour of India, scoring 440 runs at fifty-five, with four fifties and a century. That was quickly followed by a couple more hundreds in the home series against the same opponents in 1982, including a superb 208 at the Oval which was as technically accomplished an innings as anyone could wish to see. Admittedly India were not a great bowling side, Kapil Dev apart, but Botham had often exhibited a degree of vulnerability against the spinners. This innings nailed those doubts.

Willis's tenure as England skipper was always destined to be a short one, age and injury catching up with him. Looking to the future, David Gower had been installed as vice captain, but Botham also skippered England on tour on occasion. He clearly had hopes of getting another crack at the job in less taxing circumstances, but recognised that Gower was the undoubted front runner. His lingering hopes of getting the job evaporated on the infamous sex 'n' drugs 'n' rock 'n' roll tour of New Zealand and Pakistan in 1983/84. As if the bad publicity engendered, inevitably and inaccurately centring on Botham's alleged bedroom exploits, were not enough, his return home with a knee injury left Gower to step into the breach when Willis also fell ill. With Gower leading the side well and batting superbly, his selection as captain for the forthcoming summer's Tests against the West Indies was a foregone conclusion. Meanwhile, back at home, Botham was inserting his foot in his mouth, as much out of frustration as anything else. In the course of a long radio interview he made a feeble stab at a very stupid joke, suggesting that Pakistan was the kind of place you'd send your mother-in-law on holiday for a month. The diplomatic gaffe merely hardened the Establishment's prejudices that the boy was a talented loudmouth, a latter-day Fred Trueman, who couldn't be trusted to use the right knife in company. His aptitude for leading a cricket side was irrelevant; the feeling was Botham would let the side down off the field, a grossly unfair attitude given his exemplary performance in the hothouse atmosphere of Guyana in 1981. All the same, it consigned him to a future with little hope of regaining the England captaincy.

Most colleagues agree that Botham was never a great one for taking criticism, however kindly or constructively it might be meant. Especially since the trials and tribulations of his captaincy, he has taken any rebuke as being personally, rather than professionally, directed. Given the nature of so much press comment he was entitled to be sensitive, but the cricketing evidence suggests that his unwillingness to take direction embraced those who captained him. By the time Bob Willis left the England scene in 1984, the dressing room had been stripped of its senior players – Boycott, Brearley, Taylor, Willis and Underwood had all gone. Botham himself was now the senior pro, but operating without any real responsibility. He undoubtedly found it hard to take orders from players who were his own age and who had played less Test cricket than he had himself. Where Willis had in the main been able to temper Botham's ego, Gower was the first to find it hard going, the results under his leadership pointing out his comparative failure to harness Botham's talents.

In Willis's reign, Botham's role in the side was developing, changing by degrees. From being an all-rounder whose predominant value was with the ball, circumstances rotated through almost 180 degrees. Although the opposition was not always the strongest, Botham enjoyed some of his most consistent batting form when Willis was in charge, the captain giving him extra responsibility to bat for long periods and to construct an innings. To his frustration, in the past Botham had often come in at number seven, by which time he might only have the tail left for company. Willis tended to use Botham as one of his front-line batsmen from whom he expected an average of around forty. Botham complied with those needs, passing fifty on nine occasions out of thirty-one, averaging forty-one over Willis's eighteen Tests in charge. In contrast, as a bowler he would often find himself deprived of the new

109

ball, even coming on as second change. Though he managed three five-wicket hauls for Willis, it was apparent that he was not the force he'd once been. Indeed, when England had allowed New Zealand to score 307 in Christchurch on what *Wisden* described as a 'suspect pitch', Willis called the England bowling 'some of the worst' he had seen. With Willis taking four for fifty-one and Cowans three for fifty-two, *Wisden* saw Botham as the main culprit, bowling seventeen overs to take one wicket for eighty-eight, 'Hadlee [striking] 99 in 111 minutes (81 balls), taking heavy toll of a surfeit of long-hops from Botham'. It was not to be the last time Botham tried to bounce batsmen out with disastrous effects.

By that time it was becoming increasingly obvious that Botham had to play as a batting all-rounder, for his bowling was often little more threatening than Basil d'Oliveira's had been in the late sixties when he'd performed a similar role in the England side. From England's return from Australia in 1983 to the end of his career, Botham played forty-three Tests, taking 116 wickets at 37.4 each, striking every sixty-seven balls. That contrasts with his first fifty-nine Tests, studded with 267 wickets at 24.5 each, one every fifty-one balls. The decline is obvious, but the figures would have been acceptable had Botham been operating in a Steve Waugh type of role for England, picked for his batting but capable of bowling a few overs and picking up the odd wicket here and there, helping the balance of the side. It's a point many picked up on at the time. In his book *On Reflection* in 1984, Richie Benaud was already suggesting that Botham's back was in need of further treatment and that he should adapt his action to enhance the threat he posed and to protect his spine. Benaud, shrewd as ever, posed the vital question: 'Now ... does Botham have the dedication and the will to regain maximum fitness to hold off the challenge of [Kapil Dev, Richard Hadlee and Imran Khan]? Does he have the will to train hard and remain a bowling all-rounder, or will he become a batting all-rounder instead? This could be accomplished easily enough because there is no doubting his ability with the bat and his ability to win matches for a captain in that department.' Benaud was not alone in his regard for Botham's batting. In his book on the 1986/87 Australian tour *Ashes To Ashes*, Peter Roebuck wrote prior to the First Test, 'here in Brisbane, Ian Botham is steeling himself to score a century ... no man in cricket is more certain of scoring a hundred when his mind is set upon it, not even the great Richards. To Botham, these things are acts of will-power. He has an extraordinarily strong will which, if he uses it, rarely fails.'

There's little to suggest that Botham took the decline in his bowling as seriously as he should have. He remained convinced that he could roll over a side at will, yet the evidence was stacked against him. At Lord's in 1984, a pivotal Test in David Gower's career, England had the West Indians in trouble for once. Set 342 to win in five and a half hours, everyone imagined they'd be looking to bat out time. With only Bob Willis looking remotely Test match class, Gordon Greenidge took England to pieces. Botham bowled twenty overs for 117 runs where Willis bowled fifteen for forty-eight. Similar discipline from Botham might have saved the game but, recalling his prime, Botham felt he could win the match by virtue of his own aggression. As he ruefully recounted in his autobiography, his conviction that he could bounce batsmen out undid him: 'I overdid the delivery ... as far as I was concerned, the next one was bound to get him, but, of course, it never did.'

Benaud's argument that Botham needed either to get fit or to change his priorities made more sense with every passing day. Still capable of bowling well – his eight wickets for 103 in the first innings of that Lord's Test was a case in point – the good days were fewer and further between. Yet Botham's competitive instinct was so well honed that he could not stay out of the action, demanding the ball, always trying to get men out. There's no question that he continued to get wickets that no one else could. Returning to the England side against New Zealand in 1986 following his 'drugs' ban, he had Bruce Edgar caught at slip by Graham Gooch with his first ball. Eleven balls later he snapped up Jeff Crowe, leg before wicket, to move past Dennis Lillee and become the greatest wicket taker in Test match history. Nobody but Botham could conjure events like that into being, no other cricketer has ever had such a mastery of the art of the impossible, none has had such a vivid imagination. Yet at that time for every day like that when the fires burned bright there were days of humiliation, such as the beating he took from Sri Lankan captain Duleep Mendis at Lord's in the 1984 Test. In mitigation, Phil

Neale, Botham's skipper at Worcestershire, points out:

> when he was getting older, the problem was that England always desperately needed an all-rounder and often he just had to bowl. We've still not properly replaced him in that role. And you could never rule out his knack of getting a wicket – on a flat pitch, nothing happening, he'd bowl a long hop and get somebody out for you. His past record always discouraged you from ruling him out of doing anything. While he was in the side, you'd always give him the ball to see what might happen. You'd have struggled to make the decision to play him just as a batsman and stop him from bowling.

Even in the light of Neale's assertions, that decision needed to be taken for him. As much as at any other time in his professional career, in 1984 Botham needed someone to turn to, a mentor whose advice he respected. The laid back David Gower was never likely to fit into that mould. The two were friends, rivals for the cricketing public's favour, too close in age and attitude to the game and to life in general to be able to give wise counsel to each other. Botham needed an ultimatum along the lines of Benaud's question: Do you want to bowl at your best again? If so, get fit. If you don't want to, or are physically incapable, take your batting more seriously and win your place in the side on that alone. There was never any reason why Botham should not have settled into the number four or five berth for England and made it his own for another decade. He had the ability to get close to England's run scoring record as well as being its leading wicket taker. For want of good advice, that chance went begging.

So far as Ian Botham was concerned, David Gower's captaincy was disastrous. Gower had far too much faith in Botham the bowler when such a belief was no longer warranted. Phil Edmonds, for example, noted that Gower remained convinced of the power of Botham's golden arm throughout the West Indies visit of 1984, letting him bowl when there was little prospect of him making a breakthrough. Admittedly, Gower was short of quality quick bowling with the demise of Bob Willis and was enduring the same misfortune Botham had lived through – facing the West Indies early in his captaincy. Accordingly he lost many games and his own figures suffered, as did Botham's. Even bearing all that in mind, under Gower Botham averaged twenty-six with the bat and thirty-six with the ball, both much poorer than his overall figures, and only ten of his twenty-one Tests under Gower came against the West Indies. There was ample time to repair the figures elsewhere, but Gower simply could not get the best out of him on a regular basis. Most telling of all, at no time under Gower's leadership did Botham produce a genuine match winning display, though he was an important figure in the team that reclaimed the Ashes in 1985.

Of the four men who skippered Botham in ten or more Tests, it's reasonable to suggest that Gower did less for his career than any of the others. Though his overall figures under Gatting were not vastly superior, the Middlesex man was at least able to coax two match winning per-formances from his waning all-rounder; indeed, it was Botham's elec-trifying presence on that glorious Australian adventure of 1986/87 that first stamped England's dominance on the entire series, before he finally sealed the retention of the Ashes with a superb spell of intelligent medium pace bowling at the Melbourne Cricket Ground. Gatting gave Botham the freedom he required but within a sensible disciplinary framework, and also managed to keep his superstar pretty much out of the limelight on that tour, allowing Botham to concentrate on his cricket. The fact that Botham took his wife Kath with him on the trip was also a tactical masterstroke, keeping the press hounds at bay.

In contrast, the laissez-faire Gower so lost control of England's Car-ibbean trip in 1985/86 that Botham was never in any frame of mind to tackle Viv Richards' men. Again, in fairness to Gower, it's hard to see how England could have done a lot about the five-nil result, but they should surely have made a better fight of it. Just as in 1984, once Gower's team was under attack from the opposition, the wheels fell off. The 'optional practice' idea, while trying to keep the pressure off players already under withering fire, was a move that backfired, in PR terms if nothing else. In addition, while natural touch players like Gower and Botham were not always helped by long net sessions, they did set a poor example to the rest of the party, giving the impression they were unconcerned by persistent failure. Allowing Botham to do his own thing while giving him the idea that he was fireproof was an approach doomed to failure. Less gifted players struggling with their form and technique against the fast bowlers would clearly have been helped by sustained practice, though again the facilities provided were generally awful. Seeing that Botham and Gower had such disdain for practice, younger players fell in with their habits. Botham seemed not to appreciate that not all players had his strength of character, some lacking the necessary fibre to go their own way. As in everyday life, some simply followed the herd and failed to do what was best for themselves, choosing instead to court easy popularity among these heroes of the game.

While almost everyone suffered statistically at the hands of the West Indies, one would have still hoped that Botham would be the best of a poor bunch. Instead, his bowling decline was dramatically underlined. Reporting in *The Cricketer*, Christopher Martin-Jenkins had this to say of his opening spell in the Second Test in Trinidad: 'Taking the new ball when it ought to have been given to Ellison, [he] bowled five wayward, powder-puff overs which cost England no fewer than 39 runs. It also cost Botham his pride and it was a little sad to see a bowler once so dangerous blaming everyone but himself for the fact that Greenidge was laying into him with such pleasure.' The series ended with Botham fifth of five in the bowling averages behind John Emburey, Neil Foster, Richard Ellison and Greg Thomas. The batting was little better: he rolled in sixth with 168 runs at 16.8. That statistic was quite appalling since it was painfully obvious his future must lie with his batting. At a time when Botham should have become nothing more than a useful change bowler, his ego wouldn't allow it, and he demanded that he be respected as an all-rounder when he did not deserve it. Meanwhile David Gower was either unable or unwilling to initiate the very necessary transformation of Botham into a batsman who could bowl a bit, something which Gatting tried to do.

The nadir of Botham's partnership with Gower came on that tour. In his autobiography, Gower noted that 'this trademark of [Botham's], that he is in his mind always doing, or about to do, great things, is a mixed blessing. When it is going right, everyone knows what remarkable things can happen. When it's going wrong, he doesn't always step back and look closely enough at himself from the outside. The rest of the team were looking closely at him all right, and all they could see was someone who hardly bowled in the nets, and was disappearing for five an over. No wonder they got disgruntled.' The problem was that Gower was the captain of the side whose job it was to impose some kind of discipline on Botham. If his presence was affecting other players as that final comment suggests, it was up to Gower to get him back into line. He failed to do so. *Wisden's* John Thicknesse did not mince words in his summary of the trip: 'Much went wrong that with firmer captaincy and management might not have ... in cold fact, England never had a hope. That they could and should have done better, few who saw them would dispute. Their lack of commitment was reflected in their attitude to practice, a department in which West Indies showed them up to be amateurs.' Suggesting that while Gower was an excellent leader in victory, he did not have the steel in his character necessary for such a taxing trip, Thicknesse noted that 'it was not only that he had no faith in practice – a weakness exacerbated by Ian Botham's presence – but sometimes he seemed even to lack interest'. For Botham the tour was a catastrophe. Thicknesse remarked that he 'had a dreadful tour in every imaginable way ... his aversion to net practice set a bad example and only once, when he was under threat of being dropped, did he produce a good performance with the ball'.

In fairness, the media had had a major effect on Botham's form once more. Perhaps if Gooch or Gatting had been made England's leader earlier on, he might have survived the slings and arrows of outrageous tabloid speculation. They would certainly have stood more chance of keeping him in check. Although he was never wild about Gooch's management methods, the dressing room atmosphere he encouraged might have made a difference. Speaking in 1992, John Emburey, admittedly a close friend of Gooch, told the *Daily Telegraph's* Paul Weaver that on his return to Test cricket under Gower 'there was a lack of discipline, the atmosphere in the dressing room was unbelievable, noisy, loud and full of bravado. David Gower was the captain and Ian Botham and Allan Lamb were making their presence known ... Graham Gooch has done a fantastic job [as captain]. He is a disciplinarian and if players don't fit in, he won't have them.'

The vice captaincy situation in the West Indies is crucial in trying to understand the rest of Botham's career. Given the events of the 1983/84 tour, it was perfectly reasonable that Botham should have chosen not to winter in India in 1984/85, taking the opportunity to rest a body that had been pushed to the limits for ten years. Surprisingly selected as vice captain, Mike Gatting grasped the opportunity and had an excellent tour to leapfrog ahead of Botham in the pecking order. It was understandable that Gatting, now looking like an authentic Test cricketer at long last, was the automatic choice to understudy Gower in the West Indies. On Gatting's return home after having his face customised by a Malcolm Marshall bouncer, Graham Gooch was given the post, in spite of the fairly obvious mood of discontent – as captain of one of the rebel sides that had toured South Africa, he was the subject of fierce protest demonstrations and could be forgiven for having things other than cricket on his mind. To make him vice captain was as daft a decision in the circumstances as the appointment of Geoff Miller on the previous tour of the West Indies when the incapacitated Willis had jetted back to England. With Botham causing concern among some who suggested he abused the freedom Gower gave him, this was an obvious opportunity to get him back on side; it would have been a brave decision given the prevailing media attitude, but brave decisions are often the right ones. Paul Downton felt that something needed to be done, telling Rob Steen that '[Botham] was a bit of a divisive influence; he spent a lot of time in the West Indies' dressing room. I, for one, felt he was too much under Viv's sway. He wasn't a good loser or a good battler; he found it hard to believe he was doing anything wrong.'

The selection of Gooch as vice captain made it apparent once and for all that Ian Botham would never again get the call to lead his country. It had been an unlikely dream for some time, but this was the last nail in the coffin. Most damaging of all, it came at precisely the moment when Botham was less committed to his cricket than at any other time. Wearied by the sheer physical effort of bowling quick, troubled by back and knee injuries, beleaguered by the press, and carrying the weight of a faltering legal action against the *Mail on Sunday*, being England's premier sporting hero suddenly looked a less attractive job than ever before. Perhaps he realised, subconsciously at least, that he would never again scale the heights of 1981, that the rest of his career would be more humdrum than the great days he had already enjoyed. Botham was looking for new challenges, fresh fields to conquer in order to restore his vitality and appetite for the game. The England captaincy or vice captaincy might have been one such challenge, but no such offers were forthcoming. Nor were any sustained ultimatums as to his form, Gower merely pointing out to him that he'd come close to being dropped for the Fourth Test, which prompted his best game of the series. Indeed, the Establishment seemed to go out of its way to cut him off from the decision making process, making it clear that he was in the team on sufferance because it didn't dare ditch him. Refusing to accept that Botham, now in his cricketing maturity, might actually thrive on extra responsibility, the powers that be withheld the very thing that could have prolonged the usefulness of his career and kept him out of the tabloids; in the West Indies in 1985/86, he was not even co-opted onto the selection panel. Instead, he and pals like Allan Lamb were given licence to enjoy the social side of touring as much as, and perhaps to the detriment of, their cricket. Whether anyone in the party was guilty of anything untoward or not, the freedom given to Botham simply gave the sensation seekers in Wapping the chance to let their fevered imaginations run riot, this in spite of the fact that Botham spent a lot of the tour locked in his hotel room, the better to avoid the squadrons of news reporters. With more of the same to look forward to on each subsequent tour until the body finally wore out and he hung up his bat, there's little wonder that Botham was becoming disenchanted with it all.

Botham was looking for another mentor. He was desperate for someone to give him a sense of direction, but engaging Tim Hudson as his manager was a reckless cry for help. Hudson was the kind of chap that could talk the hind legs off a donkey and then persuade it to enter the Grand National. A self confessed eccentric, Hudson made his million on the west coast of America as a DJ and property developer (whether the two jobs were intertwined is, like much else that surrounds Hudson, a mystery). Botham described him as a 'likeable nutter' and Hudson certainly had the sort of character and ego to match his own. A friendship of sorts was therefore inevitable, the more so once Hudson began to make Botham sound like an exotic combination of John Wayne, Harrison Ford and Errol Flynn. ITB was the greatest thing since sliced bread and, according to Hudson, the rest of the world would soon fall at his feet.

The continuous press carping had only hardened Botham's attitude to the outside world. Since he had to read so much rubbish about himself, he felt he could only trust his own opinions, and as a man who had been proved right against the odds throughout most of his life, Botham was not one to underestimate his own value. After 1981, he believed he had the Midas touch and that it would never leave him; Hudson's views simply coincided with his own. Therefore, once Hudson began to articulate his vision of an action-packed future filled with all the money he could dream of, there was an inexorable logic about it all as far as Botham was concerned. Tiring of the circuit, no longer relishing the inescapable grind of the international cricketer, Botham wanted something else to do with the rest of his life. He began to alienate even those who were his supporters: in the course of his benefit year in 1984, he arrived very late for one game especially arranged for him at Sparkford. His couldn't care less attitude caused club captain Graham Reeve to make it clear that Botham would not be welcome there in future. Stories like these were a worrying development. One of Botham's strengths was that he had the common touch and could relate to the ordinary supporters of the game. Appearing arrogant and contemptuous of those who were helping him raise £90,000 in his benefit season did little for his image and merely helped create a climate in which people were willing to believe the worst about him. If nothing else, it fostered a growing feeling that Botham thought he was above everything. For a time, things seemed to spiral beyond Botham's control. Jaded, world weary, he seemed unable to draw a line under his problems. Cricket was no longer the seductive mistress it had been in his youth and he yearned for something to replace it in his affections. Also, approaching thirty, even he had to accept that he was nearing the latter stages of his active sporting career. While he was financially comfortable, he'd scarcely made a fortune out of the game, certainly when compared with contemporary international footballers or the rock stars with whom he was now mixing. If Hudson could provide a pot of gold, that was to be welcomed.

Hudson took charge of Botham's affairs in early 1985, just as Mike Gatting was placing himself next in line for the England captaincy and ruling Botham out of the running for good. Hudson's early tactic was to make cricket seem different, new and exciting, essential music to the

England's new hero prepares to meet Australia. Perth, December 1979.
© *Adrian Murrell, Allsport.*

(left) In the master's footsteps: Botham follows Brearley off the field. 1978. © *Allsport.*

(below) Stripped for action, Botham prepares to play for Scunthorpe United. December 1980.
© *Adrian Murrell, Allsport.*

England's captain receives advice from Ken Barrington. 1981.
© *Adrian Murrell, Allsport.*

The quiet before the storm: David Bairstow and Botham join Viv Richards and Clive Lloyd in the West Indian dressing room. 1981. © *Adrian Murrell, Allsport.*

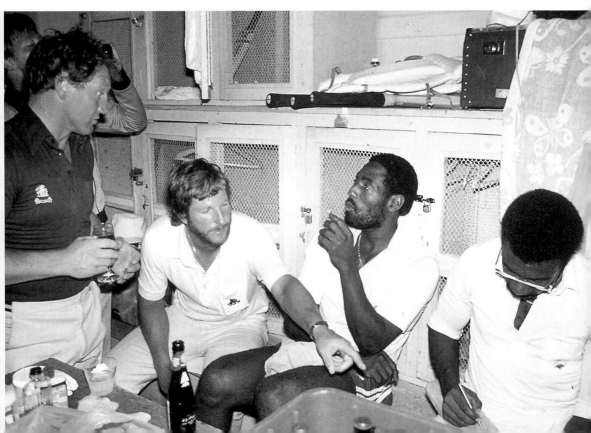

(above) The Messiah and the multitude. Headingley, 1981.
© *Adrian Murrell, Allsport.*

(left) Botham goes hunting for journalists. Indo/Pakistan border, January 1982.
© *Adrian Murrell, Allsport.*

(right) Captain Gower and bowler Botham on point duty. Lord's, 1985.
© Adrian Murrell, Allsport.

(below) 'For God's sake, keep going.' The fruits of Botham's greatest miracle. August 2 1986.
© Adrian Murrell, Allsport.

'Who writes your scripts?' Botham equals Lillee's record with his first ball back after the drugs ban. England vs. New Zealand, the Oval, 21 August 1986. From left to right: Athey, Botham, French, Gooch, Gatting, Edgar.© *Adrian Murrell, Allsport.*

Hannibal Botham arrives in Turin with his wife, Kath. April 1988.
© *Adrian Murrell, Allsport.*

(above) The King of Panto! Oh no
he isn't. Botham meets co-stars
George and Zippy. Bournemouth,
December 1991.
© *Chris Cole, Allsport.*

(right) 'Send your mother-in-law
next time!' Pakistan's revenge.
Botham dismissed by Akram for 0.
World Cup Final, March 1992.
© *Ben Radford, Allsport.*

Ian Botham always respects the validity of tabloid criticism.© *Andrew Cornaga, Allsport.*

'Come on, Both. We'll flippin' murder 'em!' Botham the motivational coach in thoughtful mood with David Lloyd in Bulawayo, December 1996.© *Clive Mason, Allsport.*

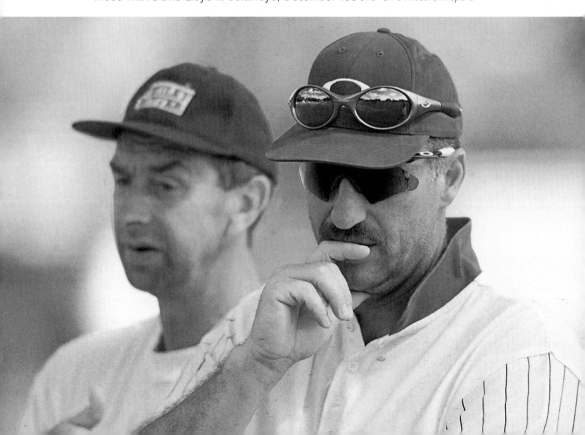

ears of the haggard Botham. Inviting Botham to his rural retreat, Birtles, in the Cheshire countryside, the talk was Packeresque and Pythonesque in its hyperbole, painting a picture of private teams captained by rock stars playing televised matches while Pink Floyd performed an evolving soundtrack from the boundary edge. There was also the range of clothing, garish concoctions that only a genuinely colour-blind man such as Botham could have been persuaded to endorse. Bit by bit the schemes became increasingly grandiose, but somehow Hudson made it all seem reasonable. Botham was enthralled by the prospect of changing the staid old game into something new, fresh, vital. So persuasive was Hudson that even Brian Close was roped in as cricket manager at Birtles.

Even so, Botham must have been at a low ebb to fall for Hudson's next ludicrous suggestion. He was going to become a Hollywood superstar, a star of the silver screen. Sporting swashbuckler he may have been, but since cricket means nothing more than 'grasshopper' in the States, Botham was a completely unknown quantity to the movie producers in Los Angeles. An unknown non-actor is unlikely to become the new James Bond, yet Botham fell in with Hudson's plans, so keen was he to make a change in his way of life. This was the real legacy of 1981. Ever since then, once he had walked upon the waters, once he'd transformed the bitter tears of defeat into the sweet champagne of victory, no one had been able to say no to him. Botham knew best because he'd proved it. He'd done things that no mere mortal could ever repeat. The people knew it, his friends knew it, the opposition knew it. Most of all *he* knew it. Headingley had shown that no challenge was too great for this man. All things were possible as long as you believed. If Ian Botham thought he could become a movie star, it was just a matter of time before it came to pass – that was how he'd reached the pinnacle of the cricketing world after all. Yet Botham was a supremely gifted cricketer, an instinctive natural athlete; there was no evidence to suggest he was a natural Marlon Brando. Of course, these seemed to be just petty details that would be addressed in due course. Nothing to worry about. The proposal was thrilling, it was novel, it was a gauntlet thrown down at the feet of a man who had done everything in cricket. The macho Botham even had his hair highlighted, something which would have been unthinkable a few years earlier.

Ultimately, it was Hudson's dreams of Hollywood that proved to be his undoing. Botham came to see him as a Walter Mitty character, an inveterate dreamer whose schemes often had little to do with reality. More sinister as far as Botham's family were concerned was the way in which Hudson seemed to live within a magic circle of followers who hung on his every word. Slowly, insidiously, Botham was drawn into the centre of this world. He was besotted with Hudson's panache and daredevilry, refusing to hear any criticism of his latest saviour. Kath, stubborn and sensible, refused to fall under the spell. She was concerned about her husband but felt he was big enough to look after himself. Her real worry was the effect Hudson would have on the children. Since Botham wouldn't listen to her criticisms, she reacted in the only manner left to her by issuing an ultimatum: either Hudson had to go or she would. Pig headed to the last, Botham allowed her to walk out on him, though her action was the wake-up call he needed. Given that she had been able to weather the sex and drugs storms whipped up by the media, her initial determination to leave underlined the seriousness of the situation. When she returned to the family home a few days later for the sake of the children, Botham's faith in Hudson had been irredeemably shaken.

A few days later, when Hudson confided in Brian Close that Kath and the family would have to go if Botham was going to become a smouldering sex symbol on the big screen, the game was up, even though it took a few more months before Botham finally sacked him as his business manager. Finally coming to his senses after a year-long interlude, Botham put his family life first and got his marriage back on an even keel. The final parting of the ways with Hudson came when, with the sex and drugs allegations flying through the air while England were in the West Indies, Hudson allegedly told the press that Botham smoked dope and didn't everybody? Given that Botham was still embroiled in legal proceedings having sued the *Mail on Sunday* over the New Zealand articles, this was not quite the sort of publicity he required. Hudson was finished, not before time as far as Botham's family were concerned. He left a legacy of eighteen months during which Botham had become more hooked on the idea of fame and fortune than at any stage, to the exclusion of his family and to the undoubted detriment of his cricket. He had failed in the Caribbean again, but once more his tour had been wrecked by external events beyond his control. When the record books show that Botham always had a terrible time against the West Indies, the other pressures that always seemed to accompany series against them need to be taken into consideration.

Free of Hudson, the remainder of Botham's career was comparatively sedate, once the 1986 drugs storm had been weathered. He seemed more willing to listen to the views of his family, notably his wife Kath, who had long been a voice of sanity amid the madness; as Botham was happy to confess later, she was the rock to which the entire family clung in the midst of the turbulence. While her husband could escape onto the pitch or into a huddle of confidants around the bar, she had nowhere to go. The kids still had to be taken to school, the visits to the supermarket had to be made. Without her, the whole family would surely have gone under. Tongue firmly placed in cheek, Bob Willis wondered aloud whether Botham might not have ended up in prison had he not married Kath so early. An exaggeration or not, the consequences for Botham in the absence of her counsel would have been desperate indeed.

On the field, too, there were people with his interests at heart. Moving to Worcestershire in 1987, he found Phil Neale to be an intelligent skipper who used him well and who allowed him to be himself, within reason. At county level, the years beneath the cathedral at Worcester were perhaps the best of his life. If nothing else, at that lower level he was still a consummate performer, a genuinely threatening all-rounder who could still make a decisive contribution with the ball. Neale was the ideal county captain for a player like Botham. Simply by getting Botham to the club he had gone out on a limb. Some members had voiced their disquiet over Botham's reputation and were worried that his arrival might disrupt the smooth running of the club. Botham was anxious to repay his new captain's confidence in him. Neale used him better than any captain since Mike Brearley, Botham stating in his autobiography that 'here was a man who knew how to handle his players and understood enough about their personalities to get the most out of them'. For his part, Neale makes the whole thing sound so easy:

Ian has a good cricket brain. I always tried to get his input wherever possible. He accepted that I was the captain and made the decisions but he was always ready and able to offer an opinion and I went out of my way to seek it. Even on the field, crossing between overs, I'd say, 'How do you think it's going, Beefy? What d'you reckon?' We only had one disagreement that I can remember which was about him wanting to carry on bowling when I wanted Graham Dilley to have a go! A lot was made of 'can you handle Ian Botham' but his commitment to the players he was working with was excellent. He's at his best when he's one of the boys in the dressing room with the team aiming for something in particular. His commitment to whatever side he's playing for means that he's not difficult to handle as long as you're sensible and you accept that he is different, that he's got a lot of other things going on in his life. You can't just treat him like any ordinary cricketer and that was our approach. I think by the time he came to Worcestershire the England captaincy ambitions had gone and at county level it would have been difficult for him to lead a side, going off to Tests and so on. He had a lot to contribute if you were prepared to ask and he was an invaluable senior professional and vice captain. If you involved him, he had a lot to contribute.

That assessment is an interesting contrast with Brian Lara as seen through the eyes of his county captain, Dermot Reeve. On his arrival at Warwickshire in 1994, Lara had just beaten Sobers' record for the highest individual Test score with his 375 in Antigua and was the biggest cricketing star since Botham. Despite the occasional problem, Lara had managed to sustain an enviable reputation as a nice young man coping well with stardom, quite the opposite to the perception of Ian Botham circa 1986. Yet in Reeve's book, *Winning Ways*, he devotes an entire chapter to the disruption that Lara caused at Edgbaston among the players and in the committee rooms. One thing that Lara understands far better than Botham ever did is the value of good public relations. If Botham had, just occasionally, done the 'right' thing, the 'expected' thing – a net session here and there, or a contrite, if insincere, apology from time to time, for example – he might have saved himself a lot of trouble. That was not the Botham way however, and he often fund himself in trouble simply because of his honesty.

Though David Graveney skippered him for a couple of inconsequential seasons at Durham, the last captain of any note in Botham's career was Graham Gooch. Though the two had a great deal of respect for each other's abilities, neither was sold on the other's means for arriving at an end, nor were they always personally compatible. In the end, Gooch was proved right, at least in so far as cricketing longevity is concerned. Even now, at the age of forty-three, Gooch could still open the innings for England in a home series and give a good account of himself, while Botham had ceased to be fit enough to play convincingly at international level even before he played his swansong games under Gooch. Just as Boycott had turned net practice into a way of life, so Gooch and England manager Micky Stewart were fetishists where physical fitness was concerned. Though Botham and Gower had never needed to worry about that early on – Gower naturally fit, Botham incredibly strong – in the second half of his career Botham would have been helped by paying a little more attention to his diet and to his overall levels of fitness. Yet even after Gooch's revolution, referring to England's out cricket on the Ashes tour of 1994/95, Peter Roebuck pointed out in *The Cricketer* that 'England's cricket takes too little heed of fitness, not too much'. Mike Atherton concurred in the December 1996 issue of *Wisden Cricket Monthly*: 'I am not a fitness fanatic and I don't enjoy it per se. But I have never known a fitter cricketer be a worse one and have known plenty who have benefited by it ... over the last two winters, my own performances have certainly suffered at the end of a long, arduous tour.' Few would suggest that Atherton's poor form with the bat in Zimbabwe was down to his being too fit, while the English team as a whole was not beset by the rash of injuries that had attended many previous tours.

In truth, Gooch and Botham were always a potentially combustible mixture because their attitudes to the game differed so much. Furthermore, circumstances conspired so that they must have viewed each other with some suspicion. Back in 1982, Graham Gooch had been the captain of the South African Breweries XI that made the rebel tour of South Africa, threatening Test cricket in its wake. Botham had been the prime target of the organisers but had turned down the opportunity. That decision was partly conscientious objection out of deference to friends like Richards and Garner and his own distaste for apartheid, partly a careful weighing up of the financial implications of such a move, and partly a refusal to betray his country by ducking out of Test cricket for a lengthy period. Having already been at odds with Gooch over fitness training in the West Indies, Botham must have felt let down by those younger players who sold out to the South Africans. Just as dispiriting for him must have been the way in which he took all the criticism for England's failure in the West Indies in 1985/86 when it was Gooch who had done as much as anyone to undermine team spirit, another legacy of that South African odyssey. Selected for the tour in the wake of his wonderful summer of 1985 against Australia, Gooch was England's great hope against the West Indian fast bowlers, but he spent much of the tour in bitter introspection as anti-apartheid demonstrators targeted him wherever he went. That was enough to wear anyone's resolve down and Gooch cut a morose, dejected figure for much of the tour, even threatening to fly home at one point after Antigua's deputy prime minister suggested, erroneously, that Gooch had apologised for going to South Africa. Just as one has to have some sympathy for Botham's outrageous treatment at the hands of the press, one must accept that Gooch was under immense pressure in the West Indies and could be forgiven for snapping. But Botham had never threatened to quit the tour as Gooch had, and yet England's poor team spirit was supposedly all his fault. His pronounced sense of injustice must have found that hard to bear.

Perhaps the final straw with Gooch came when Botham was controversially omitted from the 1989/90 tour of the West Indies, of which more later. Suffice to say at this point that Botham had turned down an extremely lucrative offer to go to South Africa that winter on the understanding that he would make the plane to the Caribbean, only to be let down at the final moment. Having made himself unavailable for just two England tours in his entire career – one to India when he was in desperate need of a rest, the other to Pakistan and the World Cup of 1987 when he was trying to avoid the press pack by wintering in Australia – he was now cast aside by a hierarchy which had apparently begged him not to go to South Africa. And the captain of that side who didn't need him? Graham Gooch, a man who had in Botham's opinion turned his back on his country in 1982. If Gooch and England manager Micky Stewart felt the presence of the 'champagne set' players like Botham and Gower undermined them, Botham must have been every bit as uneasy with their rise to the summit of English cricket.

As a reaction to these disappointments Botham had subsequently scoffed at Gooch's methods as captain, and perhaps they were too rigid, not allowing some players to be themselves. The slack that Phil Neale cut Botham at Worcester was essential for his psychological well-being, yet it has to be said that Gooch is living proof that there is some sense in the medicine he prescribed. England's up and down performances under his captaincy cannot be laid purely at his door – like many leaders before him, he was often let down by the material with which he had to work. Of course David Gower should have been selected far more regularly than he was, but it was Botham who ruled himself out of contention by reason of his own inadequacies, not Gooch or Stewart. The facts are that by 1989 Botham's bowling was not of international class and he rarely showed the application necessary to displace the likes of Allan Lamb and Robin Smith from England's top order, while it was also surely time to give up and coming players such as Alec Stewart and Mike Atherton a chance. If Gooch has some culpability in the premature end of Gower's career, his hands are clean when it comes to Botham. A healthier partnership between the two post-1989 would have been most welcome for English cricket, for potentially Botham still had a lot to offer as a batsman and even more to offer as an entertainer. Even when he was struggling, Botham had that charismatic magnetism that drew people into cricket grounds. Had he looked at his technique and health as rigorously as Gooch did, he might have been packing Test grounds for three or four years longer, enchanting his fans with pyrotechnic displays.

Like the rest of us, Botham made his good decisions and his bad, and he was unfortunate in losing those who could have made a difference at crucial times. He was not the only person who was badly advised though, for the men who run the game at Lord's all too rarely did the right thing by their hottest property.

CHAPTER FIVE

WHOM LORD'S WOULD DESTROY THEY FIRST DRIVE MAD

The Establishment

One of the more tempestuous relationships in Ian Botham's career has been that with cricket's establishment, be that the England selectors, management, or the Test & County Cricket Board. To simplify matters, these can all be classified under the all-embracing umbrella of 'Lord's'. Botham is not the first player to feel that he has grievances against the powers that be and nor will he be the last. Any cricketer who threatens to transcend the game can expect to feel the wrath of the Establishment coming down upon his head. Anyone who whips up frenzied public support, intentionally or unintentionally, while behaving in an unconventional manner is looking for trouble. And anyone who can crack a century on a couple of hours' sleep after a good night out is just too damned clever for his own good in the eyes of some.

The irony of Botham's position was unconsciously made clear in Trevor Bailey's obituary to Bill Edrich. Published in *The Cricketer* in June 1986, just after England's squad had returned from the vilification heaped on them for their lackadaisical attitude in the West Indies and Botham's banning from the game, it was hard not to smile at Bailey's portrait of Edrich: 'Bill lived and played hard, firmly believing that life was for living, not for existing. Blessed with exceptional stamina, he considered it neither necessary, nor desirable to retire to bed early simply because he happened to be batting in a Test, an outlook which did not always appeal to the establishment who did not possess the same enthusiasm for the parties.' This is of course the same Bill Edrich now commemorated at Lord's by the Compton & Edrich stand. Let's not forget that Mr Compton also knew a thing or two about parties. From Bailey's sketch, it seems likely that Edrich and Botham would have enjoyed each other's company had they been contemporaries.

Other players from the past have upset the apple cart in differing ways. Fred Trueman was as popular with the cricketing hierarchy as an outbreak of cholera simply because he spoke his mind. Consequently, he made just four of the eight England tours conducted while he was an active Test player, despite being England's most explosive bowler. He dedicated his autobiography, *Ball Of Fire*, to 'all young cricketers of independent spirit, in the hope that they might learn from it some of the pitfalls into which their pride and self-respect will surely lead them'. Although Botham and Trueman have rarely seen eye to eye, *Ball Of Fire* could have been a set text for the young Somerset all-rounder; media intrusion aside, Trueman was assailed by all the same difficulties that were to besiege Botham.

Players from Yorkshire have seemed particularly prone to problems with Lord's, proof of the existence of the north/south divide, presumably. It was a tension exacerbated by the particular strain of bloody-mindedness that made the county such a formidable outfit but which failed to endear them to the old school tie types that ruled the game. Brian Close lost the captaincy as a disciplinary measure. Ray Illingworth's relations with Lord's were rarely cordial, and even Geoffrey Boycott was heard to complain that 'the establishment seems to want my ability but not me'. In his aggressive attitude to the game, Botham's mentality was similar to that of the great Yorkshire sides of the 1950s and 1960s, though his sometimes extravagant batting would rarely have gone down well in their dressing room. It was no surprise that he was in regular conflict with Lord's.

Ian Botham's problem was simple: he was the first cricketing superstar of the media age and, as such, he swamped the game. People who didn't want to know anything about cricket wanted to know everything about Botham. He was talented, exciting, charismatic. He pulled people into the grounds wherever he went and the press and TV responded warmly to him, at first. For a time, Ian Botham was English cricket and English cricket was Ian Botham. He appeared to wield enormous power and threatened the cosy hegemony of Lord's. Understandably wary of the cult of personality which had inflated Tony Greig and Ian Chappell to the point where they could front Kerry Packer's circus, the Establishment did not wish to run the risk of Botham being able to do likewise in the company of another multi-millionaire mogul.

It's vital here to look at the priorities of the authorities. The World Series circus which was rooted in the idea of selling cricket for its true value, expanding the game's popularity, making a few more dollars for Kerry Packer, and putting a more reasonable salary in the pockets of the players, was treated as a Judas-like betrayal. Decades-old friendships were destroyed as the Establishment worried about the loss of players to this media tycoon, and yet the life of international cricket was never actually threatened, simply the position of Lord's and the MCC as the arbiters of the game. The players who plumped for Packer were reviled and Greig in particular has never been forgiven by some. All this over what is, after all, just a game. Yet when Gooch and then Gatting led rebel sides to South Africa, threatening to rip the very fabric of Test cricket on racial lines and, more importantly, giving succour, however unwittingly, to a repugnant form of government, the atmosphere was less vitriolic. The prodigal Gooch and Gatting along with others were welcomed back to the fold at the first opportunity, Gooch ascending to the England captaincy. At one stage, the MCC even tried to organise a touring side of their own for a visit to South Africa. That was perhaps its darkest hour, but then as cricket's greatest writer, C.L.R. James, points out in *Beyond A Boundary*, 'What do they know of cricket, who only cricket know?'

The governing instinct of any form of establishment is survival if only for survival's sake. It does not matter if there are no other objectives, no plans for the future. All that matters is the retention of power. Once a group's status is under threat, it is galvanised into action, taking up arms against those who would defeat it. It is the fate of any iconoclast therefore to be mistrusted and despised, to be attacked with the full might of that establishment. These authorities may appear genteel and gentlemanly but they are street fighters at heart for whom all is fair in time of war, willing to deploy all the weapons at their disposal. This is perhaps their greatest, most lethal advantage, for those who are considered their opponents are regularly taken aback by the vitriol of these city gents, their venom couched in terms of apparently sweet reason. That is not to say that rebels are always in the right. It is in the very nature of rebellion to swipe at targets indiscriminately, often behaving every bit as badly as the quarry. Perhaps this is just from a lack of thoughtful analysis, perhaps it's the natural excesses of the wayward, unconventional spirit, perhaps it's done deliberately to provoke and annoy. Whatever the case, one has to remember that the aspects of a rebel's character upon which society frowns are often the roots of their greatness. Botham's stubborn belief in himself and his refusal to 'play the game' could be exasperating at times, but without that determination to go his own way, he would not have been half the cricketer.

Truly arriving on the Test match scene in 1978, Botham was the proverbial breath of fresh air. With English cricket having lost some of its greatest personalities to Kerry Packer, most notably Tony Greig and Alan Knott, here was a man who could take the centre stage and fill the gaping void they'd left behind. In any era, Ian Botham would have been a giant; in 1978, he was the answer to cricket's prayers. To use the vernacular, he put bums on seats, more bums on a greater number of seats than any Englishman since Denis Compton. Even though the Tests against Pakistan and New Zealand were woefully one-sided affairs, spectators still came through the gates, most of them to see the latest Botham performance; Gower's arrival that year had a similar, if far less dramatic, impact.

For the next couple of years, Botham's star was relentlessly in the ascendant as he routinely picked up man of the match and series awards as England won Test after Test. He achieved the fastest Test double of 1000 runs and 100 wickets in history. Blasting the Indians into sub-mission, he missed a Test hundred before lunch at Headingley by a single run. He regularly notched up centuries and bagged five wickets in an innings as though such an achievement were routine. So completely did Botham dominate the field of action that for a while it even looked as if he might become the first man to take 500 Test wickets and score 9,000 Test runs. He was irresistible, unbeatable, unstoppable. All the while, the cash registers were whirring and ticket office telephones ringing. Botham was doing well out of the game but the game was doing much, much better out of him. It's in the nature of life that such a run of unbridled good form and fortune cannot last for ever. Yet Botham was such a phenomenon, such a force of nature, that it seemed he might rewrite every rule and every record in the book. If he continued to take on all comers and to improve at such an exponential rate then there was no telling what he might achieve in a full career. By 1979, a paranoid hierarchy at Lord's was certainly starting to become more than a little apprehensive of his potential for he was winning broad popular appeal. To the frightened men in power, this was akin to a leader of the opposition having huge support among the electorate, support that might be utilised not at all benignly or, more worrying, in the pursuit of change. Having just resolved the Packer crisis, Lord's had no wish to see its power compromised by a member of the national side.

Human nature is deeply distrustful of the messianic, with good reason. However, before we go nailing every messiah to a tree just for the sake of it, we should ask if we are doing ourselves harm in the process. In a different sphere, for instance, the public crucifixion of such left-wing leaders as Tony Benn or Nye Bevan, both adherents of the kind of radical politics that might have done the country more good than certain policies we've had since the war, did democracy a great disservice and robbed the nation of the opportunity to choose a different set of ideas and ideals to those which prevailed. The systematic humbling of Ian Botham, a man with no wider agenda than to live his life in as enjoyable a manner as possible, was handled in the same way and did the game of cricket a great injury. The attitude percolating from Lord's may well have been at the root of the eventual public vilification that threatened to destroy him, but it was achieved with the active connivance of the media, particularly the tabloid press. It's fair to say it was also achieved with the assistance of Botham himself.

It is true that those with remarkable qualities are often seen as slightly unhinged, fairly or not. Often that is evidence of little more than indifference to what people may think of them and a determination to do things their way, to behave in a manner that is ahead of their time. Those that have sometimes been derided in life – Presley, Lennon, Dean, Cobain – are often granted iconic status in death, usually because they die early before they've had the chance to ruin their iconoclastic reputation. (Had Botham conveniently passed away at the Oval in 1981 – better still, had he been assassinated by a distraught Kim Hughes – we would now have shrines to Saint Ian up and down the land.) Botham *was* different, undeniably so, and he was attacked for it by many old-stagers. He had no time for the niceties of diplomacy. He had no need to observe the time honoured social graces of the game. He was not deferential to authority, offering his support only when it was deserved. He lived hard and yet was still able to play hard. He never thought defeat was possible, no matter what the situation. He made extravagant promises that seemed to be nonsense, but then he'd go out on the field and turn them into reality. He may not always have had the composed assurance of a Viv Richards or the grace and guile of a Dennis Lillee, yet he managed to perform feats that equalled the best of either of them. His huge frame was important, just as is currently the case with the dominant All Black Jonah Lomu (a confrontation between him and Liam Botham would be worth watching), but again we must accept that the crucial difference was his self confidence. To mere mortals, seeing someone so sure of himself can be an unnerving experience. To make us feel better, we label them eccentric. They're just different, that's all.

Botham was a little unfortunate in some ways. From the point of view of the authorities he was the wrong personality at the wrong time. When, in 1962, the forces held within Pandora's Box demanded their release and the distinction between amateur and professional was abolished, the men at the top of the tree must have suspected they were living on borrowed time. That distinction was one of the most stultifying aspects of the English game, one which had become quite ludicrous by the time of its repeal. Though we are still some way from the ideal classless society, that 'upstairs downstairs' mentality was utterly repugnant in the post-war world. The end of 'gentlemen' and 'players' was a simple acceptance of the new egalitarian realities that were shaping the world. Though no one could have guessed how things would unfold, in hindsight the emergence of someone like Ian Botham was the logical conclusion of this period of change involving one day Tests, Kerry Packer, television and money. Taking the country with him, not only was he post-amateur man, he was post-Packer man too. For those at Lord's, there must have been genuine concern that these lunatics might take over their asylum – Botham was the pop star as cricketer. In truth, he was more Elton John that Johnny Rotten, but Lord's had him marked as the establishment-shredding punk rather than the outrageous entertainer.

Lord's resented Botham because he was the irreverent embodiment of change in what to them were its most repellent aspects – dear God, he was even attracting football supporters! Totally unimpressed by social ranking, Botham was in the vanguard of a meritocracy. If you deserved his respect, you got it; if you didn't, he wouldn't lower himself to worry about your values or your opinions. That refusal to suffer fools at all may have been evidence of a character lacking in tolerance, but it caught the mood of the times. The 1980s were the years when you did what you wanted to do. Who cared about anyone else? Botham was the 'me' generation gone mad and it must be said that some of his more boorish behaviour was evidence of the general coarsening of England. But against that, he was good, bloody good, at his job and he deserved the loadsamoney rewards and the power it gave him. The crowds loved him not just for his unrestrained joy and his cavalier play but because he so clearly put the fear of God into the fuddy duddies who ran the game. As part of the first wave of international cricketers who actually got paid rather well, the more so for their off the field endorsements, Botham was not beholden to Lord's. He didn't have to go cap in hand to them to apologise for any misdemeanours, real or imagined, just so that he could keep his meagre pay and his place in the side. Botham wasn't just a cricketer, he was that new phenomenon, a celebrity. He was news-worthy and therefore marketable, and with the nation on his side he didn't need to worry about his behaviour, within reason. The public demanded that he play for England and the authorities did not dare leave him out. His constituency was the country, not the committee rooms in St John's Wood.

If cricket were an American game, there's little doubt that Oliver Stone would already have turned Botham's life into an epic movie, fuelled by conspiracy theories; Botham's autobiography is sufficiently paranoid – justifiably at times – to warrant it. The estimable Mr Stone would have men in bacon and egg ties crouching behind grassy knolls at the Nursery End, concocting wildly inappropriate England teams while Alec Bedser, the poor patsy, was locked in the apparent safety of a book depository somewhere in the Long Room. Even now, bearing in mind the fact that the English cupboard was pretty bare at the time, it's hard to understand how Ian Botham came to be elevated to the captaincy of England in 1980. That our finest cricketer, the man on whom our batting and bowling rested, a man with no real experience of leading any side, should suddenly be made responsible for leading a team against the most powerful bowling arsenal that had been assembled in almost fifty years is incredible, even more unlikely than the events of Headingley a year later. It's noted elsewhere that this was a surprisingly bold move by a nation that usually insists players should be all but in their dotage before getting a whiff of the captaincy. That's probably an understatement. To have a twenty-four-year-old lad who hadn't even been to public school, let alone university, running the England side was simply bizarre. It flew in the face of English cricketing history. At the time it seemed thrilling, a break with the past and the chance to embrace a new age. Oliver Stone would suggest he was promoted above his ability in order to destroy him, particularly when looking at the itinerary he would have to face. That would be taking things a little too far, but few at Headquarters were broken-hearted when Botham fell to earth in such dramatic circumstances.

Botham had done himself little good with his innocent, if reckless, involvement in the Scunthorpe night club brawl at Christmas 1980, when as England captain that was the last sort of situation he should have been getting involved in. There were other offences to be taken into consideration too: an unwillingness to accept any blame or criticism for England's defeats; the Blofeld scuffle; and a verbal altercation with the police when stopped for speeding on the eve of the First Test in 1980, police evidence reporting that he had said, 'I am Ian Botham and I will fight this all the way.' These were unfortunate, unsavoury incidents, best learned from, forgiven and forgotten. They were hardly evidence of incipient megalomania but they were matters that anyone hostile to him could use when the time was right. Certainly they were used to keep the England captaincy away from him for good once his tenure had ended in defeat. His sad demise was cause for some relief in the corridors of power, though once he had demolished the Australians at

Headingley and re-established himself in the public mind, perhaps they might have reflected briefly that having Botham around as a loose cannon was rather more dangerous than having him on the inside.

In a candid moment, Botham would have to admit that he is in the Olympic class when it comes to bearing what he feels is a legitimate grudge. In his dealings with the members at Lord's over the course of two Tests in 1980 and 1981, he had more than enough justification for concluding that some of the MCC members were not worth the time of day. A more famous episode came when he returned to the pavilion after registering his first pair in Test cricket, his miserable walk back up the steps accompanied by a stony silence. Perhaps the members didn't know how to react to him, maybe they were genuinely embarrassed on Botham's behalf, but ignoring him was no way to treat a man who had given several virtuoso performances on that hallowed turf in the preceding seasons. What of his eight wickets and a century against Pakistan? What of his eleven wickets for 140 in the game against New Zealand? What of his five wickets against India? These great deeds were soon forgotten. In retaliation, whenever Botham made runs or took wickets at Lord's subsequently, he refused to acknowledge the members. Some might feel that was petty, but it was no less petty than their treatment of him.

His first run-in with them had come the year before during the showpiece Centenary Test against Australia. That gala occasion was ruined by bad weather and woefully inadequate ground covering; one might have expected the world's premier ground to have had rather better facilities given that cricket was now back in profit. Despite bright sunshine, following earlier heavy rain, play did not get under way on the Saturday until 3.45 p.m. In their frustration, some MCC members struck Botham and jostled umpires Dickie Bird and David Constant as they returned to the pavilion from yet another fruitless pitch inspection. When reading the leader articles in the national press castigating him after his brief flare-up with Henry Blofeld, Botham might have wondered why he was so virulently attacked when the behaviour of the MCC members had received scarcely any condemnation, despite taking place under the nose of their guest, the visiting Australian captain. Outrage targeted against Botham was rationalised on the grounds that he was a 'public figure' and 'role model', always nebulous justification. Surely bad behaviour is bad behaviour? David Frith's editorial in *Wisden Cricket Monthly* noted that the disgraceful conduct of this self appointed elite destroyed 'any concept that violence lurks only in the "outer" ', a telling point against those lamenting the loss of those far off days when cricket grounds were silent places ringing to occasional polite applause.

Not content with attacking the captain of England physically, many members of the Establishment were willing to assault him mentally too. The Centenary showpiece petered out into a dull draw, an 'honourable' one as John Arlott termed it, certainly more honourable than the members deserved. However, Botham was again seen as the villain of the piece for refusing to chase 370 to win in 350 minutes. With Boycott making a typically dour century, England were never likely to get on terms with the asking rate and Botham was blamed for turning the game into a damp squib. He should have forced his team to score more quickly to make a game of it, it wouldn't have mattered if England had lost, ran the argument. That conveniently ignores the roasting Botham would have got for losing a Test match, the more so following his unsuccessful series against the West Indies. If the result was so unimportant, why did Greg Chappell set such a stiff target? If he had wanted to make a game of it, maybe he should have set England, say, 320 in even time. Chappell certainly wasn't willing to risk defeat, though his hand was forced a little by his desire to allow Kim Hughes the chance of registering a second hundred in the game. There can be little doubt that sections of the hierarchy held against Botham this failure to give the game a glorious finale. If England had engineered a nail biting finish, that would have been the abiding memory of the match. As it was, the Centenary Test is still remembered for the inadequacy of the covers and the unforgivable irascibility of the members. Since Botham failed, indeed refused to try, to get them off the hook, he made more enemies in high places.

From then on, whenever there was an opportunity to annoy or undermine him, the authorities took it. For instance, when Botham finally took his weight problem seriously at the end of the summer, he took to playing football for Scunthorpe United. It helped him shed a few pounds and stay in trim. An edict was immediately issued to the effect that he should stop, that he was risking injury – this just before he was to face Michael Holding hurling a leather ball at his head at 90 mph. But as Jim Laker wrote in *Wisden Cricket Monthly* in December 1980, 'I cannot recall anyone offering this sort of criticism when Denis Compton, Willie Watson, Arthur Milton and scores of others were concerned.' Nevertheless, the whispering campaign intensified as results went badly. In the West Indies, Botham was then made to look foolish among his own players when Lord's refused to allow him to appoint his own vice captain once Bob Willis was forced to fly home injured.

His departure from the captaincy was a blessed relief to his admirers, like seeing a suffering dog put out of its misery. There was the inevitable lull, a drawing back from confrontation, partly because Botham concentrated on repairing his reputation, and partly because so successful was he in that, that for a time he became fireproof. Botham would occasionally do something stupid to let himself down – his haranguing of some Indian batsmen in 1981/82 was unnecessary, and his attack on Australian umpires in 1982/83 was unsportsmanlike, even if his comments were meant to be off the record, a naive hope for a man of his stature – but a truce was called in his relations with the Establishment. They had more than enough on their plate with the constantly developing situation in South Africa. Following the end of the 1981/82 tour to India, fifteen English cricketers chose to tour there with a rebel side, throwing the whole future of Test cricket into doubt. Among those who did not take the rand were Bob Willis, David Gower and Ian Botham. Botham had been offered £85,000 to make the trip but refused. In part that was a financial decision, but unlike some players who felt that politics had no place in sport, the more so since there was nothing preventing big business making money out of South Africa, Botham was a genuine opponent of the apartheid system and refused to betray his basic principles. No man could be such a close friend of Viv Richards and remain unaware of the importance of the fight for racial equality. However, even Richards understood the realities of life for a professional sportsman, and when the offer came again in 1989 Richards encouraged Botham at least to talk to the South African authorities, telling him that 'you can't play for ever'. Of course, by 1989 there was cause for optimism that the struggle in South Africa was coming to a head, and that ill timed rebel tour had far less political significance than its predecessor.

This second honeymoon between Botham and Lord's was destined to be short lived; you can't be as frank, outspoken and successful as Ian Botham without making enemies on the way up. Never a diplomat, Botham rarely cared whether he trod on sensitive toes. Not only that, had he chosen to go to South Africa, he might have been considerably more popular with the upper echelons in English cricket. Their obligatory ban aside, many of those who went to South Africa have been treated well by the authorities: Gooch was made England captain and is now a Test selector, as are David Graveney and Mike Gatting; John Emburey is involved in the coaching set up; Gatting took England's 'A' side to Australia in 1996; and Peter Willey is on the panel of umpires. Gower and Botham, two men whom the South Africans would have loved to get on board and who refused to go on both occasions, have been treated very badly in comparison. Perhaps there are other reasons, but one has to wonder if this is the payback for putting loyalty to the England side before the legitimisation of apartheid South Africa.

Cricket is still a deeply conservative game; it was even more so in 1982. There is a feeling among some that the Establishment secretly welcomed that first rebel tour and the prospect of cricket splitting along racial lines. There was bitterness, an angry reaction to their having been forced into a corner by the 'left wing' anti-apartheid movement throughout the 1970s, and having been forced to expel the South Africans from the international arena. Many MCC members had extensive business interests in South Africa and felt that the sporting boycott was the thin end of the wedge, preparatory to economic sanctions being demanded. There was a real desire to see the South Africans back in the fold. Since there was such sympathy for them, one has to wonder whether those who conferred legitimacy on them are now being rewarded at the expense of others.

The next storm broke on the 1983/84 tour of New Zealand and Pakistan under the stewardship of Bob Willis. The details of this particular episode are dealt with later but the reports carried in the national newspapers had important ramifications for Botham and his dealings with Lord's. Prior to leaving, the TCCB had again criticised him for taking 'ridiculously unnecessary risks' by playing two league games for Scunthorpe United, the board inviting him to appear before its disciplinary panel on his return. While the suits may have had a point this time – his final game was just two days before the team flew out – it was poor motivational policy to threaten him in this manner. Given Botham's flagrant disregard for authority, the reaction provoked could only be an aggressive one which might impair his cricket. In addition, as Botham pointed out in his autobiography, at the same time Lamb and Gower were off skiing and Gatting was playing local league football. There were no reprimands for them.

For the first time, an English cricket team abroad was pricking the interest of the tabloid press, specifically their news reporters. The most serious allegation, carried in the *Mail on Sunday*, was that members of the team had been smoking 'pot' in New Zealand. It was a story given credence by England's abysmal showing at Christchurch when, on a poor wicket, they allowed New Zealand to rack up 307 before losing by an innings. Such amateurism could only be achieved amid the haze of funny cigarettes, according to the newspapers. A hastily organised TCCB inquiry quickly concluded that there was no case to answer and that the team had done nothing off the field that would adversely affect their performances on it. They stopped short of exonerating the players of the use of drugs and left the door open by saying that enquiries would be renewed in the event of significant new evidence coming to light. It was hardly a ringing endorsement of the party's behaviour. For the press, this verdict, of 'not proven' rather than 'not guilty' understandably smacked of a cover up, Lord's brushing unsavoury accusations under the carpet. Our moral guardians were indignant. Given that Ian Botham was the most prominent member of the party and that he had acquired a reputation as a relentlessly enthusiastic socialiser and party-goer, most of the allegations adhered to him. The fact that he had to fly back home after the First Test in Pakistan for a knee operation was also seen as suspicious. Some tried to suggest that the TCCB had ordered him home to take the pressure off the rest of the squad (it's a little unlikely that Botham would have had his knee opened up by a surgeon purely to draw the hacks off the scent). One thing was clear, however: it was Botham who was the target of the press. He was great copy and he was also writing for the *Sun*, making him fair game for the rival publications. As one of the most celebrated figures in Britain, stories about him were the stuff of newspaper proprietors' dreams, and if no story existed, there were few problems in making one up. Once the TCCB had delivered their report, it was open season on Botham.

On tour each member of the party is an employee of the English cricketing Establishment. While that does not mean the TCCB owns them body and soul, it does mean they have a responsibility to them. Those found guilty of the charge of smoking dope could have been justifiably punished with heavy fines or a fixed term ban from the game, according to the gravity of the offence. (Given that the South African rebels were at this time still banned from Test cricket, maybe Lord's was frightened of what it might find, wary of outlawing, say, four or five more international class cricketers with a West Indian series looming.) Alternatively, the TCCB could have made a thorough investigation of the matter, rooting out the truth whatever the consequences. In the light of subsequent confessions (Ian Botham and Allan Lamb were candid in their respective autobiographies), the board must have been aware there was a certain amount of pot smoking going on in the privacy of hotel rooms. Intelligent men like A.C. Smith and Norman Gifford (manager and assistant on the New Zealand tour) were not easily hoodwinked; it is almost inconceivable that they were ignorant of the behaviour of their players. Once the facts had been established, a clearly worded statement could have been issued to the effect that, yes, certain players used pot in a social context but had absolutely not used any performance enhancing drugs, that they had been fined a percentage of their tour fee, and warned that such conduct in future would not be tolerated under any circumstances. Instead, the authorities' desperate indecision sent out ambiguous, conflicting messages suggesting that players could continue to get away with anything. It's probable that had Botham been identified as the sole culprit in this sorry saga, such fudging would not have occurred: Lord's would have taken this chance to throw the book at him à la Ed Giddins. It was ironic that Botham should have behaved with such scant regard for the repercussions on a tour headed by A.C. Smith. After all, Smith was one of the very few members of the English hierarchy for whom Botham had any time. He had proved invaluable as manager of Botham's first trip to the West Indies in 1980/81, for Smith's skills as a cricketing diplomat cannot be underestimated. Later in his career, when he was marooned at Lord's, often having to defend the indefensible in his role as chief executive of the TCCB, Smith was mercilessly and unfairly lampooned by the press for his ability to speak on any subject at length and still say nothing. It would be fairer to say that by keeping his own counsel, Smith's behaviour might have been a good example that others could have followed. Without doubt, A.C. Smith has always had the good of the game of cricket at heart. The corollary to that is that he realises the players are the most important component of the game, infinitely more important than the Establishment and as such his brief, especially on tour, was to make life as comfortable as possible for his charges. For that reason alone, he was a man to whom Botham could relate, the latter noting in his autobiography that 'he saw the players' point of view and, when he could, he backed us to the hilt'. It was a shame, then, that Botham and Lamb should have let him down during the course of the 1983/84 tour. Although Botham enjoyed Smith's recognition of the players' pre-eminence in the game, he did not yet understand Smith's view that the game was more important than any player. Nevertheless, there remains a genuine warmth between the two men for Botham is quick to appreciate anyone who gives his all to the game of cricket, in whatever capacity. Where the TCCB was concerned, he failed to find any other such kindred spirits.

With these sex 'n' drugs 'n' rock 'n' roll stories surfacing on a more or less regular basis, Botham reacted in the only way he knew how: he took the fight back to the newspapers and instituted proceedings for libel against the *Mail on Sunday*. In retrospect, it turned out to be a catastrophic decision; though the specifics were wrong, the generalities about his use of dope were correct. Even so, it's easy to see how Botham fell into the trap. If he had done and said nothing, people would have assumed the stories to be true, the pernicious 'no smoke without fire' reaction to scandals. His reputation would be shattered, his commercial value reduced. As Botham pointed out in a later *Mail on Sunday* article, 'it seemed to me that everything I had fought for and worked so hard to achieve would be at risk'. The press had also challenged his virility, tempting him to put up or shut up. He couldn't resist that kind of challenge. In addition, his children were being hurt by the publicity, friends taunting Liam with the stories about his father. Botham might have been an idiot in some respects, but a six-year-old cannot be blamed for the inadequacies of his father, nor should he be put through the wringer on his account. Botham chose to clear his name for the sake of himself and his family.

If he'd been unpopular with the authorities before, he really put himself out on a limb this time. By taking on the Fourth Estate, Botham was threatening to blow everything wide open. The press never take a libel case lying down, especially if they feel there is some evidence to be found. In the absence of it, a little more mud slinging will make it impossible for the litigant, in this case Botham, to get a fair hearing. With that in mind, the situation facing cricket became more serious. Never mind what happened to Botham, this reflected on the integrity of the game.

As cricket's popularity had grown over the previous few years – thanks in no small measure to charismatic players like Botham, Imran, Richards and Gower – the game's place in the world had changed too. The treasured image of the quiet village game had gone for good. Cricket, like it or not, was now a part of the entertainment industry, no longer part of the Corinthian sporting world. Its profile had changed irrevocably and so had the position of its players. Cricketers like Botham were glamorous, comparatively wealthy, exciting people to be around. They were just like pop stars, a cricket tour running on almost exactly the same lines as a tour by a major rock band. Young men, often unencumbered by wives and girlfriends, rolled into town for a few days before heading out again. Cricket attracted more and more hangers on, even its own groupies, drawn by that romantic cowboy ideal. With attractive young women desperate to catch the eye of an international cricketer, it wasn't difficult for a resourceful journalist to put together a story or two along the lines of 'drug addled cricketer in three in a bed orgy shock horror' filled with lots of circumstantial evidence. A lot of those stories could have been avoided if wives and girlfriends had been allowed or even encouraged to travel with their men. There are practical and logistical difficulties, of course, but these could be overcome. Lord's, however, did not approve, though happily it seems as if that message has finally got home and the policy looks set to change in future. Mike

Atherton's men touring Zimbabwe and New Zealand in 1996/97 were expected to endure the arduous three-month tour without seeing their families. Highly competitive, highly charged young men were expected to give their all for England on the field, come off the field and be tucked up in bed at nine o'clock. If we'd chosen a team of monks this would be fine. Otherwise, it is highly unrealistic and is simply inviting the press to write scandal stories, the more so if England are getting beaten.

That was essentially what went on in the West Indies in 1985/86 while the libel case was pending. The news reporters were sent out in droves to dig the dirt about Botham. The four-month tour became one long list of stories about Botham and drink, Botham and drugs, Botham and women. Had the tour gone on any longer, we'd probably have heard about Botham and a flock of sheep. Little wonder that the tour fell apart as a result, Botham living like a hermit, retreating to his hotel room, which became known as the Batcave. Rather fortuitously, Botham's father-in-law, Gerry Waller, flew out to join him in Barbados when he was at his lowest ebb. It was during this period that Mick Jagger invited Botham and some friends, Waller included, to a party at his island home. Lindy Field, a former Miss Barbados, was at the party too. A couple of weeks later, her version of events was splashed all over the tabloids, a story of cocaine and broken beds in the house of a Rolling Stone. The best alibi in the world in such circumstances is your father-in-law, and so Botham's marriage was preserved, Kath having long since realised that what you read in the tabloid press is not always the pure, unadulterated truth. Botham's reputation, however, was harder to salvage. By now, it was long gone.

Back in St John's Wood, stories such as these were just further proof of Botham's unsuitability to represent England. Yet the biggest blow was still to come. Recognising that the tabloid campaign of disinformation was unbeatable, Botham had to withdraw his libel suit. Making his peace with the *Mail on Sunday*, he was required to write a front page article that, when it appeared on 18 May 1986, confirmed he had used pot in the past. This time there was to be no reprieve for Botham. Disgusted of Tunbridge Wells would have preferred him to be strung up, but the TCCB had to act within its remit. Ironically, it had brought in a new set of guidelines the previous year dealing with the moot topic of bringing the game into disrepute. The motivation? Botham's conviction for possession of cannabis on 14 February 1985. Supporting him for once, the authorities had decided that no further action need be taken in what was, after all, a police matter utterly unconnected with the game of cricket. However, they made it clear that anyone caught in similar circumstances in future would be for the high jump. Since Botham was the first to come before the beak under these new rules, the results were inevitable.

Even so, the two-month ban he received, ruling him out of almost all of the summer's cricket, and potentially the winter's Ashes tour, seemed draconian to many. In a strongly worded editorial in July 1986's *Wisden Cricket Monthly*, David Frith was staunch in his support for Botham:

> ... banished for indiscretions that would have remained known to him alone and a few intimates had not a "newspaper" posing as a moral guardian triggered off a tragic train of events by splattering sensation all over its newspulp two years ago. Botham's punishment, laughably administered for "bringing the game into disrepute" when all he had done was bring himself into it, would have been appropriate only if he had been found guilty of misbehaviour while "in uniform". Meanwhile, his 63-day ban seems to have been calculated on the basis of suspicion of far greater misdemeanours. For giving some kind of story to the newspaper in order to avert a costly and inevitably messy court case – that newspaper's "exposé" having driven the first shaft into the national hero's body – Botham has found himself roped down by Lilliputians.

That was the crucial point. Botham had done nothing wrong 'in uniform'. Unlike the days of yore, Lord's no longer owned the souls of its cricketers. They pay them for their performances on the field of play, and after stumps are drawn their lives are their own. Of course sporting personalities become role models, but that is not of their choosing. When Ian Botham was a young boy of thirteen playing cricket on the school field, his dream was 'one day I'll play for England', not 'one day

I'll play for England, be a good role model and bring together all the peoples of the world in peace and harmony through the light of my shining example'. One would hope that all sportsmen could be articulate, clean cut, smooth examples of upright citizenship like David Gower or Gary Lineker, but it's an unrealistic expectation. Just because a fellow is able to wield a bat with distinction, this does not make him a nuclear scientist, a role model, or even a nice chap. To confuse the deeds with the doer and then to foist other responsibilities upon them is self defeating. It's also a little bizarre that the organisations that promote the likes of Botham as beacons of morality then attempt to destroy those very icons in order to boost their profits. No one will deny that Botham has a self destructive streak, but he was surely helped along the road by the media. Botham has done things of which he should not be proud, but then so have we all. Fortunately, we don't end up on the front pages of the tabloids.

There is an argument that people like Botham have no right to a private life, that because they are well paid they are public property. This is plain nonsense. Everything they do on and in connection with the cricket field is under scrutiny. That is as it should be for they are representatives of the nation. Some, Botham included, would do well to recall that not all criticism of their playing performances is vindictive, that some of it is justified, is constructively meant, and is often written with a heavy heart. If a man puts in a bad performance, the public are entitled to know whether he had a long net session or not the previous day. They are equally entitled to know whether said cricketer was up until three o'clock that morning at a riotous party, though for the sake of balance it would be nice to hear about that side of things when a batsman has just scored a hundred as well as when he has registered a duck. At those times, they are on duty and have a responsibility to the side and the cricketing public who pay at the gate. Anything that does not impact on performance, however, has little relevance. That is why punishment would have been more appropriate after the New Zealand tour than when the *Mail on Sunday* article initiated it a couple of years later. In Botham's case, he did blur the lines somewhat by going public himself. Entering the public confessional only whets the appetite for more revelations. Nevertheless, that did not change the fact that his pot smoking was not connected with his cricket. His unusual contrition made it equally clear that he was not proud of what he had done, but also asked for understanding of the difficult lifestyle thrust upon celebrities. Essentially, Botham threw himself on the mercy of the court, the court being the British public, a public who, by and large, weren't bothered by his confession. Indeed, judging by the ovation he received on his return to Test cricket at the Oval in August, his popularity had increased. He knew which way the wind was blowing, and on this occasion he was bowling with his back to it.

Had the TCCB acted with more resolution back in 1984, perhaps the whole fiasco could have been avoided. Had it stood up to the press there and then, perhaps the message might have struck home. By abdicating its responsibility at that stage, it created a crisis far worse than that which had originally existed, letting the baying hounds know there was something to hide. It was inevitable the press would do everything they could to uncover it. At times like these, the instinct for self preservation takes hold; if sacrificial lambs are required, then so be it. In the modern age, self preservation effectively translates as doing whatever the media tells us to do. If the press can be appeased, if they can be bought off by some kind of remedial action, the crisis passes for another day. In another context, former Chancellor of the Exchequer Norman Lamont made the point quite eloquently: 'we give the impression of being in office but not in power'. That describes the cricketing authorities exactly: always reacting, never shaping.

The TCCB might have felt let down by Botham's actions, particularly in view of the events of the previous February. It had just cause for feeling disappointed. However, as Frith had pointed out, if anyone had been done harm, it was Botham himself. As a drug user and as someone who had broken the law – whatever his personal opinion of that law – his judgement was called into question. The notoriety would also harm his commercial profile. These were stiffer punishments than two months away from cricket, a break that did him little harm and a great deal of good if his performances in Australia that winter were anything to go by. It also ill behoves an organisation which gratefully receives large amounts of money from tobacco companies and breweries to deliver long sermons about the evils of drugs. Predictably, the hang 'em and flog 'em brigade felt that the punishment was far too lax. Botham was setting a poor example to our children and should be drummed out of the game. Surely if a famous cricketer has a greater influence on a child than his or her own parents, it was not Botham that needed to take a good look at himself but the parents concerned. In 1986 those children were as likely to have pictures of rock and pop bands plastered over their walls as pictures of Botham. It would be a pretty sheltered child indeed who hadn't heard of the seamier side of rock 'n' roll. Were we going to ban Bananarama or Eric Clapton for all eternity? A nice idea perhaps, but a shade unfair! And just how do those parents explain away the fact that then, they felt a cricketer should get a life ban for smoking dope, while now, just a few years later, the Oval Office in Washington DC is occupied by someone who has also admitted to smoking pot?

The drugs case out of the way, Botham and the authorities co-existed in a mood of mutual suspicion. Intelligently, when selected for touring duties in Australia that winter, Botham took the family. With his wife Kath on hand at all times, unearthing another sex scandal taxed even the most zealous reporters and he enjoyed his most successful and trouble-free tour. This was meant to be Botham's swansong overseas. Signing a three-year deal with Queensland from 1987/88, he had decided to set up camp in Australia for part of the year, an arrangement that failed to last the course. Even so, things remained on an almost even keel, the more so since 1988 was written off when Botham spent the year on the sidelines nursing his back; that 1980 injury had finally deteriorated so badly that surgery became essential.

Coming back to the game in 1989, Botham was bursting with life. With things to prove to himself and the world, he had a goal once more, vital if he was to concentrate fully on his cricket. He managed to reclaim his Test place while being simultaneously courted by the South African Cricket Board to go on Gatting's rebel tour. (Gatting had been another victim of the insensitivity at the top of the game and had lost out on the English captaincy in controversial circumstances. Disenchanted with his employers, he was off to make some money and also perhaps to gain a measure of vengeance.) According to Botham, sums approaching £500,000 had been mentioned, enough to give anyone pause for thought. Viv Richards had given Botham his blessing to go to South

Africa and, with just a few cricketing years left in him, the opportunity to make that kind of money was sorely tempting. That the decision to go would have ended his Test career there could be no doubt: a four- or five-year ban for the rebels was a racing certainty. According to his autobiography, Micky Stewart 'on behalf of the England management was doing his best to persuade me not to go. They wanted me in the West Indies [that winter] he said and he pleaded with me to make myself available. They made it clear that if I did so, I was more or less guaranteed a place on the plane.' Though he hadn't been in great form in the three Tests he managed against Australia, Botham was desperately keen to go to the Caribbean one last time to exorcise the demons of his previous visits. The West Indians were the one blot on his escutcheon, the one team against which he'd never played well. Freed of his obligations to Queensland, this seemed like the ideal time to make amends. He told Ali Bacher of the South African board that he would not be making the trip.

Once the team for the West Indies was selected, all hell broke loose. Botham was not on the list. He received a call from Ted Dexter, who at least had the nerve to tell him personally of his omission. Dexter's part in events seems honourable; according to Alan Lee's biography, Dexter had always doubted whether Botham should make the trip. Gooch confirmed to Lee that 'before we even began the discussions, I was instructed to exclude both [Botham and Gower]. I think Ted and Micky wanted a new influence. They wanted to get away from the champagne-set image which had been around for a few years.' The record of the conversation between Stewart and Botham comes from Botham's autobiography. It may be that Botham wished to put a rosier tint on his omission from that tour, refusing to accept that he just hadn't done enough to be worthy of a place on the plane. It may be that there was a genuine misunderstanding between himself and Stewart or between Stewart and Dexter over the likelihood of his making it to the West Indies. Or it may be that his recollections are one hundred per cent accurate, in which case this was yet another in the ever expanding catalogue of appalling player–board relations, the result of crossed wires between Stewart and Dexter or a more malign attempt to ensure that cricket's biggest name did not go to South Africa with all the implications attendant upon that. Given that Gower was removed from the captaincy and dropped from the team at one and the same time, it's not hard to conclude that one way or another the men in charge were at fault once more. If that is the case, Botham's bitterness towards Lord's is eminently understandable. Given that they also had the power to make his life easier by offering a greater degree of support when it was needed, we the cricketing public might also feel bitter that they shortened the useful life of the most exciting player of his generation.

CHAPTER SIX

I READ THE NEWS TODAY.
OH BOY.

Life with the Fourth Estate

M ore than any sporting life since that of George Best, Ian Botham's career was one which unfolded in the pages of the newspapers. All manner of deeds, some true, some false, some exaggerated, some physically impossible, were ascribed to him over his cricketing times. Much though he protests at press intrusion and the exercising of the tabloids' collective imagination, it's hard to avoid the conclusion that, materially at least, it did him more good than harm. At a time when cricketers were anything but prosperous – his Somerset salary for 1986 when Botham was perhaps the most famous man in the country was just £15,000 – his regular appearances in the media helped make him one of the most marketable commodities in sport. Against that must be measured the psychological strain that was placed upon him and, more importantly, upon his wife and family who were frequently innocent bystanders, caught up in the storms of controversy that raged about him. Kath learned to cope with the outrageous stories, discounting the newspapers and getting all her information from the source, but it was everyday life that was difficult, having to put up with comments from friends or even complete strangers about her husband's latest apparent indiscretion. For the children, prey to playground taunts about their dad, that was a worse problem still. Perhaps if the scandalmongers were exposed to the havoc wreaked by their thoughtless use of innuendo and invention, we might finally get a responsible press. It's a forlorn hope.

Unlike contemporaries such as Gower who was always highly

regarded by the public thanks to his essentially inoffensive nature, Botham had left numerous hostages to fortune over the years. His belligerence and occasional disregard for his fans did not endear him to everyone. Failing always to be nice on the way up, there were plenty ready to remember that when he was on one of his periodic trips down. He admitted in his recent autobiography that over the course of his career he had been 'aggressive, tyrannical, chauvinistic and hot-tempered'; to that might be added terms such as boorish, thoughtless, and selfish, not all qualities that sat well with significant sections of the population. *Times* journalist Simon Barnes made the important point that 'fame' should not be confused with 'uncritical love', a failing which he termed the 'Botham Error'. In truth, people were not promising to support him for ever more but were simply responding to the cavalier nature of his deeds, the successes he had earned, the brief flurries of excitement that he brought into their workaday lives. They were also responding to the nature and wider expectations of fame and celebrity in the 1980s, a period in which you were expected to flaunt power and influence and not feel that doing so was vulgar. Woe betide those who lost the Midas touch for they were destined for the scrapheap faster than ever before. Once the great deeds had dried up and Botham ceased to be the loveable big kid let loose to wreak havoc on the sporting world, the cliché that any player is only as good as their last performance took effect. However, where some are allowed to fail and fade from view, perhaps to regroup and return later, Botham had raised expectations to such a level that he could not retreat into the calm waters of obscurity. Britain, especially England, had pinned their hopes of glory on him and a disappointed public turned on him once those expectations had been dashed. A summer can last a very long time if you are constantly losing Test matches.

The demands were far too stringent for any man to bear. Within a year of his Test match debut, Botham was no longer a mere cricketer but a symbol of the nation, a man who would make Britain great once again. Media fuelled jingoism is discussed elsewhere in reference to the 1981 Australian series when Botham revelled in the orgy of flag waving that attended the Royal Wedding, but he was a figurehead of a resurgent nationalism much earlier than that. Perhaps the origins of this new patriotism can be traced to the Silver Jubilee celebrations of 1977 when the dull greyness of British life was forgotten for a few weeks amid street parties, fireworks and bunting. While the 1979 election was finally decided by the winter of discontent, the Conservatives would probably have won without it as Margaret Thatcher deftly tapped into and then encouraged the Little Englander mood that still prevails to this day in some sections of her party. It was a message that the Conservative press had long since pandered to in their general disaffection with all things foreign. Yet to make any lasting impact, ideas need to be fleshed out by personalities. Principles need faces, willing or not.

Countless media figures looked back to the days of Empire with misty-eyed nostalgia and while it was obvious that those days could never come again, they felt no need to apologise for them either. Political correctness in the 1960s and 1970s had put the very strong case that the United Kingdom should be ashamed of its imperial past, that our colonisation of vast parts of the world was not some great adventure but an act of territorial piracy. The heroes of yester-year were held up as thieves, robbing the indigenous populations of their birthright. We should be proud of the way we gave India back to the Indians, not of the way we took it in the first place. The New Right, wrapped in the union flag and stung into action following our entry into the Common Market, dismissed these claims as heresy and tried to resuscitate the great dreams of Empire. As our international influence diminished, so their rhetoric grew louder and more strident.

In Jubilee year, comparisons with Queen Victoria were inevitable; where her court had been full of Empire-builders, explorers and adventurers par excellence, Queen Elizabeth was surrounded by dull conformity. When he burst on to the scene in 1977, Botham was a breath of fresh air, a burst of unrestrained energy whose obvious joy in his cricketing successes caught the public's imagination. He quickly filled the gap, satisfied the public need for a soldier of fortune in whom we could revel, whose deeds we could glorify. We might not run Australia any longer, but by God, we could give them a damn good thrashing on the cricket field. As the next few years unfolded and his feats became increasingly prodigious, Botham was represented as a latter-day W.G.

Grace, the embodiment of the pioneering entrepreneurial spirit that had made Britain great.

The point about Ian Botham, particularly as seen through the eyes of the tabloids, is that if he hadn't existed, they'd have been forced to invent him. That was the problem. The Ian Botham who filled the pages of the *Sun* and the *Daily Mirror* didn't exist. That swashbuckling Errol Flynn of a cricketer was only one part of his personality. The caricature that took hold in the public mind belied the realities of the doting father, loyal friend or concerned fundraiser for leukaemia research. In the brash mood of the times, that was not the image the press wanted to sell. They wanted a larger than life superman who could fight the foes, win the wars, right the wrongs. In the face of a changing world, they wanted reassuring images of simplistic certainty. The press fed off Botham and Botham fed off the press image of himself. Throughout his story, it is his astonishing self belief that is the greatest cause for comment. Never short of confidence, probably the last thing he needed as a man was to be told that he was invincible. That inevitably led to the misplaced belief that he was fireproof and that whatever he said and did would be fine. Had his notices been a little more balanced, perhaps he might have been better prepared for the pitfalls that came his way.

Off the field, Botham had his problems. When the guardians of morality advise men like Botham to turn the other cheek to provocation, they are scarcely talking from a personal acquaintance with the burden of celebrity. Equally, the public was never told of the times that Botham might have followed that code and simply walked away from trouble – 'Botham not involved in a pub brawl' is not news. Botham's confrontational style and combustible temperament was the very thing that made him so effective on the field; it's hypocritical to suggest that he should be Batman on the field and then live like a village grocer off it, a point eloquently made by Peter Tinniswood in the classic book *More Tales From A Long Room*. Where Botham did fail was in exposing himself to such threats, particularly when he was the England captain. It might be unfair to expect that a young man should turn himself into a monk upon the conferral of that title, but Botham was all too often guilty of not fully accepting his responsibilities off the field. The captaincy of England is still an honour rather than a right, and with that honour goes a duty. Ian Wooldridge summed up the problem in the *Daily Mail*, pointing out that 'Botham's electrifying deeds on the cricket field have made him an incandescent figure whose influence on impressionable youth is probably greater than that of any other British sportsman. This carries a responsibility which all too often he has not acknowledged.' It is rough justice to saddle a rumbustious young man with the position of role model for a generation, but that now goes with the territory. Today's players are perhaps happier with that since they've grown up with those expectations. As one of the first stars of the media age, when flaws were exposed with relish, Botham was exploring uncharted waters, the rules evolving around him.

The first perceptible downturn in Bothamania came in 1980 when he was reduced to the status of the mere mortal by a lethal combination of a bad back and Clive Lloyd's West Indians. The level of criticism this drew was perhaps out of proportion to England's real defects, but then this is always the case nowadays. Very few people take criticism of any kind well, but Botham and his team were remarkably thin skinned. Attacks on the side's perceived deficiencies were fair game. The press were there to write about the cricket as they saw it. If Henry Blofeld felt Botham's captaincy was childish, he must be at liberty to say so, just as Botham should be free to say that he felt Blofeld's comments were uninformed, irrelevant, or plain wrong. If a cricket correspondent watches the game, he must be given his say and players must respect that right – after all, many only get in the team once a pressman has destroyed a predecessor or written up an innings of his in glowing terms. By 1981, though, relations between the England side and the bona fide cricketing press were at a low ebb. Mike Brearley remarked that on his return to the England side in 1981, he found his players 'more embittered by the press than I'd ever known ... I myself felt that rows were planted, cultivated and encouraged ... by the modern craving for excitement and sensation'. Some cricket writers go beyond the confines of their job in order to get exclusives on the line up for the next game and so on, but generally speaking they continue to do a good job; it is often their sub-editors who add lurid headlines to pieces that are comparatively mild. But anyone who puts themselves in the public eye should be ready for attack if it's warranted; you have only to listen to the trenchant commentaries of Bob Willis to realise that it's a very different game on the other side of the boundary. Willis' comments are often accurate and well informed, but I wonder how he'd have taken to them had they been directed at him in 1980? Botham was equally upset when the press questioned his abilities but his angry reactions only gave the press more reason to taunt him on and off the field. By offering plenty of provocation, they could guarantee themselves a juicy story.

With their man weakened by poor play on the field, it only needed one moment of stupidity by the England leader to make himself front page news for all the wrong reasons. In order to keep his weight down, Botham chose to train with Scunthorpe United prior to leaving for the 1980/81 tour of the Caribbean. Immersing himself in the affairs of the club, he quickly became a vibrant part of the dressing room and consequently he joined the team on a Christmas night out at Tiffany's night club. During the course of the evening one of his colleagues, goalkeeper Joe Neenan, was given a very rough time by a few locals who blamed him for the club's FA Cup exit a few weeks earlier. As night club arguments often do, the banter soon degenerated into a fight. Botham was on hand when Neenan struck one of his tormentors, the two having chased them for 600 yards. Inevitably, the story got into the papers and was portrayed as Botham attacking some innocent bystander. Once the story had worked its way through the courts, it became apparent that Botham had not been involved in the fight. He was found not guilty.

The die was cast, however. The great thing about smears is that, unwarranted or not, they are pernicious. They corrupt because they stick in the memory – David Mellor will forever seem faintly ridiculous not because he had an extra-marital affair but because he was supposed to have made love in a Chelsea shirt, later revealed as a press invention. Although Botham was not guilty – a decision not confirmed in the Crown Court until 23 September 1981 – he was a condemned man, a front page exposé waiting to happen. That was unfair, imposing an additional pressure to conform that did not suit him. However, he was reckless in failing to respond to the warning shot he'd received. Botham being Botham, he confirmed that he would do the same thing again. His loyalty to his friends was such that had Neenan been set upon by a gang the following day, he would almost certainly have become embroiled out of a sense of obligation. That is an admirable characteristic in many ways, but it could easily have led him into even more trouble: he might have been injured or he might have inflicted an injury on someone else merely by trying to separate the fighting factions. That Scunthorpe incident could have turned out much worse than it did and as such it should have opened his eyes to the difficult position he was in. From then on, he should have had the wit to avoid similar confrontations, or at least to try to avoid situations that could get out of hand. His failure to do so was manna for the press pack that followed his every deed.

While the runs were flowing and the wickets were tumbling in the patriotic summer of 1981, all was sweetness and light. He was providing the head of Kim Hughes on a plate as a royal wedding present. It was as if he were colonising Australia all over again, such was his bullishness in keeping with the times of celebration. A great self publicist, Botham was in the headlines all the time, perpetuating the image of the superman in whose glory we all basked. Sadly, from a newspaper angle good news becomes dull if repeated day after day. It's not upsetting or startling. It doesn't sell newspapers. Rupert Murdoch's stable, which included the *Sun* and the *News Of The World*, had been leading a gradual decline in the standards employed by the tabloid press, a decline which accelerated once Robert Maxwell arrived on the scene with his rescue of the *Daily Mirror*. The intense competition for circulation between the two led to newspapers desperately trying to trump one another with increasingly bizarre stories.

On the 1982/83 tour to Australia Botham had a pretty lean time with both bat and ball as England surrendered the Ashes he had protected so successfully in 1981. In what he felt was an off the record chat to a journalist, Botham complained at some length about the poor standard of Australian umpiring. This was something of a mantra in the England camp, the more so as the series went on. Approaching the final Test two-one down, a win would save the Ashes. On the first morning and without a run on the board, Australian opener John Dyson was given not out to a confident run out appeal. Television pictures showed that he was out of his ground by a good eighteen inches. Dyson went on to score seventy-nine, anchoring an Australian innings of 314 that left them all but safe. Tired and frustrated after nearly three months away from home and with another two months of the tour to go, Botham boiled over and the result found its way into the *Sun*. The Australian Cricket Board was inevitably furious and Botham picked up a £200 fine. More importantly, it was another nail in the coffin in terms of his relations with the newspapers, coming as it did just a month after the same paper had invented a story which stated in vivid detail that he and Rodney Hogg had had a brawl in a Sydney night club. After we had had Botham built up into the world-dominating Victorian hero, the call went out for a return to Victorian values, Victorian morality. Just as putting the 'Great' back into Great Britain had needed a figurehead, so stories illustrating the dangers of immorality needed a victim. Who better than Botham to remind the ordinary man and woman of the dangers of rising above your station in life? Who more likely to offer the kind of stories they needed? Anti-Botham propaganda had as much potential as articles in his favour – the dramas attending his weight problems of 1980 had proved that. Those stories from Australia in 1982/83 were just the start of a hellish period for Botham with fact and fiction blurring until they became indistinguishable to all but those actually caught in the crossfire.

The walls really came tumbling down on the winter tour of 1983/84 when England visited New Zealand. They went there never having lost a series to the Kiwis, surrendering just two Tests out of the fifty-seven played between the countries. In their typically patronising, paternalistic fashion, the English press simply dismissed New Zealand as cannon fodder, opposition which the English giants should overcome without working up a sweat. This conveniently ignored the fact that in Richard Hadlee they had a genuine all-rounder who was in the same class as Botham, and in Martin Crowe an accomplished batsman who was beginning to fulfil his golden promise. These two great players were backed up by a very useful side of supporting actors such as John Wright, Geoff Howarth, Lance Cairns and Ewen Chatfield. Having won their first Test on English soil in the summer of 1983, they were a real threat on their own surfaces. This type of caution did not wash with a nationalistic press still unable to come to terms with the fact that countries other than England might actually be able to play a bit of sport themselves. They demanded triumph after triumph.

The first game ended with honours even, centuries from Botham, Randall, Coney and Martin Crowe leading to a high scoring draw in Wellington. The Second Test was played at Christchurch's Lancaster Park. The England side were down to twelve fit men including Tony Pigott who had been wintering in New Zealand and was called up to play for his country at a moment's notice (he was forced to postpone his wedding which was due to take place on the fourth day). He needn't have bothered because England lost in three. Playing on a pitch that resembled crazy paving, England contrived to bowl so badly that the home team reached 307 having been 137 for 5. Richard Hadlee plundered a Bothamesque ninety-nine off eighty-one balls to push the score at least 130 runs higher than should have been possible. England were inept in the field, captain Bob Willis recording in his diary that 'Ian was unbelievably bad – right back to his worst days'. England were shot out for eighty-two and ninety-three, the first time this century that both completed innings had totalled less than a hundred. Hadlee took eight wickets in the match to reinforce his claims to Botham's throne, for as Willis pointed out, 'the batting may have lacked heart but it was not the main cause of the humiliation – that came on the first day'.

Such results look like damnable capitulation from the other side of the world, and this particular reverse came before we had all become so used to seeing England taking beatings overseas. The players had let England down. Surely they weren't so bad that they could lose to little New Zealand? There must be more to it than mere cricket. Stories needed to be found, and they came back from Christchurch in abundance: England's players went out on to the playing field befuddled by an alarming collective intake of cannabis; they locked the dressing room door to outsiders and spent their time smoking it. Firstly, it's ridiculous to believe that a tour party of fourteen or fifteen players would all want to smoke, or would all condone it; secondly, as Bob Willis pointed out – and this is what really undermines the story – 'anyone with the slightest knowledge of cricket grounds would know that people wander in and out of dressing rooms all the time, rendering the thought of surreptitious pot-smoking laughable, even if anyone was that way inclined'. Sadly, since England were playing badly, people were only too happy to go along with the reports. Had England won, the allegations would not have been printed. If they had been, the average reader would have laughed them off along the lines of 'if the cricketers are winning, maybe we can get the footballers to smoke it as well'. The story would have been absurd and ineffectual; look at how similar allegations made against Phil Tufnell in the winter of 1996/97 were ignored after England had taken the series 2–0.

If you're losing, then whatever you do you will get criticised for it. If you practice for six hours a day then tuck yourself up in bed at 9.30 with a cup of cocoa and an improving volume, then you are too reserved to give free rein to your gifts; if you're out all night burning a box of candles at both ends and in the middle too, you're wearing yourself to a frazzle and wasting your talents. In today's world, where success is essential rather than a nice bonus, there is no hiding place if you lose. Botham suffered from that truism, though ironically it was the very competitiveness and refusal to accept defeat displayed by great sportsmen like him that created that kind of climate. We in England – or certainly our tabloid newspapers – don't appreciate well enough the concept of sporting competition. In any contest there will be winners and there will be losers, that is the point of competition. But just because you lose a series heavily, it doesn't mean you are dissolute or dilettante in your approach to the game. It could simply be that you have come up against a better side. That's sport, but we cannot seem to accept that. We're England. We should always win. Unfortunately, it's not that easy any more. This is one of the biggest stumbling blocks in our attempts to gain sporting supremacy once again, for it puts players under intolerable pressure and forces selectors to chop and change a side unwisely just to escape censure. If Pakistan bowl us out in a day, the headlines scream of an 'afternoon of shame'; if Shane Warne rattles through the side we're 'Warne out'; if Brian Lara hammers the English attack for 150, our bowlers should be put out to grass and the captain thrown out on his ear. But why? Test cricket is full of fine players, even great players. If they play well, better than we are playing, should we not enjoy the spectacle? As long as the best possible English team is selected and then gives of its very best, we should accept the results, win, lose or draw, not glorify or crucify the captain. Any other response is childish.

It seems that the press had gone to New Zealand in 1983/84 looking for such sensationalist stories and were only encouraged by England's defeat. Accusations of conduct unbecoming were trumped up from the outset. In the first, a businessman told the *Daily Express* that a drunken and surly rabble comprising Botham, Willis and Lamb had been in their hotel bar at one in the morning. This was shown to be a case of mistaken identity, and the bar had closed at eleven anyway, but it set the pattern for the tour. It was only a matter of time before the big stories began to appear. As noted in the previous chapter, cricket tours were starting to resemble rock 'n' roll tours; as Willis pointed out, 'ever since I have been in the game, tours have involved a certain amount of drinking and a certain amount of female hangers-on'. It was drugs that the tabloids were really after, though. The attitude to pot in New Zealand is considerably more liberal than over here. As Allan Lamb pointed out in his autobiography, 'it was so much the normal and accepted thing there, that I did get mildly involved'. The media clearly felt that here was a chance to get a compelling front page story and bring down the great adventurer Botham, reinforcing the themes of their ongoing morality play. They were out to get him as part of the wider agenda and were waiting for the first cracks to form in his legendary armour. England's defeat at Christchurch provided the opportunity. There was no documentary evidence of his use of dope, just a hopeful suspicion among the press pack. To add spice to it all, they gilded the lily and added a couple of young girls to the scenario too. 'England cricketers in sex and drugs scandal' was splashed all over the front pages. It was these unfounded allegations that caused Botham to sue so ill advisedly, when he'd have done better to follow Lamb's dismissively flippant, yet more believable, approach: 'as I pointed out at the time, if I'd got a girl in my room for a bit of the naughties, I wasn't likely to leave the door open for anyone to walk in as [the girl who sold the story and later withdrew it had] admitted she'd been able to'. Again, Botham helped get himself into this fine mess. The stories were written by the press on a separate agenda. Botham was just another victim. The point was that his general demeanour meant that the pressmen could write salacious stories about him and be believed by a lot of people. They could never have written the same stories about David Gower because he had always been perceived differently. Since Botham played up to his yobbish image at times with his over aggressive farewells to opposing players when he had taken their wicket, his theatrical appealing, those unsavoury comments about Aussie umpires a year earlier, few seemed to doubt his capability to perpetrate further crimes and misdemeanours.

By this stage, Botham had a real dilemma. He was always one of the lads, a 'new lad' before the term meant anything. He loved a few beers and a yarn in the pub. He loved to hunt, shoot, fish, play football and go out with the boys. That was the root of much of his popularity for it struck a chord with the general public. He also enjoyed that particular image, yet it made him more of a target. City boys and beer boys alike greeted Botham with a 'nudge, nudge, wink, wink, say no more!' attitude. They envied him these fictitious nights of passion with exotic New Zealand beauties, all believing that the stories were true. The macho bravura of Botham must have been tempted to play up to the audience, while the devoted father must have despaired at the mess he found himself in. If he was to preserve his position, perhaps even his marriage, he needed to improve his image. He had to update it, make himself look the mature family man.

To the press, it was part of their ongoing game, the sport they simultaneously enjoyed with the royal family or with Boy George. Here was a mighty hero brought down to earth by his all too human failings. The destruction of the House of Botham might even be seen as a dry run for the destruction of the House of Windsor. He was certainly the bridge between the factual but relatively deferential treatment of George Best and the relentless, highly focused campaign waged against Paul Gascoigne. They pushed Botham as far as they could, continually testing the waters of public morality to see how much they could get away with. It's an ongoing process even today. If Botham had 'taken his medicine' in New Zealand, no more would have been said. Indeed, the press would have organised some great pictures of the tearful reunion with the devoted wife who was standing by her man – happy endings all round in hypocrisy land. Instead, he chose to take on the press. Honest, courageous, but ultimately daft. However hard you fight, they have the typewriters and the ear of the man in the street. They can make your life a misery without ever straying from the truth, by angling it, distorting it, putting it through the wringer, adding a little spin to your every word and deed.

Without hard evidence to back up their claims about Botham's exploits in New Zealand, it was still possible he might inflict an expensive defeat on them in the courts, the more so since the public were still generally sympathetic towards him. The press, therefore, needed to discredit him. The first piece of good fortune dropped into their laps, though if Botham is right in his autobiography it was all part of an elaborate set up, his solicitor Alan Herd having warned him of the possibility some weeks in advance. Having chosen not to tour India in 1984/85, he was looking forward to a break from the game. He wanted to spend time with the family, let the aching muscles take a rest, and recharge his batteries for the visit of the Australians in 1985. On New Year's Eve, the police arrived at the family home in Epworth with a search warrant; a pair of Botham's trousers sent to a local dry cleaner's had been found to contain a small packet of drugs in the pocket. Once the police searched his home they found dope in a drawer which Botham freely admitted he left there, having been given it by a supporter some years earlier, then forgetting all about it. The whole story is bizarre, another example of Botham's naive belief that he was fireproof. The find in the local dry cleaner's sounds questionable to say the least, but then if Botham had not held drugs at his home there would have been nothing for the police to find, there would have been no charges, and there would have been no story for the press to ram down his throat. Intriguingly, it was precisely the kind of story they needed at precisely the time they needed it. The whole campaign was redolent of the orchestrated attempts to attack the Beatles and the rock fraternity in general in the late 1960s once the whole hippie ethic started to frighten the Establishment. The Beatles were no longer lovable mop-tops but supposedly a threat to society. In his exhaustive biography of John Lennon, Ray Coleman says this of the 1968 raid on Lennon and Yoko Ono:

He was always convinced that the bust was a 'set-up'. Don Short of the *Daily Mirror* had warned him three weeks previously that the police were on the way, so John said he had 'cleaned the place up, especially as I knew Jimi Hendrix [renowned for his chemical intake] had had this flat before Ringo and me'. He maintained that the dope had been planted in the trunk, a spot in which he would never have tried to hide it. 'It was a frame-up. I guess they didn't like the way the image was looking. The Beatles thing was over. No reason to protect us for being soft and cuddly any more – so bust us!'

The parallels with Botham are striking. Just as the Beatles had been at the forefront of the swinging sixties, so Botham had been representative of a resurgent Englishness; just as the Beatles threatened to take on the Establishment – 'we're more popular than Jesus now' said Lennon with good reason in 1966 – Botham's popularity was equally frightening. Both represented the rise of the working and middle classes to a position of power in society, threatening the age old supremacy of the ruling aristocracy. The Beatles supposedly controlled the minds of teenagers; Botham's legal attack on the press promised to expose their duplicity. Both needed to be put firmly in their places. The difference is that Botham didn't clear up the house. Had he done so, he would have been in the clear since there's no reason to believe that the police were involved in any conspiracy against him. What is likely is that the original find in the dry cleaner's was planted; by whom and why is a matter for speculation. Of course those who were to stand against him in the libel court gained from his public exposure as one who kept cannabis in the house. Following these dramas, according to Peter Roebuck, 'Friends told him that he had been betrayed by someone in the village, the village where he believed he was understood. He concluded that he could not stay in Epworth, though the vast majority of people there were still his friends. He decided to sell his house and move to a still more remote part of Yorkshire.'

It became public knowledge that Botham had kept drugs in the house. Whether he had intended to use them or not, it was a damaging revelation for his case against the *Mail on Sunday*. It gave added credence to one plank of their story and it would be hard for anyone to find in Botham's favour where drugs were concerned. The other side of the case, that he was a womaniser, would also need to be reinforced by the media. He knew he was comparatively safe during the English summer of 1985 and he spent that season winning over public opinion with some of the most incendiary batting ever seen. Eighty sixes in the season was a new record and his belligerent attack on the Australians helped pummel them into submission, creating the environment in which Gooch, Gatting and Gower could reap a mighty harvest of runs and recapture the Ashes. All summer, as soon as Botham got to the wicket the country stopped, just as it had in 1981. His innings were usually brief but they were always explosive – 250 runs in 289 balls in the six Tests including a spectacular eighteen off seven balls at Edgbaston.

By this stage, Botham was a wiser man. He knew full well that the tour to the West Indies in 1985/86 would be fraught with dangers for him. Having attacked him on the drugs front, it was always likely that the tabloids would try to find him *in flagrante* with another woman. They were so desperate to catch the players in the act that they even thought they might be able to use Lindsay Lamb and Ally Downton in their schemes, Allan's wife explaining in his autobiography that 'the players had gone off to Jamaica while we stayed on in Antigua, and the day they were due back, we moved from our flat into the team hotel. As we were booking in, a journalist heard the two of us asking when the players would be coming and told us that we'd be all right, as they were all keen to meet new girls!' Unfortunately, Botham was not yet wise enough to take Kath on tour with him, the single most effective safeguard against stories of this nature. Though he cut an isolated figure on this tour, restricting himself to his hotel room for the most part, he did venture out on occasion. He went, for instance, to that party thrown by Mick Jagger. The fabricated stories that came out of that evening of Botham and the former Miss Barbados Lindy Field snorting cocaine as the preamble to a night of passion destroyed any lingering hope of his libel case meeting with success. From there followed the drugs admission to the *Mail on Sunday*, the final acceptance that this was one battle that Ian Botham could not win.

Once Botham had taken his beating, draped himself in sackcloth and ashes, and prostrated himself at the feet of the Fourth Estate, normal service was resumed. While the war was being waged, the agenda had moved on yet again. Morality had gone out of the window. This was 1986, Nigel Lawson's boom was in full swing, the cry of this age was

Loadsamoney! Lager louts were in, Gordon Gecko wannabes were all the rage. Now was the time for red braces, fast cars, enjoying yourself, flaunting your wealth, and who was the best example of the ordinary lad done good? Botham. The papers loved him again, championing him as England's great saviour at a time when those messianic powers had long since deserted him. They recognised that having him in the side was exciting, certainly better copy than the athletic clones Micky Stewart and Graham Gooch were soon to be accused of fashioning. They indulged him his boorish off days once more, as was demonstrated once Allan Border had taken him off to play for Queensland. He signed a three-year deal to play for them from the winter of 1987/88 in the hope of securing their first ever Sheffield Shield title.

Initially, the new scenario appealed. He had his family with him, the pressure was all on the field rather than off it, he was back to playing cricket for the thrill of it and being handsomely rewarded into the bargain. The family situation was absolutely crucial. Botham had been trying to relaunch himself, putting the past firmly behind him. His move to Worcestershire had been a successful one and now he was hoping to mend fences within the family. Although Kath had stood by him through all the press speculation, the events of the last few years had taken their toll. Though it had been the arrival of Tim Hudson which had put their relationship under the greatest strain, life hadn't been that much fun for several years now. For the sake of her and the children, it was time Botham spent more time with the family, something which his connection with Queensland seemed to offer. In addition, it would be nice to enjoy the quiet life for a change away from the tabloid journalists who would be following England's every move in Pakistan. In one sense that worked, for following the Shakoor Rana affair when Mike Gatting had a full scale argument with the Pakistani umpire, it was the England captain who would take up the front pages for the foreseeable future. Winters in Australia had other attractions too. In spite of his pugnacious attitude to their cricketers on the field, Botham enjoyed the country and the people. He was firm friends with similar spirits such as Rodney Hogg and Dennis Lillee, and had many good memories of previous tours there. Allan Border was another good friend, and though Botham liked to include regular references to Australia's history as a penal colony whenever he discussed the country, he had a genuine affection for the place. This was hardly surprising since his approach to the game was typically Australian, brash, tough, uncompromising. If those characteristics didn't always win him favour in his homeland, they were appreciated by those Down Under. Just as Tony Greig had made a name for himself there, so too did Ian Botham.

Botham had long since been an anti-hero in Australia. Ever since he'd had that now legendary fight with Ian Chappell during his stay on the Whitbread scholarship back in 1976/77, the Aussie public had enjoyed hearing stories about this highly unconventional Englishman. On that occasion, Botham, unsurprisingly, found himself in a bar during the course of the Centenary Test. At one stage, England looked likely to be overwhelmed before a brilliant innings from Derek Randall almost snatched victory for the visitors. With England apparently out of it, Botham heard Chappell holding forth on their deficiencies, leaving no one in any doubt that the Australians were their masters. Though Botham wasn't involved in the conversation, he told Chappell to watch what he was saying about his country or there'd be trouble. Since Chappell was a former captain of Australia and was on home turf, he paid scant attention to this upstart and carried on with the attack. Botham's self control snapped after issuing a third public warning, and he belted Chappell with enough force to knock him over a table. According to Botham, Chappell then made to leave but, at the door, he turned and hurled another insult at Botham. Botham then chased him into the street, backing off only when he saw a police car come into view. Given that that argument had arisen from Botham's fierce patriotism, it was ironic that a decade or so later he should choose to forego further Test caps for three winters in Australia.

On the field with Queensland he was an all-round success, spearheading the side and playing some of his finest cricket in years. They topped the Shield table for a time and cruised towards the final. All had been quiet on the media front, but as the season was drawing to its climax the side was rocked by reports in the Australian press that, following a game between Queensland and Tasmania, Botham and Dennis Lillee had wrecked a club. Botham denies that charge but does admit to breaking a few glasses, still pretty unimpressive and rather stupid behaviour. Only too well aware of Botham's highly developed nose for controversy, officials at the Queensland Cricket Association started to get a little twitchy. Their carefully planned assault on the title was in danger of being undermined. In his defence, Botham might not have been aware of just how much success meant to Queensland, though given their position was similar to that of Somerset back in 1978 he of all people should have been in an ideal position to understand it. The sensible course would have been to fall in with the team's plans and keep religiously to the party line. Keep your head down, turn up at the nets, if only to offer moral support to the other lads, win the Shield, and then you could party like there was no tomorrow. That would have been indulged by one and all as a fitting response to a much sought after triumph. Botham had to go his own way. As the tensions rose, he fell out with Allan Border, refusing to accept his team order of no drinking prior to the games. In losing to Victoria in their final match, Queensland lost the chance of home advantage in the final, which in turn meant that a draw against Western Australia would not be enough to secure the Sheffield Shield. They had to win that last match.

On the flight out to Perth for that game, the Queensland players began bickering among themselves. With so much riding on just one match, it was inevitable that tensions would run high. While an intelligent and personable individual, it's not for nothing that Allan Border is sometimes referred to as Captain Grumpy. Although the national side realised the value of following him to the hilt, an experienced campaigner like Botham was always going to have his own opinions, some of which were valid, others less so. With Border used to getting his own way, there was always the chance the two might fall out at some stage. On the flight they got into a heated argument, the two exchanging fairly robust language. A man sitting in front turned round to remonstrate whereupon Botham, ever the diplomat, put his hands on the man's shoulders and, according to his autobiography, 'redirected his gaze so he was facing the front again and told him to mind his own business'. Allan Border later suggested that what Botham actually said was 'it's fuck all to do with you'. Cooling down later on, Botham apologised to the man as he disembarked, and hoped that that was the end of the matter. In a matter of moments, however, Botham was charged with assault and found himself stuck in jail on the eve of the most important game of the season. He was only released once Dennis Lillee turned up to stand bail. Queensland duly lost the final and the cricket association took that opportunity to sever its ties with Botham, the members' minds made up by the field day the Australian press had with his discomfort. Revenge for Headingley 1981 tasted very sweet in some quarters.

Again, Botham has complained that this episode was blown up out of proportion, but was it really? Sticking him in a prison cell was obviously an over reaction on the part of the authorities – with the Shield final about to take place, he was hardly likely to leave the country – but did Botham really have to 'redirect' the man's gaze in the first place? Could he not have thought twice about it, looked at the behaviour of himself and his colleagues, and accepted they were in the wrong? Could he not have apologised for the volume at which they were arguing and then moderate his own language? It is not always the world against Ian Botham. A simple disagreement shouldn't end up in a charge of assault. His confusion on these matters is justifiable to a degree since he was on the receiving end of so many conflicting opinions. The press had hung him out to dry over his use of dope, attacked him for fictitious flings with other women, but every time he was involved in a brawl, it made him more popular. He'd come to prominence for clouting Ian Chappell and had won a lot of friends in the press for that, presumably because Chappell was one of the hated Aussies. The Queensland plane incident was also sympathetically received in many quarters. One can only conclude that again, this was because he'd been giving as good as he got with another loudmouthed descendant of a convict – the press are still allowed to be overtly racist where white nations are concerned. The yob culture louts loved it. Botham, they wrongly surmised, was one of their own. That was good for newspaper circulation, but it wasn't good for Botham.

With his Australian dreams dashed, Botham returned to a solely domestic agenda, though his next visit to their shores was again fraught with controversy. Arriving there in time for the 1992 World Cup after a season in pantomime, he viewed the forthcoming jamboree thus: 'What could be better than to beat the Aussies in Melbourne playing in front of 100,000 convicts?' Had Botham been nursing a grievance against

Australians since the Queensland fiasco four years ago? Had he forgotten just where the convicts had come from in the first place? If that wasn't enough, on the eve of the final itself he and Gooch stormed out of the official dinner when an Australian comedian, Gerry Connolly, began to make jokes about the Queen. Botham reportedly made the ludicrous statement that 'I did it for the Queen. I love my country and I can't put up with that sort of crap.' Christopher Martin-Jenkins summed up the rather pathetic affair in the *Daily Telegraph*, commenting that

> to walk out was both pompous and rude. Lampooning the Royal Family, whether one likes it or not, is hardly unknown on British television . . . in the case of Botham, who, sensitive Australians might think, had already insulted his hosts by referring [to them as convicts], his hypocrisy is transparent. No two people's sense of humour is quite the same, as Gooch and Botham may well have already discovered from the increasing number of after-dinner speeches which both now make for considerable rewards . . . they have set themselves a dangerous precedent. The danger with celebrity is that those who achieve it take themselves too seriously.

Botham was soon to find that such actions were unpopular with his hosts. Blunt banners calling him a 'Queen Lover' appeared at the final while his dismissal for a duck got the loudest cheer of the day. A few days later, a £43-a-head dinner at which he was the main attraction pulled in fifty-seven people rather than the 500 anticipated. One of the organisers noted that the billing 'Ian Botham & Friends' was sadly inappropriate, and that the turn–out would have been better had they invited his enemies.

Botham's life, his actions and reactions, were constantly dictated by the media in the 1980s. For those who have never suffered media intrusion, the question must be why did he not simply ignore it all and lead his own life? Part of the problem is geographic and cultural. England is not a big enough country to accommodate legends. They cannot disappear and nor will our pathologically curious nature allow them to. The tabloids do on a national scale what the old woman down the street used to do on a local one; they are the source of the gossip, the scandal, the rumour and the innuendo that oil the wheels of everyday conversation. How much more exciting it is to have revealed the veritable Satyricon that was supposedly the private life of Ian Botham than the details of the new settee arriving at Mrs Dawkins' home.

Trial by tabloid is an insidious punishment that seeps into every aspect of the victim's life. Most disturbing of all, it affects the family who are often put under awful pressures by journalists trying to find another quotation to take out of context. Botham had no idea where it would all end. The 1980s were the tabloid years, the years when they were constantly pushing back the boundaries of taste and decency, searching for the limits. Just where would their quest for a story end? Any seasoned journalist could see that given enough rope, he'd hang himself. Why hit Chappell? Why not lose weight in 1980 to protect his back? Why not hang around the nets a little more, if only as a good PR exercise? Why keep dope in the house? Why take such delight in rubbing people up the wrong way? Why make so many enemies? Why leave yourself open to charges of assault on an aeroplane? Botham would say that his attitude of no surrender was crucial to his success on the field, yet surely, once the press had taken their first pot shots at him, it would have been possible to exercise a little more self discipline if only for the sake of his family. He was obviously not the monster of media invention, so why did he keep stoking the fires with such silly indiscretions? Writing in *The Times* in March 1995, Simon Barnes explained the Botham quandary: 'Botham never got the hang of fame. He was convinced he was always loved by the people and brought low by the press. Handy villains! ... the part played by the newspapers in all this was hardly edifying but they could not have done it without Botham. Uncritical public support drained away, became equivocal and for Botham, for all his million comebacks, life was never quite the same, quite as easy ever again.'

Probably the greatest lesson to be learned from 'Botham – The Tabloid Years' is that we should not be foolish enough to confuse the mighty deeds with the doer. It would be so much easier to admire and enjoy the skills of Paul Gascoigne if it were possible to erase pictures of the leering oaf with the obsession with comedy breasts, a grown man whose idea of rapier wit is to belch as frequently and loudly as possible. It's not easy to do, the more so since personalities such as Gascoigne seem to believe that such behaviour is charming and lucrative. On the latter point, they may have a case. Is Gascoigne that much more gifted than, say, Alan Shearer? Probably not, but in terms of extra-curricular activities he is a far more attractive proposition. Ignorance and boorishness have become a substitute for charisma in the relentless downmarket drive of popular culture, and for a time that suited Botham well. But when a man wants to rehabilitate his reputation and be taken seriously, the loutish moments come back to haunt him. Lord's and the media did much to make sure that Botham was never England captain again after his first fling at the job, but they didn't do as much as Botham himself.

CHAPTER SEVEN

GRACE AND DANGER
The People's Champion

It's little wonder that Ian Botham has held the attention of the nation for twenty years and more. No cricketer has better embodied all the classic ingredients of great drama: meteoric rise, swashbuckling performances, an iconoclastic turn of mind, accusations of betrayal by those he called his friends, attacks by those he knew to be his enemies, and all the while he kept on coming back for more. Even then, in the moments of his greatness, he was often to be found sowing the seeds of his own demise.

Let's talk cricket and not controversy. Grasping his chance on the Test match stage, for the better part of three years Botham launched his career with a ferocity of intent and a consistency of purpose and of results not matched since the days of Bradman. In his first twenty-five Test matches he picked up 139 wickets at eighteen each, averaging one victim every forty-five balls. Fourteen times he took five wickets or more in an innings, getting ten in a match three times. He made, or rather blasted, 1336 runs at an average of forty. He clocked up six hundreds, three times accompanying that by grabbing five wickets in an innings, a staggering feat of virtuosity and of stamina which is unparalleled in the annals of the game. *Wisden* tells us in its 1996 almanac that of the other great all-rounders Sobers managed that particular feat just twice, Miller, Imran, Wasim Akram and Benaud once each, and Hadlee and Kapil Dev not at all. Yet Botham then went on to do it twice more in his career. He completed the Test double of 1000 runs and 100 wickets in just twenty-one matches, two faster than his closest rival.

When he wasn't batting, he was taking slip catches with ease, hurling himself to left or right to clutch edges, displaying reflexes that many a top class goalkeeper might have envied, grabbing the ball with a non-chalant yet intuitive anticipation reminiscent of a great bird clamping its jaws shut around a leaping salmon. To see Botham at work in the slips was a rare privilege, his catching like some elemental force of nature, the more so since he stood with hands resting on his thighs against the advice of all the text books. In those twenty-five Tests, England won fifteen, tasting defeat just five times, three of those coming in the final four games of that triumphant period.

With those statistics to back him up, Botham's place among the greats was already assured. And yet of all the great players, Botham's place in the affection of cricket lovers has the least to do with statistics and the most to do with personality, with the manner and timing of his deeds. We don't relish memories of Botham in the physical act of reaching a hundred as we do with Boycott or Atherton, men who have chiselled their way deliberately to a milestone. It's the shots that he played on the way that endear him to us, whether it be in a two-hour century or a twenty-minute knockabout for twenty or thirty. In those early years, Botham transformed Test cricket from the dour legacy of the 1960s where matches were ground out in interminable wars of attrition into a game of glorious entertainment, transported back to its roots on the village green. Botham was the local blacksmith hurling the ball down or striking it out of the ground to the amusement of all those who looked on. As David Frith recalls, 'I'll never forget how the crowds responded to his deeds. Even fairly staid people forgot themselves in their eagerness to show their delight at his performances.'

In those glorious early years, Botham seemed never to contemplate failure. Whether he came to the wicket at 276 for 5 with England in command or 134 for 5 with England struggling, the position in the first two Pakistan Tests of 1978, his attitude was the same. If the ball was there to be hit, he hit it. Very often he hit it even if it wasn't there for that purpose. And once he did hit it, that ball stayed hit. Such aggression was unheard of; even his predecessor Tony Greig had played with some caution when deemed necessary. Botham never felt there was such a need because he never felt there was an adversary worth worrying about.

Perhaps in those early Tests he was right. Just as England suffered a nightmarish itinerary from the winter of 1979/80 into the winter of 1981/82, they were lucky in their opponents from the end of the West Indian series in 1976 until they flew out to Australia in 1979/80 to heal the Packer rift. There were comparatively cheap runs and wickets to be had. The remarkable thing is that Botham claimed so many of them himself when other Englishmen returned moderate figures over the period; Gower scored quite heavily but good players like Gooch and Gatting just could not fully establish themselves, neither registering a Test century between those dates. With the ball, a great bowler like Bob Willis couldn't match Botham, while good performers like Old and Hendrick scarcely got a look in. It's easy to construct a thesis that suggests Botham was too much for his contemporaries, that some of them found his escapades too daunting to compete with and retreated into their shell. Botham bridles at the suggestion, seeing it as a slight, intimating that he was not a team man. That is not the case at all, it's merely that others were caught in his shadow, unable to shine. Such was his all-encompassing brilliance, their efforts were lost in the shuffle or ignored by a press and public who couldn't get enough of Botham, whatever he was doing. Ultimately the confidence of some players was dented. Even though Botham made all the right noises about it being a team effort, they were not granted the same public spotlight. This must have had an effect on the self esteem of some.

Back in 1976, Botham and Mike Gatting were seen as the future of English cricket, more so than Gooch and Gower. It was nip and tuck as to who would make the biggest impact the quickest, who would go on to be the dominant personality in the English game for the next decade. Both flew out to Australia on the Whitbread scholarship scheme in 1976/77. On the field of play Gatting outshone Botham who displayed relatively unimpressive form. Nevertheless, it was Botham who caught the attention courtesy of his much reported contretemps with Ian Chappell. He also used the playing experience to good effect, rounding out his game, adding a little more Australian-style aggression to his manner, improving his fitness, and he started the 1977 season in the best form of his career thus far. In addition to his sense of physical well-being, he had a great incentive: the Packer-bound Tony Greig had to be replaced in the England side. For Gatting there was no such glaring opportunity. Some suggest that the relish with which Botham seized his day set Gatting back some years. It was the first major upset in his career and he was unsure how to deal with it. He captured a place on the tour to Pakistan and New Zealand – just ahead of David Gower, perhaps because he could offer a few overs of useful medium pace – but failed to shine. He played a Test in Pakistan while Botham was ill on the sidelines but could not grasp his opportunity, scoring just five and six before falling to the spinners. In New Zealand he managed one match too, failing to score as Botham plundered fifty-three and took five wickets. This established a pattern for the first half of Gatting's career and one which Graeme Hick is in real danger of repeating. A bully of county attacks, he was initially diffident, sometimes too cautious in Test matches; the image that endures is of him padding up to a ball on off stump only to be out lbw time and time again.

It's interesting that while Botham was struggling for form and fitness at home in 1980 and 1981, Gatting seemed more at home on the international stage, making a greater impression on the team. When Botham returned to the ranks and began to flay all and sundry once more, Gatting seemed browbeaten again. Perhaps this was the work of coincidence, but by 1984, with a poor summer against the West Indies behind him, it looked as though Gatting would never make the transition to Test cricketer. He finally made the step up once David Gower chose to take him to India as vice captain on a tour that Botham missed. Batting with renewed vigour, Gatting scored 136 in the First Test, 207 in the Fourth, and totalled 575 runs at almost ninety-six for the series. From that time on he was established as one of England's leading players. Not only did Botham's aura of invincibility inhibit the opposition, it seems to have troubled less robust team–mates, though one might argue that Gower was the first England captain to display the requisite faith in Gatting's talents.

Botham's innate self confidence meant that he was never overawed by the Test atmosphere. This was crucial to his success. But even in his early career, his sense of certainty could be overbearing. He made enemies in the press and in the England set up because he overshadowed the efforts of everyone else. Some, such as Willis and Brearley, were delighted to have this breath of fresh air on the scene, but others were less positive. The annoying thing about Botham from their point of view was that he made it all look so bloody easy. Once he had made his mark, nets were there for him to loosen up, not to hone technique; while Boycott was grinding out his third hour with the club bowlers, Botham would have been long gone. If he was about to bat, he might have five minutes blasting the ball into the far distance and then walk out and bat in exactly the same manner, tearing Test match sides apart. If he had to bowl, he'd send down a couple of looseners in the nets, take the field, bowl another wild delivery and find the ball nestling in the hands of the man at cover point. That golden arm reputation has been overdone over the years, David Frith asking us to 'forget the fabled long-hops that took wickets and remember instead the late-swerving outswinger (from an inswing action)'. Even so, it does reinforce the point that here was a cricketer who made things happen. Life was never dull when he was around; in the dressing room that was equally true as his practical jokes maintained the morale of those with like minds, but irritated others.

One skill he never learned was that of diplomacy. His attitude on the pitch made it clear he had little respect for some of his opponents. He delighted in their humiliation, their utter defeat, a vital part of his combative approach. Botham's game wasn't simply built on his quality with the bat or ball, much of his menace came from his psychological impact. He wanted, indeed *had*, to intimidate opponents, make them feel they had no place on the same field as him, that they were there simply to be brushed aside. When he was running through the Pakistanis at Lord's in 1978, it was obvious they didn't want to face him. There was nothing physically threatening about his pace especially when Willis might be pounding in from the other end; it was his bristling aggression that had so completely overwhelmed them. Some of those batsmen were dismissed even before they'd reached the crease. It's an attitude that Dominic Cork has tried to adopt with mixed results, but the man who learned most from Botham's tactics was big Merv Hughes. His sheer size and appearance were enough to put the fear of God into any opponent. When he added a lengthy follow through after delivery so he could eyeball the batsman who had just played and missed outside off stump, here was a bowler who could walk over the faint hearted. Botham was the same. That's why both were able to take wickets with seemingly innocuous deliveries. It was the cumulative effect of their hostile actions that got so many scalps. Botham understood this only too well and always looked to dominate Hughes in their meetings. In the First Test of 1986/87 when Merv was still a relatively new Test match cricketer, Botham laid into him to the tune of twenty-two off one over on his way to 138, before bowling him for a duck. Thereafter Hughes was no real threat in that series, Botham having categorically established his authority. Things had changed by 1989 when Hughes was a crucial component in Border's triumphant team that recaptured the Ashes.

Fiery at play, Botham was a Jekyll and Hyde character. He was a genuinely relaxed and friendly individual off the field in those early days before his cynicism grew in response to the tabloid maulings, driving him back into his shell. Get him down the pavilion steps and a whole new character emerged. Much of it was bravado, macho pride that insisted no challenge was too great for him. That was perhaps at the root of his disdain for nets. Real men – great men – don't need to practice, they just do the job. Since he took little advice from anyone, there was no need for coaching either. It was this fault that led him into his first trough of form. As suggested, stamping his authority on a series was a matter of pride for Botham. He had to assert his dominance in order to weave his magic. If he could cow the opposition into believing he was a superman, then he could perform like one. However, it was always likely that the West Indians would be the side to finish his golden run. His technical and temperamental weaknesses against express pace have been outlined elsewhere. He had to fight fire with fire to assert his masculinity. This character that he and the press had created could not back down in the face of enemy assault. That veneer of confidence was crucial, but of course he wasn't as good as he pretended to be; nobody in the history of the game has ever been *that* good. Consequently, he could bully bowlers with his power, implying a great eye but not necessarily a watertight game. The very best bowlers soon realised that this was a facade that could be crushed if they aimed their fire at the fault lines.

The West Indies targeted his flaws ruthlessly. Though it is always the over that Holding bowled to Boycott in Jamaica in 1980/81 that is discussed in hushed tones of reverence, he bowled one that was every bit as quick to Botham later in the game. Botham was left looking like the worst number eleven, all at sea against the onslaught, scratching his head in response to bowling that was almost inhuman. Some commentators suggest that this was psychological warfare aimed at Boycott, but it's just as likely that Holding was simply underlining his mastery and his majesty for Botham's benefit since he recognised that he would be around for a lot longer than the Yorkshireman would. It was a lesson that stayed long in his psyche; it may never have been fully erased.

That West Indian side was fearsome, brimming with exciting natural talent. That in itself is enough to explain Botham's failing form against them, but was there more to it than that? His need to hold the psychological upper hand has been demonstrated. Against every side in the country, then every side in the world, there was no man who could strike fear into Botham's heart. There was seemingly only one contemporary cricketer whom he held in awe, his Somerset team-mate Vivian Richards. Watching Richards bat when in full flow was a remarkable thing to behold. Be it in a Test or a one dayer, at the top of his game Viv was the master. Just as Botham loved to dominate, so too did Richards. That lazy, unconcerned stroll out to the wicket, the nonchalant fiddling with a sweat band, the cold stare down the pitch at the bowler, these were all calculated movements that said 'I'm here, I'll stay as long as I feel like it and you can't stop me'. For seven or eight years, that was no idle boast. Phenomenally powerful, Richards had the finest eye in cricket. Apparently able to see the ball so much quicker than anyone else, he could whip a ball from outside off stump into the crowd at midwicket, a shot he performed again and again at Lord's in the 1979 World Cup Final. That knock took the trophy away from England and underlined the fact that here was a batsman who could rank with the very greatest from any era. Botham saw innings like that day in, day out with Somerset. He admitted that, Ken Barrington aside, Viv Richards was the only man from whom he sought advice. They were great friends, but on the field Richards was the first among these equals.

Inevitably, then, Botham must have gone out to face the West Indies with confidence dimmed. No longer was he leaving the pavilion expecting to win, sure that he would steamroller his opponents. Richards must have loomed large in all his thoughts; the world's greatest batsman was on the other side, a batsman whom Botham rated as at least the equal of Bradman. Botham the bowler, injured and ailing, must have wondered about his own capacity to dismiss him. Looking around the side, he must have questioned just who else could get Richards out. It was that psychological blow as much as the genuine quality of the West Indian cricket that finally beat him. How else to explain his consistent failures against them, whether burdened by the captaincy or not? Why else would he have failed to impose himself on them once his back injury had eased and was causing fewer problems; once it had improved by the following year, the Aussies still felt his presence. The common denominator in all these failures was Viv Richards, the only man consistently to psych Botham out of the game and therefore the only man to overcome him, though it could be argued that Imran Khan was to have a similar effect on him later in the decade.

Defeat can have different effects on different personalities. Some are wrecked by it, nerve and confidence shattered for ever. Some accept it as just the inevitable turning of the wheel, certain that their turn will come again in the fullness of time. Others simply ignore it, incapable of dealing with it and its consequences. Botham seems to fall into the latter category. It enabled him to dismiss the previous twelve months against the West Indians as an aberration caused largely by his back injury, those who had meddled with his captaincy back at the TCCB, and the influences in his side that had not been wholly benign. None of the problems revolved around Botham, his occasionally naive tactics, his inability to get the best out of the side, the fact that the West Indies were too good for him, the step up in quality of opposition exposing failings in his game. That kind of talk was defeatist nonsense. Just give him another go and he'd show everybody. All he needed was a fair chance. Headingley 1981 provided it. Without that psychological armour and selective memory, Botham could not have created the miracle at Leeds. Instead of fretting about his position in the side, he approached that Test like any other, knowing that he could win the game and that the selectors would have to be mad to leave him out.

Yet just as defeat can be damaging, so too can victory. Those three Tests which he won 'single-handed', according to popular legend, established him as an icon but ruined his never too reliable sense of perspective. Thereafter he was Indiana Jones, the lone adventurer who firmly believed he was the man for all eventualities, that he could turn any game however dire the situation, a mistaken belief that continued into his cricketing dotage. Failing to accept that the events of 1981 were built around a set of circumstances unlikely to be replicated, he apparently believed that he alone had fashioned the results, rather than being the beneficiary of wild circumstances. He couldn't have done it without being hugely gifted, but great deeds are often the result of being in the right place at the right time. There are times when getting down to some hard graft is essential, when pulling out a dull but worthy performance is more valuable than the swashbuckling approach which goes wrong as often as it goes right. Ironically, where most players are remembered for their failures as much as their successes, so over-whelming was Botham, so exciting his style of play, that his many failures do not linger in the mind. The images of Botham on the field are, Lord's 1981 apart, completely positive ones, a blur of runs, wickets and catches.

Initially, all the signs were that Botham had been a little chastened by his poor form against the West Indies in 1980 and 1981. Reminded that his gifts could be recalled by a capricious fate, he knuckled down to the job of Test cricket, accepting it as a rather harder grind than had hitherto been the case. In India he was exemplary. He accepted the dead nature of the surfaces England encountered once India had won the First Test. There were occasional bursts of hostility with the ball but he quickly realised that was futile, exhausting work. Helping captain Keith Fletcher by operating in a stock bowling role for much of the series, it was as a batsman that he shone. Unveiling a technique that was solid in all departments, he proved that he could build an innings and be depended upon as a front line batsman. Keith Fletcher must take credit here for promoting him to number five in the order, giving him responsibility for the side in the wake of the loss of the captaincy. That was psycho-logically vital. Accumulating 440 runs at fifty-five, the most notable facet of his play was his discipline. It seemed he was ready to use his gifts to the full, nurturing them accordingly. That impression continued into the English season of 1982 when he batted beautifully against the Indians, having bowled superbly in the first innings of the first game at Lord's. Building on that, he went to the Oval for the third and final Test match with England one up and batted the tourists into oblivion. Rather than the blood and thunder of Headingley in 1981, Botham now played with controlled aggression. Admittedly the Indians weren't the strongest bowling side, but Botham went about his job with such concentrated determination that it seemed he had achieved cricketing maturity. Without the customary blazing away, he still achieved Test cricket's fastest double century in terms of balls received, just 220.

Yet even in this hour of glory, Botham was about to hit another decline in his form. A puzzle over the years has been his stubborn refusal to concentrate on his batting once it became clear that his general level of fitness meant he was becoming less of a threat with the ball. Keen-eyed judges such as Ted Dexter felt he was such a naturally good technician that he was potentially the best of England's four premier batsmen of the mid-eighties. It was his firm belief that Botham could bat at four and hold together the order with Gooch, Gower and Gatting slotting in around him. That's a big claim given that Gooch and Gower both managed more than 8,000 Test runs, but it's a shrewd one. Botham played pretty straight, hit the ball cleanly, had a good eye and a basically secure game. His weakness against the fastest bowling could have been worked on and perhaps eradicated or at least alleviated since in part it was a temperamental as much as a technical shortcoming. In 1982 it seemed increasingly clear that his future lay with the bat.

In that 1982 season, despite a fine performance against India in the First Test, all was not well with Botham the bowler. In the second innings of that game he managed just one wicket for 103, one for eighty-six in the second game and two for eighty-five in the final match. The decline continued against Pakistan in the second half of the summer. He picked up nine wickets for 334 in the first two games, with his bowling at Lord's particularly inconsequential. He ended the season on a high, snapping up nine wickets on a helpful track at Headingley, but that did not disguise the long term decline in his powers since that back injury had robbed him of his zip. He was still taking wickets, but they were taking longer to fall and costing him far more than previously: since April 1980, he'd taken 110 wickets in twenty-nine Tests at a rate of one every fifty-nine balls, a 33 per cent increase in his strike rate compared with those first twenty-five games. They now cost twenty-nine each too, a rise of 59 per cent per wicket.

Statistics can be misleading, of course. Even in that 'decline', those returns look good against the records of many Test bowlers. It's a similar record to that of John Snow's entire career, for instance, and Snow was a very fine player; if England could unearth another Snow tomorrow, many of Mike Atherton's problems would be over. Nevertheless, Botham's early success rate ensured he would be judged by the very highest standards. He'd performed as remarkably as Sydney Barnes, the choice of many historians as the game's greatest bowler. If he couldn't be expected to maintain such dizzy heights indefinitely, then the trend and the steepness of the downward curve gave cause for concern as did the physical reasons for it. It was a trend that was never reversed: in his final forty-eight Tests, he took just six hauls of five wickets in an innings; his first fifty-four Tests had seen twenty-one such feats. When people criticise Botham's lack of application at the nets or his lifestyle, his constant retort is 'look in the record books'. A powerful argument in total terms, but one wonders whether Botham took a look at his bowling figures beyond the first third of his career. His failure to do so meant that mentally he saw himself as still living in some golden age, while in reality the golden arm had become base metal.

He continued to pound in and unleash bouncer after bouncer, willing himself to take wickets. Somewhere along the way, he lost the plot and changed from an intelligent swing bowler into a man who apparently thought he was Bob Willis. He did not have the pace to blast good players out on decent pitches any longer and the results show that. Peter Roebuck pointed out that he seemed to mislay his complete control of devilish swing in both directions: 'In his early years [he] was a master of swing. He was strong, fit and very, very good. Easy to forget that he could also bat superbly giving himself licence with the ball ... the late inswinger with the old ball, turning nought for seventy into four for ninety, the transformation at which Botham was the greatest of all.' That nip off the pitch, that little zip through the air, had gone, taken by that back complaint and the way in which his body had filled out, distorting that once beautiful action. No longer could he be relied upon to roll over the opposition tail, wrapping up the last five wickets for thirty or forty.

A lot is made of Botham boosting his figures by insisting on bowling at tail-enders, arguing that his reputation was cheaply made. Certainly he did a lot of that but then he was very good at it; so is Waqar Younis. It's a much maligned skill but Mike Atherton knows only too well how useful it can be, having seen New Zealand's last pair put on more than a hundred to save the First Test in Auckland on the 1996/97 tour. In his prime, they'd have put on a dozen before Botham would have grabbed the ball, said 'bugger this for a game', and finished the match in an over or two. In these days when the lower order batsmen are increasingly well organised, such ability can mean the difference between winning and losing a game. Yet time took that talent away too.

Roebuck is especially accurate in his assertion that Botham gave himself licence with the ball with his excellent batting. The reverse is equally true. If he'd already got five wickets in a game, he'd go to the crease knowing he'd done his job and that any runs were a bonus. Once the wickets dried up, it had a detrimental effect on his batting. Botham was unsuited to being anything other than an all-rounder. In his head, he was always taking wickets and scoring hundreds. It was not an either/or situation. A crisis in one department heralded a crisis in the other. For a man whose whole reputation and career was built upon the enormous foundations of his self belief, it seems that that was quite a fragile base. Post-1982, there were 134 more wickets at thirty-eight each, a strike rate of sixty-eight balls. That's pretty mundane − of the England bowlers with more than those 134 wickets in a career, only Emburey has a similarly high average. Yet at the very time you'd expect him to be making more runs in order to compensate, he scored just 2204 more at twenty-nine, disappointing when so many batsmen improve with age and experience. As a combination, these are very useful figures indeed and better than the career figures of any other English all-rounder in history apart from Tony Greig, but again, Botham's greatness early on demands that we judge him by the very highest standards. He failed to live up to them, in spite of propaganda to the contrary.

It was in 1982/83 that the balance in his game seemed to be terminally upset. In Australia his bowling lost all its penetration. Significantly, his batting was woeful too. Robbed of the central plank of his bowling strategy, captain Bob Willis could do nothing but surrender the Ashes. Botham bowled without rhythm, and in his book on the series the first notes of doubt crept in: 'I believe I have two years left in me as a strike bowler in Test cricket.' Bearing that comment in mind, there is a counter argument as to why Botham did not give his full attention to his batting. Perhaps all the blame for his all-round decline should not be laid at his door. As he noted in the same passage of that book, who would replace him as a bowler, especially as Willis was nearing the end of the road? In that 1982/83 series, it was his wickets rather than runs that were sadly missed. From an English point of view, Botham was needed primarily as a bowler; with Gower, Gatting, Randall and Lamb to pack the middle order, runs were often less crucial. Botham was overworked in the field, particularly in the light of his suspect back, but his captains often had little choice. In his diary of the subsequent 1983/84 tour, Willis noted that during that disastrous defeat in New Zealand 'I was criticised for allowing him too long a spell. But we only had four bowlers in the side – two had to bowl into the wind for long periods and one of these, Tony Piggott, was a Test rookie. Botham simply had to bowl.' Just as Alec Stewart has been sacrificed in recent years, forced to bat at six and keep wicket in order to balance the side, Botham was the victim of equally insensitive handling.

As one who always liked to be involved, Botham was never going to hold up his hands and say he was finished as a Test bowler, capable only of a filling-in role, a handful of overs as and when required. It's in his nature to take on all comers at all times. The selectors and management had to make that decision for him. That, though, might have meant leaving him out – was he a reliable enough batsman to replace any one of Gatting, Gower, Lamb and Randall in the top order, assuming they were in good form? In 1982 the answer would have been yes; a year later, things were nothing like as clear cut. Perhaps that was one challenge Botham didn't relish. If he had been forced into that position, consider how the team might have improved. In the West Indies in 1985/86, for example, the team in the final Test was Gooch, Slack, Robinson, Gower, Lamb, Gatting, Botham, Downton, Ellison, Emburey, Foster. The bowling was to be done by Foster, Ellison, Botham and Emburey, yet it was obvious that Botham was struggling to take wickets. Gower was trying to bowl out the West Indies with three bowlers, with Emburey tight but lacking in penetration, Ellison relatively inexperienced, and Foster a perennial injury worry. How much better to have gone into the game with six front line batsmen, leaving out Slack, promoting Robinson to open and Gatting to bat at three. With Botham at six and made fully aware of his responsibilities to get around a hundred runs in the two innings, that would have left a berth free for another front line bowler. Botham could then have filled in with the ball as and when necessary – again we come back to him playing the Steve Waugh role. That would have better suited his changing abilities and would surely have prolonged his career at the top, protecting his back from further punishment. Allowing him only to bowl when fresh, he might have recaptured the form that made him so dangerous. If you bat at seven as Botham often did, you have to be considered a bowler first, yet English selectors have long been so concerned about batting frailties that they try to pack the tail. Surely it's time to take a tip from the Australians, something we seem to be learning at last. Specialists win Test matches. If you have six good specialist batsmen, you shouldn't need runs from the tail. If they come, they're a bonus. And surely, if the top six have gone for 100, the last five aren't likely to muster many. Players have to be judged on results, and on those results Botham was no longer a genuine all-rounder, i.e. a player who would get in the side as batsman and bowler. However, he did maintain his place in the side with ease. That was down to a potent combination of reputation and the paucity of talent in English cricket. With a wicketkeeper who usually batted in the lower half – French, Downton, Richards – England were crying out for an all-rounder. When they went to India without Botham in 1984/85 they took Chris Cowdrey and Richard Ellison, neither of whom were remotely in the same class with bat or ball. That tour underlined the fact that Botham had to play, had to bowl, and any runs were viewed as a pleasing extra bonus.

With the strain placed upon him on and off the field, it's little wonder he was inconsistent. Even so, he had a good year in 1985. Walking straight back into the team and faced with the Australians, his confidence was fully restored, the sight of the old enemy summoning up the blood and stiffening the sinew. His absence had made it clear that he was England's number one – probably England's only – all-rounder. In a microcosm of his whole career, that season he blasted the Aussies with bouncer upon bouncer, smashed their bowlers all around the grounds, had a war of words with umpire Alan Whitehead, and generally behaved as though he owned every ground he played upon. Hammering sixes like they were going out of fashion, this was vintage Botham. There was a faint hope that the winter he'd had off had recharged his batteries, renewed his enthusiasm and set him up for a second coming. These were vain hopes, for that Australian visit of 1985 was Botham's final great series, at least on these shores.

Time had taken its toll on him. For eight years he'd held England together with bat and, especially, with ball. He'd been worked into the ground but, a willing workhorse, he had always come back for more. That willingness to bowl was his undoing. The body had taken a pounding; besides the back, he'd had a knee operation and was continually pestered by minor but significant ailments. Worse than that, he'd become a circus freak show, his life, or something vaguely like it, unfolding in the press each day. That distracted him from his cricket, reduced his mental preparation for matches, and his game did suffer as a consequence. His cricket became less and less important as other matters became central to his daily existence. It's equally true to say that he was losing his interest in the game. The captaincy of Somerset had turned sour, the England captaincy would clearly never come again. By the time of his return from the West Indies in April 1986, he'd done everything there was to do in the game several times over. The ill starred Tim Hudson interlude had shown one thing: he needed more than cricket in his life. There was nothing left to achieve on the field though a little necessary prompting came his way with his drugs ban. When he returned from that, he was fully fired up with something to prove once again; the fact that he came into the last Test with New Zealand fresh after the enforced hiatus from the game showed what he could still achieve granted the right sort of handling.

Botham clearly felt victimised by the Establishment's handling of him; given the sympathetic and far more intelligent treatment meted out to the likes of Paul Merson in recent years, a man who used harder drugs far more widely, he must still wonder why he was dealt with so summarily. Yet this jolt provided new impetus. It was self righteous wrath that propelled him into a powerful response. At the Oval against New Zealand he promptly broke Dennis Lillee's record to become the greatest wicket taker in Test history. For good measure, he then hit the joint second fastest fifty in Test cricket too, his half century coming in only thirty-two balls. Clearly the old magic was still there when the blood was up. That happened less frequently as he seemed to care less and less about results, more and more about making an impact. Perhaps after the media battering he'd taken, he wanted the public to love him again as they'd done in 1981. Any man who could be so destructive with the bat as he was in 1985 and 1986 was clearly still a considerable player. This was not wild slogging but strong, selective hitting of the ball, slamming bowlers into submission. Yet if he could score so rapidly, why did he not score more heavily? Simply put, he no longer had the appetite for it all. The game and all its attendant controversies seemed to bore him. Why else would such a rampant patriot opt out of the England scene by signing a contract to winter in Australia from 1987/88 to 1989/90?

The Hudson escapades suggested that Botham had become an adrenalin junkie, needed the impetus of new challenges to invigorate him. Why try to revisit past glories on the field? Even if he achieved them, they would lack the sweetness of the first time and there'd be plenty of experts on hand to point out that this was not as good an innings as Old Trafford in 1981, or that he'd bowled better in 1978 at Lord's. Perhaps cricket might have lost his services earlier had it not been for his move to Worcestershire in 1987, his subsequent period with Queensland, and then the back surgery of 1988. Between them they offered him a chance to prove himself as a player once again, gave him some time away from the game to think about how much it all meant to him, allowed the body some respite and gave him the ultimate challenge of reclaiming his spot in the Test side. Having back surgery is just about as serious as it gets for a quick bowler. A few have come back from it, like Dennis Lillee and Ian Bishop, but they were struck down as young men with still excellent physiques. For them there was always a light at the end of the tunnel for they had time to play with. When Botham returned from his surgery at the start of 1989 his new sylph-like figure stunned many, but it was an indication of the seriousness of his intent. Looking fitter than he had done in years, that still did not disguise the fact that he had passed his thirty-third birthday the winter before and that Father Time was catching up with him.

The 1989 season was make or break for Botham. However hard he had prepared for the season, it was only when he got out on the field that he'd know whether his back operation had been an unqualified success or not. All the requisite rewards were on offer: a visit from the Australians in the summer, and a final trip to the West Indies in the winter, the two foes he most wanted to face. Coming on as second change for Worcestershire, bowling well within himself at a pace he would have been well advised to adopt three years earlier, he made a promising start with the ball, though his batting form was scratchy. Nevertheless, he got into the England party for the Texaco trophy, his first representative duties in twenty-one months. There the pattern continued, economical with the ball, loose with the bat. Even so, Botham was named in the side for the First Test but was then struck by a ball from Steve Barwick of Glamorgan, the result a depressed fracture of the right cheekbone. The muddle headedness of England's selectors was then exposed when Robin Smith was called up as his replacement. After all the years of persisting with Botham as all-rounder, apparently he had now been chosen primarily as a batsman at the time when he was in awful form with 128 runs from eight completed innings – that was the only conclusion to be drawn from the elevation of Smith.

Back within three weeks, Botham walked into the England side for the Third Test at Edgbaston with Gower's England already two down and starting to panic in the wake of massive defeats. To make way for Botham, Paul Jarvis, the opening bowler, was dropped; selection policy was still hard to fathom. Nevertheless, Botham performed creditably with the bat: his two and a half hour vigil for forty-six helped carry the team from 75 for 5 to 171 for 6 in reply to Australia's 424. England avoided the follow on and with the help of the weather salvaged a draw. If anything, this game should have been the pointer for Botham's next four years in the game – batting sensibly, holding the side together in adversity, and bowling within himself (in the Australian second innings, he did not bowl at all). Things started to go wrong in the next game at Old Trafford where he failed both times with the bat when a decent performance in either innings would have saved a game lost by nine wickets. Admittedly, like most of the team, Botham's thoughts were elsewhere, for on the final day the rebel tour party for South Africa was announced.

Injury hampered the rest of his season – he dislocated a finger in the Fifth Test when trying to hold a hard chance at slip and that effectively ended his international season. He left the ground looking set for a winter in the West Indies following the assurances he felt he'd received from Micky Stewart. When, on 8 September, the touring party was announced, Botham's name was conspicuous only by its absence. It was a volte-face Botham has never forgiven, one that left him forever suspicious of the motives of Stewart, the newly appointed England captain Graham Gooch, and chairman of the selectors, Ted Dexter, all of whom he belittled in his autobiography. Dexter explained the decision on the grounds that his form had 'not even nearly approximated to Test standard this year'. The furore that Botham might have expected to follow was lost amid the sympathy for David Gower, stripped of the captaincy and then dropped from the touring party, apparently on the grounds of fitness since he needed a shoulder operation two months before the party flew out. Had Gower retained the Ashes, would his shoulder have been an issue?

In fact, it was Gower's omission that gave the strongest clue as to why Botham had been left at home too. Looking through the Test series, Botham was one of England's better players at Edgbaston in the Third Test, played poorly in the Fourth, and was injured and so was unable to contribute in the Fifth. This was hardly enough to condemn a man coming back from serious surgery. If anyone should have been questioned, it was the selectors for bringing him back into Test cricket too early. Perhaps choosing him at all was the greatest error. Rather than giving him hope for the future, England might have been better served pensioning him off there and then. His selection in 1989 was surely borderline, yet in selecting him then, it made no sense to leave him out of the winter touring party. Certainly his form in the domestic game had been less than inspired with the bat – 276 Championship runs at sixteen – but the back injury would not harm his batting. The niggling injuries which disrupted the flow of his season were at the root of that lack of runs and Dexter and company had had enough confidence in him as a batsman to pick him for the First Test when he'd scarcely scored a run to that point. Having adhered to the 'form is temporary, class is permanent' argument at the start of the summer, it was cast aside in September. The decision was all the more peculiar since, on the plus side, his bowling was much more reliable for having the pace taken out of it. Fifty-one wickets at twenty-two suggested that he might be able to turn his arm over quite usefully on occasion. He was closer to being considered a genuine all-rounder than he had been in several years. Look at the squad England took to the West Indies and those that replaced him. The batsmen were Gooch, Lamb, Rob Bailey (one Test), Nasser Hussain (no Tests), Wayne Larkins (six Tests), Robin Smith (eight Tests) and Alec Stewart (no Tests, reserve wicketkeeper). The two all-rounders were David Capel and Phil DeFreitas. At that stage of their careers, it's hard to see how Stewart, Hussain or Capel got the nod ahead of Botham on cricketing ability alone if Botham had been considered a good enough player to make the side in 1989. There had to be another agenda to explain the selection policy.

The Australian series of 1989 had degenerated into disaster by its close. Gower's leadership was again ineffectual, but he was also beset by problems. Every side England selected had to be changed before it took the field because of a spate of injuries. At the tail end of the season, half the side made it clear they had no interest in playing for England by signing up to go to South Africa – since those negotiations had gone on for much of the summer, they must have undermined team spirit. To blame Gower alone for the heavy defeat against Border's highly focused troops would be unfair. Nevertheless, as Ted Dexter pointed out, a change of direction was necessary. England could not go on simply surrendering to every half decent side they met. Better leadership was required while the team as a whole needed to be fitter, sharper, more dedicated to their game. This must have dawned on them earlier in the season when things began to accelerate downhill. Of course Stewart and Dexter knew of the South African tour that was coming up. Botham insists that Stewart talked him out of going by promising him a place in the side going to the West Indies, a decision that cost him £500,000, enough to make anyone bitter. With Gower's days as captain obviously numbered and Mike Gatting off on the rebel trip, what better time to make wholesale changes?

Graham Gooch had been England's captain for the final West Indian Test in 1988 and the game against Sri Lanka, doing a reasonable job at a difficult time. He had been chosen to lead the side to India that winter in a tour aborted because of the South African connections of some in the party, Gooch included. With that in mind, it might have been sensible to assume that he would have been England captain for the start of 1989. However, with Peter May resigning as chairman of the selectors a change was always possible, and Gower it was who took charge of the side through that troublesome summer. Gooch, unluckily, returned to the ranks and had an awful year with the bat, tormented by Terry Alderman and Geoff Lawson, even standing down from the England side at one point. With all these things in mind and a South African rebel tour in the offing, Gooch might have been thought of as the prime candidate to lead the side. He'd planned to winter with Western Province in 1988/89 before his elevation to the England job and still had strong links with the country. This time, however, Gooch was against going, knowing only too well the trouble that went with the money. With Gatting definitely going on the trip, though, a window of opportunity was opening once again for Gooch; with Gower gone as well, he was the only real choice left to the selectors.

Gooch and Stewart were always likely to make a united team at the top of English cricket. Gooch's devotion to physical fitness was already well known in the game and the punishing schedule which he set himself was surely instrumental in his long stay at the top. He was unimpressed by Gower's captaincy against Australia, noting in his auto-biography that 'more and more, [he] seemed to let the game drift ... one thing which was plain to see during the English depression of that series was how fast disillusion can set in for a badly beaten side'. These sorts of sentiments chimed in perfectly with those of Stewart, who had never wanted Gower as captain anyway, preferring the more pugnacious figure of Gatting. With Gatting gone, Gooch stepped into a similar role with ease.

Before selecting the touring party, Dexter and Stewart had settled on the policy they would follow. On arrival at the selection meeting, Gooch was told that Gower and Botham would not be considered. This fell in with his own feelings for, as he wrote, 'I had set my heart on changing losing attitudes and needed concentrated single-mindedness without any non-cricketing distractions'. This was at the heart of Botham's omission. It was not so much a question of form, more one of attitude. If Botham went to the Caribbean, would he become a media sideshow yet again to the detriment of everyone? Quite simply it came down to a question of trust. Would Ian Botham stick to the party line, keep his head down and basically do as he was told, or might he instead be the liability he'd been in 1985/86? Ironically, now that he had resolved to take Kath with him on future tours, he might well have been the more sober tourist Stewart and Gooch were looking for, but his past reputation, on and off the field in the West Indies, let him down. In that sense, one can hardly blame them for leaving him to kick his heels at home. They deliberately went for a young side that would fall in behind Gooch, mimicking the Australian line Allan Border had so successfully taken. Essentially, Botham and Gower were seen as a malign influence at the heart of the English team, bon viveurs who cared more about the recreational rather than the net facilities. They were seen as likely to lead the younger players into bad habits at a stage when Stewart and Gooch wanted to school them in the old-fashioned virtues of Test cricket – hard work, good technique, physical fitness. This is a moot point of course, for under Stewart and Gatting in Australia in 1986/87 Botham had been lauded as an excellent team man and a key figure in the Ashes series victory. Nevertheless, the die was cast and the England hierarchy had acted finally to break up the trio of Botham, Gower and Lamb whose apparently flippant attitude to their work troubled them.

Little has been made of Lamb's part in this for in the public eye he was a distant third among these musketeers. While his profile was lower, his form was also much better and throughout the second half of the 1980s he was the mainstay of England's fragile batting, notably so against the fast bowlers. But Lamb was no slouch when it came to having a good time. He and Botham were great friends because they shared a similar outlook on life, the classic live hard, play hard mentality – the two once put firecrackers on Bob Willis's run up inducing another panic attack for umpire Dickie Bird who thought the ground had been infiltrated by gunmen. The two were inveterate practical jokers and could generally be found in each other's company after stumps had been drawn. Lamb was often on hand when Botham ended in the mire – New Zealand 1983/84, West Indies 1985/86 – and it was to prevent just this sort of clique forming that the selectors acted. With Botham out of the way, Lamb was elevated to a position of responsibility, becoming Gooch's vice captain and actually leading the side in a Test when his captain was injured. Lamb was able to respond to that greatest need when you are upsetting the powers that be by being yourself; to preserve your skin, you have to play better than everyone else. For Botham scaling such heights was a distant memory, and so he was vulnerable to the great purge.

For all Botham's protestations that he should have made the plane – and if Stewart had made a promise to him, it should either have been honoured or Stewart should have resigned if he had made such a statement without the authority to do so – England did pretty well without him, much better than they had in many years against the West Indies. They won the First Test, and were denied the chance of going two up by rain and time-wasting tactics in Trinidad before losing the final two games of the series. Moreover, *Wisden* remarked, 'Gooch rapidly commanded an unfailing respect among his players and earned it by his quiet, individual counselling, his caring touch and his thoughtful tactics. In his own way, he was the most impressive England captain since Brearley.' Equally, Lamb was 'gregarious and positive . . . just what was required as a support for the more complex ways of Gooch'. If the ends justify the means, the dropping of Gower and Botham was revealed as a masterstroke.

England were entering a new era and Botham would have been well advised to accept that. Things were changing and he was no longer viewed as an integral part of the England set up. He continued to perform well for Worcestershire and managed the occasional comeback when the resources of the national team were stretched, but his England days were long gone. Well into his thirties, surely this was no surprise, for not even a Botham can go on for ever, especially after the pounding he'd given his body throughout his career. But, like the Princess of Wales, he was not disposed to go quietly. Perhaps Graham Gooch and Micky Stewart did start to overdo the physical fitness side of things to the detriment of the side's sharpness, but to carp on continually about how this was costing England Test matches rang hollow. The more Botham attacked the Establishment, the easier it was for them to label him a malign influence and leave him out of the side.

The message finally struck home in 1993 as Botham waged an impressive publicity-led campaign for his reselection for the England side to take on the Aussies. Given that England had played poorly in India that winter, a change in personnel was likely, but would picking an ailing thirty-eight-year-old really be a step forward? Botham bowled well at the start of the season in a meaningless game for the Duchess of Norfolk's XI against Australia at Arundel, taking two for twenty-nine in ten tidy overs. To Botham, this was evidence that he still held the Indian sign over the Australians. This was absurdly naive. Sadly, the unworldly Ted Dexter was crass in remarking that it looked as though the Aussies were trying to play Botham into the Test team. An off the cuff joke it might have been, and the underlying point that the game proved nothing was a good one, but it was still grossly insulting to a figure of Botham's stature.

Botham was no longer good enough to play Test cricket, but he continued to play for Durham in the hope the call might come. It's true that England were in trouble again against Australia that summer, but it was time to move on. If changes had to be made, bring in some youngsters, not those whose day had gone. Sadly, Botham was starting to resemble those old stagers who knew it all whom he'd despised in his earlier career. The time had come for him to look to the future. Ironically, it was Dexter who offered him the chance to take a place in the England set up, asking him to lead an England 'A' side on a brief visit to Holland in July. Sure, this was not the big time he'd been used to, but as a service to English cricket and a first toe in the water towards a coaching position in the hierarchy, it had potential. Botham refused, complaining in his book that Dexter had asked him to go on a 'clog-dancing mission'. This was hardly the action of a patriot who wanted to do all he could to help the development of the national side and the spread of the game of cricket.

Perhaps Botham had come fully to embody Ralph Waldo Emerson's view of heroism: 'self-trust is the essence of heroism ... [it is] scornful of petty calculations and scornful of being scorned. It persists; it is of an undaunted boldness and a fortitude not to be wearied out. Its jest is the littleness of common life ... heroism is obedience to a secret impulse of an individual's character.' This was Ian Botham, it had always been so, but as his career wound down it seemed more the case than ever. His greatest admirers were often angered by England's poor use of his gifts and equally saddened by his own refusal or inability to settle down to the hard work that even the greats must do, produce the weight of runs of which he was capable, and demand inclusion as a specialist batsman. That did not appeal. Botham was an artist, not an artisan. If he had been the intrepid adventurer in his early days, he was to adopt another of W.G.'s mantles, that of the great impresario. People flocked to watch any game in which he was involved because they knew they would see a cameo of Botham's greatness. That seemed to be enough for him, to dazzle briefly and then retire to the seclusion of the dressing room to prepare himself for *A Question Of Sport*, a speaking tour, or a pantomime. Again, like W.G., his very presence was enough for many; perhaps also like W.G., he came to believe that he was bigger than the game.

Certainly it's easier to make out a case that the Pakistani series of 1987 should have been his last. His back surgery of 1988 prolonged his useful life as a county cricketer but he was left short of Test quality since he seemed unwilling or unable to score the runs required of him. If Test matches are there to be won, if they are the supreme test of national sporting fortitude, the best side needs to be selected. Botham did not meet those requirements any longer. He knew the end was coming, and it frustrated him. He joined the long list of cricketers to be niggled by Dermot Reeve – nothing strange in that – but this irascibility was more pointed, more heartfelt, no longer just part of the act. According to

Reeve's autobiography, 'Ian was beginning to be under pressure for his all-rounder spot in the England team [when] we had our spat in 1990 ... he hadn't made the England tour party to the West Indies in '89/90 and that had hurt him ... he was still having to rack up some performances to get back in the England side.' That pressure rattled him. A characteristically unorthodox knock from Reeve against Worcestershire was ended by Botham who, on dismissing him, roared 'Go on, fuck off.' Reeve's typically succinct rejoinder was 'You've had your day mate.'

Reeve was right, closer to the truth than Botham would have liked. Even so, his competitive instinct helped him to fight off all comers for far longer than was necessary or good for English cricket. Just as he had overshadowed Mike Gatting early in his career, so the shadow of his legend has loomed large over those who have looked to replace him. That's a mighty long list now. Phil DeFreitas was the first real contender, but he was a good bowler who was well short of Test class with the bat. Dermot Reeve himself could have been effective in the Test arena, might even have made a good England captain, but few rated his all-round skills highly enough to give him an extended opportunity. That much is also true of Dominic Cork, though his batting shows some promise and he may yet become a genuine international all-rounder. Like Reeve, he has the bloody-mindedness of Botham, a fierce determination to win and to impose himself on the opposition. Never overawed, his problem may be that which beset Botham: as England's only regular wicket taker, he is in danger of being bowled into the ground, his useful life shortened. Darren Gough is similar to Cork in terms of quality and the two could forge a useful new-ball partnership for England. If both stay fit and in form, the two together might equal Botham as batsman. That's always been the problem post 1985 – England need two players to replace him. Perhaps the man most affected by the Botham legend has been Chris Lewis. If any English all-rounder could come close to Botham, it is him. A great natural talent, Lewis's toughest opponent seems to be himself. There has been many a false dawn in his career when it seems he has finally established himself only for him to fall out of the picture once again. The pressure of expectation always seems to be too much for a player who should be dominating the

England side in an attack with Cork, Gough, Tufnell and one other, guaranteeing that England could bat usefully down to number nine.

Despite Botham's detrimental though wholly innocent effect on those that would follow, many players have benefited from playing alongside him. Phil Neale is particularly bullish about the impact he had on Worcestershire once he arrived at New Road:

> His presence was important. He came here because he knew we were a good side and that he wouldn't have to carry us. His arrival meant we went from being a picturesque little club playing nice cricket in a cosy little atmosphere but which hadn't won anything in a while, to a club that was looking for success. Suddenly Ian came and the press came with him. That's a double edged thing, we had to be careful about what we said, but also it attracted attention that the others thrived on. That got a number of our lads into the England side. When Ian got injured in 1988, it looked like a crippling blow because we looked on him as a main part of the side but the guys came in and filled the hole – Martin Weston deputised superbly well. People had thought Ian's arrival meant the end for him but he played his best cricket while Ian was at the club and related very well to him. I know Ian had a very positive influence on guys like him and Stuart Lampitt. In that season, though he couldn't play, he was very supportive and a positive influence about the dressing room. The thing that struck me was Ian was totally committed and very focused on Worcestershire being successful. He was the first to get a plan in the mind about how the season would go – which games we ought to win, where we'd need to work hard, he was determined that we would be successful.

At England level, the Botham effect was less obvious on the field, but his presence had an impact nonetheless. Tony Lewis, writing in the *Daily Telegraph*, noted that

> these days [his] cricket is as much aura as reality. When he was recalled at The Oval [in 1991] a golden glow settled on the England dressing room ... it was Robin's return to Sherwood Forest. The lesser merry men gathered around him and heard words devoid of apprehension, loaded with self-confidence and found themselves thrust to the centre

of the country's news media concern ... 'Both' was back, all would be well now ... his batting these days lacks continuity because he struggles to find the linking strokes between defence and thundering hits ... at his best he often picked up singles by turning the straight ball to leg but now there are false messages from eye to the body and the strokes are sometimes flawed ... although the terrific assaults of 1981 may never be repeated and though he is unlikely to get five wickets in a Test innings again, Ian Botham is a cricketer who makes things happen.

That perhaps is the most fitting epitaph for Botham's cricketing career. He made glorious things happen, the unexpected, the thoroughly impossible. To him, the impossible was commonplace so it is not surprising that he felt he could go on repeating those feats ad infinitum. Consequently his time with Durham was an unhappy one. We were faced with the dispiriting sight of this colossus blaming others for not realising he could still beat the Aussies when, by his own admission, it was an effort just to get out of bed.

Having brought down the curtain, and with cricket finally out of his life, Botham needed new battles to fight. His court case against Imran bore the hallmarks of a man who needed to vanquish a foe once again; perhaps that litigation was used to suppress the withdrawal symptoms that all greats suffer once they leave the stage. Certainly he has a pronounced sense of injustice and a desire to right any perceived wrongs, but given that courtroom decisions are every bit as uncertain as events on a cricket field, he was ill advised to fight an alleged libel published in a small circulation magazine. Better by far to have laughed off such risible accusations of racism – would Viv Richards have a racist as his closest friend? – and meaningless jibes about his lack of breeding. They meant nothing to anyone but Botham and his fellow litigant, Allan Lamb. Few had seen the article, fewer still believed it. More unwise still was Botham's attack on an article appearing under Imran's name in the *Sun* which accused all of England's great bowlers, and most of those in the rest of the world, of cheating at one time or another, though none was actually named. Botham felt this to be a smear and acted, while Trueman, Statham, Bedser, Tyson, Snow, Willis, Lillee, McKenzie,

McDermott, Hall, Holding, Ambrose, Walsh *et al* laughed off Imran's charges as too contemptible to be worthy of comment. Appropriately enough for such a risible and unnecessary case, the trial itself often degenerated into farce over the course of its thirteen days in Court 13. Among the moments of prime comedy there was Allan Lamb unable to tell the difference between 'condemning' and 'condoning', Brian Close refusing to confirm that Geoff Boycott was an honest man, and Boycott attempting verbally to lay into Close and narrowly avoiding facing contempt of court charges.

Botham's pride may have been wounded by Imran's apparent accusations but his failure to let sleeping dogs lie cost him dearly. With Imran securing the services of George Carman QC in his defence, it was obvious that Botham would not be given an easy ride. During his fourteen-hour spell in the witness box, all the sordid tabloid stories of the past twenty years were unearthed in a squalid and thoroughly distasteful attempt to blacken his character, putting himself and his family life under the microscope yet again, a process that must have been painful but one which he must have expected. His performance was persuasive, making it perfectly clear that the sanctity of his reputation was paramount and that not just he but his parents, his wife and his children had all been hurt by Imran's comments. Even so, it did little to show why he felt he had had to resort to legal action, especially since Imran had offered to publish a full letter of apology in *The Times*, one which would have exonerated Botham and would have severely damaged the standing of his opponent.

In the course of the trial, perhaps Botham got the vindication he wanted without getting the result – rather like scoring a hundred but finishing up on the losing side. Certainly Imran was forced to recant on his accusations that he was a cheat for having put together a lengthy video which purported to show members of the English team wilfully altering the condition of a ball; he withdrew it from evidence once Botham and David Gower took the stand to refute his accusations. This meant that the defence of 'justification' had collapsed, this after Imran had called a number of star witnesses – Mike Atherton, Derek Pringle, David Lloyd, Lloyd actually doing more for Botham's case by discounting all the tales of ball tampering that he'd recounted in a book as 'stories. And good 'uns!' – to back up his theory that tampering was widespread in the game.

With this central plank of Imran's defence disappearing beneath him, the result of the trial seemed a foregone conclusion. There was genuine amazement when the jury finally found in favour of Imran since he had now admitted that Botham was no cheat. After days of semantic argument centring around what might or might not be defined as 'cheating' within the laws of the game, and with little time given over to the possibly more important accusations of racism beyond emotional denials of the charge from the Botham and Lamb camps, it appeared that the jury still couldn't see what all the fuss was about. If their verdict meant anything at all, it seemed to say that all those involved should have known better and not wasted their time, that if Imran had indeed impugned the integrity of Lamb and Botham, they should have been men enough to accept a suitably fulsome apology, shake hands and leave it at that. The final word on the whole affair would be Botham's, a comment he made on the second day when Carman asked why he had failed to sue the Sunday newspapers over the Lindy Field story. Having pointed out that he hadn't the means to take on the tabloids, he added, 'at the end of the day, they were just fish-and-chip wrapping'. Perhaps the unconscious irony of that statement was not lost on the jury.

In the final analysis, competition was in Botham's blood. It was that which made him great, it was that which was his downfall. He turned the competitive instinct into an art form, that was his gift, yet it left him tainted. He was unfortunate to live in an era when everything is played out under the microscopic gaze of the media; back in the 1950s he'd have been loved as a cavalier playboy like Denis Compton. Truth be told, he *was* loved by the majority of the English cricketing public. The sermons he attracted in the tabloids were forgotten as another lofty drive dropped into the members' enclosure for six. He gave so many people such extraordinary pleasure that perhaps he should have been indulged his wilder moments. Yet sport has come to mean too much, games are taken out of all proportion to their worth. If England win a meaningless one day match in Madras, they are the finest side the world's ever seen. If they lose a similar game two days later in Calcutta, they are a disgrace to the nation and should be brought home immediately. Neither response is intelligent, neither is true, neither is helpful. Under such ludicrous pressures it's small wonder that volatile young men go off the rails. Forty years ago, if Keith Miller got Compton's wicket with a full toss in front of a full house in Melbourne with the Ashes riding on it, both men would have laughed at the preposterousness of it all. The crowd would have applauded, would have revelled in their enjoyment. Botham brought that enjoyment back to cricket. While he was winning, all was well, but when he smiled at his demise in a Test in Christchurch – caught by fluke off a full blooded shot – he was castigated for his couldn't-care-less attitude; in the 1950s he'd have been cherished as a character. Now, he was a 'mixed blessing' for the game, a yob. Isn't that absurd? For the sake of himself and his family, Botham may be better off without cricket. For all his faults, cricket is still immeasurably the poorer without him.

CHAPTER EIGHT

ANGELS IN THE ARCHITECTURE

Who Is The Greatest?

The perennial question which surrounded Botham's years at the top concerned his position among the great all-rounders – did he compare with Keith Miller, was he in the same class as Garfield Sobers? Cricket has changed so rapidly over the last twenty post-Packer years that such judgements are impossible to make; there is more cricket played today, under different circumstances and under different pressures. All we can safely say is that Botham would have been successful in Miller's era just as Miller would be a hit today. The more sensible comparison is surely with the other three great all-rounders who played in Botham's era. Who was the greatest – Ian Botham, Imran Khan, Kapil Dev or Richard Hadlee? To consider the question in 1980 would have been the work of a moment, for Botham was the undisputed number one. As time passed, Botham slipped down the field. All four left the game around the same time in the early 1990s, by which time he had the weakest credentials of any of them, playing for England more on reputation than results, while the others remained true champions.

Any such argument must be a subjective one and there will be as many different views as there are people. As a starting point, it's useful to look at their comparative statistics with bat and ball. Each meets the all-rounder criteria. In their prime they would have deserved selection for the national side as either batsman or bowler, with Hadlee perhaps the only borderline case, his batting never quite as robust as that of the others, though it should be pointed out that in a crisis he regularly made crucial runs. Each has won games for his country with bat and ball.

	TESTS	INNS	N.O.	RUNS	H.S.	AVGE	100s	50s
Botham	102	161	6	5200	208	33.55	14	22
Hadlee	86	134	19	3124	151*	27.16	2	15
Imran	88	126	25	3807	136	37.69	6	18
Kapil	131	184	15	5248	163	31.05	8	27

	BALLS	RUNS	WKTS	AVGE	STRIKE	BEST	5WI	10WM
Botham	21,815	10,878	383	28.40	56.96	8/34	27	4
Hadlee	21,918	9612	431	22.30	50.85	9/52	36	9
Imran	19,458	8258	362	22.81	53.75	8/58	23	6
Kapil	27,740	12,867	434	29.65	63.92	9/83	23	2

Each numbers among the greatest cricketers his nation has ever produced. Each would grace virtually any side in the history of the game.
But who is the greatest of the four?

Kapil Dev is in many ways the most unlikely of the quartet. Until his
arrival on the scene in 1978/79, the very idea of the Indians unleashing
a highly successful quick bowler was quite laughable. Opening bowlers
were there simply to take the shine off the ball so that spinners such as
Bishan Bedi and Bhagwat Chandrasekhar could get on to beguile for
over after over; the sight of military medium trundlers such as Abid Ali
taking the new ball in a Test match rarely struck terror into the opposing
openers. On the featherbed pitches regularly produced throughout
India's Test match history right up until the Golden Jubilee of 1979/80,
fast bowling was a back breaking, heart breaking business. It was an
occupation that was fruitless and few took up the challenge. Those that
did generally had short careers. In consequence, at home on turning
pitches, India were a formidable force, the attacking thrust of their
opponents blunted by the surfaces upon which they toiled. Away from
home, however, they were perpetually vulnerable. Unused to playing
fast bowling, their batsmen could often be unhinged by belligerence;
Trueman's destruction of them at Headingley in 1952 was a case in
point, the punch drunk tourists collapsing to 0 for 4, the worst ever

start to a Test match innings. Just prior to Kapil's arrival on the scene, India's tour to the West Indies in 1975/76 was plagued by injury inflicted by Clive Lloyd's lightning fast pacemen. The nadir came at Sabina Park when the Indian second innings closed for ninety-seven with only five wickets down, captain Bedi insisting that there were no more batsmen fit enough to take to the crease – he had declared at 306 for 6 in the first innings as a protest against intimidatory bowling which had caused both Gaekwad and Patel to retire hurt, while Viswanath broke a finger in getting out.

If the batsmen were at sea against the quicks, when India took to the field they would often find themselves bowling on tracks tailor made for seam and swing bowlers, offering nothing for the spinners. Once Kapil Dev arrived in Indian sides, home teams could no longer produce fast pitches knowing they were free from any retaliation. He turned the prevailing logic on its head and was the single most important reason for India enjoying its most consistently successful period in Test cricket throughout the 1980s and into the 1990s. In addition, it was his charismatic leadership and dynamic batting that captured the World Cup in 1983, surely the most popular win until Sri Lanka's success on the subcontinent in 1996.

In his early career, Kapil was a constant threat to the batsmen, his bowling a whirl of activity and aggression unusual among the traditionally gentle Indian sides. Though a smile was rarely far from his face, Kapil could bowl like a demon, hurrying up to the wicket and hurling down deliveries that were distinctly nippy. It was his misfortune that India lacked an equally potent threat from the other end. Ghavri was a useful foil, but just how much more dangerous would Kapil have been had he been partnered by the current pairing of Javagal Srinath and Venkatesh Prasad, two men clearly inspired by Kapil's example? As it was, batsmen were happy just to keep Kapil out, attempting to score their runs at the other end; this was certainly the case in matches held beyond India's sunny clime where colleagues like Shastri or Doshi were equally threatening with the turning ball. The benefit Kapil did enjoy was that he had less competition in the side and more opportunity to bag lots of wickets – if no one else in the side could break through, then he would eventually. In England's 633 for 5 at Edgbaston in 1979, for example, Kapil got all five wickets. As his strike rate illustrates, he had to do a lot more bowling to get his victims, a combination of batsmen's caution and his having to play a high proportion of matches on fairly lifeless pitches.

As a batsman, there were few more pleasing sights than Kapil Dev in full flow. He allied a typically wristy Indian approach to deceptive physical power, his wiry frame uncoiling like a spring to clatter the ball to the boundary. Those who saw it can never forget his batting at Lord's in 1990. India, with their last pair at the crease, required twenty-four to avoid the follow on after Gooch had made his magnificent 333. Facing a new over from Hemmings, the first two deliveries brought no runs. Then, as if suddenly aware of the vulnerability of his partner at the other end, Kapil launched into four quite monumental hits, each sending the ball sailing over the boundary ropes, saving the follow on in a manner none could have imagined possible. It was a feat that would even have stretched Botham in 1981. As David Frith remarked, 'Kapil could touch the sublime in carefree batsmanship'. Certainly few have ever batted with his abandon on such a regular basis.

He and Botham are similar in many ways. Both had a tendency to play from the heart at times when they might have been better advised to play from the head. Yet as Botham proved, such a tendency is often the root of genius; to ignore convention, trust yourself and give free rein to the spirit can create moments of pure magic. Kapil did that most memorably in 1983 in a Prudential World Cup game at Tunbridge Wells. Choosing to bat first against Zimbabwe, India crashed to 17 for 5 with Gavaskar, Patil, Amarnath, Srikkanth and Yashpal Sharma all out. Given that the opposition were relative minnows, the sensible course for Kapil would have been to try to bat out the fifty-five overs with the help of his colleagues, shielding them and not taking any undue risks, looking to post a target of 150 or so. Instead he thrashed 175, a tournament record, as India reached 266 to make qualification for the next stage a formality. It was an innings that transformed the tournament and did as much as anything to capture the trophy. Only those who fit Emerson's definition of heroism could perform so irresponsibly in conventional terms and yet be so successful.

Like Botham, Kapil had his detractors. Certainly he was not as incisive a bowler in his latter years when he seemed to be continuing partly because there was no replacement on the horizon, and partly to accumulate yet more records. He bagged forty-five of his wickets against Sri Lanka, then a relatively weak nation – this equates to Botham picking up scalps in the Packer period, though Botham took far more wickets than that. Yet picking up cheap wickets against poor opposition is not the formality it sometimes appears; you still need to be a fine bowler regularly to get five or six wickets in an innings. Poor sides might represent an easier foe, but they still have to be beaten. If we look at Kapil's displays against the West Indies, they are exemplary, and indicate he was a considerable bowler. Of course, Kapil did more bowling than the other three and so would expect to get more wickets. His strike rate is the poorest of the four, but given that he often played on lifeless pitches in India, that's to be expected. It should be remembered too that Botham's strike rate was built up in his first forty Tests and that the rest of his career was far less dramatic. At a time when Botham should have been benefiting from the accumulated wisdom of experience, he was often bowling like a drain. The other three seldom did so, cutting their cloth according to their physical well-being, letting brain do the work that had formerly been the preserve of brawn.

In that regard Kapil, like Imran and Hadlee, had a physical advantage over Botham. Where Botham was a naturally large framed man, one who was always going to fill out into a bulky individual, the others were more wiry. If that gave Botham the greater reserves of stamina which allowed him to bowl long spells, it also put a greater strain on him as he got older. Bowling quick is a debilitating business and the extra weight he naturally carried gave his lower body a pounding. It also made it harder for him to maintain the superb action he had before he had matured fully, placing additional stress on that perpetually fragile back. Kapil remained a naturally lithe figure and was therefore better able to maintain his fitness and so his form. As Botham's star burst into the heavens in a blaze of glory only to extinguish itself as swiftly, Kapil's burned with a consistent intensity, lighting up the sky long after Botham had become yesterday's man. Yet in terms of performances over a career it is almost impossible to separate Botham and Kapil Dev. Their records are similar, their feats stupendous, their achievements equally immense –

for Botham's regular destruction of Australia, read Kapil hauling India into the modern age.

Sir Richard Hadlee is a different matter altogether, the only one of the four who might struggle to call himself a genuine all-rounder. As fierce a striker of the ball as any of the others, it was as one of the very greatest bowlers of all time that he truly made his reputation; in that sense, he is the only one of the four who might not get in a World XI as an all-rounder, yet the only one who would make it on the strength of just one of the two disciplines. Surely he would be the first choice for the best quick bowler of the 1980s, Malcolm Marshall perhaps his worthiest challenger for that crown. In his *Wisden* appreciation of Hadlee in 1991, Don Mosey termed him 'the most intelligent fast bowler the world has seen'. David Frith selects him of all the great all-rounders in history 'to bowl for my life'. These are judgements from the game's historians that are worthy of respect; they're yet more remarkable when you consider Hadlee's early years in Test cricket were not wildly successful. It wasn't until the start of the 1980s, some seven years after his debut, that Hadlee began to construct his wonderful figures. To that stage he'd played twenty-six Tests and taken 107 wickets at a cost of thirty. The rest of his career saw him capture 324 wickets in sixty Tests at a cost of just 19.7, an astonishing performance given that he was playing for one of the weakest Test nations over that period. Like Kapil, he was short of the very best support, though the likes of Chatfield and Cairns were reliable performers, more threatening than India's seamers. As New Zealand matured as a side in the 1980s, picking up victories all around the world, men like Martin Crowe and John Wright deserve great credit for the invaluable part they played. Essentially, though, Hadlee carried the hopes of the New Zealand team on his shoulders. It's no surprise that his best batting often came when the side was either in trouble or urgently seeking to press home an advantage. If New Zealand won a Test, it was fair to assume that another sterling performance from Hadlee was at the root of it all. Certainly, he was *the* decisive factor in more Tests and over a greater period of time than Botham could ever lay claim to.

It's become a cliché that Botham was the greatest competitor in the cricketing world, but does that bear scrutiny? Certainly his desire, his will to win, was staggering, but did that make him the greatest? Hadlee was every bit as determined. Although the acuity of Botham's cricketing brain is not in doubt, it was often clouded by the red mists of competition, the need to bounce a batsman out or hit a bowler out of the attack. On occasion such tactics worked, but as he aged they worked less frequently, ended more depressingly. Hadlee, on the other hand, rarely allowed himself to be consumed by the frenzied atmosphere of a Test match. Instead he drew back from the emotions of the day, concentrating, always concentrating, on the job in hand. He probed for weaknesses in a batsman, searched through his filing system to recall modes of dismissal, looked for the ones and twos when he was batting to break up the field before he hit out, turning the game into a science rather than an art form. In that sense he outstrips Botham and Kapil Dev. Yet in terms of the all-rounder debate, one has to question his performance as a batsman. The most interesting statistic is that, like his bowling, his batting improved with age. Surely that is the hallmark of a great all-round cricketing mind rather than just a gifted all-round cricketer? Hadlee never sold himself short. He stretched his gifts to the absolute maximum, which is all that can be asked of any player.

Botham is perhaps the hardest to judge. Undeniably he was the most heroic, the most theatrical, the easiest to warm to or take offence against. If your prime motivation in watching cricket was to be entertained, Botham was your man. Whether he was playing superbly or in the lowest trough of form, life was never dull while he was around. His early runs and wickets were often taken against poor or weakened sides, but they were taken nevertheless, voraciously so. In addition, it's perhaps his misfortune that he played against poorer sides when at his best. If a full strength West Indian or Australian side had toured England in 1979, maybe Botham would have shredded their batting orders too. It's unfortunate that those games are still relatively fresh in the memory and we remember the weakened state of the opposition. How many other epic displays have been given in such circumstances? Hutton's 364 at the Oval in 1938 was achieved on a perfect pitch against a bowling attack in which only Tiger O'Reilly could truly be called great – the back up of Waite, McCabe, Barnes and Fleetwood-Smith was not awe-inspiring, especially on that blameless surface. Sobers was equally fortunate in the Pakistani attack that toiled against him in vain at Sabina Park in 1957/58 when he eclipsed Hutton, only Fazal Mahmood a worthy adversary. So let's not be too quick to condemn Botham for the heinous crime of being too good for the opposition. Much of the case against him rests on his performances against the West Indies. Throughout the 1980s, the West Indies provided the supreme test. This is how the four fared against them with bat and ball:

	TESTS	INNS	N.O.	RUNS	H.S.	AVGE	100s	50s
Botham	20	38	1	792	81	21.40	0	4
Hadlee	10	15	3	389	103	32.42	1	1
Imran	18	33	5	775	123	27.68	1	3
Kapil	25	39	4	1,079	126*	30.82	3	4

	BALLS	RUNS	WKTS	AVGE	STRIKE	BEST	5WI	10WM
Botham	3,609	2,146	61	35.18	59.16	8/103	3	0
Hadlee	2,506	1,124	51	22.04	49.13	6/50	4	1
Imran	3,488	1,695	80	21.19	43.60	7/80	6	1
Kapil	4,639	2,216	89	24.90	52.12	9/83	4	1

If these comparisons tell us anything, it is that against the best side in the world Botham was the only one to be systematically reduced to the role of mere mortal in both departments of the game. Hadlee's performance is significantly better than his career averages, while Kapil and Imran were both more successful bowlers against the West Indies compared with their overall career figures. Looked at in these cold statistical terms, Botham looks ineffective. But, of course, Disraeli was right and if these statistics don't actually lie, they need to be viewed in the light of mitigating circumstances.

As a bowler, Botham never faced the West Indies when at his fittest, all his games against them coming in the wake of his back problems. His tours to the Caribbean were beset with problems, some of his own making, others not. Whoever was at fault, it is only fair to concede that his run ins with the press would have had an egregious effect on the form of the most thick skinned individual and so the tabloids must take some of the blame for his under achieving in the West Indies. Most damaging, perhaps, he played in an England side that regularly lacked the fibre to fight back against the West Indians, sapping even his morale. The sides that took the field under Gower against the West Indies often seemed rudderless ships. For all his gifts, Gower was palpably unsuited to the role of leading England against the West Indies; once things were going badly for them, no one seemed able to take responsibility, to marshal the troops and instigate a fightback. Certainly in the West Indies the pitches were very poor indeed and the home bowling extremely fearsome, but to lose ten straight Tests was woeful. Like rabbits caught in the headlights, England were regularly run down by the oncoming juggernaut driven by Vivian Richards. As England's most explosive cricketer, Botham should have been the one to produce the goods under pressure, but so demoralised was the side as a whole and so big a part did the soap opera of his life play in that demoralisation, it was beyond even him. The Lord's Test of 1984 was a case in point: he took eight West Indian victims in the first knock, his highest score against them of eighty-one in the second. Yet with the West Indians facing a stiff target of 342 in the fourth innings, Botham and his colleagues bowled with all the discipline of an alcoholic village green eleven to be beaten out of sight by nine wickets. So strong was the psychological hold the West Indies had on England that even Botham could not escape its grip.

It's equally true to say that for deep rooted historical reasons, the West Indians prize victory over England more than any other, even when England are in dire straits and clearly no match for them. Under Lloyd and then Richards, they attacked England's weaknesses ruthlessly and never offered a moment's respite. Yet despite this convincing barrage of excuses, we must still face the fact that Botham's performances against the West Indies were desperately ordinary. Taking that on board, all the evidence still suggests that Botham's greatest moments – in 1978 against Pakistan, in 1979/80 against India, and then against the Australians in 1981 – were a little overrated. The nature, as much as the scale, of his achievements tended to sweep people away in the heat and glory of the moment; cooler analysis indicates that Botham, although England's greatest ever all-rounder, may not have been foremost of this quartet.

Perhaps Botham's greatest failing in comparison with the others was his attitude of no surrender, the very attitude that had launched his career. He had to score quickly, hit hard, bowl fast, even when the ability was no longer quite there, even if circumstances argued that he should show caution. There were some glimpses of him batting with the required measure of responsibility – Sydney in 1979, the Oval in 1987, Edgbaston in 1989 – but these were relatively few and far between. Botham genuinely believed that he would best serve his team by playing according to type. For a time when he was young, fully fit and incredibly strong, that worked supremely well. Later, he needed to keep a check on his temperament but rarely managed to do so. Had Botham been endowed with Hadlee's calculating brain, his appetite for hard work off the field, his desire to probe for weaknesses and to maximise his gifts, his figures would be yet more awesome than they are; if you could weigh the natural talents of all four on a set of kitchen scales, they would tip in the Englishman's favour. The talent was there to the end, but the appetite for the basics waned. In the West Indies in 1985/86, for example, his one good performance came when he was told that he'd been on the verge of losing his place in the side. If that said anything, it was that as you get older, natural talent isn't enough. The reflexes slow, the eye dims, you need to work harder at your game. Botham seemed to feel he was still twenty-one.

John Arlott once said of Botham that he didn't realise what a com-plicated game cricket was and that that was at the root of his success. He played in an uncomplicated way – a gleeful swing of the bat, a wholehearted delivery, an improbable leap to grasp a dazzling slip catch. That was wonderful while it lasted, but once injury robbed him of his zip he needed to go back to the drawing board. Temperamentally, he could not seem to do so. He still had to try to bounce players out when he was no more threatening than an ordinary medium pacer. If he'd followed the Gooch regimen to keep in trim, remodelled his action and bowled at a reduced pace, he could still have been a top class bowler, following the example of Lillee or Hadlee. As it was, Botham played with the heart more than the head and couldn't, or wouldn't, change. That attitude gave us Headingley 1981; it also gave us the second innings at Lord's in 1984 when Gordon Greenidge humbled him. That was Botham, the glorious and the grotesque. That was what made him the most unpredictable cricketer of the four, one of the most exciting ever. Yet in some ways, Botham wasn't the great cricketer of folklore, certainly not in performance terms beyond his initial four-year explosion; a man like Bradman, a true legend of the game, earned that status year after year by performances on the field, so too did Headley, Trueman, Sobers, Richards, Border and the like. Botham was as much a phenomenon as he was a cricketer, legendary for his impact on the world as much as for his deeds on the field. That made him a great competitor, wonderful theatre, a potential match winner, but not a wholly reliable performer.

The acid test comes when selecting the World XI to play the invading Martians for the future of the earth. If selections relate to career performances, then I don't believe Botham should be the first choice all-rounder from these four. That honour must surely go to Imran Khan, Botham's *bête noire*, particularly if one allows that Hadlee would be selected purely on the strength of his bowling. Imran and Botham again have a lot in common: both are extremely charismatic characters on and off the field; each has his admirers who will defend him to the hilt; each is capable of opening the mouth before the brain is fully engaged, leading himself into trouble; each has done a huge amount of valuable charity work, Botham for leukaemia research, Imran for the construction of a specialist cancer hospital in Pakistan. Time and again, though, the two have crossed swords, going right back to their first Test encounters in England in 1982, an ill tempered series that the Pakistanis felt was stolen from them by poor, or in their eyes malicious, English umpiring. Given that the English have been complaining about the standard of Pakistani umpiring, with good reason, since we first set foot in their country, the Pakistanis had every right to question one or two dubious decisions that went England's way. However, even though the hairline decisions may have tilted the balance in a tight three-Test series, Imran did himself little good in the eyes of the sporting world by bemoaning the fact time and again. It suggested he was lacking in sportsmanship, failing to look closely at his own side's shortcomings and preferring to blame others for an unacceptable defeat. On the field, that series was a modest one for Botham but one in which Imran was superb – 212 runs at fifty-three and twenty-one wickets at 18.6 compared with Botham's 163 runs at twenty-seven and eighteen wickets at 26.6. Never mind the cricket though, the real feature of the series was the animosity that threatened to engulf Anglo-Pakistan relations – a boil that continued to fester until good relations were restored by Wasim Akram and Mike Atherton in 1996 – and a rivalry which developed between Imran and Botham that apparently seethes to this day.

If Imran was unchivalrous in 1982, Botham was crass in 1984, making comments about Pakistan that he was soon to regret. Living as he does in a country that still regards Bernard Manning as a comedian, it's understandable that Botham should have made a feeble joke about his mother-in-law in relation to the standard of accommodation on offer to tourists in Pakistan. It was not meant offensively for in England it passed without comment, such was the everyday nature of the jibe, but it was nonetheless a stupid thing to say. Though Pakistani hotels may not measure up to those in the west, the people are hospitable and genuinely welcoming, something which is far more important and which should be appreciated by those who visit. Not only were Botham's comments offensive, they were rude to his hosts; more important still, since there are many people of Pakistani origin who live in this country and have to deal with the oppressive weight of casual racism every day, it's vital that public figures such as Botham do nothing to stoke those fires, however inadvertently. If it was easy to see why Botham thought nothing of the comment at the time, it was just as reasonable that the Pakistanis should take offence against these flippant remarks. Even so, as an educated man and one with wide experience of British culture, Imran should have been able to rise above the jibe, to treat it as a contemptible irrelevance, and he should not have responded at any time. His comments that painted Botham as a racist in *India Today* were unworthy – racists rarely send messages of support to anti-apartheid rallies as Botham has done. Imran's accusations did far more damage to his reputation than that of Ian Botham, not least because it made him seem petty, while the worst that can be said about Botham was that his initial off the cuff remark was thoughtless.

Ball tampering is another issue altogether. Imran's admission that he did occasionally scratch the side of the ball and lift the seam must inevitably take the shine off some of his performances as a bowler, but equally we must respect his claims that these were the isolated incidents he described them as. As a genuinely hostile fast bowler, he often measured up to the standards set by Hadlee and Lillee. Incisive with the new ball, he could be every bit as penetrative with the old, pioneering that latest bowling innovation, reverse swing. He taught his successors well too. The advent of reverse swing in recent years and the ability of the Pakistani bowlers, notably Wasim Akram and Waqar Younis, to make the old ball deviate prodigiously has been viewed with suspicion, yet as Derek Pringle explained in 1995's *Wisden*, it is no surprise that such a skill should emanate from the subcontinent: 'A perfect example of man's triumph over an unhelpful environment . . . playing on grassless pitches of low bounce with hard, bare outfields, where cricket balls rapidly deteriorate, Pakistan's bowlers developed a method of swinging an old ball. It requires a creation of opposites on the ball's surface, a kind of Yin and Yang effect where one side is kept smooth and damp while the other is allowed to roughen but is kept scrupulously dry.' As Jack Bannister pointed out in the 1993 almanack 'remember that Wasim and Waqar have played in county cricket but no other Lancashire or Surrey bowler has suddenly developed the ability to swing the old ball so much . . . even more significantly, the Pakistan support bowler Aqib Javed has not benefited anything like as much from any so-called doctoring'. Perhaps we should accept that the two are quite exceptional bowlers. No one suggested that Bob Massie tampered with the ball when he took sixteen wickets on his debut at Lord's in 1972, or when Botham himself made the ball go like a boomerang at Lord's in 1978 against Pakistan. These were natural but uncommon occurrences. Perhaps Imran and then Waqar and Wasim have learned how to control the freakish? Given that English bowlers such as Darren Gough are now reverse swinging the ball, perhaps we can accept that it is a new addition to the quick bowler's armoury and congratulate the Pakistanis. As Bannister continued, 'any genuine innovation in sport is fascinating to watch'; we should note too that Shane Warne, prior to his recent injury, seemed able to develop a completely new kind of delivery almost each year, so it is possible to revolutionise the fundamentals of the game. Therefore, in the absence of any firm evidence to the contrary, we should admire the ingenuity of Imran and his colleagues rather than castigate them.

Yet the Pakistanis continue to upset Botham more than any other cricketing nation. It must be significant that he decided to opt out of touring just in time to ensure that he missed the World Cup, held in India and Pakistan in 1987, and then the England tour of Pakistan in 1987/88. Perhaps this was nothing more than mere coincidence, yet it certainly suggested that the problem was not physical. Botham was willing to put up with the rigours of an Australian winter but not another jaunt into Asia. His weariness with the press pack was obviously the major factor in his decision making, but from a Pakistani perspective, it looked calculated and ungracious. Little wonder that the Pakistanis were always keen to put one over on him, something in which they often succeeded.

In the face of such resolve, it was inevitable that Botham would be sucked into controversy. It is true that Pakistan have at times been an annoying side to play against. They have their superficial irritants like the hyperactive Javed Miandad, they have been known to appeal over-zealously, Salim Yousuf being a prime culprit at Headingley in 1987, but it is Imran who really seemed to get under Botham's skin. Perhaps it was Imran's patrician streak, his assumption of aristocratic bearing that simply got up Botham's egalitarian nose. Perhaps, as with Viv Richards, Botham was unnerved by an opponent who represented a superior force, a talent greater than his own. Certainly in that rain ruined 1987 series, Imran held the upper hand as Pakistan won the only completed game of the rubber. Scoring a magnificent century at the Oval, Imran totalled 191 runs at forty-eight and took twenty-one wickets at twenty-two, Botham responding with 232 runs at thirty-three and seven wickets at sixty-two. It was clearly Imran's series, one in which he installed himself as perhaps the premier all-rounder. He'd long been seen as a superb opening bowler, but in the latter stages of his career in particular he became one of the finest technicians in the world with the bat, combining an enviable ability to dominate the best attacks with the intelligence and craft to combat top class bowling on helpful wickets. He was good enough to get into a strong Pakistani side purely as a batsman on a number of occasions when he was troubled by injuries that prevented him bowling, and responded to crises with a cool head.

Yet more valuable – and most remarkable of all, the feature that sets him apart from Kapil, Hadlee and Botham – was his skill as a captain. Learning from his own shortcomings when touring England in 1982, he rarely allowed himself to become flustered by events subsequently, displaying a great ability to calm the volatile talents that surrounded him. His presence in the middle was a steadying influence that allowed his team to make best use of their substantial gifts. In its report of the 1987 tour of England, *Wisden* reported that 'without Imran's leadership, or his ability as a player, such triumphs [as Pakistan's first series victory in England, having previously achieved a similar first in India] would not have been celebrated'. As a skipper, he followed Clive Lloyd's lead and presided over a dressing room that had often been beset by quarrels and feuds; just as the West Indies had sometimes been weakened by internal strife, so Pakistan were oft wounded by internecine conflict. Like Lloyd, Imran gave strong leadership, setting standards and imposing a sensible level of discipline on a hitherto undisciplined side. This was powerfully illustrated in a Test match at Headingley in 1987. His wicketkeeper Salim Yousuf claimed a catch off Botham when he'd clearly dropped the ball first. *Wisden* notes that Botham 'reacted angrily, and umpire Palmer had to be quick to separate them. Imran also acted smartly, dressing down Yousuf in no uncertain manner.' Too many captains would defend the indefensible on their own side – Miandad did so when Aqib Javed showed dissent to umpire Palmer at Old Trafford in 1992, for example. As a mature cricketer, Imran refused to let himself be blind to his own side's inadequacies of temperament.

It was Imran's strength of purpose and of character that carried Pakistan to victory in the World Cup of 1992, the final glorious swansong for both himself and Botham. Both had distinguished tournaments, Botham rousing himself to heights that had long seemed beyond him, fired by the dream of winning the World Cup, performing supremely in almost all of England's eight qualifying games. More impressive still was Imran who transformed a bedraggled outfit into potential winners with his now legendary exhortation to his men to fight like the cornered tiger. Having been mauled by the West Indies, skittled out by England for seventy-four in a game ended by rain, beaten heavily by India, and thoroughly outplayed by the South African novices, qualification for the semi-finals seemed an unlikely pipe dream at best. Imran's career was heading for an ignominious end, yet he rallied his side to beat Australia and Sri Lanka with ease, before New Zealand were brushed aside to seal a semi-final showdown against the same opposition. By now, they were looking like the team to beat and a solid victory in Auckland put them through to the final to be held under the lights in Melbourne.

England, asked to field by Imran, started well with Pringle taking two early wickets. But it was Imran with a sensible, then explosive, seventy-two who took the game away from them, the Pakistanis posting 249 as Botham toiled through seven overs to take one wicket – ironically that of Imran – for forty-two. Succeeding as pinch hitter through the tournament, Botham opened with Gooch. With just six on the board, Botham was caught behind for nought off Wasim Akram, causing Aamir Sohail to wonder aloud why he hadn't sent his mother-in-law in to bat instead. When Stewart followed fifteen runs later and then Hick and Gooch fell in quick succession, the game was up. Though expensive, Imran had the satisfaction of taking the last wicket when Richard Illingworth succumbed with England twenty-two runs behind. Imran's role was a deep and decisive one. His leadership along with his exhilarating play had transformed a beaten side into world champions; in its way, his achievement ranked with Botham's rearrangement of the Ashes series in 1981. It offered final confirmation, were it needed, that this was a very substantial cricketer indeed. Since Imran was a great captain when Botham clearly was not, he must shade Botham, Hadlee and Kapil Dev in the cricketing argument, and claim his place as the greatest of these four eminent all-rounders.

Is that a volcano erupting on Alderney?

CHAPTER NINE

OUT OF TIME

Where Do We Go From Here?

N ow that Ian Botham has played his final game, what will be his role for the rest of his working life? It may be that he has already stumbled across it. The ventures into pantomime might have seemed crazy at the time, but they were hugely successful; when he appeared in *Cinderella* at Wimbledon in the winter of 1994/95, he helped make it London's most profitable panto of the season. Oh yes he did. Despite reviews that pointed out he was as wooden as the stage, the kids loved seeing him and he loved working with them; after all, he was the biggest kid in the place. Nevertheless, an actor's life was not for Botham on the incontrovertible grounds that he can't act. Speaking tours were much more his line, allowing him to capitalise on the goodwill won over his spell on *A Question Of Sport* where he and Bill Beaumont became a much loved double act accorded the warmth usually reserved for the likes of Morecambe and Wise. Their honest good humour and obvious enjoyment of the show made it one of the BBC's great success stories of recent years. The two bowed out at the top, perhaps sensibly allowing new blood to revitalise an old formula, and their shows will always be remembered with affection.

A *Question Of Sport* was the ideal vehicle for Botham, for it allowed him to relax and be himself in front of the TV cameras, an excellent grounding for a future career in television journalism, the avenue he is now pursuing with Sky Sports. How much longer he remains with them is a question that can only be answered by the authorities at Lord's for any role he might take up as a national selector would require him to step down. That would be ironic, for Botham used *A Question Of Sport* as a platform from which to launch his unsuccessful bid for elevation to the selection committee in 1996. That particular scramble for power was marked by its almost surreal nature, a comedy of errors that left English cricket looking rather stupid, though that's by no means a rare experience. Following the dismal World Cup showing, Botham was proposed as a selector by Surrey and Derbyshire ensuring that a ballot was necessary. Illingworth supported the ageing Brian Bolus and Fred Titmus before the latter's withdrawal, then gave his blessing to John Edrich's candidature. The field eventually expanded to include Chris Cowdrey, Kim Barnett, Graham Gooch, David Graveney and Geoff Miller prior to a mid-April election. The TCCB members found it incumbent upon them to remind the counties that the full-time media work of one candidate was incompatible with his election. It was inevitable thereafter that Botham would fail to gain election, the panel eventually being made up of Gooch and Graveney along with new coach David Lloyd and chairman Ray. Indeed Graveney might have been installed as chairman had not the Professional Cricketers' Association for whom he worked forced him to stand down from the contest. The whole sorry mess unfolded in the pages of the press over several weeks making sense to few and saddening many, notably those who supported Botham. However, there was much sense in Alan Lee's column in *Wisden Cricket Monthly* once the results were announced. Noting that Botham 'would be utterly miscast as a selector', he went on to point out that his supporters 'beat the drum for his election without any explanation of how their man was going to alter the habits of a lifetime for a job that involves all the detail, observation and analysis that he detests'. Lee's analysis was quite correct. Never a great watcher of the game, the very idea of Botham trawling the country for fresh new talent was hard to credit.

Surely, though, English cricket, now under new management with the introduction of Lord MacLaurin, can find a place for the most charismatic player of his generation? One would like to think so, but it begs the very tough question of just what that place should be. Over recent years, English cricket has been overwhelmed with supposedly messianic figures who were there to cure all our ills and take the national side to the peaks of the game. Peter May, Ted Dexter and Raymond Illingworth all started their reigns as chairman of selectors amid a blaze of optimistic publicity, only to have their hopes dashed once they took office. Given that these three were all eminent men with acute cricketing brains, one has to wonder if they were at fault or whether they were asked to operate within the fabric of an unworkable system. A little of both is the case, for the English cricket season is so designed that it seems impossible for us to unearth a fast bowler who can stay fit in body and mind for long enough to make an enduring impact on the Test scene. That has been our greatest failing since Bob Willis bowed out of international cricket in 1984. Devon Malcolm has threatened to replace him on occasion, but insensitive handling and Malcolm's own inconsistency meant that his promise never fully came to fruition. Had Malcolm become the centrepiece of England's attack, our record would have been significantly improved over recent years. The tragedy is that he has been the only England fast bowler of note in more than a decade. Clearly, then, there is something wrong with the system that will bedevil anyone who is linked with the fortunes of the national side.

Nonetheless, what the May, Dexter and Illingworth years have shown us is that England need a backroom staff of men who are closer to the players' ages rather than those who played most of their cricket nearly thirty years ago. However shrewd they might have been when it comes to the basic disciplines of the game, they are too divorced from an era where cricket has evolved at a bewildering pace. Anyone who played the game in the pre-Packer era can have little idea of the different pressures today's players face. I reiterate that that doesn't make the current shape of cricket better or worse than it was in 1956, 1966 or 1976, but it is a dramatically different shape. One day cricket was almost unheard of when Illingworth led England for the last time in 1973 – he actually played just three such internationals, managing one win, one defeat and one no result, the full hand. His disdain for such matches is obvious and he was shocked by the public backlash which attended England's dismal one day form in South Africa and then the World Cup in 1996; to him, these games seemed unimportant. Illingworth was clearly out of touch with the public and it is they to whom he is finally accountable.

Botham is, of course, still revered by much of the cricketing public and significant sections of the tabloid press, including the *Mirror* for whom he contributes a column. He was scathing in his criticism of the English performances in the World Cup, suggesting that for the first time he wanted to see England humbled in the hope that changes might be made. These were the opening salvoes in Botham's own bid for the premiership in English cricket, a long campaign that rumbled on into the early weeks of the 1996 season. In the revised paperback edition of his autobiography published recently, he pushed his claims for Illingworth's job, while making the point that England should be coached by players like Lamb, Gower, Boycott, Gooch and himself. That England need leadership from a man more in touch with the players' own experiences is undeniable, an argument that will prove to be irresistible over the coming years. At the same time, one needs to question the names he puts forward. Boycott, for example, is a fine technician who clearly knows the game inside out and has helped many English players informally. However, as one who makes his living from the media and who is not afraid to offer vigorous criticism of what he sees as poor cricket, he is not wildly popular with the players.

Lamb, Gower and Botham were all exorcised from the English set up in part because they were felt to be a disruptive influence by Dexter, Stewart and Gooch – though Botham was ostensibly dropped from the West Indies tour of 1989/90 on the grounds of poor form, that was a handy excuse. The selectors wanted to change direction. It is a matter of opinion as to whether or not that was a necessary decision or not. However, one must remember that the 1980s for England were not one long period of constant success; memories of that decade are too often swayed by thoughts of Headingley in 1981. But let's remember too the West Indian blackwashes of 1984 and 1985/86 and the 4–0 defeat in 1988. There were series defeats at the hands of New Zealand in 1983/84 and 1986 along with a drawn rubber in 1987/88, losses to India in 1981/82 and 1986, to Pakistan in 1983/84, 1987 and 1987/88. These were not the glory years. What made the 1980s special was beating Australia in 1981, 1985 and 1986/87. Even then, they hammered us in return in 1979/80 and 1989, also winning in 1982/83. Our great players in these less than distinguished years were Botham, Gower, Lamb, Gooch and Gatting, with Botham's own record standing as played 102, won 35, lost 30, drawn 37, not as great as memory alone might suggest, though rapturous statistics in the light of England's recent offerings. Interestingly, post-1982, the record is played 48, won 11, lost 21, drawn 16, suggesting that perhaps lifestyle had got in the way of the cricket. Given that the Gooch/Stewart partnership bore some fruit in the West Indies before fitness training became a wearisome obsession, the loss of Botham and Gower was not the grievous blow it might have appeared.

But of course they do represent a wealth of experience which should be tapped in some way, even if only in an advisory capacity alongside a different kind of coach, one who is open to new methods and the latest techniques for maximising an individual's performance on the field. A modern, forward-thinking coach is desperately important if England are to progress. David Lloyd's appointment was a step in the right direction, presenting the players with someone on the same wavelength, someone who understood the demands of the game as it's played in 1997. He looks to be building on the work Graham Gooch did in his time as England skipper. If Gower's demise came more swiftly and far less graciously than was necessary, Gooch, Dexter and Stewart were right in calling time on 'the champagne set'. Men like Botham, Lamb and Gower were great players, relying on flair, instinct, natural timing. They had gifts beyond the ordinary and consequently they could get away with a few late nights and still perform well; they were also around at the right time, for now such licence could not be given to players. Touring was not quite so intensive even six or seven years ago and England's away matches were not captured live on television as they are by Botham's current employers, Sky. A poor performance on the other side of the world was criticised but was not put under the spotlight as it is today. The rewards have grown enormously, but so have the pressures. Those who are merely very good players need to work harder than a Gower or a Botham did at their peak. Sure, they need a drink or two in the evening to unwind, but equally they need to adopt a highly focused and rigorously professional attitude to what is an increasingly professional game. The foundations laid by Gooch have borne fruit in the determined and utterly committed approach of men like Mike Atherton and Alec Stewart. Dermot Reeve made the point in *Winning Ways* that 'Goochy had difficulty understanding why others in the team lacked his dedication and desire to succeed . . . I was impressed with the way he led by example and trained so hard. Goochy was quite right to say that times had changed, that you couldn't have a good night out and then expect to turn it on at full power in a vital game. He felt you had to treat your body like an engine, putting the best oil in it, with regular services . . . he loved a laugh, enjoyed a drink at the right times and encouraged the players fully.'

That attitude is true of the very best coaches in the game. Look at the dramatic advances made by the South Africans in a very short time under the eye of Bob Woolmer. He is not afraid to admit he is still learning about the game, is not dogmatic, fosters a good team spirit and is ready to encourage the players to express themselves. His is an original mind capable of lateral thinking. He employs nutritonists, dieticians, medical experts on every form of physical fitness. Botham himself seems unimpressed by this aspect of the modern game and though he would like to be involved in the England set up, he admits that 'I don't see myself strutting around the nets in a tracksuit.' Comments like that suggest that he has learned little from the advances made by Australia and South Africa in recent years and that he is living in as much of a time warp as Illingworth ever was. The lackadaisical days have gone. Australia win so regularly not simply because they have good players but because they work hard. It's a cliché to say that the Aussies are as fresh at the end of a long day as they are at the start, but it happens to be true. The Waughs, Taylor, Elliott *et al* are capable of playing the very long innings that Test cricket demands because their concentration does not waver with fatigue. Their bowlers can be relied upon to bowl with the same control in the final session as they did in the first. As a team, they are fiercely fit for they have recognised that the last thirty minutes of a day are every bit as important as the first thirty. Much of that comes down to preparation, something at which Botham was poor.

Since Botham was impatient with some of Gooch's methods, it seems unlikely that he would be the best man to deal with the differing demands of players. Just as Gooch could not deal with Gower's relaxed attitude to his cricket, Botham seems unhappy with those who are keen to get into the best physical shape, or have their own attitude to getting ready for a game. Therefore, instead of having a hands-on role elsewhere, Botham would surely be of most use in the dressing room in a motivational role, firing the players up for battle. He is still a commanding figure in the game. He could be an extremely useful supporting player alongside a supremo figure like Lloyd or Dermot Reeve – now that would be a pairing! But it would need to be a supporting role, for the number one position is not one to which he is suited.

It could even do him harm. Botham is a team player but his popular image is too big for the wider world to accept him as simply that. The selection committee would be cast as Botham and Botham would be cast as the selection committee, that much is inescapable. Still respected by the public, a stint as the face of English cricket might damage his reputation and consequently his commercial well-being; after all, though England are scarcely world beaters at present, just who are the names lurking in county cricket that might transform them into a side capable of winning regularly all around the globe? Botham could help pick a side; sadly he couldn't be transported back to his early twenties too. Raymond Illingworth went from being the *éminence grise* of English cricket to being an object of derision in just eighteen months. Wouldn't the same fate befall Botham – recall the captaincy years for evidence of the fickle nature of both the media and the public. After his years in the job, Ray Illingworth is now in effective retirement. No longer wanted as a commentator, the *Express* is the only outlet for him. In two years, if England have been beaten in an Ashes series, lost in the West Indies, and gone down against South Africa with Botham at the helm, where would that leave him? Botham's retort would be that with him in command such results would not come about, but is that realistic? Would any bookmaker make England favourites for any of those series? Which new players might appear to turn England into winners? Isn't it more accurate to say that whoever leads England in the next eighteen months is looking down the barrel of a gun?

There are good players in English cricket, many of whom are under achieving. Darren Gough, for example, looked a top class Test match prospect just two years ago, but since then injury and loss of form have come his way. Dominic Cork had a decidedly average second season in Test cricket, bowed down by too much work. What of Chris Lewis,

Mark Ramprakash, Phil Tufnell? These men, along with established players such as Atherton, Stewart, Knight, Crawley and Thorpe, offer a nucleus of talent that should at least make England hard to beat. Why then were they so easily swept aside by Pakistan in 1996 why was the 1996 World Cup such a disaster, why have England slipped down the world rankings? Perhaps Botham might be able to get the very best out of these men by his mere presence, but if he was seen to be associated with losers, might not the lucrative speaking tours and advertisements dry up? Would Sky want him back if his tenure ended in ignominy? If nothing else, it would end all the arguments that fly back and forth between himself and Ray Illingworth as to who is the greatest, but perhaps Botham is better off leaving that unanswered.

Clearly the selection of Ray Illingworth as English manager and chairman of selectors was, in hindsight, a mistake. His blunt public pronouncements for many years on TV must have rankled with those who came under his stewardship. Allowing him to make regular newspaper pronouncements on the players he'd picked and discarded was equally stupid – that's something that might affect Botham in due course. It's little wonder that Robin Smith, for example, fell away so badly once Illingworth was installed, having had to listen to his trenchant criticism of his technique against spinners for a number of years. His treatment of Angus Fraser and Devon Malcolm was less than inspirational. More than anything else, Illingworth seemed an anachronism. He wanted a side that could win the Ashes as they were fought for in 1972. Botham is close to falling into the same trap. His impatience with authority has been well documented. He has always wanted to do things his own way, but might that way not be out of date too? Think back to that quotation from Peter Roebuck's *It Sort Of Clicks* when discussing Botham's captaincy of Somerset: 'he had a vision of a beautiful world ... where he and his mates, arriving in eccentric clothes to upset the fuddy-duddies, would laugh and drink the nights away, and then storm around defeating all the conventional types with their managers and their serious faces'. It didn't work then and it certainly could not work now. It may be prosaic, but good, successful cricket is built upon masses of hard work. Brian Lara is a regular visitor to the nets whatever his form.

Other dangers lurk for Botham in his work for the *Mirror* and for Sky Sports. Though informally co-opted into the England think tank for the winter tour of Zimbabwe and New Zealand, he was caught off guard at times when donning his broadcasting hat. During the First Test against New Zealand in Auckland in 1996/97 during a particularly torpid piece of English cricket when Cork and Gough were unable to score the quick runs required, Botham was asked about England's game plan. His reply made it clear that he was unimpressed, wondering aloud whether a game plan existed. Commenting on Sky's coverage, Roy Hattersley noted in the *Express* that on the first day when England bowled poorly, 'there was the constant implication that in their fast bowling days, Bob Willis and Ian Botham would have run through the New Zealanders before lunch'. Like Boycott before him, Botham may soon have to choose between commentary and country lest he make his position with the latter untenable with remarks made for the benefit of his paymaster.

One thing is perfectly clear, he's unlikely to fit in with the Lord's hierarchy, so a job with the newly established England & Wales Cricket Board seems like a non-starter. Botham would clearly love to put something back into the game and transform the England side into winners, but is that the best job for him given his outside interests? Cricket is about to undergo the greatest revolution in its history. Just as football and rugby have been irrevocably changed by Murdoch's television millions, so too will cricket be. It's amazing in many ways that the current structure of Test cricket has stayed intact for so many years for, essentially, it's utterly meaningless. A beautiful absurdity. We play against one country one year, another the next but, an Ashes series apart, what's the point? Where does it lead? Arguments go on about who are the world champions, but no one can ever prove it conclusively. A world championship of Test cricket is the inevitable next step if it is to survive as the most important form of the game. When this revolution comes, the game will be turned upside down by money, the old structures swept away. The players will become superstars, as important as Shearer, Cantona or Gullit. We will watch cricket on TV all the year round from all over the world, beamed to us at odd times from odd locations to maximise the profitability for the TV companies that will underwrite the game. Change will come so quickly and in such dramatic fashion that the Packer revolution will seem mild by comparison and the experience of those who played in the 1980s will be as redundant to the new realities as those who played in the 1960s are to today. When that day comes – and it is not far off – professionalism will be vital and an era of charismatic personalities will be consigned to the dustbin of history, a delightful eccentricity from a forgotten age. The personalities will be off the field since the faceless players will be worked so hard and will be so determined to stay at the top that they won't have the time or the freedom to get involved in the kind of escapades that Gower or Botham or Miller or Compton or Sobers or Benaud did. Great personalities will be needed to front the programmes, to remind us of a time when sport was fun, when there were laughs to be had, when it wasn't all a matter of life and death. What will be required are heroes of the past who have a ready wit, are comfortable in front of the camera, who have shown themselves to have a genuine rapport with the public, someone to whom they respond warmly. Now *that* sounds like a job for Ian Botham.

WALK THIS WAY
Leukaemia Research

I t's a pretty sad reflection of the times in which we live that when a public figure tries to do something for a worthwhile cause, the first question that's asked is always 'What's in it for them?' Admittedly, plenty of celebrities have tried to cash in on causes over the years, turning their apparent charitable concern into one glorious photo opportunity to further their own careers. The public has a right to be cynical about it all, but that doesn't mean that every good turn is done in the hope of boosting an ego or raising a profile.

It must be conceded that when the plans for his great John o'Groats to Land's End walk were first unveiled in 1985, Ian Botham was not at his most universally popular. The New Zealand/Pakistan tour of 1983/84 had been a disaster on and off the field. The great Botham had not overcome the West Indians in the home series of 1984. His press was unflattering and he was surrounded by an unpleasant atmosphere, almost one of decay. It was something he could not dispel however hard he tried. His critics leapt upon the walk idea as evidence that he was trying to bribe his way back into the public affection; unable to charm them on the field any longer, the yob was pretending to have a con-science. Given that Botham had already been quietly helping the cause for eight years and has subsequently pounded his way across thousands of miles and raised millions for leukaemia research, perhaps those critics are proud of their contribution.

Had they taken the trouble to find out the reasons for Botham's interest in the subject, they'd have found they were deeply rooted. It

227

dated back to the summer of 1977 when he'd picked up an injury while fielding in the Australian second innings of the Fourth Test at Headingley. Standing on the ball in his attempt to field it, he managed to break a bone in his left foot. Unaware of that at the time, he ignored the injury and continued to bowl, further aggravating the damage. Back in Taunton after the game he went to the local Musgrove Park Hospital for further treatment, passing through the children's ward while he was there. It was then that he was informed that two of the children, who looked right as rain to the naked eye, had little time left. Struck down by leukaemia, they were incurable. Already in a highly emotional state himself since Kath was in the final days of her pregnancy with Liam, Botham was stunned by this news, news of a disease that, like so many of us back then, he'd barely heard of. With his own child about to be born, his mood could be summed up as 'there but for the grace of God go my family'.

His initial response was typically generous. On hearing that the annual party for the children had been cancelled, he handed over fifty pounds to make sure it would go ahead. Many would have left it at that, happy to have made some contribution, unsure of what to do next until all thoughts of the disease were pushed out of mind by the demands of day to day living. Given the frantic lifestyle that Botham lived, it would be excusable for him to have forgotten all about it in a matter of months. But that is not his way. Certainly he can be arrogant and rude at times, but equally he is a committed father and, when approached in the right way, cannot do enough for those he chooses to help. When you take into account everything else that was going on in his life, he was surely one of the greatest charity fundraisers of the 1980s, and while the sums raised can't quite compare with Live Aid, the amount of work he and Kath undertook in arranging the nightmarish itineraries that attended the walks, organising help from local businesses and so on, compares with that done by Sir Bob Geldof. Perhaps both the Bothams deserved that kind of recognition too.

Where the walks are concerned, Botham deserves every last word of praise that he has received. Of course the walks have done his reputation no harm, but that was never a consideration. Had he been solely interested in looking after his battered public image, he could easily have engaged the services of a media guru, had a make over, appeared contrite at his failings and come out the other end smelling of roses. That would have required virtually no effort on his part and might even have earned him some lucrative new commercial contracts. That would have been an easy option, one guaranteed to succeed. Instead, he did what he wanted to do and stuff the consequences. When, on the eve of a vitally important Test match tour to the West Indies, someone as busy as Ian Botham gives up a month of his life to walk the length of Britain, he deserves to be taken seriously, deserves to be taken at face value. That alone underlined that he was interested in the cause. In its way, this was a more remarkable effort than anything he'd ever done on the field of play, far more heroic in its scale and purpose, the more so since the huge physical effort might even have taken its toll on his performance on the cricket field, laying him open to criticism from all sources.

That first long trudge through October and November 1985 lasted thirty-five days amid a whirl of publicity. A 'Who's Who' of English cricket accompanied him at one stage or another, Jack Bannister filing an on the sport report for *Wisden Cricket Monthly* which demonstrated just how badly Botham had been misunderstood over the years:

> his treatment of the crowd was exemplary, with the very young and the aged receiving special consideration . . . a woman approached him and stuffed a £10 note in one hand and a scribbled note in the other. He read it and silently handed it to me. It read "My little one has got it. For God's sake, keep going" . . . on Day 34 Botham still had enough instinct for the right action at the right time to present an old lady in an invalid chair with a long-stemmed red carnation . . . he struck chords of empathy with the public, young and old alike, which will reverberate for a long while.

In the face of those reactions, it's hard to see how anyone could criticise him as self-serving.

His need for new challenges – substitute Headingleys – is detailed elsewhere. If there was any selfish motive involved in his fundraising walks, it was in providing him with another mighty challenge. The leukaemia walk, created out of a genuine passion to help the helpless, was another Headingley. It was a classic example of his core philosophy: nothing is impossible. If Botham can imagine it, he can turn it into reality. After a year when the press had scarcely been off his back, who else would emerge from the security and privacy of his own home and lay himself out in the open before the public for the greater part of five weeks? The reaction was impossible to predict; given the level of media hostility towards him, he could have been ignored, booed, attacked, he could have had things thrown at him, failed to raise any money and been made to look ridiculous. Instead he swept the whole country along with him, manipulating the newspapers that had victimised him so remorselessly over the years.

Hardbitten journalists were among the first to fall under the Pied Piper's latest spell, dispelling any lingering thoughts that this was a glorified PR exercise. They were swept along on the rising tide of public feeling, responding to Botham as the rest of the country did. Even when the novelty had worn off five years later, commentators such as the *Mail on Sunday*'s Patrick Collins were sufficiently touched by Botham's obvious feeling for the cause that they filed glowing reports about less glamorous walks such as the East Coast March from Aberdeen to Ipswich. Catching up with him in Grimsby, Collins reported one of the local mayor's attendants saying 'He's got his critics has Ian Botham, but after this, I shan't have a word said against him.' 'For what it's worth,' added Collins, 'neither shall I. There are those who suspect that Botham has used these walks to enhance his frequently dubious image. After attempting to match his stride on a single 25-mile, six-hour slog, I can give the lie to that cynicism.' Botham himself pointed out that 'sure it's a struggle. I mean, after about an hour every day, my hands start swelling incredibly and my feet feel like they don't belong to me. But I get a good rest every night and I'm ready next morning. It's got to be done hasn't it?' When Collins remarked that the Test team was about to depart for Australia, Botham offered a stunning rejoinder: 'Not for me, mate. I don't want it any more. I wouldn't swop this for anything.'

The first walk, John o'Groats to Land's End, raised a sum not far short of £1,000,000 from a slew of donations and was indicative of the Botham determination to make a difference in the face of a terrible disease. It was a genuinely inspiring, genuinely heroic effort that allowed the whole country to take part in what became a moral crusade in the mould of Live Aid. Aside from the mind-boggling statistics of the walk itself, it did represent a welcome opportunity for Botham to meet the people and to change the public perception of him in the wake of the constant drug allegations. The Ian Botham that we saw on the charity walk was the real man, warts and all. There were the moments when his temper got the better of him, striking out at a police officer who, fortunately, made nothing of the incident, understanding that physical exhaustion can play havoc with perspective. There were the moments of bravado – running thirty-six miles in bursts, turning somersaults on the road. There were the moments of generosity, tenderness and genuine communication with the people. There were the moments designed purely for the crowds: finishing the walk in top hat and tails, leaping into the Atlantic off Land's End. There was the spirit of camaraderie that existed between Botham and his fellow walkers, Alan Border's brother John, journalist Chris Lander and Mancunian businessman Phil Rance, men who took Botham at face value and who wanted nothing from him but his friendship, a spirit which carried them through to their goal.

Inevitably, efforts were made to rain on his parade. One freelance journalist made unsubstantiated allegations that Botham and friends had been smoking pot. Since the quartet had had a police escort virtually every step of the way and had been mobbed wherever they went, it was difficult to see how they could possibly have got away with any such thing. The charge was investigated by police and quickly dismissed out of hand. It must have saddened Botham though to see his generous enterprise sullied by such pettiness. And while not wishing to condone the use of illegal substances, even if the four *had* been fuelled by any or every soft drug on the list, those leukaemia sufferers who have been helped by the walk would not have cared less.

This trek up and down the country, along with further walks such as Belfast to Dublin, around the Channel Islands, the East Coast March detailed above, from Land's End to Margate, or retracing Hannibal's journey across the Alps, have swelled the coffers for the cause. In truth, Botham is far better suited to this role than that of an international cricketer in the media age. He is a bigger spirit than the staid game of cricket can handle. He is a bolder man than the little world of opinion formers can bear. He has a mission, he has ambitions, he has the common touch. It requires an indomitable and generous spirit to undertake anything as ostensibly impossible as his charity walks. That humanity can spill over, his exuberance can cause difficulties in a world of petty regulations, while his sense of certainty in everything that he does can lead him into trouble on the occasions when he hasn't got it right. When he is out of touch he resembles a dinosaur, for everything he does is on such a grand scale. Mistakes look worse just as triumphs seem unimaginably enormous. He has got many things wrong in his time but he's got far more things right. Still his generosity shines through the occasionally surly demeanour he adopts when discussing cricket. In New Zealand he had his head shaved, an action which according to Sky Sports managed to raise £50,000 for charity. That's a mark of his open and giving nature and also a tribute to his enduring legend. Who else would have raised £5,000, never mind £50,000, from such a simple action?

Ian Botham will always have his critics. He pretends to ignore them but his willingness to take legal action against those whom he feels have transgressed illustrates his surprisingly thin skin. Botham, above all, wants to be loved by the people, wants to rekindle the flame of affection that he felt throughout his golden years. That may well be beyond him for those were the headiest of days. He would be better served by far to draw satisfaction from his deeds. Forget the runs, catches and wickets. When he gets to bed at night, he need only recall that the leukaemia research laboratories in Glasgow have been named in his honour as a tribute to his tireless fundraising activities. That is enough for any man. No one who could react so spontaneously and vigorously to an anonymous disease could be anything but a very great man. The last word on that score goes to Vivian Richards: 'he responds, he's human, he's not a plastic guy'.

24/11/55	Born in Heswall, Cheshire – weight 10lb 1oz.
1969	Debut for Somerset Under 15s.
1971	Plays for the South West in the English Schools' Under 15 cricket festival, Liverpool.
8/71	Has trial for Lord's groundstaff and is invited back for the following year.
1972	Spends summer on Lord's groundstaff.
1973	Invited to return to Lord's, but spends most of the summer playing for Somerset Second Eleven.
2/9/73	Makes Somerset debut versus Sussex at Hove in John Player League. Scores two, bowls three overs (0/22) and takes one catch to dismiss Tony Greig.
8/5/74	First class debut for Somerset against Lancashire at Taunton. Scores thirteen, bowls three overs for fifteen, catches Jack Simmons.
27/5/74	Takes first first class wicket, Gloucestershire's Dunstan.
12/6/74	Struck in the face by an Andy Roberts bouncer but still guides Somerset to victory in Benson & Hedges quarter-final against Hampshire.
26/6/74	Meets Kathryn Waller at the Benson & Hedges Cup semi-final at Leicester.
13/7/74	Maiden first class fifty, fifty-nine against Mike Brearley's Middlesex at Taunton.
9/74	Completes debut season with 441 runs and thirty wickets in first class cricket.
9/75	Season of improvement sees him finish with 584 runs and sixty-two wickets.
31/1/76	Marries Kathryn Waller.

3/8/76	Maiden first class hundred, 167 not out against Nottinghamshire at Trent Bridge.
26/8/76	Makes international debut against West Indies in one day international at Scarborough. Scores one, bowls three overs for twenty-six, takes wicket of Lawrence Rowe.
9/76	Ends season with 1022 runs and sixty-six wickets.
Winter 76/7	Spends winter on Whitbread scholarship in Australia.
28/7/77	Test match debut versus Australia at Trent Bridge. Takes 5/74 in first innings, first Test wicket being Greg Chappell. Scores twenty-five in only innings. England win by seven wickets.
26/8/77	Son Liam is born.
9/77	Completes season with two Test caps and selection for winter tour to Pakistan and New Zealand. Scores 738 runs and takes eighty-eight wickets in season.
Winter 77/8	Plays all three Tests against New Zealand. Scores maiden hundred, 103, in second game at Christchurch – runs Boycott out in second innings on Willis's instructions. Also takes eight wickets in match. Gets a further five and another fifty in third game. Returns home as England's number one all-rounder.
4/78	Selected as one of *Wisden*'s Five Cricketers of the Year.
19/4/78	Takes hat-trick for MCC against Middlesex – Radley, Barlow, Featherstone, all bowled.
6/78	Scores two centuries and takes thirteen wickets in home series against Pakistan. At Lord's, becomes first man to score a hundred and take eight wickets in an innings in Test history.
8/78	Takes twenty-four wickets in home series against New Zealand.
9/78	Ends season with selection for Australian tour.

10/78	Injures hand by putting it through glass in a revolving door at a pub in Epworth. Unfit at start of tour to Australia.
Winter 78/9	Scores 291 runs and takes twenty-three wickets in triumphant series for England.
3/2/79	Daughter Sarah is born.
23/6/79	Plays in defeated England side in Prudential World Cup Final against West Indies.
6/8/79	Takes 100th Test wicket when Brearley catches Gavaskar at Lord's. Completes feat in two years, nine days, a new record. It is his nineteenth Test.
20/8/79	Scores 99 before lunch for England against India at Headingley.
30/8/79	Reaches 1000 Test runs in his twenty-first Test. Records the fastest ever Test match double of 1000 runs and 100 wickets.
8/9/79	Plays in Somerset side that wins Gillette Cup at Lord's, beating Northamptonshire by forty-five runs. It is Somerset's first ever trophy.
9/9/79	Helps Somerset clinch John Player League with victory over Nottinghamshire at Trent Bridge.
Winter 79/80	Tours Australia with England and tops bowling averages, third in batting averages. England play the Golden Jubilee Test in India on their way home. Botham scores a hundred, takes six wickets in first innings and seven in second, an unparalleled individual performance.
4/80	Sustains back injury during game versus Oxford University.
5/80	Appointed England captain.
24/5/80	Registers highest career score, 228 not out in 184 minutes against Gloucestershire at Taunton.
28/5/80	First match as England captain, Prudential Trophy game at Headingley. West Indies win by twenty-four runs.

England win second game at Lord's on 30/5, Botham hitting the winning runs.

30/5/80	Appointed captain for first two Tests against West Indies.
4/6/80	Stopped for speeding by police.
5/6/80	Leads England in a Test match against West Indies at Trent Bridge. Scores a total of sixty-one runs and has match figures of four for ninety-eight. England lose by two wickets.
12/8/80	England lose West Indian series by one game to nil.
30/8/80	Assaulted by MCC members during suspension of play in Centenary Test.
1/9/80	Appointed England captain for tour of West Indies. Is ordered to lose weight.
23/12/80	Involved in a night club incident in Scunthorpe. Comes to aid of friend, Joe Neenan of Scunthorpe United, but is later charged with assault. Is later acquitted.
15/2/81	On rest day of First Test in Trinidad, Botham suggests that if England don't get a draw 'heads will roll'. England lose by an innings.
2/81	Robin Jackman's visitor's permit is revoked in Guyana. The Second Test is cancelled and tour placed in jeopardy.
14/3/81	Ken Barrington dies of a heart attack in Barbados.
18/3/81	Shell-shocked England lose Third Test by 298 runs.
15/4/81	Series ends in two-nil defeat, England salvaging draws in last two games. Botham ends series with seventy-three runs at ten and fifteen wickets at thirty-three – tops bowling averages.
4/81	Jostles Henry Blofeld at Nassau airport following disagreement over a press article.
5/81	Appointed England captain for Australian series on match by match basis.
8/6/81	England lose Prudential Trophy series by two to one.

21/6/81	England lose First Test by four wickets.
7/7/81	Botham registers pair at Lord's in drawn Second Test. Returns to pavilion to stony silence. Resigns captaincy.
21/7/81	Completes innings of 149 not out as England win Third Test at Headingley having followed on, first such Test match occurrence since 1894/95.
25/7/81	Plays in Somerset side that wins Benson & Hedges Cup, beating Surrey at Lord's by seven wickets.
2/8/81	Takes five wickets for one run in final burst to seal victory in Fourth Test at Edgbaston.
15/8/81	Scores century in Fifth Test to clinch series win at Old Trafford, described as one of the finest innings ever.
31/8/81	Dismisses Rodney Marsh to claim 200th Test wicket at the Oval. Completes ten wickets in a Test match for the final time.
1/9/81	Man of the Series versus Australia: 399 runs at thirty-six, thirty-four wickets at twenty-one.
23/9/81	Is cleared of charges relating to Neenan incident on 23/12/80.
12/81	Voted BBC Sports Personality of the Year.
Winter 81/2	Tours India under Keith Fletcher. Tops batting averages with 440 runs at fifty-five. On 1 December, completes 2000 runs in Tests. Fastest ever double double – forty-two Tests. On 22 January 1982 scores the fastest ever century on Indian soil against Central Zone at Indore – fifty minutes, forty-eight balls.
13/3/82	Sends message of support to anti-apartheid rally in Trafalgar Square.
17/5/82	Crashes two Saab motor cars in a celebrity race day at Thruxton.
9/7/82	Completes highest Test score, 208, versus India at the Oval. Fastest ever Test double hundred in balls received – 220.

24/7/82	Plays in Somerset side which retains the Benson & Hedges Cup with a nine wicket win over Nottinghamshire.
Winter 82/3	Tours Australia. On 12 November reaches 3000 runs in fifty-fifth Test. Otherwise, an ordinary tour as England lose the Ashes. Is fined £200 by tour manager Doug Insole for comments about Australian umpires.
6/83	Defies TCCB attempts to end his *Sun* column.
22/6/83	Plays in England side beaten by India in Prudential World Cup semi-final.
25/8/83	Scores last Test century on home soil, 103, against New Zealand at the Oval.
3/9/83	Captains Somerset side that wins the NatWest Bank Trophy at Lord's, beating Kent by twenty-four runs.
24/11/83	Appointed as Somerset's captain.
Winter 83/4	Tours with England in New Zealand and Pakistan. Tour is marred by newspaper allegations regarding drug taking by England players. Botham decides to sue the *Mail on Sunday*. Returns home early from Pakistan for a knee operation. While in hospital, gives an interview in which he says Pakistan 'is the kind of place to send your mother-in-law for a month, all expenses paid'. Is subsequently fined £1000 by TCCB.
4/84	Begins first season as Somerset captain – it is also his benefit year.
2/7/84	Reaches 4000 runs in his sixty-ninth Test.
3/7/84	Ends most personally successful Test against West Indies – eighty-one and 8/103 – on the losing side at Lord's. On final day, bowls twenty overs for 117 runs.
26/7/84	Announces he will be unavailable for England's winter tour of India.
7/84	Arrives late for his benefit game at Sparkford, Club captain Graham Reeve complains about Botham's atti-

tude and makes it clear he will not be welcome in future.

9/8/84	Takes his 300th wicket in his seventy-second Test, the first man to complete 4000 runs and 300 wickets.
9/84	Completes first season as county captain. Somerset are seventh in the Championship, quarter-finalists in the two cup competitions, and thirteenth on Sundays.
31/12/84	Police search Botham's Epworth home and find a small quantity of cannabis.
14/2/85	Pleads guilty to possession of cannabis at Scunthorpe Magistrates Court. Is fined £100.
3/85	Engages Tim Hudson as manager.
1/7/85	Dismisses Australia's Graeme Wood at Lord's to become England's greatest wicket taker in Tests.
13/7/85	Has argument with Umpire Whitehead during Trent Bridge Test. Given severe warning about future conduct by TCCB.
26/7/85	Scores fastest hundred of the season against Warwickshire at Edgbaston in forty-nine minutes. Registers twelve sixes in his innings of 138 not out.
8/85	It's announced that his 1984 benefit season raised £90,822, a Somerset record.
9/85	Completes season with a world record of eighty sixes in the summer. Season ends with Somerset bottom of County Championship.
8/10/85	Botham resigns the Somerset captaincy.
13/11/85	Daughter Rebecca is born.
10 & 11/85	First marathon walk in aid of leukaemia research from John o'Groats to Land's End.
Winter 85/6	Tours West Indies with England. Tour is dogged by further press allegations concerning drugs and extra-marital affairs. Botham manages 168 runs at seventeen and eleven wickets at forty-nine. Prior to Fourth Test comes close to being dropped for the first time since

1977/78. Ends series with 354 wickets, one behind Dennis Lillee.

22/1/86   A portrait of Botham by John Bellany is unveiled in the National Portrait Gallery, the first cricketer to be so honoured since W.G. Grace. The portrait receives a mixed reaction.

3/86   Sacks Tim Hudson as manager.

5/86   Is made a vice president of Scunthorpe United.

18/5/86   In a *Mail on Sunday* article, Botham confesses that he has used pot in the past.

29/5/86   TCCB ban Botham from cricket from 29 May until 31 July, on the grounds of bringing the game into disrepute with his newspaper article, denying in the past that he had used cannabis and making public pronouncements without the clearance of his county.

2/8/86   Returns to first class cricket against Worcestershire at Weston-super-Mare.

3/8/86   Scores 104 not out from sixty-six balls in sixty-four minutes.

21/8/86   Returns to Test cricket against New Zealand at the Oval. Dismisses Bruce Edgar with first ball. Eleven balls later, dismisses Jeff Crowe to become the leading wicket taker in Test match history.

25/8/86   Hits the second fastest half century in Test history. Takes twenty-four from one over off Derek Stirling to equal the Test record set by Andy Roberts off Botham in 1980/81.

8/86   Viv Richards and Joel Garner are informed their playing contracts with Somerset will not be renewed. Botham threatens to leave unless they are reinstated.

9/86   A new waxwork of Botham is unveiled at Madame Tussaud's.

10/86   Announces that he will spend the next three winters playing for Queensland.

8/11/86   Special General Meeting of Somerset CCC backs the cricket committee. Richards and Garner are not reinstated. Botham says he will leave the club on the expiry of his contract on 31/12/86.

Winter 86/87 Tours Australia with England. During First Test on 15/11/86, registers last Test match century. In the Second Test, he captures his 100th catch in Tests on 3/12/86, the eighth outfielder to do so. In the Fourth Test, takes 5/41 on 26/12/86, his final five-wicket haul in Tests. *Wisden* notes that he has been an excellent influence on the side and has gone out of his way to help the younger players throughout the tour.

10/1/87   Signs a contract to play for Worcestershire.

4/87   Walks 150 miles from Belfast to Dublin in aid of leukaemia research.

25/4/87   Makes Championship debut for Worcestershire in a two-wicket win over Kent at New Road.

8/8/87   Concedes 217 runs from fifty-two overs against Pakistan at the Oval, the most conceded by any Englishman in Tests.

10/8/87   Scores his 5000th run in his ninety-fourth Test.

13/9/87   Scores sixty-one as Worcestershire clinch the Refuge Assurance League by beating Northamptonshire at Worcester. In the final four games, Botham and Tim Curtis share four century partnerships.

Winter 87/8 Plays for Queensland in Australia. Helps them reach the Sheffield Shield final. An altercation on the flight to the final in Perth ends with Botham's brief arrest. Following defeat in the final, Queensland terminate Botham's three-year contract after just one season.

4/88	Walks from Perpignan to Turin in the footsteps of Hannibal in aid of leukaemia research.

20/5/88   Botham finally bows to his back injury. He announces that he requires an operation to fuse two vertebrae and will miss the remainder of the season. He is an important influence in the dressing room as Worcestershire win the County Championship and retain the Refuge Assurance League.

14/12/88   Taken to Chelsea police station to answer charges of assault on one Kevin James Batten. Charges withdrawn, though not before the allegations make the front page of the *Sun*. They make an out of court settlement.

15/4/89   Botham returns to first class cricket, playing for Worcestershire against MCC.

2/7/89   Is struck in the face by a drunken youth in an unprovoked attack in a Northampton pub.

31/8/89   Botham helps Worcestershire retain the County Championship by beating Gloucestershire at New Road.

9/89   Following an indifferent season, Botham is omitted from England's party to tour West Indies. His failure to make the party is overshadowed by the dropping of David Gower, England captain throughout the previous summer.

5/11/89   Appears on BBC Radio's Desert Island Discs.

14/7/90   Plays in Worcestershire team beaten in the Benson & Hedges Cup Final by Lancashire.

11/90   Walks 630 miles in twenty-six days from Aberdeen to Ipswich in aid of leukaemia research.

Winter 90/91   Takes part in *Jack & The Beanstalk* pantomime at Bradford Alhambra.

14/7/91   Plays in Worcestershire team that beat Lancashire by sixty-five runs in the Benson & Hedges Cup Final.

9/91   Announces that he will to move Durham for their inaugural Championship season in 1992.

15/9/91   Ends Worcestershire career by playing in the team that beats Lancashire by seven runs to win the Refuge Assurance Cup.

9/91   Is selected for England tour to New Zealand and then Australia for the Benson & Hedges World Cup series. Is given permission to join the tour late so that he may discharge his commitments to the Bournemouth pantomime, *Jack & The Beanstalk.*

6/2/92   Plays his 100th Test, against New Zealand in Wellington.

25/3/92   Plays in the England side that loses the World Cup Final to Pakistan by twenty-two runs.

25/4/92   Makes his first class debut for Durham against Leicestershire in their inaugural Championship match at Durham University. Takes Durham's first Championship wicket when he dismisses Nigel Briers.

29/4/92   Scores 105 on Durham debut. It is their first Championship century.

13/6/92   Is appointed OBE in the Queen's Birthday Honours.

21/6/92   Completes his final Test match for England at Lord's as they lose to Pakistan by two wickets. Scores two and six, takes none for nine and holds two catches. His final record is 102 Tests, 5200 runs at 33.55 with fourteen centuries. He has 383 wickets at a cost of 28.40. He has also held 120 catches, an English record he holds with Lord Cowdrey.

24/8/92   He plays his final game in England colours, the Fifth Texaco Trophy game against Pakistan at Old Trafford, a game England win by six wickets. Botham bowls eleven overs for forty-three runs and does not bat. His one day record is 116 games, 2113 runs at 23.2, thirty-six catches and 145 wickets at 28.54.

243

10/92	Walks 546 miles from Land's End to Margate in aid of leukaemia research.
11 & 12/92	Appears on a speaking tour in the UK with Viv Richards – 'The King & I'.
Winter 92/93	Takes part in *Jack & The Beanstalk* pantomime in Stockport.
2/93	Takes the 'King & I' show to Australia.
18/7/93	Announces his immediate retirement from the game during Durham's match with the touring Australians.
19/7/93	Completes his final first class game by keeping wicket in the final over without pads or gloves. His final first class figures are 402 matches, 19,399 runs at 33.97 with thirty-eight centuries. He held 354 catches and took 1171 wickets at 27.22.
Winter 93/4	Takes part in *Dick Whittington* pantomime in Bath.
Winter 94/5	Takes part in *Cinderella* pantomime in Wimbledon.
3/95	Goes on speaking tour with Allan Lamb – 'Beef & Lamb In A Stew'.
5/95	Joins Sky Sports as commentator and analyst.
4/96	Accepts nomination as England selector. Fails to get elected to panel.
15/7/96	Begins the first of thirteen days in the Royal Court of Justice, taking action against Imran Khan for alleged libels in the *Sun* and *India Today*.
31/7/96	Trial ends. On both counts, the jury find in favour of Imran by a majority of 10–2. Later, Botham and Lamb decide to appeal against the decision.
11/96	Further speaking tour with Lamb – 'Balls 'n' all'.
Winter 96/7	Works alongside David Lloyd in an informal coaching and motivational capacity on England's tour of Zimbabwe and New Zealand.

Below is a match by match summary of Ian Botham's Test career. The left hand column details all of his Test match victims, mode of dismissal, and his full bowling analysis for each innings. The right column gives similar details of his batting performances, indicating his score, how he was out, and who dismissed him. For example, in his first game at Trent Bridge in 1977 he took the wickets of Chappell, Walters, Marsh, Walker and Thomson, taking five for seventy-four in the first innings and none for sixty in the second. When he batted, he scored twenty-five before being bowled by Max Walker.

ENGLAND VS AUSTRALIA AT TRENT BRIDGE
July 28, 29, 30, August 1, 2, 1977. England won by 7 wkts.

G.S. Chappell	bowled	19	20–5–74–5	b Walker	25
K.D. Walters	c Hendrick	11	25–5–60–0		
R.W. Marsh	lbw	0			
M.H.N. Walker	c Hendrick	0			
J.R. Thomson	c Knott	21			

ENGLAND VS AUSTRALIA AT HEADINGLEY
August 11, 12, 13, 15, 1977. England won by an innings and 85 runs.

D.W. Hookes	lbw	24	11–3–21–5	b Bright	0
K.D. Walters	c Hendrick	4	17–3–47–0		
R.W. Marsh	c Knott	2			
M.H.N. Walker	c Knott	7			
J.R. Thomson	bowled	0			

ENGLAND VS NEW ZEALAND AT BASIN RESERVE
February 10, 11, 12, 14, 15, 1978. New Zealand won by 72 runs.

J.G. Wright	lbw	55	12.6–2–27–2	c Burgess b Hadlee	7
S.L. Boock	bowled	4	9.3–3–13–2	c Boock b Hadlee	19
M.G. Burgess	c Boycott	6			
D.R. Hadlee	c Roope	2			

ENGLAND VS NEW ZEALAND AT LANCASTER PARK
February 24, 25, 26, 28, March 1, 1978. England won by 174 runs.

M.G. Burgess	c Roope	29	24.7–6–73–5	c Lees b Boock	103

B.E. Congdon	lbw	20	7–1–38–3	not out	30
W.K. Lees	c Miller	0			
R.O. Collinge	c Edmonds	32			
E.J. Chatfield	c Edmonds	3			
R.O. Collinge	c Miller	0			
S.L. Boock	c Taylor	0			
E.J. Chatfield	lbw	6			

ENGLAND VS NEW ZEALAND AT EDEN PARK
March 4, 5, 6, 8, 9, 10, 1978. Match drawn.

R.W. Anderson	c Gatting	17	34–4–109–5	c Edwards b Collinge	53
M.G. Burgess	c Randall	50	13–1–51–0		
B.E. Congdon	c Miller	5			
J.M. Parker	lbw	14			
R.J. Hadlee	c Roope	1			

ENGLAND VS PAKISTAN AT EDGBASTON
June 1, 2, 3, 5, 1978. England won by an innings and 57 runs.

Mudassar Nazar	c and b	14	15–4–52–1	c Qasim b Liaquat	100
			17–3–47–0		

ENGLAND VS PAKISTAN AT LORD'S
June 15, 16, 17, 19, 1978. England won by an innings and 120 runs.

Mudassar Nazar	c Taylor	10	5–2–17–0	b Liaquat	108
Haroon Rashid	bowled	4	20.5–8–34–8		
Talat Ali	c Roope	40			
Wasim Raja	c and b	1			
Wasim Bari	c Taylor	2			
Sikander Bakht	c Roope	1			
Iqbal Qasim	bowled	0			
Javed Miandad	c Gooch	22			

ENGLAND VS PAKISTAN AT HEADINGLEY
June 29, 30, July 1, 3, 4, 1978. Match drawn.

Haroon Rashid	c Brearley	7	18–2–59–4	lbw Sarfraz	4
Sadiq Mohammad	c Brearley	97			
Wasim Raja	lbw	0			
Sarfraz Nawaz	c Taylor	4			

ENGLAND VS NEW ZEALAND AT THE OVAL
July 27, 28, 29, 31, August 1, 1978. England won by 7 wkts.

G.P. Howarth	c Edmonds	94	22–7–58–1	c Bracewell b Boock	22

R.W. Anderson	c Taylor	2	19–2–46–3
J.G. Wright	lbw	25	
M.G. Burgess	lbw	7	

ENGLAND VS NEW ZEALAND AT TRENT BRIDGE
August 10, 11, 12, 14, 1978. England won by an innings and 119 runs.

B.A. Edgar	c Taylor	6	21–9–34–6	c Hadlee b Boock	8
R.W. Anderson	lbw	19	24–7–59–3		
M.G. Burgess	c Taylor	5			
B.E. Congdon	c Hendrick	27			
G.N. Edwards	c Taylor	0			
R.J. Hadlee	c Gooch	4			
B.E. Congdon	c Brearley	4			
B.L. Cairns	lbw	0			
R.J. Hadlee	c Taylor	11			

ENGLAND VS NEW ZEALAND AT LORD'S
August 24, 25, 26, 28, 1978. England won by 7 wkts.

J.G. Wright	c Edmonds	17	38–13–101–6	c Edgar b Collinge	21
M.G. Burgess	lbw	68	18.1–4–39–5		
B.E. Congdon	c Emburey	2			
R.W. Anderson	bowled	16			
R.J. Hadlee	c Brearley	0			
G.P. Howarth	c Taylor	123			
B.A. Edgar	bowled	4			
J.G. Wright	bowled	12			
J.M. Parker	c Taylor	3			
M.G. Burgess	c Hendrick	14			
R.O. Collinge	bowled	0			

ENGLAND VS AUSTRALIA AT WOOLLOONGABBA
December 1, 2, 3, 5, 6, 1978. England won by 7 wkts.

K.J. Hughes	c Taylor	4	12–1–40–3	c Maclean b Hogg	49
R.M. Hogg	c Taylor	36	26–5–95–3		
A.G. Hurst	c Taylor	0			
P.M. Toohey	lbw	1			
R.H. Hogg	bowled	16			
A.G. Hurst	bowled	0			

ENGLAND VS AUSTRALIA AT WACA GROUND
December 15, 16, 17, 19, 20, 1978. England won by 166 runs.

| | | 11–2–46–0 | lbw Hurst | 11 |
| | | 11–1–54–0 | c Wood b Yardley | 30 |

ENGLAND VS AUSTRALIA AT MELBOURNE CRICKET GROUND
December 29, 30, 1978, January 1, 2, 3, 1979. Australia won by 103 runs.

K.J. Hughes	c Taylor	0	20.1–4–68–3	c Darling b Higgs	22
G.N. Yallop	c Hendrick	41	15–4–41–3	c Maclean b Higgs	10
J.A. Maclean	bowled	8			
G.M. Wood	bowled	34			
R.M. Hogg	bowled	1			
K.J. Hughes	c Gower	48			

ENGLAND VS AUSTRALIA AT SYDNEY CRICKET GROUND
January 6, 7, 8, 10, 11, 1979. England won by 93 runs.

P.M. Toohey	c Gooch	1	28–3–87–2	c Yallop b Hogg	59
G. Dymock	bowled	5		c Wood b Higgs	6

ENGLAND VS AUSTRALIA AT ADELAIDE OVAL
January 27, 28, 29, 31, February 1, 1979. England won by 205 runs.

A.R. Border	c Taylor	11	11.4–0–42–4	c Wright b Higgs	74
P.H. Carlson	c Taylor	0	14–4–37–1	c Yardley b Hurst	7
B. Yardley	bowled	28			
W.M. Darling	c Willis	15			
W.M. Darling	bowled	18			

ENGLAND VS AUSTRALIA AT SYDNEY CRICKET GROUND
February 10, 11, 12, 14, 1979. England won by 9 wkts.

P.M. Toohey	c Taylor	8	9.7–1–57–4	c Carlson b Yardley	23
P.H. Carlson	c Gooch	2			
G.N. Yallop	c Gower	121			
A.G. Hurst	bowled	0			

ENGLAND VS INDIA AT EDGBASTON
July 12, 13, 14, 16, 1979. England won by an innings and 83 runs.

C.P.S. Chauhan	c Gooch	4	26–4–86–2	b Dev	33
Kapil Dev	lbw	1	29–8–70–5		
A.D. Gaekwad	c Gooch	15			
G.R. Viswanath	c Taylor	51			
M. Amarnath	lbw	10			
Kapil Dev	c Hendrick	21			
S. Venkataraghavan	lbw	0			

ENGLAND VS INDIA AT LORD'S
August 2, 3, 4, 6, 7, 1979. Match drawn.

C.P.S. Chauhan	c Randall	2	19–9–35–5	b Venkataraghavan	36

A.D. Gaekwad	c Taylor	13	35–13–80–1
Kapil Dev	c Miller	4	
Yashpal Sharma	c Taylor	11	
B. Reddy	lbw	0	
S.M. Gavaskar	c Brearley	59	

ENGLAND VS INDIA AT HEADINGLEY
August 16, 17, 18, 20, 21, 1979. Match drawn.

| | | | 13–3–39–0 | c Ghavri | 137 |
| | | | | b Venkataraghavan | |

ENGLAND VS INDIA AT THE OVAL
August 30, 31, September 1, 3, 4, 1979. Match drawn.

S.M. Gavaskar	c Bairstow	13	28–7–65–4	st Reddy	38
				b Venkataraghavan	
G.R. Viswanath	c Brearley	62	29–5–97–3		
K.D. Ghavri	c Bairstow	7			
B. Reddy	c Bairstow	12			
S.M. Gavaskar	c Gower	221			
Yashpal Sharma	lbw	19			
Yajurvindra Singh	lbw	1			

ENGLAND VS AUSTRALIA AT WACA GROUND
December 14, 15, 16, 18, 19, 1979. Australia won by 138 runs.

B.M. Laird	lbw	0	35–9–78–6	c Toohey b Thomson	15
A.R. Border	lbw	4	45.5–14–98–5	c Marsh b Lillee	18
G.S. Chappell	c Boycott	19			
R.J. Bright	c Taylor	17			
D.K. Lillee	c Taylor	18			
G. Dymock	bowled	5			
K.J. Hughes	c Miller	4			
P.M. Toohey	c Taylor	3			
R.W. Marsh	c Gower	4			
R.J. Bright	lbw	12			
J.R. Thomson	bowled	8			

ENGLAND VS AUSTRALIA AT SYDNEY CRICKET GROUND
January 4, 5, 6, 8, 9, 1980. Australia won by 6 wkts.

K.J. Hughes	c Taylor	18	17–7–29–4	c Chappell b Pascoe	27
A.R. Border	c Gooch	15	23.3–12–43–0	c Wiener b Chappell	0
D.K. Lillee	c Brearley	5			
G. Dymock	c Taylor	4			

ENGLAND VS AUSTRALIA AT MELBOURNE CRICKET GROUND
February 1, 2, 3, 5, 6, 1980. Australia won by 8 wkts.

K.J. Hughes	c Underwood	15	39.5–15–105–3	c Marsh b Lillee	8
G. Dymock	bowled	19	12–5–18–1	not out	119
A.A. Mallett	lbw	25			
R.B. McCosker	lbw	2			

ENGLAND VS INDIA AT WANKHEDE STADIUM
February 15, 17, 18, 19, 1980. England won by 10 wkts.

S.M. Gavaskar	c Taylor	49	22.5–7–58–6	lbw Ghavri	114
S.M. Patil	c Taylor	30	26–7–48–7		
Yashpal Sharma	lbw	21			
Kapil Dev	c Taylor	0			
N.S. Yadav	c Taylor	8			
D.R. Doshi	c Taylor	6			
R.M.H. Binny	lbw	0			
G.R. Viswanath	c Taylor	5			
S.M. Patil	lbw	0			
S.M. Gavaskar	c Taylor	24			
S.M.H. Kirmani	c Gooch	0			
Yashpal Sharma	lbw	27			
N.S. Yadav	c Taylor	15			

ENGLAND VS WEST INDIES AT TRENT BRIDGE
June 5, 6, 7, 9, 10, 1980. West Indies won by 2 wkts.

A.I. Kallicharran	bowled	17	20–6–50–3	c Richards b Garner	57
A.M.E. Roberts	lbw	21	16.4–6–48–1	c Richards b Roberts	4
J. Garner	c Lever	2			
I.V.A. Richards	lbw	48			

ENGLAND VS WEST INDIES AT LORD'S
June 19, 20, 21, 23, 24, 1980. Match drawn.

C.G. Greenidge	lbw	25	37–7–145–3	lbw Garner	8
D.L. Haynes	lbw	184			
D.L. Murray	c Tavare	34			

ENGLAND VS WEST INDIES AT OLD TRAFFORD
July 10, 11, 12, 14, 15, 1980. Match drawn.

A.I. Kallicharran	c Knott	13	20–6–64–3	c Murray b Garner	8
I.V.A. Richards	bowled	65		lbw Holding	35
D.L. Murray	bowled	17			

ENGLAND VS WEST INDIES AT THE OVAL
July 24, 25, 26, 28, 29, 1980. Match drawn.

I.V.A. Richards	c Willey	26	18.2–8–47–2	lbw Croft	9
J. Garner	c Gatting	46		c Greenidge b Garner	4

ENGLAND VS WEST INDIES AT HEADINGLEY
August 7, 8, 9, 11, 12, 1980. Match drawn.

C.G. Greenidge	lbw	34	19–8–31–1	c Richards b Holding	37
				lbw Marshall	7

ENGLAND VS AUSTRALIA AT LORD'S
August 28, 29, 30, September 1, 2, 1980. Match drawn.

K.J. Hughes	lbw	84	22–2–89–0	c Wood b Pascoe	0
			9.2–1–43–1		

ENGLAND VS WEST INDIES AT QUEEN'S PARK OVAL
February 13, 14, 16, 17, 18, 1981. West Indies won by an innings and 79 runs.

M.A. Holding	lbw	26	28–6–113–2	lbw Croft	0
J. Garner	lbw	4		c Holding b Richards	16

ENGLAND VS WEST INDIES AT KENSINGTON OVAL
March 13, 14, 15, 17, 18, 1981. West Indies won by 298 runs.

E.H. Mattis	lbw	16	25.1–5–77–4	c Murray b Holding	26
A.M.E. Roberts	c Bairstow	14	29–5–102–3	c Lloyd b Roberts	1
M.A. Holding	c Gatting	0			
J. Garner	c Bairstow	15			
D.L. Haynes	lbw	25			
C.H. Lloyd	lbw	66			
A.M.E. Roberts	c Bairstow	0			

ENGLAND VS WEST INDIES AT ST JOHN'S
March 27, 28, 29, 31, April 1, 1981. Match drawn.

D.L. Haynes	c Downton	4	37–6–127–4	c Lloyd b Croft	1
H.A. Gomes	c Gower	12			
E.H. Mattis	c Butcher	71			
D.A. Murray	c Boycott	1			

ENGLAND VS WEST INDIES AT SABINA PARK
April 10, 11, 12, 14, 15, 1981. Match drawn.

M.A. Holding	c Downton	0	26.1–9–73–2	c Greenidge b Marshall	13
C.E.H. Croft	c sub	0		c Garner b Holding	16

ENGLAND VS AUSTRALIA AT TRENT BRIDGE
June 18, 19, 20, 21, 1981. Australia won by 4 wkts.

G.F. Lawson	c Gower	14	16.5–6–34–2	b Alderman	1
A.R. Border	c and b	63	10–1–34–1	c Border b Lillee	33
G.N. Yallop	c Gatting	6			

ENGLAND VS AUSTRALIA AT LORD'S
July 2, 3, 4, 6, 7, 1981. Match drawn.

J. Dyson	c Gower	7	26–8–71–2	lbw Lawson	0
A.R. Border	c Gatting	64	8–3–10–1	b Bright	0
T.M. Chappell	c Taylor	5			

ENGLAND VS AUSTRALIA AT HEADINGLEY
July 16, 17, 18, 20, 21, 1981. England won by 18 runs.

G.M. Wood	lbw	34	39.2–11–95–6	c Marsh b Lillee	50
K.J. Hughes	c and b	89	7–3–14–1	not out	149*
G.N. Yallop	c Taylor	58			
A.R. Border	lbw	8			
G.F. Lawson	c Taylor	13			
R.W. Marsh	bowled	28			
G.M. Wood	c Taylor	10			

ENGLAND VS AUSTRALIA AT EDGBASTON
July 30, 31, August 1, 2, 1981. England won by 29 runs.

R.J. Bright	lbw	27	20–1–64–1	b Alderman	26
R.W. Marsh	bowled	4	14–9–11–5	c Marsh b Lillee	3
R.J. Bright	lbw	0			
D.K. Lillee	c Taylor	3			
M.F. Kent	bowled	10			
T.M. Alderman	bowled	0			

ENGLAND VS AUSTRALIA AT OLD TRAFFORD
August 13, 14, 15, 16, 17, 1981. England won by 103 runs.

A.R. Border	c Gower	11	6.2–1–28–3	c Bright b Lillee	0
R.J. Bright	c Knott	22	36–16–86–2	c Marsh b Whitney	118
D.K. Lillee	c Gooch	13			
K.J. Hughes	lbw	43			
T.M. Alderman	lbw	0			

ENGLAND VS AUSTRALIA AT THE OVAL
August 27, 28, 29, 31, September 1, 1981. Match drawn.

G.M. Wood	c Brearley	66	47–13–125–6	c Yallop b Lillee	3
M.F. Kent	c Gatting	54	42–9–128–4	lbw Alderman	16
K.J. Hughes	hit wicket	31			
R.J. Bright	c Brearley	3			
T.M. Alderman	bowled	0			
M.R. Whitney	bowled	4			
M.F. Kent	c Brearley	7			
R.W. Marsh	c Gatting	52			
R.J. Bright	bowled	11			
D.M. Wellham	lbw	103			

ENGLAND VS INDIA AT WANKHEDE STADIUM
November 27, 28, 29, December 1, 1981. India won by 138 runs.

G.R. Viswanath	c Boycott	8	28–6–72–4	c Gavaskar b Doshi	7
S.M. Patil	lbw	17	22.3–3–61–5	c Azad b Dev	29
S.M. Gavaskar	c Taylor	55			
Kapil Dev	c Taylor	38			
D.B. Vengsarkar	c Tavare	5			
S.M. Gavaskar	c Taylor	14			
S.M. Patil	lbw	13			
G.R. Viswanath	c Taylor	37			
D.R. Doshi	bowled	7			

ENGLAND VS INDIA AT KARNATAKA STATE C.A. STADIUM
December 9, 10, 12, 13, 14, 1981. Match drawn.

K. Srikkanth	c Gooch	65	47–9–137–2	c Madan b Doshi	55
S.M.H. Kirmani	lbw	9			

ENGLAND VS INDIA AT FEROZ SHAH KOTLA
December 23, 24, 26, 27, 28, 1981. Match drawn.

G.R. Viswanath	bowled	107	41–6–122–2	c Azad b Madan	66
Kapil Dev	c Gooch	16			

ENGLAND VS INDIA AT EDEN GARDENS
January 1, 2, 3, 5, 6, 1982. Match drawn.

D.B. Vengsarkar	c Taylor	70	27–8–63–2	c Gavaskar b Dev	58
S.M.H. Kirmani	bowled	10	11–3–26–0	c Yadav b Doshi	31

ENGLAND VS INDIA AT CHIDAMBARAM STADIUM
January 13, 14, 15, 17, 18, 1982. Match drawn.

| Yashpal Sharma | c Tavare | 140 | 31–10–83–1 | c Kirmani b Shastri | 52 |
| | | | 8–1–29–0 | | |

ENGLAND VS INDIA AT GREEN PARK
January 30, 31, February 1, 3, 4, 1982. Match drawn.

| Pranab Roy | bowled | 5 | 25–6–67–1 | st Kirmani b Doshi | 142 |

ENGLAND VS SRI LANKA AT SARAVANAMUTTU STADIUM
February 17, 18, 20, 21, 1982. England won by 7 wkts.

S. Wettimuny	c Taylor	6	12.5–1–28–3	b De Mel	13
L.R.D. Mendis	lbw	17	12–1–37–0		
G.R.A. De Silva	c Emburey	12			

ENGLAND VS INDIA AT LORD'S
June 10, 11, 12, 14, 15, 1982. England won by 7 wkts.

G.A. Parkar	lbw	6	19.4–3–46–5	c Malhotra b Madan	67
G.R. Viswanath	bowled	1	31.5–7–103–1		
S.M. Gavaskar	bowled	48			
Madan Lal	c Tavare	6			
D.R. Doshi	c Taylor	0			
Kapil Dev	c Cook	89			

ENGLAND VS INDIA AT OLD TRAFFORD
June 24, 25, 26, 27, 28, 1982. Match drawn.

| G.R. Viswanath | c Taylor | 54 | 19–4–86–1 | b Shastri | 128 |

ENGLAND VS INDIA AT THE OVAL
July 8, 9, 10, 12, 13, 1982. Match drawn.

| D.B. Vengsarkar | c Edmonds | 6 | 19–2–73–2 | c Viswanath b Doshi | 208 |
| S.M. Patil | c sub | 62 | 4–0–12–0 | | |

ENGLAND VS PAKISTAN AT EDGBASTON
July 29, 30, 31, August 1, 1982. England won by 113 runs.

Mudassar Nazar	lbw	0	24–1–86–2	b Imran	2
Mohsin Khan	c Willis	26	21–7–70–4	lbw Tahir	0
Mudassar Nazar	lbw	0			
Mansoor Akhtar	c Taylor	0			
Mohsin Khan	lbw	35			
Wasim Bari	c Taylor	12			

ENGLAND VS PAKISTAN AT LORD'S
August 12, 13, 14, 15, 16, 1982. Pakistan won by 10 wkts.

Mansoor Akhtar	c Lamb	57	44–8–148–3	c Mohsin b Qadir	31
Haroon Rashid	lbw	1	7–0–30–0	c Sarfraz b Mudassar	69
Imran Khan	c Taylor	12			

ENGLAND VS PAKISTAN AT HEADINGLEY
August 26, 27, 28, 30, 31, 1982. England won by 3 wkts.

Mohsin Khan	c Taylor	10	24.5–9–70–4	c sub b Sikander	57
Mudassar Nazar	bowled	65	30–8–74–5	c Majid b Mudassar	4
Abdul Qadir	c Willis	5			
Ehteshamuddin	bowled	0			
Mansoor Akhtar	c Randall	39			
Zaheer Abbas	lbw	4			
Javed Miandad	c Taylor	52			
Majid Khan	c Gower	10			
Imran Khan	c Randall	46			

ENGLAND VS AUSTRALIA AT WACA GROUND
November 12, 13, 14, 16, 17, 1982. Match drawn.

A.R. Border	c Taylor	8	40–10–121–2	c Marsh b Lawson	12
R.W. Marsh	c Cook	0	6–1–17–0	b Lawson	0

ENGLAND VS AUSTRALIA AT WOOLLOONGABBA
November 26, 27, 28, 30, December 1, 1982. Australia won by 7 wkts.

J. Dyson	bowled	1	22–1–105–3	c Rackemann b Yardley	40
K.J. Hughes	c Taylor	0	15.5–1–70–0	c Marsh b Thomson	15
R.W. Marsh	c Taylor	11			

ENGLAND VS AUSTRALIA AT ADELAIDE OVAL
December 10, 11, 12, 14, 15, 1982. Australia won by 8 wkts.

J. Dyson	c Taylor	44	36.5–5–112–4	c Wessels b Thomson	35
K.C. Wessels	c Taylor	44	10–2–45–1	c Dyson b Yardley	58
B. Yardley	c Gower	38			
J.R. Thomson	c and b	3			
K.C. Wessels	c Taylor	1			

ENGLAND VS AUSTRALIA AT MELBOURNE CRICKET GROUND
December 26, 27, 28, 29, 30, 1982. England won by 3 runs.

A.R. Border	bowled	2	18–3–69–1	c Wessels b Yardley	27
J. Dyson	c Tavare	31	25.1–4–80–2	c Chappell	46
				b Thomson	
J.R. Thomson	c Miller	21			

ENGLAND VS AUSTRALIA AT SYDNEY CRICKET GROUND
January 2, 3, 4, 6, 7, 1983. Match drawn.

K.C. Wessels	c Willis	19	30–8–75–4	c Wessels b Thomson	5
K.J. Hughes	c Cowans	29	10–0–35–1	lbw Thomson	32
G.F. Lawson	c and b	6			
J.R. Thomson	c Lamb	0			
K.C. Wessels	lbw	53			

ENGLAND VS NEW ZEALAND AT THE OVAL
July 14, 15, 16, 17, 18, 1983. England won by 189 runs.

J.G. Bracewell	c and b	7	16–2–62–4	b Hadlee	15
R.J. Hadlee	c and b	84	4–0–17–0	run out	26
B.L. Cairns	c Lamb	2			
E.J. Chatfield	c Willis	0			

ENGLAND VS NEW ZEALAND AT HEADINGLEY
July 28, 29, 30, August 1, 1983. New Zealand won by 5 wkts.

26–9–81–0	c Howarth b Cairns	38
0.1–0–4–0	c Howarth b Coney	4

ENGLAND VS NEW ZEALAND AT LORD'S
August 11, 12, 13, 15, 1983. England won by 127 runs.

M.D. Crowe	bowled	46	20.4–6–50–4	lbw Cairns	8
E.J. Gray	c Lamb	11	7–2–20–1	c Coney b Chatfield	61
B.L. Cairns	c Lamb	5			
I.D.S. Smith	c Lamb	3			
J.G. Wright	c Taylor	12			

ENGLAND VS NEW ZEALAND AT TRENT BRIDGE
August 25, 26, 27, 28, 29, 1983. England won by 165 runs.

T.J. Franklin	c Smith	2	14–4–33–1	lbw Snedden	103
			25–4–73–0	c Edgar b Gray	27

ENGLAND VS NEW ZEALAND AT BASIN RESERVE
January 20, 21, 22, 23, 24, 1984. Match drawn.

J.G. Wright	c Cook	17	27.4–8–59–5	c Crowe b Cairns	138
B.A. Edgar	c Taylor	9	36–6–137–1		
G.P. Howarth	c Gower	15			
R.J. Hadlee	c Gatting	24			
I.D.S. Smith	lbw	24			
J.J. Crowe	lbw	3			

ENGLAND VS NEW ZEALAND AT LANCASTER PARK
February 3, 4, 5, 1984. New Zealand won by an innings and 132 runs.

M.D. Crowe	c Tavare	19	17–1–88–1	c Chatfield b Cairns	18
				c Crowe b Boock	0

ENGLAND VS NEW ZEALAND AT EDEN PARK
February 10, 11, 12, 14, 15, 1984. Match drawn.

	29–10–70–0	run out		70

ENGLAND VS PAKISTAN AT NATIONAL STADIUM
March 2, 3, 4, 6, 1984. Pakistan won by 3 wkts.

Zaheer Abbas	c Lamb	0	30–5–90–2	c Ramiz b Qadir	22
Abdul Qadir	c Lamb	40		b Tausif	10

ENGLAND VS WEST INDIES AT EDGBASTON
June 14, 15, 16, 18, 1984. West Indies won by an innings and 180 runs.

C.H. Lloyd	c Pringle	71	34–7–127–1	c Garner b Harper	64
				lbw Garner	38

ENGLAND VS WEST INDIES AT LORD'S
June 28, 29, 30, July 2, 3, 1984. West Indies won by 9 wkts.

C.G. Greenidge	c Miller	1	27.4–6–103–8	c Richards b Baptiste	30
H.A. Gomes	c Gatting	10	20.1–2–117–0	lbw Garner	81
D.L. Haynes	lbw	12			
C.H. Lloyd	lbw	39			
I.V.A. Richards	lbw	72			
P.J.L. Dujon	c Fowler	8			
R.A. Harper	c Gatting	8			
J. Garner	c Downton	6			

ENGLAND VS WEST INDIES AT HEADINGLEY
July 12, 13, 14, 16, 1984. West Indies won by 8 wkts.

	7–0–45–0	c Dujon b Baptiste	45
		c Dujon b Garner	14

ENGLAND VS WEST INDIES AT OLD TRAFFORD
July 26, 27, 28, 30, 31, 1984. West Indies won by an innings and 64 runs.

D.L. Haynes	c Cowans	2	29–5–100–2	c Garner b Baptiste	6
P.J.L. Dujon	c Downton	101		c Haynes b Harper	1

ENGLAND VS WEST INDIES AT THE OVAL
August 9, 10, 11, 13, 14, 1984. West Indies won by 172 runs.

C.G. Greenidge	lbw	22	23–8–72–5	c Dujon b Marshall	14
I.V.A. Richards	c Allott	8	22.3–2–103–3	c Marshall b Garner	54
P.J.L. Dujon	c Tavare	3			
R.A. Harper	bowled	18			
M.A. Holding	lbw	0			
M.D. Marshall	c Lamb	12			
D.L. Haynes	bowled	125			
M.A. Holding	lbw	30			

ENGLAND VS SRI LANKA AT LORD'S
August 23, 24, 25, 27, 28, 1984. Match drawn.

S.A.R. Silva	lbw	8	29–6–114–1	c sub b John	6
S. Wettimuny	c Gower	13	27–6–90–6		
R.S. Madugalle	bowled	3			
R.L. Dias	lbw	38			
A. Ranatunga	lbw	0			
L.R.D. Mendis	c Fowler	94			
A.L.F. De Mel	c Ellison	14			

ENGLAND VS AUSTRALIA AT HEADINGLEY
June 13, 14, 15, 17, 18, 1985. England won by 5 wkts.

C.J. McDermott	bowled	18	29.1–8–86–3	b Thomson	60
S.P. O'Donnell	lbw	0	33–7–107–4	b O'Donnell	12
G.M. Ritchie	bowled	46			
G.M. Wood	c Lamb	3			
A.R. Border	c Downton	8			
S.P. O'Donnell	c Downton	24			
G.F. Lawson	c Downton	15			

ENGLAND VS AUSTRALIA AT LORD'S
June 27, 28, 29, July 1, 2, 1985. Australia won by 4 wkts.

K.C. Wessels	lbw	11	24–2–109–5	c Ritchie b Lawson	5
D.C. Boon	c Downton	4	15–0–49–2	c Border b Holland	85
G.M. Ritchie	lbw	94			
W.B. Phillips	c Edmonds	21			
A.R. Border	c Gooch	196			
A.M.J. Hilditch	c Lamb	0			
G.M. Wood	c Lamb	6			

ENGLAND VS AUSTRALIA AT TRENT BRIDGE
July 11, 12, 13, 15, 16, 1985. Match drawn.

G.M. Wood	c Robinson	172	34.2–3–107–3	c O'Donnell b McDermott	38
G.F. Lawson	c Gooch	18			
S.P. O'Donnell	c Downton	46			

ENGLAND VS AUSTRALIA AT OLD TRAFFORD
August 1, 2, 3, 5, 6, 1985. Match drawn.

D.C. Boon	c Lamb	61	23–4–79–4	c O'Donnell b McDermott	20
W.B. Phillips	c Downton	36	15–3–50–0		
G.R.J. Matthews	bowled	4			
G.F. Lawson	c Downton	4			

ENGLAND VS AUSTRALIA AT EDGBASTON
August 15, 16, 17, 19, 20, 1985. England won by an innings and 118 runs.

G.M. Wood	c Edmonds	19	27–1–108–1	c Thomson b McDermott	18
A.M.J. Hilditch	c Ellison	10	14.1–2–52–3		
S.P. O'Donnell	bowled	11			
C.J. McDermott	c Edmonds	8			

ENGLAND VS AUSTRALIA AT THE OVAL
August 29, 30, 31, September 2, 1985. England won by an innings and 94 runs.

G.M. Wood	lbw	22	20–3–64–3	c Phillips b Lawson	12
A.M.J. Hilditch	c Gooch	17	17–3–44–3		
D.R. Gilbert	bowled	1			
G.M. Wood	bowled	6			
K.C. Wessels	c Downton	7			
W.B. Phillips	c Downton	10			

ENGLAND VS WEST INDIES AT SABINA PARK
February 21, 22, 23, 1986. West Indies won by 10 wkts.

R.B. Richardson	lbw	7	19–4–67–2	c Patterson b Marshall	15
J. Garner	c Edmonds	24		b Marshall	29

ENGLAND VS WEST INDIES AT QUEEN'S PARK OVAL
March 7, 8, 9, 11, 12, 1986. West Indies won by 7 wkts.

B.P. Patterson	c Gooch	9	9.4–0–68–1	c Richardson	2
				b Marshall	
				c Payne b Marshall	1

ENGLAND VS WEST INDIES AT KENSINGTON OVAL
March 21, 22, 23, 25, 1986. West Indies won by an innings and 30 runs.

P.J.L. Dujon	c sub (Slack)	5	24–3–80–1	c Dujon b Patterson	14
				c Dujon b Garner	21

ENGLAND VS WEST INDIES AT QUEEN'S PARK OVAL
April 3, 4, 5, 1985. West Indies won by 10 wkts.

P.J.L. Dujon	c Downton	5	24.1–3–71–5	b Holding	38
I.V.A. Richards	lbw	87	3–0–24–0	c Gomes b Marshall	25
R.A. Harper	lbw	21			
M.A. Holding	bowled	25			
B.P. Patterson	c Downton	3			

ENGLAND VS WEST INDIES AT ST JOHN'S
April 11, 12, 13, 15, 16, 1986. West Indies won by 240 runs.

C.G. Greenidge	bowled	14	40–6–147–2	c Harper b Garner	10
I.V.A. Richards	c Gooch	26	15–0–78–0	b Harper	13

ENGLAND VS NEW ZEALAND AT THE OVAL
August 21, 22, 23, 25, 26, 1986. Match drawn.

B.A. Edgar	c Gooch	1	25–4–75–3	not out	59
J.J. Crowe	lbw	8	1–0–7–0		
J.V. Coney	c Gooch	38			

ENGLAND VS AUSTRALIA AT WOOLLOONGABBA
November 14, 15, 16, 18, 19, 1986. England won by 7 wkts.

C.D. Matthews	c Gatting	11	16–1–58–2	c Hughes b Waugh	138
M.G. Hughes	bowled	0	12–0–34–1		
D.C. Boon	lbw	14			

ENGLAND VS AUSTRALIA AT WACA GROUND
November 28, 29, 30, December 2, 3, 1986. Match drawn.

G.R. Marsh	c Broad	15	22–4–72–1	c Border b Reid	0
			7.2–4–13–0	c Matthews b Reid	6

ENGLAND VS AUSTRALIA AT MELBOURNE CRICKET GROUND
December 26, 27, 28, 1986. England won by an innings and 114 runs.

G.R. Marsh	c Richards	17	16–4–41–5	c Zoehrer	29
				b McDermott	
A.R. Border	c Richards	15	7–1–19–0		
T.J. Zoehrer	bowled	5			
C.J. McDermott	c Richards	0			
M.G. Hughes	c Richards	2			

ENGLAND VS AUSTRALIA AT SYDNEY CRICKET GROUND
January 10, 11, 12, 14, 15, 1987. Australia won by 55 runs.

			23–10–42–0	c Marsh b Taylor	16
			3–0–17–0	c Wellham b Taylor	0

ENGLAND VS PAKISTAN AT OLD TRAFFORD
June 4, 5, 6, 8, 9, 1987. Match drawn.

Javed Miandad	c French	21	14–7–29–1	c Wasim b Tauseef	48

ENGLAND VS PAKISTAN AT LORD'S
June 18, 19, 20, 22, 23, 1987. Match drawn.

			Did not bowl	c Miandad b Wasim	6

ENGLAND VS PAKISTAN AT HEADINGLEY
July 2, 3, 4, 6, 1987. Pakistan won by an innings and 18 runs.

			Did not bowl	c Yousuf b Mudassar	26
				c Mudassar b Mohsin	24

ENGLAND VS PAKISTAN AT EDGBASTON
July 23, 24, 25, 27, 28, 1987. Match drawn.

Ijaz Ahmed	lbw	20	48–13–121–1	c and b Wasim	37
Salim Malik	c and b	17	20.3–3–66–2	c Mohsin b Wasim	6
Ijaz Ahmed	bowled	11			

ENGLAND VS PAKISTAN AT THE OVAL
August 6, 7, 8, 10, 11, 1987. Match drawn.

Ramiz Raja	bowled	14	52–7–217–3	b Qadir	34
Mudassar Nazar	c Moxon	73		not out	51
Salim Malik	c Gower	102			

ENGLAND VS AUSTRALIA AT EDGBASTON
July 6, 7, 8, 10, 11, 1989. Match drawn.

| G.R. Marsh | lbw | 42 | 26–5–75–1 | b Hughes | 46 |

ENGLAND VS AUSTRALIA AT OLD TRAFFORD
July 27, 28, 29, 31, August 1, 1989. Australia won by 9 wkts.

| G.R. Marsh | c Russell | 47 | 24–6–63–2 | b Hohns | 0 |
| D.M. Jones | bowled | 69 | | lbw Alderman | 4 |

ENGLAND VS AUSTRALIA AT TRENT BRIDGE
August 10, 11, 12, 14, 1989. Australia won by an innings and 180 runs.

| | | | 30–4–103–0 | c Waugh b Hohns | 12 |

ENGLAND VS WEST INDIES AT THE OVAL
August 8, 9, 10, 11, 12, 1991. England won by 5 wkts.

R.B. Richardson	c Stewart	20	11–4–27–1	hit wkt b Ambrose	31
P.V. Simmons	c Lewis	36	16–4–40–2	not out	4
C.B. Lambert	lbw	14			

ENGLAND VS SRI LANKA AT LORD'S
August 22, 23, 24, 26, 27, 1991. England won by 137 runs.

R.S. Mahanama	c Russell	2	10–3–26–1	c Mahanama	22
				b Ramanayake	
			6–2–15–0		

ENGLAND VS NEW ZEALAND AT BASIN RESERVE
February 6, 7, 8, 9, 10, 1992. Match drawn.

C. L. Cairns	c Russell	33	14–4–53–1	c Cairns b Su'a	15
J.G. Wright	c Russell	0	8–1–23–2	lbw Patel	1
B.R. Hartland	lbw	19			

ENGLAND VS PAKISTAN AT EDGBASTON
June 4, 5, 6, 7, 8, 1992. Match drawn.

| | | | 19–6–52–0 | | |

ENGLAND VS PAKISTAN AT LORD'S
June 18, 19, 20, 21, 1992. Pakistan won by 2 wkts.

| | | | 5–2–9–0 | b Waqar | 2 |
| | | | | lbw Waqar | 6 |

TEST MATCH BATTING & BOWLING RECORDS

Batting by Opponents

OPPT	TESTS	INNS	N.O.	RUNS	H.S.	AVGE	100s	50s
Australia	36	59	2	1673	149*	29.35	4	6
India	14	17	0	1201	208	70.65	5	5
New Zealand	15	23	2	846	138	40.29	3	4
Pakistan	14	21	1	647	108	32.35	2	3
Sri Lanka	3	3	0	41	22	13.67	0	0
West Indies	20	38	1	792	81	21.40	0	4
TOTAL	**102**	**161**	**6**	**5200**	**208**	**33.55**	**14**	**22**

Batting by Captain

CAPT	TESTS	INNS	N.O.	RUNS	H.S.	AVGE	100s	50s
Brearley	26	38	2	1489	149*	41.36	7	3
Gower	21	35	0	933	85	26.66	0	6
Willis	18	31	0	1276	208	41.16	4	5
Botham	12	21	0	276	57	13.14	0	1
Gatting	10	15	2	480	138	36.92	1	2
Fletcher	7	9	0	453	142	50.33	1	4
Gooch	5	7	1	81	31	13.50	0	0
Boycott	3	5	1	212	103	53.00	1	1
TOTAL	**102**	**161**	**6**	**5200**	**208**	**33.55**	**14**	**22**

Bowling by Opponents

OPPT	BALLS	RUNS	WKTS	STRIKE	AVGE	5WI	10WM	BEST
Australia	8479	4093	148	57.29	27.65	9	2	6/78
India	3371	1558	59	57.14	26.41	6	1	7/48
New Zealand	3284	1500	64	51.31	23.44	6	1	6/34
Pakistan	2491	1271	40	167.27	57.18	2	0	8/34
Sri Lanka	581	310	11	52.82	28.18	1	0	6/90
West Indies	3609	2146	61	59.16	35.18	3	0	8/103
TOTAL	**21,815**	**10,878**	**383**	**56.96**	**28.40**	**27**	**4**	**8/34**

Bowling by Captain

CAPT	BALLS	RUNS	WKTS	STRIKE	AVGE	5WI	10WM	BEST
Brearley	6690	2815	150	44.60	18.77	15	4	8/34
Gower	4421	2680	74	59.74	36.22	5	0	8/103
Willis	3958	2133	61	64.89	34.97	3	0	5/46
Botham	2211	1158	35	63.17	33.09	0	0	4/77
Gatting	1601	811	19	84.26	42.68	1	0	5/41
Fletcher	1592	725	20	79.60	36.25	1	0	5/61
Gooch	534	245	7	76.29	35.00	0	0	2/23
Boycott	808	311	17	47.53	18.29	2	0	5/73
TOTAL	**21,815**	**10,878**	**383**	**56.96**	**28.40**	**27**	**4**	**8/34**

BIBLIOGRAPHY

Benaud, Richie, *On Reflection* (Collins, 1984)

Benaud, Richie, *The Appeal Of Cricket* (Hodder & Stoughton, 1995)

Botham, Ian & Peter Smith, *The Incredible Tests 1981* (Pelham, 1981)

Botham, Ian & Ian Jarrett, *Botham Down Under* (Collins, 1983)

Botham, Ian & Peter Roebuck, *It Sort Of Clicks* (Collins, 1986)

Botham, Ian & Peter Hayter, *My Autobiography: Don't Tell Kath* (Collins, 1995)

Boycott, Geoff & Terry Brindle, *Opening Up* (Arthur Barker, 1980)

Chappell, Greg & David Frith, *The Ashes '77* (Angus & Robertson, 1977)

Close, Brian & Don Mosey, *I Don't Bruise Easily* (Futura, 1979)

Coleman, Ray, *John Ono Lennon* (Sidgwick & Jackson, 1984)

Collins, Patrick, *The Sportswriter* (Virgin, 1996)

Doust, Dudley, *Ian Botham The Great All-rounder* (Granada, 1981)

Eagar, Patrick, *Botham* (Kingswood Press, 1985)

Gooch, Graham & Frank Keating, *My Autobiography* (Collins, 1995)

Gower, David & Martin Johnson, *The Autobiography* (Fontana, 1993)

James, C.L.R., *Beyond A Boundary* (Stanley Paul, 1963)

Lamb, Allan & Jack Bannister, *My Autobiography* (Collins, 1996)

Lee, Alan, *Lord Ted* (Vista, 1996)

Martin-Jenkins, Christopher, *The Jubilee Tests* (MacDonald & Jane's, 1977)

McDonald, Trevor, *Viv Richards: The Authorised Biography* (Sphere, 1984)

McLellan, Alastair, *The Enemy Within* (Blandford, 1994)

Murphy, Patrick, *Botham: A Biography* (J.M. Dent & Sons, 1988)

Reeve, Dermot & Patrick Murphy, *Winning Ways* (Boxtree, 1996)

Richards, Viv & David Foot, *Viv Richards* (World's Work, 1979)

Roebuck, Peter, *Slices of Cricket* (George Allen, 1982)

Roebuck, Peter, *It Never Rains . . .* (George Allen, 1984)

Roebuck, Peter, *Ashes To Ashes* (Heinemann, 1987)

Roebuck, Peter, *From Sammy To Jimmy* (Partridge Press, 1991)

Savidge, Michele & Alastair McLellan, *Real Quick* (Blandford, 1995)

Sobers, Sir Garfield & Ivo Tennant, *The Changing Face Of Cricket* (Ebury Press, 1996)

Steen, Rob, *David Gower: A Man Out Of Time* (Gollancz, 1995)

Trueman, Fred, *Ball Of Fire* (J.M. Dent, 1976)

West, Peter & Wendy Wimbush, *The Battle For The Ashes*
   (*Daily Telegraph*, 1987)

Willis, Bob & Alan Lee, *Diary Of A Cricket Season* (Pelham, 1979)

Willis, Bob & Alan Lee, *The Captain's Diary* (Collins, 1984)

Wisden Cricketers' Almanack   *The Times*

Wisden Cricket Monthly   *Daily Telegraph*

The Cricketer   *Mail on Sunday*

                                    Guardian

Aamir Sohail 216
Abid Ali 202
Alderman, Terry 42, 79, 81, 82, 86, 190
Amarnath, M. 204
Ambrose, Curtley 198
Amiss, Dennis 44
Antigua 26, 65, 122
Aqib Javed 213, 215
Arlott, John 52, 87–8, 135, 210
Arundel 193
Ashes, the 35, 44, 45, 76, 81, 86, 99,
    108, 113, 143, 155, 163, 176, 183,
    191, 200, 216, 223, 224, 225
    (see also Australia, England)
Ashes To Ashes (Peter Roebuck) 110
Atherton, Michael 20, 54, 123, 125,
    142, 172, 181, 182, 198, 212, 221,
    224
Athey, Bill 59
Auckland, New Zealand 182, 216, 225
Australia 14, 43, 56, 110, 173, 186, 222,
    230; cricket academy 8; Sheffield
    Shield 23, 164–7; Worcestershire
    deal 35; cricket board 156; 1992
    World Cup 216; v.
    England: (1936/37) 88;
    (1970/71) 99; (1974/75) 77;
    (1978/79) 54, 107; (1979/80) 44–5,
    51, 55, 173, 220; (1982/83) 136, 155–
    6, 183, 220; (1986/87) 110, 113, 191,
    220; (1994/95)123; v. West Indies:
    (1975/76) 54; (1996/97) 22 (see
    England)
Azharuddin, Mohammad 55

Bacher, Ali 147

Bailey, Rob 189
Bailey, Trevor 80, 107, 126–7
Bairstow, David 64
Ball Of Fire (Fred Trueman) 127
Bannister, Jack 66, 213, 229
Barclay, J.R.T. 16
Barlow, G.D. 234
Barnes, Simon 150, 169
Barnes, Sydney 181, 207
Barnett, Kim 218
Barrington, Ken 61, 63, 65, 70, 78, 91,
    93, 97, 104–7, 177, 236
Barwick, Steve 38, 187
Basin Reserve (New Zealand) 1
Batten, Kevin James 242
Beaumont, Bill 4, 217
Bedi, Bishan 202, 203
Bedser, Alec 42, 69, 133, 197
Bellany, John 240
Benaud, Richie 110, 111, 112, 171, 226
Benson & Hedges Cup 12, 14, 16, 17,
    18, 19, 20, 25, 36, 38, 85, 97
Best, George 3, 149, 160
Beyond A Boundary (C.L.R. James) 128
Bird, Dickie 134, 192
Bishop, Ian 187
Blofeld, Henry 59, 133, 134, 153, 236
Bodyline 61
Bolus, Brian 218
Bombay, India 41, 45, 78
Boon, David 24, 71
Border, Allan 24, 29, 70, 82, 83, 85, 86,
    164, 166, 176, 191, 211, 231
Border, John 231
Bore, Mike 18
Botham family

Ian Botham: birth and childhood 8–10, 93; England Schools 9, 13; Lord's groundstaff 10, 93–6; Whitbread scholarship 14, 173; Somerset games 12, 14–19, 52, 70, 85; maiden first-class hundred 14; Test call-up 15; first Test wicket 100; maiden Test hundred 102; Somerset captaincy 25; Somerset affair 25–34; England captaincy 18–19, 25, 40, 41, 46, 50–1, 53–7, 66–71, 103; resigns captaincy 76; v. Australia: 15, 41, 68, 80–7, 107, 113, 134–5, 136, 155, 162–3, 183, 185, 187–8; v. India: 45, 108, 134, 136, 179–80; v. New Zealand: 101–2, 110, 111, 134, 156–7, 186; v. Pakistan: 101, 102, 134, 172, 175; v. Sri Lanka: 111; v. West Indies: 46–8, 50, 59, 64, 66, 111, 114, 153, 177–8, 184; signs for Worcestershire 34–6, 121–2, 196; signs for Durham 39, 193; signs for Queensland 146, 164–7; breaks Lillee's wickets record 186; decline in bowling prowess 180–4; fails to be selected 39–40, 188–9, 191, 192, 197; plays in 1992 World Cup 167; injury 12, 18, 37–8, 48–9, 103, 108, 110, 116, 153, 174, 178, 185, 186–7, 194; and rebel tours 123–4, 136–7, 146–7, 190; relations with authority 31, 39, 126–48; and Ken Barrington 61, 63, 65, 91, 104–7; and Mike Brearley 42, 52, 81, 83, 85, 91, 93, 100–4, 107; and Tom Cartwright 96–7, 99, 107; and Brian Close 11, 12–14, 23, 46, 47, 91, 96–101, 107; and Graham Gooch 58, 60, 123–5, 188; and David Gower 112–15; and Tim Hudson 117–21; and Allan Lamb 192; and Viv Richards 11–12, 17, 23–4, 28–9, 31–2, 90, 116,

177–8; and Bob Willis 108, 121; and with the media 27, 33, 49, 51, 64, 115, 116, 118, 120, 140–3, 149–70, 220; Neenan incident 66, 104, 135, 15·l–5; Chappell punch 15, 165, 167, 169, 173; diplomatic gaffes 108–9, 167–8, 175; sex and pot-smoking 28, 108, 121, 137, 138–40, 142, 145–6, 156–64; disillusionment with cricket 118, 124–5, 147–8; disdain for training 114, 123–4, 222; court battle with Imran Khan 197–9; candidature for England selector 218; leukaemia walks 227–32; journalism 220, 225; as Sky commentator 217, 221, 225; pantomime 167, 194, 217; *A Question Of Sport* 194, 217–18; compared with all-rounder rivals 201–16; shortcomings 16, 19, 28, 38, 48, 52, 70–1, 90–1, 111, 114–15, 134, 150, 167, 169–70, 177, 178–9; qualities 4, 13, 30, 47, 87, 102, 109, 174–5, 176; achievements 1–2, 5, 18, 88, 129, 171–3, 221; iconic image 2–3, 29, 32–4, 75–6, 89, 127–8, 130–2, 144, 150–3, 160, 179

Kathryn Botham (née Waller, wife) 49, 52, 93, 99, 113, 120, 121, 142, 146, 149, 163, 191, 228, 233

Liam Botham (son) 49, 131, 141, 228, 234

Sarah Botham (daughter) 23

Rebecca Botham (daughter) 239

Les Botham (father) 8

Marie Botham (mother) 8

Dale Botham (sister) 8

Gerry Waller (father-in-law) 142

Boycott, Geoffrey 22, 44, 46, 47, 59, 60, 64, 68, 76, 78, 80, 82, 97, 101, 106, 109, 123, 127, 135, 172, 175,

177, 198, 220, 225; and rebel
   tours 57, 63
Bradman, Don 1, 2, 36, 55, 86, 88, 171,
   178, 211
Breakwell, Dennis viii, 11
Brearley, Mike 5, 42–7, 52, 57, 59, 65,
   68, 76–85, 86, 91, 92, 93, 101–4, 106,
   107, 109, 121, 153, 174, 233, 234
Bridgetown (Barbados) 61, 63, 64, 105
Briers, Nigel 243
Bright, Ray 81
Burgess, Graham 11, 18
Burke, J.W. 107

Cairns, Lance 156, 206
Capel, David 189
Carman, George 198, 199
Cartwright, Tom 93, 96–9, 105, 107
Chandrasekhar, B.S. 202
Changing Face Of Cricket, The (Garfield
   Sobers) 90–1
Chappell, Greg 42, 43, 55, 57, 78, 82,
   89, 100, 135, 234
Chappell, Ian 15, 128, 165, 167, 169,
   173
Chappell, Trevor 82
Chatfield, Ewen 156, 206
Christchurch, New Zealand 102, 110,
   138, 157, 159, 200
Clapp, Bob 12
Close, Brian 11, 12–14, 15, 23, 28, 46–
   7, 91, 96, 97–101, 102, 104, 106, 107,
   119, 120, 127, 198
Coleman, Ray 161
Collins, Patrick 230
Compton, Denis 1, 2, 76, 86, 127, 129,
   136, 199, 200, 226
Coney, Jeremy 157
Connolly, Gerry 168
Constant, David 134

Cook, Geoff 39
Cork, Dominic 7, 175, 195, 196, 223,
   225
Cowans, Norman 110
Cowdrey, Chris 42, 184, 218
Cowdrey, Colin 243
Crawley, John 224
Cricketer, The 53, 68, 100, 114, 123, 126
Croft, Colin 46, 60, 64, 78
Cronje, Hansie 79
Crowe, Jeff 111, 240
Crowe, Martin 25, 27, 29–31, 156, 157,
   206
Curtis, Tim 36, 241

Daily Express 159, 223, 225
Daily Mail 153
Daily Mirror 152, 155, 161, 220, 225
Daily Telegraph 90, 115, 168, 196
DeFreitas, Phil 189, 195
Denness, Mike 42, 43
Denning, Peter 17
Derbyshire CCC 218
Dexter, Ted viii, 40, 42, 147, 180, 188–
   91, 193–4, 219, 220–1
Diary Of A Cricket Season (Bob Willis) 28
Dilley, Graham 24, 35, 41, 47, 64, 65,
   80, 83, 122
D'Oliveira, Basil 62, 110
Donald, Allan 22, 24
Doshi, D.R. 203
Downton, Ally 163
Downton, Paul 116, 184
Dunstan, M.S.T. 233
Durham CCC 39–40, 123, 193, 197;
   Chester-le-Street 39
Dyson, John 82, 83, 155

Eagar, Patrick 87
Edgar, Bruce 111, 240

Edgbaston (Birmingham) viii, 7, 43, 52, 84–5, 88, 90, 92, 98, 122, 163, 187, 188, 203, 210

Edmonds, Phil 24, 47, 53, 112

Edrich, Bill 126–7

Edrich, John 98, 107, 218

Elliott, Matthew 222

Ellison, Richard 114, 184

Emburey, John 24, 42, 47, 59, 64, 65, 84, 85, 92, 114, 115, 137, 182, 184

Enemy Within, The (Alastair McLellan) 23–4

England 7, 14, 15, 18, 21–2, 27, 38, 43, 49, 65, 109, 125, 133, 142, 158, 218–25; v. Australia: (1938) 207; (1953) 76; (1972) 213; (1977) 15, 57; (1981) 42, 68, 79–91, 150, 155, 209, 220; (1985) 1, 113, 124, 161, 185, 220; (1989) 187–8, 210, 220; (1993) 39–40, 193; Centenary Test, Lord's 67, 78, 134–5; v. India: (1952) 202; (1979) 203; (1982) 67, 108, 180; (1990) 204; v. New Zealand: (1978) 129; (1986) 185–6, 220; v. Pakistan: (1978) 102, 129, 172, 213; (1982) 67, 211; (1987) 194, 210, 214–15, 220; v. Sri Lanka: (1984) 111; v. West Indies: (1976) 12, 54–5, 66, 173; (1980) 50–2, 53, 56, 69, 179; (1984) 111, 174, 209, 210, 220; v. Zimbabwe: (1996/97) 54, 142, 225 (see other countries for away series); World Cup: (1979) 177; (1987) 124; (1992) 215–16, 218; (1996) 219, 220, 224; England 'A' 137

Essex CCC 29, 36, 77

Fazal Mahmood 208

Fearnley, Duncan 34, 35

Featherstone, N.G. 234

Felton, N.A. 25

Field, Lindy 142, 163, 199

Fleetwood CC 79

Fleetwood-Smith, L. 207

Fletcher, Keith 43, 45, 67, 77, 107–8, 179, 237

Foot, David 26, 27

Foster, Neil 114, 184

Fraser, Angus 224

French, Bruce 184

Frith, David viii, 5, 64, 68, 89, 97, 107, 135, 143, 145, 172, 175, 204, 206

From Minor To Major (Simon Hughes) 4

From Sammy To Jimmy (Peter Roebuck) 28, 31

Gaekwad, A.D. 203

Garner, Joel 16, 17, 18, 25–32, 46, 48, 50, 64, 78, 124, 240, 241

Gascoigne, Paul 2, 4, 160, 169–70

Gatting, Mike 5, 24, 45, 47, 80, 83, 85, 116, 138, 163, 164, 173–4, 180, 183, 184, 195, 221; and the England captaincy 67, 76, 107, 113, 114, 115, 118,137, 191; and rebel tours 128, 146, 190

Gavaskar, Sunil 204, 235

Ghavri, K.D. 203

Giddins, Ed 139

Gifford, Norman 139

Giles, Ashley 23

Gillette Cup 11, 16, 17

Gimblett, H. 32

Glamorgan CCC 10, 15, 19, 21, 27, 187

Gloucestershire CCC 18

Gooch, Graham 5, 7, 24, 35, 45, 47, 53, 59, 60, 65, 105, 111, 163, 168, 173, 180, 184, 189, 204, 216; and the England captaincy 58, 61, 76, 115–16, 123–5, 137, 147, 188, 190–3, 220–2;

fitness regime 58, 164, 193, 210, 221; and rebel tours 107, 123, 128, 137; as England selector 218

Gower, David 5, 15, 22, 24, 35, 44, 45, 47, 50, 53, 59, 60, 65, 80, 102, 107, 123, 125, 129, 136, 137, 138, 141, 147, 163, 173, 174, 180, 183, 184, 198, 220, 222, 226; image and reputation 33, 144, 149–50, 159–60; and the England captaincy 41, 42, 51, 56, 67, 70, 76, 108, 109, 111, 112–17, 148, 187, 188–92, 209, 221, 242; and rebel tours 136

Gough, Darren 195, 196, 213, 223, 225

Grace, W.G. 1, 2, 86, 152, 194, 240

Graveney, David 39, 123, 137, 218

Graveney, Tom viii, 90

Greenidge, Gordon 46, 59, 78, 111, 114, 210

Greig, Tony 3, 14–15, 43, 44, 47, 54–5, 66, 101, 128, 129, 165, 172, 173, 182, 233

Guyana (1981 affair) 61–3, 105, 109

Hadlee, Richard 24, 110, 156, 157, 171, 201–2, 205, 206–7, 208, 210, 211, 213, 215, 216

Hall, Wes 198

Hammond, Wally 86

Hampshire CCC 12

Hassan, S.B. 18

Hattersley, Roy 225

Haynes, Desmond 46, 50, 59, 78

Headingley (Leeds) 13, 38, 41, 42, 50, 55, 77, 80–4, 86, 88–90, 92, 119, 129, 133, 134, 167, 178, 180, 202, 210, 214, 215, 220, 228, 229

Headley, George 211

Healy, Ian 71

Hemmings, Eddie 204

Hendrick, Mike 24, 47, 100, 173

Herd, Alan 161

Hick, Graeme 20, 36, 174, 216

Hobbs, Jack 1, 86

Hogg, Rodney 42, 79, 156, 164

Holding, Michael 24, 46, 47, 50, 53, 55, 64, 78, 98, 136, 177, 198

Hookes, David 82

Howarth, Geoff 156

Hudson, Tim 117–21, 164, 185, 186, 239, 240

Hughes, Kim 42, 55, 70, 78, 81, 82, 84, 85, 89, 131, 135, 155

Hughes, Merv 71, 175–6

Hughes, Simon 4

Hussain, Nasser 189

Hutton, Len 207, 208

Illingworth, Ray 13, 42, 99, 127, 218, 219, 220, 222, 223, 224

Illingworth, Richard 216

Imran Khan 16, 110, 141, 171, 178, 197–9, 201, 205, 208, 211–12, 214–16, 244

Incredible Tests, The (Ian Botham & Peter Smith) 52

India 27, 42, 44, 53, 1, 20, 46, 67, 77, 90, 129, 134, 174, 193, 202–4; v. England: (1976/77) 43; (1979/80) 209; (1981/82) 108, 136, 179–80, 220; (1984/85) 116, 161, 184; World Cup (1992) 215 (see England)

India Today 212, 244

Insole, Doug 238

It Never Rains. . . (Peter Roebuck) 31

Jackman, Robin 59, 61–3, 64, 65, 70, 105, 236

James, C.L.R. 128

Jardine, Douglas 61
Jarvis, Paul 187
Javed Miandad 55, 214, 215
Jessop, Gilbert 81, 86
John Player League 11, 16, 18, 25
Jones, Dean 24
Jones, Mike 35

Kallicharran, Alvin 46
Kapil Dev 45, 108, 110, 171, 201–6, 207, 208, 215, 216
Kent CCC 17, 19, 37
Kingston (Jamaica) 24, 177
Knight, Nick 23, 224
Knight, Roger 45
Knott, Alan 44, 47, 86, 129

Laker, Jim 44, 86, 105, 136
Lamb, Allan 115, 117, 125, 138, 139, 140, 159, 183, 184, 189, 191–2, 197–9, 220, 221, 244
Lamb, Lindsay 163
Lampitt, Stuart 38, 39, 196
Lander, Chris 231
Lara, Brian 1, 2, 122, 158, 224
Larkins, Wayne
Lawry, Bill 107
Lawson, Geoff 54, 79, 190
Lee, Alan 147, 218
Lennon, John 161, 162
Lever, J.K. 36, 47
Lewis, Chris 195, 223
Lewis, Tony 196
Lillee, Dennis 1, 2, 42, 43, 45, 49, 54, 78, 79, 81, 83, 84, 85, 86, 111, 131, 164, 165, 167, 186, 187, 197, 210, 213, 240
Lloyd, Clive 42, 46, 54, 55, 57, 59, 68, 70, 78–9, 104, 153, 203, 209, 215
Lloyd, David 198, 218, 221, 222, 244

Lord's Cricket Ground 1, 2, 11, 13, 19, 50, 68, 70, 85, 87, 89, 97, 98, 102, 111, 175, 177, 179, 180, 186, 204, 209, 210, 213; the 'Establishment' 45, 61, 66, 76, 88, 125, 126–48, 170, 217; Centenary Test 67, 78, 134–5; groundstaff 10, 93–6

McCabe, Stan 207
McDermott, Craig 71, 198
McDonald, Trevor 90
McKenzie, G.D. 197
MacLaurin, Lord 218
McLellan, Alastair 23
Mail on Sunday 26, 33, 116, 120, 138, 140, 142, 144, 162–3, 230, 238, 240
Malcolm, Devon 219, 224
Marks, Vic 12, 18, 23, 25, 27, 28
Marlar, Robin 106
Marsh, Geoff 71
Marsh, Rodney 78, 83, 237
Marshall, Malcolm 46, 78, 116, 206
Martin-Jenkins, Christopher 114, 168
Massie, Bob 213
Maxwell, Robert 155
May, Peter 42, 190, 219
MCC 10, 70, 128, 134, 137
MCG (Melbourne) 1, 41, 78, 113, 167, 200, 216; Centenary Test 43, 165
Melford, Michael 55
Mendis, Duleep 111
Middlesex CCC 17, 19, 70, 113
Miller, Geoff 47, 61, 218
Miller, Keith 5, 171, 200, 201, 226
Milton, Arthur 136
More Tales From A Long Room (Peter Tinniswood) 152
Moseley, Hallam 12
Mosey, Don 206

Muncer, Len 94–6
Murdoch, Rupert 155, 225
Murphy, Pat 93, 97

NatWest Trophy 19, 20, 25, 36, 37, 70
Neale, Phil 21, 34, 37, 38, 112, 121–2, 125, 196
Neenan, Joe 66, 104, 154–5, 236, 237
New Zealand 27, 44, 111, 120, 129, 134, 174, 185, 206; v. England: (1977/78) 101; (1983/84) 28, 108, 110, 137–8, 144, 156–61, 183, 192, 220, 227; (1996/97) 142, 182, 225; World Cup (1992) 216 (see England)
News Of The World 155
Northamptonshire CCC 7, 17, 36
Nottinghamshire CCC 14, 15, 18, 19

Old, Chris 41, 47, 58, 80, 81, 82, 84, 101, 173
Old Trafford (Manchester) 1, 41, 51, 86, 88, 90, 91, 186, 188, 215
On Reflection (Richie Benaud) 110
Ontong, Rodney 10
Opening Up (Geoffrey Boycott) 57
O'Reilly, Bill 'Tiger' 207
Oval (Kennington, London) 29, 86, 108, 131, 145, 180, 186, 196, 207, 210, 214
Oxford University 48

Packer, Kerry 3, 15, 43, 44, 45, 57, 62, 101, 128, 129, 130, 131, 173, 201, 205, 219, 226
Pakistan 1, 42, 45, 67, 102, 129, 134, 138, 158, 172, 175, 180, 209, 224; v. England: (1977/78) 101; (1983/84) 108, 137, 174, 220, 227; (1987/88) 214; World Cup: (1987) 124, 214; (1992) 215–16; effect of Packer 44;

and controversy 164, 211–15 (see England)
Palmer, Roy 215
Patel, B.P. 203
Patil, S.M. 204
Pigott, Tony 157, 183
Popplewell, Nigel 25, 32
Port of Spain (Trinidad) 17, 59–61, 66, 80, 90, 114, 192
Prasad, Venkatesh 203
Preston, Norman 13
Pringle, Derek 198, 213, 216
Professional Cricketers' Association 218

Queensland 33, 146, 147, 164, 165–7, 168, 186; cricket association 166
Question Of Sport, A 4, 194, 217–18

Radley, Clive 234
Ramprakash, Mark 13, 224
Rance, Phil 231
Randall, Derek 24, 47, 54, 157, 165, 183
Reeve, Dermot 79, 122, 194–5, 221, 222
Reeve, Graham 118, 238
Refuge Assurance League 37, 38
Richards, C.J. 184
Richards, Vivian 14, 46, 48, 57, 60, 78, 87, 104, 106, 113, 141, 209, 211, 214, 232, 244; friendship with Botham 11, 90, 93, 124, 177, 197; as a batsman 12, 64, 86, 111, 131, 178, 211; at Somerset 17–18, 23–4, 25–34, 240, 241; and rebel tours 136, 146
Roberts, Andy 12, 24, 46, 50, 53, 78, 233, 240
Robinson, Tim 184
Roebuck, Peter 10, 12, 18, 24, 25, 27–33, 39, 100, 110, 123, 162, 181, 182, 224

Rose, Brian 12, 16, 17, 18, 19, 25, 59, 60
Rowe, Lawrence 234

Sabina Park (West Indies) 1, 66, 203, 208
Salim Yousuf 214, 215
SCG (Sydney) 1, 24, 54, 107, 210
Scunthorpe United FC 135, 137, 154
Shakoor Rana 164
Sharp, Harry 94–6
Shastri, Ravi 203
Short, Don 161
Shropshire CCC 10
Simmons, Jack 233
Slack, Wilf 184
Slocombe, P.A. 12
Smith, Alan (A.C.) 61, 63, 104, 139–40
Smith, David 36
Smith, Robin 125, 187, 189, 224
Snow, John 181, 197
Sobers, Garfield 1, 2, 90–1, 122, 171, 201, 207, 211, 226
Somerset CCC 8, 10, 15, 16, 23–4, 36, 46, 95, 100, 149, 166; County Championship 15, 17, 19; John Player League 11, 16, 18; Gillette Cup 11, 16, 17; Benson & Hedges games 12, 16, 17, 19, 97; dismissal of Richards and Garner 25–34; second XI 10, 96; Taunton 12, 13, 15, 26, 30, 70, 96, 228
South Africa 222, 223; v. England (1995/96) 219; rebel tours and boycotts 57, 61–3, 72, 107, 116, 123–5, 128, 136–7, 139, 146–7, 188–90; cricket board 146
Sri Lanka 102, 190, 203, 205, 216
Srikkanth, K. 204
Srinath, Javagal 203
St Vincent (West Indies) 57

Statham, Brian 197
Steen, Rob 116
Stewart, Alec 125, 183, 189, 216, 221, 224
Stewart, Micky 123, 125, 147, 164, 188–93, 220–1
Stirling, Derek 240
Sun 51, 138, 152, 155, 156, 197, 238, 242, 244
Sunday Express 59
Sunday League 20
Surrey CCC 17, 26, 36, 61, 218
Sussex CCC 16, 19
Swanton, E.W. 5

Taylor, Bob 44, 47, 80, 84, 109
Taylor, Derek 11, 18
Taylor, Mark 22, 71, 83, 222
TCCB 67, 104, 126, 137–40, 142, 145, 178, 218
Texaco Trophy 187
Thicknesse, John 86, 115
Thomas, Greg 114
Thomson, Jeff 43, 84
Thorpe, Graham 7, 224
The Times 150, 169, 198
Titmus, Fred 218
Topley, Don 36
Trent Bridge (Nottingham) 14, 15, 18, 53, 68, 79
Trueman, Fred 1, 2, 109, 127, 197, 202, 211
Trumper, Victor 86
Tufnell, Phil 158, 196, 224
Turner, Jack 37
Tyson, Frank 197

Underwood, Derek 47, 109

Viswanath, G.R. 203

Waite, M.G. 207

Walsh, Courtney 22, 24, 198

Walters, Doug 82

Warne, Shane 24, 87, 158, 213

Warwickshire CCC 7, 18, 19, 23, 32, 34, 52, 122

Wasim Akram 24, 171, 212, 213, 216

Watson, Willie 136

Waugh, Mark 71, 87, 222

Waugh, Steve 71, 87, 110, 184, 222

Waqar Younis 24, 182, 213

Weaver, Paul 59, 115

West, Peter 82

Wellard, A.W. 32

West Indies 30, 42, 43, 45, 46–8, 52–62, 69, 77, 78, 98, 102, 108, 111, 112, 116, 126, 135, 136, 147, 173, 174, 176–8, 187, 188–90, 205, 208–9, 223, 227; v. England: (1973/74) 50; (1980/81) 55, 57–64, 104–6, 139, 154, 177, 179; (1985/86) 53, 113–14, 117, 120–1, 124, 142, 184, 191, 192, 210, 220; (1989/90) 38, 50, 124, 188–90, 195, 220; v. Australia (1996/97) 22; World Cup: (1979) 44; (1992) 215 (see England)

Weston, Martin 38, 196

Whitehead, Alan 185, 239

Whitney, Mike 79, 86

Willey, Peter 76, 80, 137

Willis, Bob 5, 15, 24, 47, 49, 52, 59, 76, 87, 100, 102, 111, 121, 154, 159, 173, 174, 175, 181, 192, 197, 219, 225,

234; and the England captaincy 67, 101, 108, 109–10, 137, 157, 183; v. Australia (1981) 41, 79–80, 81–4, 86, 89, 92; injury 60–1, 66, 116, 136

Winning Ways (Dermot Reeve) 122, 221

Wisden 1, 12, 13, 14, 19, 26, 27, 36, 38, 40, 55, 59, 82, 86, 97, 106, 110, 115, 171, 192, 206, 213, 215, 234, 241

Wisden Cricket Monthly 5, 26, 27, 44, 52, 59, 64, 68, 107, 123, 135, 136, 143, 218, 229

Wood, Graeme 82, 84, 239

Woodcock, John 86

Woods, S.M.J. 32

Wooldridge, Ian 153

Woolmer, Bob 44, 106, 222

Worcestershire CCC 18, 21, 34–9, 112, 121–2, 164, 186, 187, 193, 196; New Road 36, 38, 196

World Cup (1979) 44, 177, 235; (1983) 204; (1987) 124, 214; (1992) 215, 218; (1996) 219, 220, 224

World Series, see Kerry Packer

Worrell, Frank 70

Wright, John 156, 206

Wyatt, R.E.S. 25

Yallop, Graham 86

Yashpal Sharma 204

Yorkshire CCC 17, 98, 11, 127

Zimbabwe 54, 61, 123, 142, 204, 225